Steam Railway Directory

The Ultimate Steam Railway Guide
for the UK and Ireland

**Containing over 200 Railway Centres, with
over 3,000 locomotives and rolling stock.**

**Also available on CD-ROM
Updated daily on www.hccsteamrailway.com**

The next generation directories

i

Steam Railway Directory

Publishing Director: Howard Cox

Sales Manager: Neil Stokes

Project Manager: Julian Grattidge

Design & Production Manager: Lucy Hibbert
Design & Production Assistant: Paul Harrison
Design & Production Assistant: Mathew Jennings

Editor: Sarah Martin

Data Research Manager: Claire Thorpe

Researchers: Sally Webster, Lise Taylor, Michelle Malbon, Angela Evans, Sarah Lockett, Faye Jackson, James Lloyd, Marie Devaney, Sarah Murray.

Editorial Programmer: Matthew Corne
CD programming: Paul Crossley
Website design and programming: Martin Robinson

Publisher: HCC Publishing Ltd

ISBN: 1-903897-09-2

Cover Photographs:
Main Picture: © Ed Hurst
Top Left : © Chris English

Further Information:

Emails: steamrailway@hccpublishing.co.uk
contactus@hccpublishing.co.uk

Website: www.hccsteamrailway.com

Address: Meaford Power Station, Meaford, Stone, Staffordshire, ST15 0UU.

Tel: 0870 7541666 (From outside the UK +441782 371184)
Fax: 0870 7541667 (From outside the UK +441782 371167)

Foreword

Railway preservation is no longer a movement for dedicated railway enthusiasts; it is a big and growing industry and a key factor in tourism programmes in many areas.

Nearly 8 million people visited steam railway centres in 2000 and spent over £40m at these locations. In fact, in 1999 the National Railway Museum was named as one of England's top three tourist attractions and during the year 2000 they welcomed around 450,000 visitors.

Correspondingly, there have been many directories and publications, which describe steam railways very professionally, and in some cases in considerable detail, that have become best sellers in recent years.

Up until now, no publisher has managed to give the enthusiast or the tourist the ability to locate steam railway facilities and stock at each centre from only knowing the locomotive's name or type. For example unless you are familiar with its location, how would you locate the "Canadian Pacific" or certain stock that has a particular wheel arrangement?

Well the waiting is over!

"The ultimate guide to steam railways" in the UK and Ireland is now available. This massive compilation of steam railways is available as a handy sized directory, interactive CD-ROM and sophisticated website.

EMAP's "Steam Railway", the top-selling magazine, is pleased to place their name on this unique and essential guide to locating railway centres, locomotives and rolling stock information.

The "Steam Railway Directory" is more than an up to date compilation of steam railway centres today. For the first time you can locate over 3,000 locomotives and stock by the date built, who built it, where it is located and, if you can see it operating, under restoration or on static display. You can select a station by its facilities, or even by the price, gradient or views of a journey.

There are so many ways to interrogate the "Steam Railway Directory".

In addition to this hard copy format, the Steam Railway Directory is also available as a powerful interactive CD-ROM, which gives you a million extra ways to locate the railway of your choice. In addition to the detailed station and stock information, there are over 800 photos, maps, and timetables to view as well as an interactive diary.

Purchasing the Steam Railway Directory in either form also allows membership to the www.hccsteamrailway.com website, giving access to a whole host of restored railway and locomotive information, which is updated on a daily basis.

So enjoy the "Steam Railway" searching experience, we certainly have!

Sarah Martin
Editor

Background

Restored railways and rail museums continue to attract a vast cross section of enthusiasts, all of whom want something slightly different from their visit. Whilst the majority may be interested in steam locomotives, others may prefer to locate diesel, electric or petrol locomotives. Some may want to visit miniature railways, whilst others may want to view restored locomotives in use or on static display.

You may be planning a family day out, so need to know what facilities are available before you get there, i.e. a café, guided tours, or perhaps disabled access. You might like to know what journeys are available from a particular railway line and the features you can expect from the journey, such as the gradient of the line, what the views are like, or how much it will cost to travel.

Maybe you and your enthusiast friends are looking for railways that offer training courses, history lectures or even driver footplate experience. Whatever your preference, how do you locate restored railways or museums that suit your particular requirements?

This has been the age-old problem with the majority of conventional directories. They do not provide the enquirer with the information they want, in the way that they want it. Most directories set out with good intentions, however, as the modern rail enthusiast becomes more discerning, sophisticated, and even demanding, these 'one-dimensional' directories tend to leave the enquirer "short-changed" and invariably frustrated.

With years of expertise in market research, database management, and publishing, the team at HCC knew what was needed. A truly 'searchable' directory, structured in such a way that any rail enthusiast, no matter what their requirements, would be able to pick up the book and find 'useable' information, presented in a structured manner that was easy on the eye.

Welcome to the Steam Railway Directory, one of the Next Generation Directories from HCC Publishing.

Searching Made Simple .....

Your Involvement

We welcome your input; in fact we positively encourage your comments about any inaccuracies that may be apparent. We also welcome your recommendations about Steam Railways, locomotives or rolling stock not currently covered in this directory. So let's hear your constructive criticism. It is our aim to continue to improve the most comprehensive source of information about UK & Irish Steam Railways currently available to you. So please contact us about railways and stock included or not included in the Steam Railway Directory.

Data issue points to be aware of whilst using the Steam Railway Directory.

1. Information given by businesses is usually obtained using sophisticated "data collection" questionnaires. If you would like to receive one, please contact us by telephone on 0870 754 1666 or you can also email us at: steamrailway@hccpublishing.co.uk

2. London (Greater) is listed as a county (we know it is not). Sub-areas of London have been recognised as a locality and are entered when they are known (e.g. Camden, Waterloo etc).

3. The Channel Islands are listed under England.

4. Some areas of information are incomplete due to lack of any co-operation by a business representative. That person, for unclear reasoning, prefers that you do not know more than they want to divulge.

5. In certain sections some names have been shortened to enable a uniform layout, but remain recognisable.

6. All telephone numbers have been corrected to the British Telecom recommended layout, including international numbers (any changes to numbers after publication is in the hands of BT). Don't forget that the international code for the UK is +44 and Ireland is +353

7. All prices listed are in UK pounds. Irish Punts and Euros have been converted to UK pounds at the time of publishing.

Standard Abbreviations

Ass - Association
Ave - Avenue
Cl - Close
Co - Company
Coun - Council
Cres - Crescent
Ctre - Centre
Ctry - Country
Dept - Department
Est - Estate
Gr - Grove
Grp - Group
Gt - Great
Hse - House
Ind - Industrial
Nat - National
Nr - Near
Org - Organisation
Pk - Park
Pl - Place
Prde - Parade
Pres - Preservation
Rd - Road
Rlwy - Railway
Sq - Square
St - Street
St. - Saint
Sv - Service
Svs - Services
Tnsprt - Transport
Trce - Terrace
UK - United Kingdom

Glossary

Railways

Beamish – North of England Open Air Museum
BHES – Barrow Hill Engine Shed
BR – British Rail
Bress – Bressingham Steam Centre & Gardens
CVR – Churnet Valley Railway
DFR – Dean Forest Railway
DRC – Darlington Railway Centre & Museum
Eastleigh – Eastleigh Railway Preservation Society
ELR – East Lancashire Railway
Embsay – Embsay and Bolton Abbey Steam Railway
GCR (N) – Great Central Railway
GWR – Great Western Railway
GWS – Great Western Society
HLPG – Humberside Locomotive Preservation Group
Hull – Hull Street Life Museum
IOW – Isle of Wight Steam Railway
KESR – Kent & East Sussex Railway
LBR – Leighton Buzzard Railway
LBSCR – London Brighton & South Coast Railway
LCDR – London Chatham & Dover Railway
LMS – London Midland & Scottish Railway
LNER – London & North Eastern Railway
LSWR – London & South Western Railway
LTM – London Transport Museum
MLST – Main Line Steam Trust
MMSI – Manchester Museum of Science & Industry
MOWT – Ministry of Works and Transport
MR – Metropolitan Railway
MRC – Midland Railway Centre
NRM – National Railway Museum
NVR – Nene Valley Railway
NYMR – North York Moors Railway
RA – Railway Age
ScM – Science Museum
SECR – South Eastern & Chatham Railway
SER – South Eastern Railway
SR – Southern Railway
SRM – Stephenson Railway Museum
STEAM – Steam Museum
StLREC – St Leonards Railway Engineering Centre
SVR – Severn Valley Railway
THM – Timothy Hackworth Museum
TransM – Glasgow Museum of Transport
WD – War Department
WLLR – West Lancashire Light Railway
WSR – West Somerset Railway

Glossary

Locos & Diesel Multiple Units

A1A – A1A – 3 Axles per bogie, central not driven

B-B – 2 Axles per bogie coupled by drive shafts

BE – Battery Electric

Bo-Bo – 2 Independently driven axles per bogie

Co-Co – 3 Independently driven axles per bogie

DE – Diesel Electric

DH – Diesel Hydraulic transmission via cardan shaft

DM – Diesel Mechanical

DMBS – Driving Motor Brake Second

DMU – Diesel Multiple Unit

DTCL – Driving Trailer Composite

E – Overhead Electric

EMU – Electric Multiple Unit

F – Fireless

G – Geared

GH – Gas Hydraulic

IST – Inverted Saddle Tank

PH - Petrol Hydraulic

PM – Petrol Mechanical

PT – Pannier Tank

R – Railcar

ST – Saddle Tank

STT – Saddle Tank and Tender

T – Side Tank

T – Tank Loco

VB – Vertical Boiler

WT – Well Tank

4w – 4 Wheel

4w – 4w – Carried on two powered four wheel bogies

Glossary

Rolling Stock

BCK – Brake Composite Corridor
BFK – Brake First Corridor
BG – Brake Gangwayed
BGP – Gangway Brake Pigeon
BSK – Brake Second Corridor
BTK – Brake Third Corridor
BZ – Brake 6w
CCT – Covered Carriage Truck
CK – Composite Corridors
CL – Composite Lavatory
FK – First Corridor
FO – First Open
GBL – Gangwayed Bogie Luggage
GUV – General Utility Van
KB – Kitchen Buffet
LB – Lounge Buffet
PMV – Parcels & Miscellaneous Van
RBR – Restaurant Buffet Refurbished
RMB – Restaurant Miniature Buffet
RU (B) – Restaurant Unclassified (Buffet)
SK – Second Corridor
SO – Second Open
SOB – Semi Open Brake
SOBT – Semi Open Brake Third
TO – Third Open
TPO – Travelling Post Office
TSL – Trailer Second with Lavatory
TSO – Tourist Second Open

Contents

Contents

A-Z of Steam Railways and Museums.

SECTION 1A

This is the main section of the directory. It can be used to locate Steam Railways and Museums you already know the name of. Or alternatively, it can be used for finding out information on a railway/museum you have located after accessing the other sections of the directory.

What information can I find?

An alphabetical listing of railways/museums showing name, address, contact details, year opened, type of complex, type of organisation, type of gauge, number of volunteers, stock overview, background, facilities, opening times, location, journeys available at the railway and stations on the journey.

ABBEY LIGHT RAILWAY

ABBEY LIGHT RAILWAY Bridge Rd, Kirkstall, Leeds, **YORKSHIRE (WEST),** LS5 3BW, **ENGLAND**.

(T) 0113 2675087

Type of Complex: Operational Railway Line

Type of Organisation: Volunteer, Non-Profit

Gauge: Narrow   **No. Volunteers:** 10

Stock Overview:

No. Diesel Locos: 7

TV/Film Appearances: Brother to the Ox (ITV)

Background: Abbey Light Railway rebuilt the railway and now operate it as a 2 foot gauge railway. All track and stock used has been restored by them.

Facilities: Driver footplate experience, Enthusiast galas, Courses on how to renovate.

Opening/Closing Times:

Spring: **Opens** Sun 13:00, **Closes** Sun 17:00
Summer: **Opens** Sun 13:00, **Closes** Sun 17:00
Autumn: **Opens** Sun 13:00, **Closes** Sun 17:00
Winter: **Opens** Sun 13:00, **Closes** Sun 17:00
Other: Open Bank Holidays.

Location:

Main Road: A65   **Mainline Station:** Headingley

Contact(s):

● **Owner:** Mr Peter Lowe

Journeys Available At This Railway:

Bridge Road, Kirkstall to Kirkstall Abbey
Track Type: Single   Direction: West
Features: Views of Urbanisation, Water, Woods. Cistercian Abbey - founded 1152. Maximum gradient of 1 in 30 (For 30 metres).
Bridges: 1 'over'   **Level Crossings:** 1   **Rivers:** 1   **Journey Duration:** 15 mins   **Journey Length:** 0.25 mile(s)
Price: £1.00 (Adult Standard) £1.00 (Child Standard)
Available on Journey: Drinks, Commentary.

Stations On This Journey:

Station Name	St	Al	Bd	Tl	DT	PA	CP	Ph	Mu	WR	Sh	VS	WS	VW	SB	VSB
Bridge Road	✔		✔									✔	✔	✔	✔	
Kirkstall Abbey	✔			✔		✔	✔		✔							

ABBEY PUMPING STATION

ABBEY PUMPING STATION Corporation Rd, Off Abbey Lane, Leicester, **LEICESTERSHIRE,** LE4 5XP, **ENGLAND**.

(T) 0116 2995111   **(F)** 0116 2995125

Affiliated Bodies: Transport Trust

Type of Complex: Museum

Stock Overview:

No. Diesel Locos: 1 (1 Pre-Group)

Facilities: Disabled access, Souvenir shop.

Opening/Closing Times:

Spring: **Opens** Mon - Sat 10:00, Sun 14:00, **Closes** Mon - Sun 17:00
Summer: **Opens** Mon - Sat 10:00, Sun 14:00, **Closes** Mon - Sun 17:00
Autumn: **Opens** Mon - Sat 10:00, Sun 14:00, **Closes** Mon - Sun 17:00
Winter: **Opens** Mon - Sat 10:00, Sun 13:30, **Closes** Mon - Sat 16:30 Sun 16:30
Other: Closed December 24th, 25th, 26th and January 1st.

Location:

Bus: 54, 54K   **Mainline Station:** Leicester Main Line

Contact(s):

Key: *St* = Stops   *Al* = Alight   *Bd* = Board   *Tl* = Toilets   *DT* = Disabled Toilets   *PA* = Kids Play Area   *CP* = Free Car Park   *Ph* = Pay Phone   *Mu* = Museum
WR = Waiting Room   *Sh* = Sheds   *VS* = Can Visit Sheds   *WS* = Workshops   *VW* = Can Visit Workshops   *SB* = Signal Box   *VSB* = Can Visit Signal Box

● **Volunteer:** Mr Tony Kendal

ALDERNEY RAILWAY

ALDERNEY RAILWAY Braye Road Station, Alderney, St. Anne, **CHANNEL ISLANDS,** GY9, **ENGLAND**.
(T) 01481 824385

Type of Complex: Railway Station, Operational Railway Line

Gauge: Standard

<u>Stock Overview:</u>

No. Diesel Locos: 1

<u>**Facilities:**</u> Santa Special, Souvenir shop, Books for sale, Children's events, Trains for hire.

<u>Opening/Closing Times:</u>

Spring: **Opens** Sat, Sun 14:00, **Closes** Sat, Sun 16:00

Summer: **Opens** Sat, Sun 14:00, **Closes** Sat, Sun 16:00

<u>Location:</u>

Nearest Town/Village: St Annes

<u>Contact(s):</u>

● **Chairman:** Mr A Le Blanc

● **Operations Manager:** Mr E A Kaye   **(T)** 01481 823580

<u>Journeys Available At This Railway:</u>

Braye Road to Mannez Quarry
Track Type: Single
Features: Views of Open Fields, Sea, Water.
Level Crossings: 5   **Journey Length:** 2 mile(s)
Price: £2.50 (Adult Standard) £1.50 (Child Standard)

<u>Stations On This Journey:</u>

Station Name	St	Al	Bd	Tl	DT	PA	CP	Ph	Mu	WR	Sh	VS	WS	VW	SB	VSB
Braye Road	✔	✔					✔									
Mannez Quarry	✔	✔					✔					✔		✔		

ALFORD VALLEY RAILWAY

ALFORD VALLEY RAILWAY Alford Station, Alford, **ABERDEENSHIRE,** AB33 8HH, **SCOTLAND**.
(T) 01975 562811

Type of Complex: Railway Station, Operational Railway Line, Museum

Gauge: Narrow

<u>Stock Overview:</u>

No. Steam Locos: 1 (1 Pre-Nationalisation)

No. Diesel Locos: 3

<u>**Facilities:**</u> Disabled access, Santa Special, Children's events, Picnic area.

<u>Opening/Closing Times:</u>

Spring: **Opens** Sat, Sun 13:00, **Closes** Sat, Sun 17:00

Summer: **Opens** Mon - Sun 13:00, **Closes** Mon - Sun 17:00

Autumn: **Opens** Sat, Sun 13:00, **Closes** Sat, Sun 17:00

<u>Location:</u>

Nearest Town/Village: Aberdeen   **Main Road:** A944

<u>Contact(s):</u>

● **Director:** Mr James Gordon   **(T)** 01975 562045

● **Treasurer:** Mr Margaret Black

<u>Journeys Available At This Railway:</u>

Alford to Murray Park
Features: Views of Open Fields, Woods.
Journey Length: 2 mile(s)
Price: £2.00 (Adult Standard) £1.00 (Child Standard)

<u>Stations On This Journey:</u>

Station Name	St	Al	Bd	Tl	DT	PA	CP	Ph	Mu	WR	Sh	VS	WS	VW	SB	VSB
Alford	✔	✔					✔		✔							
Haughton Park	✔	✔					✔									
Haughton									✔							
Murray Park									✔							

ALMOND VALLEY HERITAGE TRUST

ALMOND VALLEY HERITAGE TRUST Millfield, Livingston, **LOTHIAN (WEST),** EH54 7AR, **SCOTLAND**.

(T) 01506 414957   **(F)** 01506 497771

(E) info@almondvalley.co.uk

(W) www.almondvalley.co.uk

Affiliated Bodies: Heritage Railway Association

Type of Complex: Operational Railway Line, Museum

Stock Overview:

No. Diesel Locos: 6 (2 Pre-Group)

Facilities: Café, Disabled access.

Entry Fees: Adults: £2.80   **Children:** £1.60

Opening/Closing Times:
Spring: Opens Mon - Sun 10:00, **Closes** Mon - Sun 17:00
Summer: Opens Mon - Sun 10:00, **Closes** Mon - Sun 17:00
Autumn: Opens Mon - Sun 10:00, **Closes** Mon - Sun 17:00
Winter: Opens Mon - Sun 10:00, **Closes** Mon - Sun 17:00
Other: Closed December 25th - 26th and January 1st - 2nd.

AMBERLEY WORKING MUSEUM

AMBERLEY WORKING MUSEUM Station Rd, Amberley, Arundel, **SUSSEX (WEST),** BN18 9LT, **ENGLAND**.

(T) 01798 831370   **(F)** 01798 831831

(E) office@amberleymuseum.co.uk

(W) www.amberleymuseum.co.uk

Affiliated Bodies: Heritage Railway Association, Transport Trust

Complex Size: 36 Acres   **Year Opened:** 1979

Type of Complex: Railway Station, Operational Railway Line, Museum, Restoration Site

Type of Organisation: Charity, Non-Profit

Gauge: Narrow   **No. Staff:** 10   **No. Volunteers:** 250

Stock Overview:

No. Steam Locos: 7 (1 Pre-Group, 5 Pre-Nationalisation)

No. Diesel Locos: 17 (11 Pre-Group)

TV/Film Appearances: Time Tourists (2000), View to a Kill (1984)

Facilities: Café, Disabled access, Training courses, Enthusiast galas, Souvenir shop, Books for sale, Videos for sale, Main credit cards taken.

Entry Fees: Adults: £6.50   **Children:** £3.50

Opening/Closing Times:
Spring: Opens Mon, Thurs - Sun 10:00, **Closes** Mon, Thurs - Sun 18:00
Summer: Opens Mon, Thurs - Sun 10:00, **Closes** Mon, Thurs - Sun 18:00
Autumn: Opens Mon, Thurs - Sun 10:00, **Closes** Mon, Thurs - Sun 18:00
Other: Open 20 March - 3 November. Also open Bank Holidays and 7 days a week during school holidays.

Location:

Nearest Town/Village: Arundel   **Main Road:** B2139   **Mainline Station:** Amberley

Restaurant: The Boathouse

Contact(s):

Key: *St* = Stops   *Al* = Alight   *Bd* = Board   *Tl* = Toilets   *DT* = Disabled Toilets   *PA* = Kids Play Area   *CP* = Free Car Park   *Ph* = Pay Phone   *Mu* = Museum
     WR = Waiting Room   *Sh* = Sheds   *VS* = Can Visit Sheds   *WS* = Workshops   *VW* = Can Visit Workshops   *SB* = Signal Box   *VSB* = Can Visit Signal Box

● **For Bookings:** Ms Wendy Rundle
● **Technical Info:** Ms Sara Isted
Journeys Available At This Railway:

Amberley to Brockham
Features: Views of Hills, Woods.

AMERTON RAILWAY

STAFFORDSHIRE NARROW GAUGE RAILWAY SOCIETY Amerton Farm, Stowe-by-Chartley, Stafford, **STAFFORDSHIRE, ST18 0LA, ENGLAND**.
(T) 01785 850965　　**(F)** 01785 850965
Year Opened: 1992
Type of Complex: Railway Station, Operational Railway Line, Restoration Site
Type of Organisation: Charity, Heritage Project, Limited Company, Volunteer, Non-Profit
Gauge: Narrow　　**No. Volunteers:** 12
Stock Overview:
No. Steam Locos: 3 (2 Pre-Nationalisation)
No. Diesel Locos: 8 (4 Pre-Group)
Facilities: Restaurant, Ticket office, Santa Special, Enthusiast galas, Souvenir shop, Books for sale, Videos for sale, Photos for sale.
Opening/Closing Times:
Spring:　Opens Sat, Sun 12:00, **Closes** Sat, Sun 17:00
Summer:　Opens Sat, Sun 12:00, **Closes** Sat, Sun 17:00
Autumn:　Opens Sat, Sun 12:00, **Closes** Sat, Sun 17:00
Other:　　Sundays only in March. Open Bank Holidays.
Location:
Instructions: Signposted 'Amerton Farm'.
Nearest Town/Village: Stafford　　**Main Road:** A518　　**Mainline Station:** Stafford
Contact(s):
● **Chairman:** Mr Peter Bell
Journeys Available At This Railway:

Amerton to Amerton (round trip)
Track Type: Single
Features: Views of Open Fields. Maximum gradient of 1 in 35 (For 100 metres).
Bridges: 2 'over'　**Signal Boxes:** 1　**Rivers:** 2　**Journey Duration:** 20 mins　**Journey Length:** 1 mile(s)
Price: £1.30 (Adult Standard) £0.70 (Child Standard)
Stations On This Journey:

Station Name	St	Al	Bd	Tl	DT	PA	CP	Ph	Mu	WR	Sh	VS	WS	VW	SB	VSB
Amerton Station	✓	✓		✓	✓	✓	✓	✓			✓	✓			✓	✓
Chartley Rd			✓													

APPLEBY-FRODINGHAM RAILWAY

APPLEBY-FRODINGHAM RAILWAY PRESERVATION SOCIETYPO Box 44, Brigg, **LINCOLNSHIRE (NORTH), DN20 8DW, ENGLAND**.
(T) 01652 656661
(E) afrps@afrps.co.uk
(W) www.afrps.co.uk
Type of Complex: Operational Railway Line
Stock Overview:
No. Steam Locos: 2 (2 Pre-Nationalisation)
Background: Based on the Scunthorpe site of Corus, one of the worlds major metals companies.
Opening/Closing Times:
Other:　Pre booking is essential. Limited places available. Contact for opening times.
Location:
Nearest Town/Village: Brigg　　**Main Road:** A18
Contact(s):

● **For Bookings:** Brigg Tourist Information Centre   **(T)** 01652 657053

ARMLEY MILLS

ARMLEY MILLS LEEDS INDUSTRIAL MUSEUM Armley Mills, Canal Rd, Armley, Leeds, **YORKSHIRE (WEST)**, LS12 2QF, **ENGLAND**.

(T) 0113 2637861   **(F)** 0113 2637861

(E) armleymillsindmuseum@virgin.net

Type of Complex: Museum

Gauge: Narrow

Stock Overview:

No. Steam Locos: 8 (1 Pre-Group, 4 Pre-Nationalisation)

No. Diesel Locos: 17 (10 Pre-Group, 1 Pre-Nationalisation)

Facilities: Disabled access, Cinema, Lecture room, Souvenir shop, Picnic area and demonstration track.

Entry Fees: Adults: £2.00   **Children:** £0.50

Opening/Closing Times:

Spring: **Opens** Tues - Sat 10:00, Sun 13:00, **Closes** Tues - Sun 17:00
Summer: **Opens** Tues - Sat 10:00, Sun 13:00, **Closes** Tues - Sun 17:00
Autumn: **Opens** Tues - Sat 10:00, Sun 13:00, **Closes** Tues - Sun 17:00
Winter: **Opens** Tues - Sat 10:00, Sun 13:00, **Closes** Tues - Sun 17:00
Other: Open Bank Holidays.

Location:

Bus: 5A, 14, 66, 67.

Contact(s):

● **Curator:** Mr Daru Rooke

AUDLEY END MINIATURE RAILWAY

AUDLEY END MINIATURE RAILWAY Estate Office, Brunketts, Wendens Ambo, Saffron Walden, **ESSEX**, CB11 4JL, **ENGLAND**.

(T) 01799 541354

Year Opened: 1964

Type of Complex: Operational Railway Line

Gauge: Narrow

Facilities: Disabled access, Santa Special, Souvenir shop, Books for sale, Models for sale, Children's events, Picnic area.

Opening/Closing Times:

Spring: **Opens** Sat - Sun 14:00, **Closes** Sat - Sun 17:00
Summer: **Opens** Mon - Sun 14:00, **Closes** Mon - Sun 17:00
Autumn: **Opens** Sat - Sun 14:00, **Closes** Sat - Sun 17:00
Other: Open in December for Santa Specials.

Location:

Instructions: Situated opposite the main gates of Audley End House (signposted Audley End Estate).

Nearest Town/Village: Saffron Walden   **Main Road:** B1383   **Mainline Station:** Audley End

Contact(s):

● **Financial Manager:** Mr Gordon Perry

● **Railway Superintendent:** Mr Steve Crow

Journeys Available At This Railway:

Features: Views of Open Fields, Woods.

Bridges: 1 'over', 1 'under'   **Tunnels:** 2   **Signal Boxes:** 1   **Rivers:** 1   **Journey Length:** 1.5 mile(s)

Price: £2.20 (Adult Standard) £1.20 (Child Standard)

Key: *St* = Stops   *Al* = Alight   *Bd* = Board   *Tl* = Toilets   *DT* = Disabled Toilets   *PA* = Kids Play Area   *CP* = Free Car Park   *Ph* = Pay Phone   *Mu* = Museum
     WR = Waiting Room   *Sh* = Sheds   *VS* = Can Visit Sheds   *WS* = Workshops   *VW* = Can Visit Workshops   *SB* = Signal Box   *VSB* = Can Visit Signal Box

A-Z STEAM RAILWAYS

Avon Valley Railway — Bala Lake Railway

AVON VALLEY RAILWAY

BITTON RAILWAY CO LTD T/A AVON VALLEY RAILWAY Bitton Station, Bath Rd, Bristol, **BRISTOL,**
BS30 6HD, **ENGLAND**.
(T) 0117 9325538   **(F)** 0117 9325935
(E) enquiries@avonvalleyrailway.co.uk
(W) www.avonvalleyrailway.co.uk
Affiliated Bodies: Heritage Railway Association
Complex Size: 36 Acres
Type of Complex: Operational Railway Line
Gauge: Standard
Stock Overview:
No. Steam Locos: 6 (4 Pre-Group, 1 Pre-Nationalisation)
No. Diesel Locos: 12 (3 Pre-Group)
Facilities: Café, Guided tours available, Driver footplate experience, Santa Special, 'Thomas' event,
Courses on how to drive Locos, Souvenir shop, Books for sale, Videos for sale, Main credit cards
taken, Dining experience available.
Location:
Nearest Town/Village: Bristol   **Main Road:** A431   **Bus:** 332, 632   **Mainline Station:** Keynsham
Contact(s):
● **General Manager:** Mr Chris Kemp
Journeys Available At This Railway:

Bitton to Bitton (round trip)
Price: £3.50 (Adult Standard) £2.00 (Child Standard)
Stations On This Journey:

Station Name	St	Al	Bd	Tl	DT	PA	CP	Ph	Mu	WR	Sh	VS	WS	VW	SB	VSB
Bitton	✔	✔	✔	✔			✔									

BALA LAKE RAILWAY

BALA LAKE RAILWAY The Station, Llanuwchllyn, Bala, **GWYNEDD,** LL23 7DD, **WALES**.
(T) 01678 540666   **(F)** 01678 540535
(W) www.bala-lake-railway.co.uk
Affiliated Bodies: Heritage Railway Association, Transport Trust
Type of Complex: Operational Railway Line
Gauge: Narrow
Stock Overview:
No. Steam Locos: 2 (1 Pre-Nationalisation)
No. Diesel Locos: 3 (1 Pre-Group)
Facilities: Café, Ticket office, Santa Special, Souvenir shop, Books for sale, Videos for sale.
Opening/Closing Times:
Spring: **Opens** Tues - Thurs, Sat, Sun 10:00, **Closes** Tues - Thurs, Sat, Sun 17:30
Summer: **Opens** Mon - Sun 10:00, **Closes** Mon - Sun 17:30
Autumn: **Opens** Tues - Thurs, Sat, Sun 10:00, **Closes** Tues - Thurs, Sat, Sun 17:30
Other: Open in winter for Santa Specials only.
Location:
Nearest Town/Village: Llanuwchllyn   **Main Road:** B4403   **Taxi:** Global Taxis - 01678 540560
Hotel: Bala Lake   **Restaurant:** Badell Aur Restaurant
Contact(s):
● **General Manager:** Mr Roger Hine
Journeys Available At This Railway:

Llanuwchllyn to Bala
Features: Views of Open Fields, Water. Maximum gradient of 1 in 70.
Rivers: 1   **Journey Length:** 4.5 mile(s)
Price: £6.70 (Adult Standard) £3.00 (Child Standard)

Stations On This Journey:

Station Name	St	Al	Bd	Tl	DT	PA	CP	Ph	Mu	WR	Sh	VS	WS	VW	SB	VSB
Llanuwchllyn	✔	✔	✔	✔		✔					✔	✔	✔	✔		
Llangower																
Bala	✔	✔	✔													

BARLEYLANDS MINIATURE RAILWAY

H R PHILPOT & SONS (BARLEYLANDS) LTD Barleylands Rd, Billericay, **ESSEX,** CM11 2UD, **ENGLAND**.
(T) 01268 532253   **(F)** 01268 290229
(E) barleyfarm@aol.com
Complex Size: 4 Acres   **Year Opened:** 1989
Type of Complex: Operational Railway Line
Type of Organisation: Limited Company
No. Staff: 1   **No. Volunteers:** 16
Stock Overview:
No. Steam Locos: 6
Facilities: Café, Restaurant, Trains for hire.
Opening/Closing Times:
Spring: **Opens** Sun 10:00, **Closes** Sun 15:30
Summer: **Opens** Sun - Fri 10:00, **Closes** Sun - Fri 16:00
Autumn: **Opens** Sun 10:00, **Closes** Sun 15:30
Other: Railway open for rides on Sunday afternoons (March to October) and daily throughout
August (except Saturdays).
Location:
Nearest Town/Village: Billericay   **Main Road:** A129   **Bus:** 100   **Mainline Station:** Billericay
Restaurant: Magic Mushroom
Contact(s):
- **For Bookings:** Ms Kerry Summers
- **General Manager:** Mr Brian Connell
- **General Manager:** Ms Kelly Richardson
- **Owner:** Mr Chris Philpot

Journeys Available At This Railway:

Farm Museum to Boot Fair Station
Track Type: Single   Direction: East
Features: Views of Open Fields, Woods.
Level Crossings: 2   **Journey Duration:** 10 mins   **Journey Length:** 0.5 mile(s)
Price: £1.00 (Adult Standard) £1.00 (Child Standard) £1.00 (Adult Special) £1.00 (Child Special)

Stations On This Journey:

Station Name	St	Al	Bd	Tl	DT	PA	CP	Ph	Mu	WR	Sh	VS	WS	VW	SB	VSB
Farm Museum	✔			✔	✔	✔	✔				✔	✔	✔	✔		
Boot Fair	✔															

BARROW HILL ROUNDHOUSE

BARROW HILL ROUNDHOUSE Railway Centre, Campbell Drive, Barrow Hill, Chesterfield, **DERBYSHIRE,**
S43 2PR, **ENGLAND**.
(T) 01246 472450
Affiliated Bodies: Heritage Railway Association
Type of Organisation: Heritage Project, Limited Company
Gauge: Standard
Stock Overview:
No. Diesel Locos: 12
Facilities: Café, Buffet, Disabled access, Santa Special, 'Thomas' event, Enthusiast galas, Souvenir

---

Key: St = Stops   Al = Alight   Bd = Board   Tl = Toilets   DT = Disabled Toilets   PA = Kids Play Area   CP = Free Car Park   Ph = Pay Phone   Mu = Museum
    WR = Waiting Room   Sh = Sheds   VS = Can Visit Sheds   WS = Workshops   VW = Can Visit Workshops   SB = Signal Box   VSB = Can Visit Signal Box

shop, Books for sale, Facilities for hire.

Opening/Closing Times:
Spring: **Opens** Sat, Sun 09:00, **Closes** Sat, Sun 17:00
Summer: **Opens** Sat, Sun 09:00, **Closes** Sat, Sun 17:00
Autumn: **Opens** Sat, Sun 09:00, **Closes** Sat, Sun 17:00
Winter: **Opens** Sat, Sun 09:00, **Closes** Sat, Sun 17:00

Location:
Nearest Town/Village: Chesterfield   **Main Road:** A619   **Bus:** 25, 56

Contact(s):
- **Chairman:** Mr Mike Jackson   **(T)** 01246 472450
- **Membership Secretary:** Mr Martyn Brailsford
- **Secretary:** Mr Mervyn Allcock   **(T)** 01246 854921

Alternative Contact Details:
- 266 Williamthorpe Rd, North Wingford, Chesterfield, Derbyshire, S42 5NS, England

Journeys Available At This Railway:

BATTLEFIELD LINE

SHACKERSTONE RAILWAY SOCIETY LTD Station Drive, Shackerstone, Nuneaton, **WARWICKSHIRE,** CV13 6NW, **ENGLAND**.

(T) 01827 880754   **(F)** 01827 881050

(W) www.battlefield-line-railway.co.uk

Affiliated Bodies: Heritage Railway Association, Transport Trust

Complex Size: 20 Acres   **Year Opened:** 1976

Type of Complex: Railway Station, Operational Railway Line, Museum, Restoration Site

Type of Organisation: Limited Company, Volunteer

Gauge: Standard   **No. Volunteers:** 120

Stock Overview:
No. Steam Locos: 10 (3 Pre-Group, 1 Pre-Nationalisation)

No. Diesel Locos: 5 (1 Pre-Group)

Facilities: Café, Buffet, Ticket office, Disabled access, Waiting room, Left luggage office, Platform tickets, Photo line side permit available, Advanced booking available, Driver footplate experience, Santa Special, 'Thomas' event, Enthusiast galas, Souvenir shop, Books for sale, Videos for sale, Camera film for sale, Main credit cards taken, Children's events, Trains for hire.

Opening/Closing Times:
Spring: **Opens** 11:00, **Closes** 17:30
Summer: **Opens** 09:30, **Closes** 18:00
Autumn: **Opens** 11:00, **Closes** 17:30
Winter: **Opens** 11:00, **Closes** 17:30

Location:
Nearest Town/Village: Shackerstone

Contact(s):
- **For Bookings:** Mr Maurice Brooks
- **For Donations:** Mr Maurice Brooks
- **General Manager:** Mr Maurice Brooks
- **Technical Info:** Mr Maurice Brooks

Journeys Available At This Railway:

Shackerstone to Shenton
Track Type: Single   Direction: North to South
Features: Views of Open Fields, Woods. Shenton Station is the entry to Bosworth Battlefield. Maximum gradient of 1 in 200.
Bridges: 3 'over', 7 'under'   **Signal Boxes:** 2   **Journey Duration:** 20 mins   **Journey Length:** 5 mile(s)
Price: £6.00 (Adult Standard) £3.00 (Child Standard) £7.00 (Adult Special) £4.00 (Child Special)
Available on Journey: Refreshments, Drinks, Alcohol, Buffet, Commentary.

Stations On This Journey:

Station Name	St	AI	Bd	TI	DT	PA	CP	Ph	Mu	WR	Sh	VS	WS	VW	SB	VSB
Shackerstone	✔	✔	✔	✔	✔	✔	✔	✔	✔	✔	✔		✔		✔	
Shenton	✔	✔		✔	✔			✔		✔						

BEAMISH

BEAMISH, THE NORTH OF ENGLAND OPEN AIR MUSEUM Beamish, Stanley, **COUNTY DURHAM,** DH9 0RG, **ENGLAND**.

(T) 0191 3704000   **(F)** 0191 3704001

(E) museum@beamish.org.uk

(W) www.beamish.org.uk

Complex Size: 300 Acres   **Year Opened:** 1971

Type of Complex: Museum

Type of Organisation: Heritage Project, Conservation Project

Gauge: Standard   **No. Staff:** 50

Stock Overview:

No. Steam Locos: 10 (6 Pre-Nationalisation)

No. Diesel Locos: 2

TV/Film Appearances: Monocled Mutineer, Distant Bridges, Act of Will, Sons & Lovers, Our Friends In The North

Background: An open air museum recreating life in the North of England in the 1800's and early 1900's. Features colliery village, working farm, Pockerley Manor and the 1825 Railway.

Facilities: Café, Function room, Waiting room, Advanced booking available, Souvenir shop, Books for sale, Videos for sale, Photos for sale, Paintings/drawings for sale, Camera film for sale, Models for sale, Main credit cards taken, Facilities for hire.

Opening/Closing Times:

Spring: **Opens** Tues - Thurs, Sat, Sun 10:00, **Closes** Tues - Thurs, Sat, Sun 17:00

Summer: **Opens** Mon - Sun 10:00, **Closes** Mon - Sun 17:00

Autumn: **Opens** Mon - Sun 10:00, **Closes** Mon - Sun 17:00

Winter: **Opens** Tues - Thurs, Sat, Sun 10:00, **Closes** Tues - Thurs, Sat, Sun 16:00

Other: Railway is only open during the Summer season.

Location:

Instructions: Follow the A1 (M) and exit at junction 63. Take the A693 for approximately 4 miles towards Stanley.

Nearest Town/Village: Chester-Le-Street   **Main Road:** A693   **Bus:** 709, 720, 775   **Taxi:** Stanley Taxis   **Mainline Station:** Newcastle Central   **Hotel:** Beamish Park Hotel   **Restaurant:** Shepherd & Shepherdess

Contact(s):

- **For Bookings:** Mrs Chris Watson **(T)** 0191 3704026   **(E)** bookings@beamish.org.uk
- **For Bookings:** Ms Lorraine Watson   **(T)** 0191 3704026   **(E)** bookings@beamish.org.uk
- **Museum Director:** Ms Miriam Harte
- **Technical Info:** Mr Jim Rees

BEER HEIGHTS

BEER HEIGHTS LIGHT RAILWAY (THE) Pecorama, Beer, Seaton, **DEVON,** EX12 3NA, **ENGLAND**.

(T) 01297 21542   **(F)** 01297 20229

(W) www.peco-uk.com

Complex Size: 16 Acres   **Year Opened:** 1975

Type of Complex: Railway Station, Operational Railway Line

Type of Organisation: Limited Company

Gauge: Narrow   **No. Staff:** 3   **No. Volunteers:** 10

Stock Overview:

No. Steam Locos: 6

No. Diesel Locos: 1

TV/Film Appearances: Holiday (2001)

Facilities: Café, Restaurant, Buffet, Ticket office, Disabled access, Lecture room, Function room, Waiting room, Advanced booking available, Enthusiast galas, Souvenir shop, Books for sale, Videos for sale, Camera film for sale, Models for sale, Main credit cards taken, Children's events, Facilities for hire.

Opening/Closing Times:

Key:	*St* = Stops	*Al* = Alight	*Bd* = Board	*Tl* = Toilets	*DT* = Disabled Toilets	*PA* = Kids Play Area	*CP* = Free Car Park	*Ph* = Pay Phone	*Mu* = Museum
	WR = Waiting Room	*Sh* = Sheds	*VS* = Can Visit Sheds	*WS* = Workshops	*VW* = Can Visit Workshops	*SB* = Signal Box	*VSB* = Can Visit Signal Box		

Spring: **Opens** Mon - Sun 10:00, **Closes** Mon - Fri, Sun 17:30, Sat 13:00
Summer: **Opens** Mon - Sun 10:00, **Closes** Mon - Fri, Sun 17:30, Sat 13:00
Autumn: **Opens** Mon - Sun 10:00, **Closes** Mon - Fri, Sun 17:30, Sat 13:00

Location:
Instructions: Follow A3052 eastbound from Exeter, westbound from Lyme Regis. Take turning towards Beer (B3174) and follow tourist signs to Pecorama.
Nearest Town/Village: Seaton　**Main Road:** A3052　**Bus:** Axe Valley Buses　**Taxi:** Clapps Taxis, Seaton　**Mainline Station:** Axminster　**Hotel:** Dolphin

Contact(s):
- **For Bookings:** Mr Mark Ridgers
- **General Manager:** Mr Mark Ridgers
- **Owner:** Mr Michael Pritchard
- **Technical Info:** Mr J Macdougall CME

Journeys Available At This Railway:

Much Natter to Much Natter (round trip)
Track Type: Single　Direction: East to West
Features: Views of Hills, Open Fields, Sea, Water, Woods. Views of Beer Village, Lyme Bay and the Devon countryside. Also passes through gardens of 'Pecorama'. Maximum gradient of 1 in 70 (For 75 metres).
Bridges: 2 'over', 5 'under'　**Tunnels:** 1　**Level Crossings:** 2　**Signal Boxes:** 2　**Journey Duration:** 12 mins
Journey Length: 1 mile(s)

Stations On This Journey:

Station Name	St	Al	Bd	Tl	DT	PA	CP	Ph	Mu	WR	Sh	VS	WS	VW	SB	VSB
Much Natter		✔	✔	✔	✔		✔	✔	✔			✔		✔		

BICTON WOODLAND RAILWAY

BICTON WOODLAND RAILWAY Bicton Pk, East Budleigh, Budleigh Salterton, **DEVON,** EX9 7DP, **ENGLAND**.
(T) 01395 568465
Year Opened: 1963
Gauge: Narrow

Stock Overview:
No. Steam Locos: 1 (1 Pre-Group)
No. Diesel Locos: 2
Facilities: Restaurant, Disabled access, Souvenir shop, Main credit cards taken, Indoor play area. Dogs allowed (on leads).

Opening/Closing Times:
Spring: **Opens** 10:00, **Closes** 18:00
Summer: **Opens** 10:00, **Closes** 18:00
Autumn: **Opens** 10:00, **Closes** 18:00
Winter: **Opens** 10:00, **Closes** 17:00
Other: Closed Christmas Day.

Location:
Instructions: From Exeter, head east on A3052 for 8 miles and then turn right onto B3178 at Newton Poppleford for 2 miles. The entrance to the park is just after the Bicton College entrance.
Nearest Town/Village: Budleigh Salterton　**Main Road:** B3178　**Mainline Station:** Exeter

Contact(s):
- **Owner:** Ms Valerie Lister

Journeys Available At This Railway:

Main Station to Hermitage Station
Price: £4.75 (Adult Standard)　£2.75 (Child Standard)

Stations On This Journey:

Station Name	St	Al	Bd	Tl	DT	PA	CP	Ph	Mu	WR	Sh	VS	WS	VW	SB	VSB
Main Station	✔	✔	✔													
Hermitage Railway	✔	✔	✔													

BIDEFORD RAILWAY MUSEUM

BIDEFORD RAILWAY MUSEUM Bideford Station, Railway Trce, East-the-Water, Bideford, **DEVON,** EX39 4BB, **ENGLAND**.

(T) 01237 423585

(W) www.bidefordrailway.freeserve.co.uk

Type of Complex: Museum

Facilities: Souvenir shop, Books for sale.

Opening/Closing Times:

Spring: **Opens** Sun, Tues, Thurs 14:00, **Closes** Sun, Tues, Thurs 17:00
Summer: **Opens** Sun, Tues, Thurs 14:00, **Closes** Sun, Tues, Thurs 17:00
Autumn: **Opens** Sun, Tues, Thurs 14:00, **Closes** Sun, Tues, Thurs 17:00
Winter: **Opens** Sun 14:00, **Closes** Sun 17:00

Location:

Nearest Town/Village: Bideford

BLISTSHILL VICTORIAN TOWN

BLISTSHILL VICTORIAN TOWN Coleport Rd, Blistshill, Madeley, Telford, **SHROPSHIRE,** TF7 5DU, **ENGLAND**.

(T) 01952 583003

Type of Complex: Museum

Background: An open air museum. A small Victorian town has been created with grocers shop, chemist, bank and other replications of Victorian life. Part of the Ironbridge Gorge Museum Trust.

Facilities: Disabled access, Souvenir shop, Books for sale, Videos for sale, Main credit cards taken, Children's events.

Entry Fees: Adults: £7.50   **Children:** £5.00

Opening/Closing Times:

Spring: **Opens** Mon - Sun 10:00, **Closes** Mon - Sun 17:00
Summer: **Opens** Mon - Sun 10:00, **Closes** Mon - Sun 17:00
Autumn: **Opens** Sat - Wed 10:00, **Closes** Sat - Wed 17:00
Winter: **Opens** Sat - Wed 10:00, **Closes** Sat - Wed 17:00
Other: Contact for details of steaming days. Half price entry during winter.

Location:

Nearest Town/Village: Telford   **Main Road:** M54, J4   **Mainline Station:** Telford

Contact(s):

● **Technical Info:** Mr Jeff Copson

BLUEBELL RAILWAY

BLUEBELL RAILWAY PLC (THE) Sheffield Pk Station, Sheffield Pk, Uckfield, **SUSSEX (EAST),** TN22 3QL, **ENGLAND**.

(T) 01825 720800   **(F)** 01825 720804

(W) www.bluebell-railway.co.uk

Affiliated Bodies: Heritage Railway Association, Transport Trust

Type of Complex: Railway Station, Operational Railway Line, Museum, Restoration Site

Gauge: Standard

Stock Overview:

No. Steam Locos: 26 (8 Pre-Group, 5 Pre-Nationalisation)

TV/Film Appearances: Railway Children (1999), Wind in the Willows

Facilities: Restaurant, Disabled access, Santa Special, 'Thomas' event, Enthusiast galas, Souvenir shop, Books for sale, Videos for sale, Main credit cards taken, Dogs welcome at railway. Golden Arrow dining train available for meals and Sunday lunches.

Opening/Closing Times:

Spring: **Opens** Sat, Sun 10:30, **Closes** Sat, Sun 17:00
Summer: **Opens** Mon - Sun 10:30, **Closes** Mon - Sun 17:00
Autumn: **Opens** Sat, Sun 10:30, **Closes** Sat, Sun 17:00

Key: St = Stops   Al = Alight   Bd = Board   Tl = Toilets   DT = Disabled Toilets   PA = Kids Play Area   CP = Free Car Park   Ph = Pay Phone   Mu = Museum
WR = Waiting Room   Sh = Sheds   VS = Can Visit Sheds   WS = Workshops   VW = Can Visit Workshops   SB = Signal Box   VSB = Can Visit Signal Box

A-Z STEAM RAILWAYS

Bluebell Railway — Bodmin & Wenford Railway

Winter: **Opens** Sat, Sun 10:30, **Closes** Sat, Sun 17:00
Other: Contact for opening times during half terms.

Location:
Nearest Town/Village: Lewis   **Main Road:** A275   **Bus:** 121, 270, 473

Contact(s):
● **Operations Manager:** Mr Chris Nibs **(T)** 01825 720810   **(E)** chris.nibs@bluebell-railway.co.uk

Journeys Available At This Railway:

Sheffield Park to Hosted Keynes
Track Type: Single
Features: Views of Open Fields, Water, Woods. Maximum gradient of 1 in 60.
Bridges: 5 'over', 10 'under'   **Tunnels:** 1   **Signal Boxes:** 4   **Rivers:** 1   **Journey Length:** 9.5 mile(s)
Price: £5.80 (Adult Standard)   £2.90 (Child Standard)

Stations On This Journey:

Station Name	St	Al	Bd	Tl	DT	PA	CP	Ph	Mu	WR	Sh	VS	WS	VW	SB	VSB
Sheffield Park	✓	✓	✓	✓	✓	✓		✓		✓	✓	✓			✓	✓
Kingscote	✓	✓	✓	✓	✓										✓	✓
Hosted Keynes	✓	✓	✓	✓			✓						✓		✓	

BODMIN & WENFORD RAILWAY

BODMIN & WENFORD RAILWAY Bodmin General Station, Bodmin, **CORNWALL,** PL31 1AQ, **ENGLAND**.
(T) 01208 73666
(E) bodwenf@aol.com
Affiliated Bodies: Heritage Railway Association
Year Opened: 1989
Type of Complex: Railway Station, Operational Railway Line, Restoration Site
Gauge: Standard

Stock Overview:
No. Steam Locos: 10
No. Diesel Locos: 11

Facilities: Café, Disabled access, Driver footplate experience, Santa Special, 'Thomas' event, Enthusiast galas, Courses on how to drive Locos, Souvenir shop, Books for sale, Videos for sale, Models for sale.

Opening/Closing Times:
Summer: **Opens** Mon - Sun 09:00, **Closes** Mon - Sun 18:00
Other: Opening days in March, April, May, October and November vary. Contact for details.

Location:
Nearest Town/Village: Bodmin   **Main Road:** A30   **Mainline Station:** Bodmin Parkway

Contact(s):
● **General Manager:** Mr Roger Webster

Journeys Available At This Railway:

Bodmin General to Bodmin General (round trip)
Track Type: Single
Features: Views of Open Fields, Urbanisation. Features 20 bridges on journey. Maximum gradient of 1 in 47.
Signal Boxes: 1   **Journey Length:** 6.5 mile(s)
Price: £5.00 (Adult Standard)   £3.00 (Child Standard)

Stations On This Journey:

Station Name	St	Al	Bd	Tl	DT	PA	CP	Ph	Mu	WR	Sh	VS	WS	VW	SB	VSB
Bodmin General	✓	✓		✓	✓		✓				✓	✓	✓	✓	✓	
Bodmin Parkway Station	✓	✓														
Boscarne Junction	✓	✓														
Colesloggett	✓	✓														

BO'NESS & KINNEIL RAILWAY

SCOTTISH RAILWAY PRESERVATION SOCIETY (THE) Bo'ness Station, Union St, Bo'ness, **LOTHIAN (WEST),** EH51 9AQ, **SCOTLAND**.

(T) 01506 822298

(E) enquiries@railway.srps.org.uk

(W) www.srps.org.uk

Affiliated Bodies: Heritage Railway Association, Transport Trust

Type of Complex: Railway Station, Operational Railway Line, Museum

Gauge: Standard

Stock Overview:

No. Steam Locos: 22 (2 Pre-Group, 1 Pre-Nationalisation)

No. Diesel Locos: 19

Facilities: Buffet, Driver footplate experience, Santa Special, 'Thomas' event, Enthusiast galas, Courses on how to drive Locos, Souvenir shop, Books for sale, Videos for sale, Main credit cards taken, Children's events, Facilities for hire, Trains for hire, Picnic area.

Opening/Closing Times:

Spring: **Opens** Sat, Sun 11:00, **Closes** Sat, Sun 16:30

Summer: **Opens** Tues - Sun 11:00, **Closes** Tues - Sun 16:30

Autumn: **Opens** Sat, Sun 11:00, **Closes** Sat, Sun 16:30

Location:

Instructions: Situated off junction 5 and 3 of the M9 and junction 1 of the M90.

Nearest Town/Village: Bo'ness   **Main Road:** A904   **Mainline Station:** Linlithgow

Contact(s):

● **Vice Chairman:** Mr Jim Watson

Journeys Available At This Railway:

Bo'ness to Birkhill

Track Type: Single

Features: Views of Open Fields, Woods.

Tunnels: 1   **Level Crossings:** 4   **Signal Boxes:** 1   **Journey Length:** 3.5 mile(s)

Price: £4.50 (Adult Standard) £2.00 (Child Standard)

Stations On This Journey:

Station Name	St	Al	Bd	Tl	DT	PA	CP	Ph	Mu	WR	Sh	VS	WS	VW	SB	VSB
Bo'ness	✔	✔		✔	✔		✔		✔		✔	✔	✔	✔	✔	✔
Kinneil	✔															
Birkhill	✔	✔		✔	✔						✔					

BOWES RAILWAY

BOWES RAILWAY Springwell Village, Gateshead, **TYNE AND WEAR,** NE9 7QJ, **ENGLAND**.

(T) 0191 4161847

(W) www.bowesrailway.co.uk

Affiliated Bodies: Heritage Railway Association

Year Opened: 1975

Type of Complex: Railway Station, Operational Railway Line, Museum, Restoration Site

Type of Organisation: Charity, Non-Profit

Gauge: Standard

Stock Overview:

No. Steam Locos: 3

No. Diesel Locos: 5

Background: The worlds only operational preserved standard gauge rope hauled railway.

Facilities: Café, Guided tours available, Driver footplate experience, Santa Special, Souvenir shop, Books for sale, Videos for sale, Children's events, Facilities for hire.

Opening/Closing Times:

Key: *St* = Stops   *Al* = Alight   *Bd* = Board   *Tl* = Toilets   *DT* = Disabled Toilets   *PA* = Kids Play Area   *CP* = Free Car Park   *Ph* = Pay Phone   *Mu* = Museum
WR = Waiting Room   *Sh* = Sheds   *VS* = Can Visit Sheds   *WS* = Workshops   *VW* = Can Visit Workshops   *SB* = Signal Box   *VSB* = Can Visit Signal Box

Spring: **Opens** Mon - Fri 11:00, **Closes** Mon - Fri 17:00
Summer: **Opens** Mon - Fri 11:00, **Closes** Mon - Fri 17:00
Autumn: **Opens** Mon - Fri 11:00, **Closes** Mon - Fri 17:00
Winter: **Opens** Mon - Fri 11:00, **Closes** Mon - Fri 17:00
Other: Contact for details of operational days.

Location:

Nearest Town/Village: Gateshead   **Main Road:** B1288   **Bus:** 56A, 187, 188, X2, X3, X4, X5, X85, X90, X94   **Mainline Station:** Newcastle Central Station

Contact(s):

- **Chairman:** Mr Philip Dawe
- **Secretary:** Mr Peter Norman
- **Technical Info:** Mr John Young

Journeys Available At This Railway:

Springwell to Pelaw Main Junction
Track Type: Single
Features: Views of Urbanisation. Maximum gradient of 1 in 50.
Level Crossings: 1   **Signal Boxes:** 1   **Journey Length:** 1 mile(s)
Price: £2.50 (Adult Standard) £1.00 (Child Standard)

Stations On This Journey:

Station Name	St	Al	Bd	Tl	DT	PA	CP	Ph	Mu	WR	Sh	VS	WS	VW	SB	VSB
Springwell	✔	✔					✔			✔		✔		✔		
Pelaw Main Junction	✔	✔														

BRECON MOUNTAIN RAILWAY

BRECON MOUNTAIN RAILWAY Pant Station, Merthyr Tydfil, **MERTHYR TYDFIL,** CF48 2UP, **WALES**.
(T) 01685 722988   **(F)** 01685 384854
(E) enquiries@breconmountainrailway.co.uk
(W) www.breconmountainrailway.co.uk
Year Opened: 1980

Stock Overview:

No. Steam Locos: 1

Facilities: Café, Disabled access, Santa Special, Enthusiast galas, Souvenir shop, Main credit cards taken, Children's events, Holiday accomodation is available in the old signal box at Pontsticill.

Opening/Closing Times:

Spring: **Opens** Sat, Sun, Tues - Thurs 09:30, **Closes** Sat, Sun, Tues - Thurs 16:30
Summer: **Opens** Sat, Sun, Tues - Thurs 09:30, **Closes** Sat, Sun, Tues - Thurs 16:30
Autumn: **Opens** Sat, Sun, Tues - Thurs 09:30, **Closes** Sat, Sun, Tues - Thurs 16:30

Location:

Nearest Town/Village: Merthyr Tydfil   **Main Road:** A465   **Bus:** 30, 31   **Mainline Station:** Merthyr Tydfil

Contact(s):

- **For Bookings:** Ms Kelly Williams
- **General Manager:** Mr A J Hills

Journeys Available At This Railway:

Pant to Pant (round trip)
Features: Views of Hills, Water. Taf Fechan reservoir. Maximum gradient of 1 in 44.
Signal Boxes: 1   **Journey Length:** 3.5 mile(s)
Price: £6.80 (Adult Standard) £3.40 (Child Standard)

Stations On This Journey:

Station Name	St	Al	Bd	Tl	DT	PA	CP	Ph	Mu	WR	Sh	VS	WS	VW	SB	VSB
Pant	✔	✔		✔	✔		✔				✔	✔	✔	✔		
Pontsticill	✔	✔		✔									✔			

BREDGAR & WORMSHILL

BREDGAR & WORMSHILL LIGHT RAILWAY The Warren, Bredgar, Sittingbourne, **KENT,** ME9 8AT, **ENGLAND**.

(T) 01622 884254   **(F)** 01622 884668

(W) www.bwlr.co.uk

Affiliated Bodies: Heritage Railway Association

Complex Size: 25 Acres   **Year Opened:** 1975

Type of Complex: Railway Station, Operational Railway Line, Museum, Restoration Site

Type of Organisation: Trust, Volunteer, Non-Profit

Gauge: Narrow   **No. Staff:** 2   **No. Volunteers:** 14

Stock Overview:

No. Steam Locos: 12

TV/Film Appearances: Southern Steam (2001), Great Day Out (2001)

Facilities: Café, Waiting room, Guided tours available, Driver footplate experience, Santa Special, Enthusiast galas, Courses on how to drive Locos, Souvenir shop, Books for sale, Videos for sale, Facilities for hire, Trains for hire, Picnic areas, vintage cars, model railway and working beam engine.

Entry Fees: Adults: £5.00   **Children:** £2.50

Opening/Closing Times:

Spring: **Opens** 11:00, **Closes** 17:00

Summer: **Opens** 11:00, **Closes** 17:00

Location:

Nearest Town/Village: Sittingbourne   **Main Road:** M20, J8   **Taxi:** A2 Taxis   **Mainline Station:** Sittingbourne   **Hotel:** Jarvis Hotel   **Restaurant:** Hollingbourne

Contact(s):

- **For Bookings:** Mr Bill Best
- **General Manager:** Mr David Best   **(T)** 01795 428139
- **Manager:** Mr Bill Best
- **Owner:** Mr Bill Best
- **Technical Info:** Mr Bill Best

Journeys Available At This Railway:

Warren Wood to Stony Shaw

Track Type: Single   Direction: North to South

Features: Views of Open Fields, Woods. Maximum gradient of 1 in 50 (For 100 metres).

Signal Boxes: 2   **Journey Duration:** 5 mins   **Journey Length:** 0.5 mile(s)

Stations On This Journey:

Station Name	St	Al	Bd	Tl	DT	PA	CP	Ph	Mu	WR	Sh	VS	WS	VW	SB	VSB
Warren Wood	✔	✔	✔	✔		✔			✔	✔	✔	✔	✔		✔	
Stony Shaw	✔	✔			✔										✔	

BRESSINGHAM STEAM

BRESSINGHAM STEAM MUSEUM TRUST Bressingham, Diss, **NORFOLK,** IP22 2AB, **ENGLAND**.

(T) 01379 687386   **(F)** 01379 688085

(E) info@bressingham.co.uk

(W) www.bressingham.co.uk

Affiliated Bodies: Transport Trust

Year Opened: 1961

Type of Complex: Operational Railway Line, Museum, Restoration Site

Type of Organisation: Charity, Trust

Gauge: Narrow & Standard   **No. Staff:** 10   **No. Volunteers:** 100

Stock Overview:

No. Steam Locos: 13

No. Diesel Locos: 1

Key:	St = Stops	Al = Alight	Bd = Board	Tl = Toilets	DT = Disabled Toilets	PA = Kids Play Area	CP = Free Car Park	Ph = Pay Phone	Mu = Museum
	WR = Waiting Room	Sh = Sheds	VS = Can Visit Sheds	WS = Workshops	VW = Can Visit Workshops	SB = Signal Box	VSB = Can Visit Signal Box		

Facilities: Café, Restaurant, Ticket office, Disabled access, Lecture room, Function room, Line permit needed, Advanced booking available, Driver footplate experience, Santa Special, 'Thomas' event, History lectures, Movie shows, Courses on how to drive Locos, Souvenir shop, Books for sale, Videos for sale, Paintings/drawings for sale, Main credit cards taken, Children's events, Facilities for hire, Trains for hire.

Opening/Closing Times:
Spring: **Opens** Mon - Sun 10:30, **Closes** Mon - Sun 17:30
Summer: **Opens** Mon - Sun 10:30, **Closes** Mon - Sun 17:30
Autumn: **Opens** Mon - Sun 10:30, **Closes** Mon - Sun 16:30
Winter: **Opens** Mon - Sun 11:00, **Closes** Mon - Sun 16:30
Other: Contact for information on steaming days.

Location:
Nearest Town/Village: Diss   **Main Road:** A1066   **Mainline Station:** Diss   **Hotel:** Park Hotel

Contact(s):
● **Events Manager:** Mr Ray King
● **General Manager:** Mr Howard Stephens
● **Technical Info:** Mr David Madden   (E) madden@which.net

Journeys Available At This Railway:
Track Type: Single
Features: Views of Open Fields, Woods. Views of world famous Dell Garden. Maximum gradient of 1 in 38.
Journey Length: 5.2 mile(s)
Price: £10.00 (Adult Standard) £8.00 (Child Standard)

Stations On This Journey:

Station Name	St	Al	Bd	Tl	DT	PA	CP	Ph	Mu	WR	Sh	VS	WS	VW	SB	VSB
Waveney	✔	✔		✔	✔	✔	✔	✔	✔		✔			✔	✔	

BRISTOL HARBOUR RAILWAY

BRISTOL INDUSTRIAL MUSEUM Princes Wharf, Wapping Rd, Bristol, **BRISTOL,** BS1 4RN, **ENGLAND.**
(T) 0117 9251470   **(F)** 0117 9297318
(W) www.bristol-city.gov.uk
Affiliated Bodies: Heritage Railway Association
Complex Size: 3 Acres   **Year Opened:** 1978
Type of Complex: Operational Railway Line, Museum
Type of Organisation: Non-Profit
Gauge: Standard   **No. Staff:** 1   **No. Volunteers:** 15

Stock Overview:
No. Steam Locos: 3
No. Diesel Locos: 1

TV/Film Appearances: Casualty

Facilities: Disabled access, Advanced booking available, Driver footplate experience, Souvenir shop, Books for sale, Videos for sale, Photos for sale, Models for sale, Main credit cards taken, Facilities for hire, Trains for hire.

Opening/Closing Times:
Spring: **Opens** Sat - Wed 10:00, **Closes** Sat - Wed 17:00
Summer: **Opens** Sat - Wed 10:00, **Closes** Sat - Wed 17:00
Autumn: **Opens** Sat - Wed 10:00, **Closes** Sat - Wed 17:00
Winter: **Opens** Sat, Sun 10:00, **Closes** Sat, Sun 17:00

Location:
Nearest Town/Village: Bristol   **Main Road:** Cumberland Rd   **Mainline Station:** Temple Meads
Hotel: Jury's

Contact(s):
● **For Bookings:** Mr David Martin
● **For Donations:** Mr David Martin
● **General Manager:** Mr Andy King (E) andy_king@bristol-city.gov.uk
● **Technical Info:** Mr David Martin

Journeys Available At This Railway:

Bristol Industrial Museum to Create Centre or SS Great Britain

Track Type: Single   Direction: East to West
Features: Views of Urbanisation, Water.
Bridges: 2 'under'   **Journey Duration:** 10 mins   **Journey Length:** 1 mile(s)
Price: £1.00 (Adult Standard)
Stations On This Journey:

Station Name	St	Al	Bd	Tl	DT	PA	CP	Ph	Mu	WR	Sh	VS	WS	VW	SB	VSB
Bristol Industrial Museum	✔	✔	✔	✔	✔				✔							
Create Centre		✔			✔	✔		✔								
SS Great Britain		✔	✔	✔												

BROOKSIDE MINIATURE

BROOKSIDE MINIATURE RAILWAY Macclesfield Rd, Poynton, **CHESHIRE**, SK12 1BY, **ENGLAND**.
(T) 01625 872919   **(F)** 01625 859119
Affiliated Bodies: Britains Great Little Railways
Complex Size: 7 Acres   **Year Opened:** 1989
Type of Complex: Operational Railway Line, Museum
Type of Organisation: Limited Company
Gauge: Narrow
Stock Overview:
No. Steam Locos: 2
No. Diesel Locos: 3
TV/Film Appearances: World In Action (1998)
Background: This extensive miniature railway and museum is located within the grounds of a large modern garden centre. There is also a large collection of Railwayana.
Facilities: Café, Restaurant, Ticket office, Disabled access, Function room, Waiting room, Guided tours available, Santa Special, Training courses, Enthusiast galas, Souvenir shop, Books for sale, Videos for sale, Photos for sale, Paintings/drawings for sale, Camera film for sale, Models for sale, Main credit cards taken, Children's events, Facilities for hire, Trains for hire.
Location:
Instructions: Railway situated on main A523, midway between Hazel Grove and Poynton. Follow brown tourist signs.
Nearest Town/Village: Stockport   **Main Road:** A523   **Bus:** 191   **Taxi:** Lynx 0161 4831114
Mainline Station: Poynton   **Hotel:** Alma Lodge Hotel
Contact(s):
- **For Bookings:** Mr S Cameron
- **For Bookings:** Mr D McFarlane
- **For Donations:** Mr C Halsall
- **General Manager:** Mr D McFarlane
- **Owner:** Mr C Halsall
- **Technical Info:** Mr D McFarlane
- **Technical Info:** Mr S Cameron
Journeys Available At This Railway:

Brookside Central to Brookside Central (round trip)
Track Type: Single
Features: Maximum gradient of 1 in 40 (For 50 metres).
Bridges: 3 'over'   **Tunnels:** 2   **Level Crossings:** 1   **Signal Boxes:** 1   **Rivers:** 1   **Journey Duration:** 8 mins
Price: £1.00 (Adult Standard) £0.50 (Child Standard) £1.00 (Adult Special) £5.50 (Child Special)
Stations On This Journey:

Station Name	St	Al	Bd	Tl	DT	PA	CP	Ph	Mu	WR	Sh	VS	WS	VW	SB	VSB
Brookside Central	✔	✔	✔	✔	✔		✔		✔	✔			✔	✔		

Key: St = Stops   Al = Alight   Bd = Board   Tl = Toilets   DT = Disabled Toilets   PA = Kids Play Area   CP = Free Car Park   Ph = Pay Phone   Mu = Museum
WR = Waiting Room   Sh = Sheds   VS = Can Visit Sheds   WS = Workshops   VW = Can Visit Workshops   SB = Signal Box   VSB = Can Visit Signal Box

BUCKINGHAMSHIRE RLWY CTRE

QUAINTON RAILWAY SOCIETY LTD Quainton Rd Station, Quainton, Aylesbury, **BUCKINGHAMSHIRE,** HP22 4BY, **ENGLAND**.

(T) 01296 655720

(W) www.bucksrailcentre.org.uk

Affiliated Bodies: Heritage Railway Association

Complex Size: 34 Acres

Type of Complex: Railway Station, Operational Railway Line, Museum, Restoration Site

Type of Organisation: Charity

Gauge: Standard

Stock Overview:

No. Steam Locos: 32 (2 Pre-Group)

No. Diesel Locos: 11

TV/Film Appearances: Dr Who (1981)

Facilities: Café, Disabled access, Santa Special, 'Thomas' event, Courses on how to drive Locos, Souvenir shop, Books for sale, Main credit cards taken, Facilities for hire.

Opening/Closing Times:

Spring: **Opens** Mon - Sun 10:30, **Closes** Mon, Tues, Thurs - Sun 17:30, Wed 16:30

Summer: **Opens** Mon - Sun 10:30, **Closes** Mon, Tues, Thurs - Sun 17:30, Wed 16:30

Autumn: **Opens** Mon - Sun 10:30, **Closes** Mon, Tues, Thurs - Sun 17:30, Wed 16:30

Location:

Nearest Town/Village: Aylesbury   **Main Road:** A41   **Bus:** 16, 17   **Mainline Station:** Aylesbury

Contact(s):

- **Chairman:** Mr Andrew Bratton
- **Membership Secretary:** Mr David Potter
- **Sales Development Manager:** Mr David Jenner

Journeys Available At This Railway:

Quainton Road to Quainton Road (round trip)
Track Type: Single

Stations On This Journey:

Station Name	St	Al	Bd	Tl	DT	PA	CP	Ph	Mu	WR	Sh	VS	WS	VW	SB	VSB
Quainton Road	✓	✓	✓	✓		✓					✓	✓	✓	✓	✓	
Rowley Road				✓												

BURE VALLEY RAILWAY

BURE VALLEY RAILWAY Aylsham Station, Aylsham, Norwich, **NORFOLK,** NR11 6BW, **ENGLAND**.

(T) 01263 733858   **(F)** 01263 733814

(E) info@bvrw.co.uk

(W) www.bvrw.co.uk

Affiliated Bodies: Heritage Railway Association, Transport Trust

Type of Complex: Railway Station, Operational Railway Line, Museum

Gauge: Narrow

Stock Overview:

No. Steam Locos: 4

No. Diesel Locos: 3

Facilities: Restaurant, Ticket office, Disabled access, Santa Special, 'Thomas' event, Courses on how to drive Locos, Souvenir shop, Facilities for hire, 'Broadland Boat Train' combines a journey by steam with a cruise on the Norfolk Broads. Bicycle hire is available at Aylsham and Wroxham.

Opening/Closing Times:

Spring: **Opens** Mon - Sun 10:15, **Closes** Mon - Sun 16:30

Summer: **Opens** Mon - Sun 10:15, **Closes** Mon - Sun 16:30

Autumn: **Opens** Sun - Thurs 10:15, **Closes** Sun - Thurs 16:30

Other: Closed during November, January, February and March for driver training. Open December for Santa specials.

Location:
Nearest Town/Village: Aylsham   **Main Road:** A140

Contact(s):
- **Director:** Mr Paul Conibeare

Journeys Available At This Railway:

Aylsham to Wroxham
Track Type: Single
Features: Views of Open Fields, Water.
Bridges: 1 'over', 16 'under'   **Tunnels:** 1   **Level Crossings:** 1   **Rivers:** 1   **Journey Length:** 9 mile(s)
Price: £4.00 (Adult Standard) £2.75 (Child Standard)

Stations On This Journey:

Station Name	St	Al	Bd	Tl	DT	PA	CP	Ph	Mu	WR	Sh	VS	WS	VW	SB	VSB
Aylsham	✔	✔	✔	✔	✔		✔						✔	✔	✔	
Brampton	✔	✔	✔													
Buxton	✔	✔	✔													
Coltishall	✔	✔	✔													
Wroxham	✔	✔	✔	✔	✔		✔									

CADEBY LIGHT RAILWAY

CADEBY LIGHT RAILWAY The Old Rectory, Cadeby, Market Bosworth, Hinckley, **LEICESTERSHIRE,** CV13 0AS, **ENGLAND**.
(T) 01455 290462
Affiliated Bodies: Heritage Railway Association, Transport Trust
Type of Complex: Operational Railway Line
Gauge: Narrow
Stock Overview:
No. Steam Locos: 2 (2 Pre-Group)
No. Diesel Locos: 12 (9 Pre-Group, 1 Pre-Nationalisation)
Facilities: Santa Special, Children's events, Brass rubbing centre and model railway.
Opening/Closing Times:
Other: Open selected Saturdays throughout the year. Contact for details.
Location:
Nearest Town/Village: Hinckley   **Main Road:** A447   **Mainline Station:** Hinckley
Contact(s):
- **Owner:** Ms Audrey Boston

CALEDONIAN RAILWAY

CALEDONIAN RAILWAY (BRECHIN) LTD2 Park Rd, Brechin, **ANGUS,** DD9 7AF, **SCOTLAND**.
(T) 01561 377760
(W) www.caledonianrailway.co.uk
Affiliated Bodies: Heritage Railway Association
Year Opened: 1981
Type of Complex: Railway Station, Operational Railway Line, Museum, Restoration Site
Type of Organisation: Charity, Heritage Project, Conservation Project, Limited Company, Volunteer, Non-Profit
Gauge: Standard   **No. Volunteers:** 30
Stock Overview:
No. Steam Locos: 6 (3 Pre-Group, 2 Pre-Nationalisation)
No. Diesel Locos: 10
Facilities: Buffet, Ticket office, Disabled access, Waiting room, Left luggage office, Advanced booking available, Guided tours available, Driver footplate experience, Santa Special, Enthusiast galas, Souvenir shop, Books for sale, Videos for sale, Photos for sale, Children's events, Facilities for hire,

Key: *St* = Stops   *Al* = Alight   *Bd* = Board   *Tl* = Toilets   *DT* = Disabled Toilets   *PA* = Kids Play Area   *CP* = Free Car Park   *Ph* = Pay Phone   *Mu* = Museum
WR = Waiting Room   *Sh* = Sheds   *VS* = Can Visit Sheds   *WS* = Workshops   *VW* = Can Visit Workshops   *SB* = Signal Box   *VSB* = Can Visit Signal Box

or hire.

ning/Closing Times:

Spring:	**Opens** 10:45, **Closes** 17:05
Summer:	**Opens** 10:45, **Closes** 17:05
Autumn:	**Opens** 10:45, **Closes** 17:05
Winter:	**Opens** 10:45, **Closes** 17:05
Other:	Open Sundays from June - September. Also open for Santa specials and Easter weekend.

Location:

Nearest Town/Village: Brechin   **Main Road:** A90   **Mainline Station:** Montrose   **Hotel:** The Northern Hotel   **Restaurant:** The Northern Hotel

Contact(s):

- **Chairman:** Mr Andrew Webster   **(T)** 01241 828345
- **For Bookings:** Ms Ena Wilkie **(T)** 01561 377760
- **For Donations:** Mr Bob Smith   **(T)** 01674 762165
- **General Manager:** Mr Andrew Webster   **(T)** 01241 828345
- **Technical Info:** Mr Steve Pegg   **(T)** 01382 732035

Alternative Contact Details:

- Fernlea, 248 High St, Laurencekirk, Aberdeenshire, AB30 1BP, Scotland

Journeys Available At This Railway:

Brechin to Bridge of Dun
Track Type: Single
Features: Views of Open Fields, Urbanisation, Woods. Maximum gradient of 1 in 70.
Bridges: 3 'over', 5 'under'   **Journey Length:** 4 mile(s)
Price: £4.50 (Adult Standard) £2.50 (Child Standard)

Stations On This Journey:

Station Name	St	Al	Bd	Tl	DT	PA	CP	Ph	Mu	WR	Sh	VS	WS	VW	SB	VSB
Brechin	✓		✓	✓			✓		✓	✓	✓		✓			
Bridge of Dun	✓		✓	✓			✓			✓						

CAMBRIAN RAILWAY SOCIETY

CAMBRIAN RAILWAY SOCIETY LTD Oswald Rd, Oswestry, **SHROPSHIRE,** SY11 1RE, **ENGLAND**.
(T) 01691 671749
(W) www.cambrianline.co.uk
Affiliated Bodies: Heritage Railway Association
Type of Complex: Museum
Gauge: Standard   **No. Volunteers:** 35

Stock Overview:

No. Steam Locos: 1 (1 Pre-Nationalisation)
No. Diesel Locos: 2

Facilities: Café, Santa Special, Enthusiast galas, Souvenir shop, Books for sale, Models for sale, Main credit cards taken.

Entry Fees: Adults: £1.00   **Children:** £0.50

Opening/Closing Times:

Spring:	**Opens** Mon - Sun 09:00, **Closes** Mon - Sun 17:00
Summer:	**Opens** Mon - Sun 09:00, **Closes** Mon - Sun 17:00
Autumn:	**Opens** Mon - Sun 09:00, **Closes** Mon - Sun 17:00
Winter:	**Opens** Mon - Sun 09:00, **Closes** Mon - Sun 17:00
Other:	Trains run March - September.

Location:

Nearest Town/Village: Oswestry   **Main Road:** A5   **Mainline Station:** Gobowen

Contact(s):

- **General Manager:** Mr Mark Hignett

CAVAN & LEITRIM RAILWAY

CAVAN & LEITRIM RAILWAY (THE) Dromod, **COUNTY LEITRIM, IRELAND**.

(T) 078 38599

(E) dromod@eircom.net

Type of Complex: Operational Railway Line, Museum

Gauge: Narrow

Stock Overview:

No. Steam Locos: 1

No. Diesel Locos: 2

Facilities: Santa Special, Souvenir shop, Books for sale, Children's events.

Opening/Closing Times:

Spring:	**Opens** Mon - Sun 10:00, **Closes** Mon - Sun 14:30
Summer:	**Opens** Mon - Sun 10:00, **Closes** Mon - Sun 17:30
Autumn:	**Opens** Mon - Sun 10:00, **Closes** Mon - Sun 14:30
Winter:	**Opens** Mon - Sun 10:00, **Closes** Mon - Sun 14:30
Other:	Closed 23rd December - 5th January.

Location:

Nearest Town/Village: Dromod   **Main Road:** N4   **Mainline Station:** Dromod

Contact(s):

● **General Manager:** Mr Michael Kennedy

Journeys Available At This Railway:

Stations On This Journey:

Station Name	*St*	*Al*	*Bd*	*Tl*	*DT*	*PA*	*CP*	*Ph*	*Mu*	*WR*	*Sh*	*VS*	*WS*	*VW*	*SB*	*VSB*
Dromod	✔	✔		✔			✔		✔	✔	✔	✔	✔	✔	✔	✔

CHASEWATER RAILWAY

CHASEWATER RAILWAY Chasewater Country Pk, Pool Rd, Brownhills, Walsall, **MIDLANDS (WEST)**, WS8 7LT, **ENGLAND**.

(T) 01543 452623   **(F)** 01922 648380

(E) info@chasewaterrailway.co.uk

(W) www.chasewaterrailwater.co.uk

Affiliated Bodies: Heritage Railway Association, Lichfield District Tourism Association, Transport Trust

Year Opened: 1959

Type of Complex: Railway Station, Operational Railway Line, Restoration Site

Type of Organisation: Charity, Trust, Heritage Project, Limited Company, Volunteer, Non-Profit

Gauge: Standard   **No. Volunteers:** 30

Stock Overview:

No. Steam Locos: 7

No. Diesel Locos: 6

Background: This railway is the sole remaining section of the Colliery Railways of South Staffordshire. A new three platform station at Brownhills West opened in 2001. Two further stations are due to open in Easter 2002.

Facilities: Buffet, Ticket office, Disabled access, Waiting room, Santa Special, Souvenir shop, Books for sale, Children's events, Facilities for hire, Trains for hire.

Opening/Closing Times:

Spring:	**Opens** 11:30, **Closes** 17:00
Summer:	**Opens** 11:30, **Closes** 17:00
Autumn:	**Opens** 11:30, **Closes** 17:00

Location:

Instructions: Situated in Chasewater Country Park. Entrance is off Pool Road and is signposted from

---

Key: *St* = Stops   *Al* = Alight   *Bd* = Board   *Tl* = Toilets   *DT* = Disabled Toilets   *PA* = Kids Play Area   *CP* = Free Car Park   *Ph* = Pay Phone   *Mu* = Museum
WR = Waiting Room   *Sh* = Sheds   *VS* = Can Visit Sheds   *WS* = Workshops   *VW* = Can Visit Workshops   *SB* = Signal Box   *VSB* = Can Visit Signal Box

the southbound A5.

Nearest Town/Village: Walsall   **Main Road:** A5, A452   **Bus:** 156A, 362, 394A   **Mainline Station:** Walsall

Contact(s):
- **Chairman:** Mr D M Bathurst
- **General Manager:** Mr Steve Organ

Alternative Contact Details:
- 36 Spring Court, Birmingham Rd, Walsall, Midlands (West), WS1 2NS, England

Journeys Available At This Railway:

Brownhills West to Norton Lakeside
Track Type: Single   Direction: West to East
Features: Views of Open Fields, Water, Woods. The Railway passes through Chasewater Country Park. Includes a lengthy causeway between 2 lakes.
Level Crossings: 1   **Journey Duration:** 20 mins   **Journey Length:** 2 mile(s)
Price: £2.45 (Adult Standard) £1.45 (Child Standard)

Stations On This Journey:

Station Name	St	Al	Bd	Tl	DT	PA	CP	Ph	Mu	WR	Sh	VS	WS	VW	SB	VSB
Brownhills West	✓	✓		✓	✓	✓	✓		✓	✓	✓			✓		
Norton Lakeside	✓	✓														
Chasewater Heaths	✓	✓		✓	✓				✓				✓			
Chasetown	✓	✓														

CHINNOR & PRINCES RISBOROUGH

CHINNOR & PRINCES RISBOROUGH RAILWAY CO LTD Station Rd, Chinnor, Princes Risborough, **OXFORDSHIRE,** OX39 4ER, **ENGLAND**.

(T) 01844 353535
(E) info@cprra.co.uk
(W) www.cprra.co.uk
Affiliated Bodies: Heritage Railway Association
Year Opened: 1994
Type of Complex: Railway Station, Operational Railway Line, Restoration Site
Type of Organisation: Charity, Conservation Project, Limited Company, Volunteer
Gauge: Standard   **No. Volunteers:** 70

Stock Overview:
No. Diesel Locos: 4

Facilities: Buffet, Ticket office, Disabled access, Waiting room, Santa Special, 'Thomas' event, Souvenir shop, Books for sale, Videos for sale, Photos for sale, Tapes for sale, Models for sale, Main credit cards taken, Children's events, Facilities for hire, Trains for hire.

Opening/Closing Times:
Spring: **Opens** Sat, Sun 11:00, **Closes** Sat, Sun 16:00
Summer: **Opens** Sat, Sun 10:00, **Closes** Sat, Sun 17:30
Autumn: **Opens** Sat, Sun 11:00, **Closes** Sat, Sun 16:00
Other: Open during certain holidays and Bank Holidays. Contact for details.

Location:
Nearest Town/Village: Princes Risborough   **Main Road:** B4009   **Bus:** 232, 331, 332   **Mainline Station:** Princes Risborough

Contact(s):
- **Advertising Manager:** Mr Eric Samuel   **(T)** 01494 437395   **(E)** eric.samuel@cprra.co.uk
- **General Manager:** Mr Graham Petts **(T)** 020 84289637   **(E)** graham.petts@btinternet.com
- **Membership Secretary:** Mr Peter Harris **(T)** 01296 433795   **(E)** pete4heus@aol.com
- **PR Manager:** Mr Eric Samuel **(T)** 01494 437395   **(E)** eric.samuel@cprra.co.uk
- **Press Officer:** Mr Eric Samuel   **(T)** 01494 437395   **(E)** eric.samuel@cprra.co.uk

Alternative Contact Details:
- 37 Lytham Ave, Watford, Hertfordshire, WD1 6XA, EnglandPress Officer, 2 Coates Lane, High Wycombe, Buckinghamshire, HP13 5HE, England

Journeys Available At This Railway:

Chinnor Station to Chinnor Station (round trip)
Track Type: Single   Direction: South to North
Features: Views of Hills, Open Fields, Woods. Views of Chiltern Hills and Vale of Aylesbury. Maximum gradient of 1 in 66.
Bridges: 2 'over', 1 'under'   **Level Crossings:** 2   **Rivers:** 2   **Journey Duration:** 45 mins   **Journey Length:** 8 mile(s)
Price: £5.00 (Adult Standard) £3.00 (Child Standard) £6.00 (Adult Special) £4.00 (Child Special)
Available on Journey: Refreshments, Drinks, Alcohol, Buffet.

Stations On This Journey:

Station Name	St	Al	Bd	Tl	DT	PA	CP	Ph	Mu	WR	Sh	VS	WS	VW	SB	VSB
Chinnor Station	✔	✔	✔	✔	✔		✔			✔						
Wainhill Halt																
Bledlow Bridge Halt																
Trame Junction																

CHOLSEY & WALLINGFORD RAILWAY

CHOLSEY & WALLINGFORD RAILWAY PRESERVATION SOCIETY St John's Rd, Wallingford,
OXFORDSHIRE, OX10 0AN, **ENGLAND**.
(T) 01491 835067   **(F)** 01491 651696
Affiliated Bodies: Heritage Railway Association
Complex Size: 1 Acres   **Year Opened:** 1985
Type of Complex: Operational Railway Line, Museum
Type of Organisation: Charity, Limited Company, Volunteer
Gauge: Standard
Stock Overview:
No. Diesel Locos: 4
Facilities: Café, Ticket office, Disabled access, Waiting room, Advanced booking available, Santa
Special, 'Thomas' event, Souvenir shop, Books for sale, Videos for sale, Camera film for sale, Models
for sale, Main credit cards taken, Children's events.
Opening/Closing Times:
Spring: **Opens** 11:00, **Closes** 17:00
Summer: **Opens** 11:00, **Closes** 17:00
Autumn: **Opens** 11:00, **Closes** 17:00
Winter: **Opens** 11:00, **Closes** 17:00
Location:
Instructions: From Wallingford, follow signs for Hithercroft Industrial Estate.
Nearest Town/Village: Wallingford   **Main Road:** A329   **Mainline Station:** Cholsey
Contact(s):
● **For Bookings:** Ms Jo Clyde
● **For Donations:** Ms Jo Clyde
● **General Manager:** Ms Jo Clyde **(E)** jo.clyde@filands.co.uk
● **Technical Info:** Ms Jo Clyde
Alternative Contact Details:
● General Manager, 7 Weedon Cl, Wallingford, Oxfordshire, OX10 9RD, England**(T)** 01491 652842
Journeys Available At This Railway:

Wallingford to Cholsey
Track Type: Single   Direction: North to South
Features: Views of Open Fields.
Bridges: 2 'over', 1 'under'   **Level Crossings:** 1   **Rivers:** 2   **Journey Duration:** 15 mins   **Journey Length:** 2.5
mile(s)
Price: £3.50 (Adult Standard) £2.50 (Child Standard)
Stations On This Journey:

Station Name	St	Al	Bd	Tl	DT	PA	CP	Ph	Mu	WR	Sh	VS	WS	VW	SB	VSB
Wallingford	✔	✔	✔	✔	✔	✔			✔	✔						
Cholsey	✔	✔	✔	✔					✔		✔					

Key: St = Stops   Al = Alight   Bd = Board   Tl = Toilets   DT = Disabled Toilets   PA = Kids Play Area   CP = Free Car Park   Ph = Pay Phone   Mu = Museum
WR = Waiting Room   Sh = Sheds   VS = Can Visit Sheds   WS = Workshops   VW = Can Visit Workshops   SB = Signal Box   VSB = Can Visit Signal Box

CHURNET VALLEY RAILWAY

CHURNET VALLEY RAILWAY Cheddleton Station, Station Rd, Cheddleton, **STAFFORDSHIRE,** ST13 7EE, **ENGLAND**.
(T) 01538 360522   **(F)** 01538 361848
(W) www.churnet-valley-railway.co.uk
Affiliated Bodies: Heritage Railway Association
Type of Complex: Railway Station, Operational Railway Line
Type of Organisation: Heritage Project, Volunteer
Stock Overview:
No. Steam Locos: 7
No. Diesel Locos: 9
Facilities: Café, Santa Special, 'Thomas' event, Training courses, Courses on how to drive Locos, Souvenir shop.
Location:
Nearest Town/Village: Leek   **Main Road:** A520   **Bus:** 16, 106/107   **Hotel:** Bank End Farm Motel
Restaurant: The Avenue
Contact(s):
● **General Manager:** Ms Margaret Mountford
Journeys Available At This Railway:

Kingsley & Froghall or Cheddleton to Kingsley & Froghall or Cheddleton (round trip)
Track Type: Single
Features: Views of Hills, Open Fields, Water, Woods. Maximum gradient of 1 in 201.
Tunnels: 1
Available on Journey: Buffet.
Stations On This Journey:

Station Name	St	Al	Bd	Tl	DT	PA	CP	Ph	Mu	WR	Sh	VS	WS	VW	SB	VSB
Kingsley & Froghall	✓	✓	✓				✓									
Consall	✓	✓	✓								✓					
Cheddleton	✓	✓	✓	✓	✓		✓				✓	✓				
Leekbrook Junction																

CLEETHORPES LIGHT RAILWAY

CLEETHORPES COAST LIGHT RAILWAY Lakeside Station, Kings Rd, Cleethorpes, **LINCOLNSHIRE (NORTH EAST),** DN35 0AG, **ENGLAND**.
(T) 01472 604657
Affiliated Bodies: Heritage Railway Association
Year Opened: 1948
Type of Complex: Railway Station, Operational Railway Line, Museum
Gauge: Narrow
Stock Overview:
No. Steam Locos: 3
No. Diesel Locos: 3
Facilities: Café, Disabled access, Guided tours available, Santa Special, 'Thomas' event, History lectures, Enthusiast galas, Courses on how to drive Locos, Souvenir shop, Main credit cards taken, Children's events, Facilities for hire, Trains for hire, Picnic area.
Opening/Closing Times:
Spring: **Opens** Sat, Sun 11:00, **Closes** Sat, Sun 17:00
Summer: **Opens** Mon - Sun 11:00, **Closes** Mon - Sun 17:00
Autumn: **Opens** Sat, Sun 11:00, **Closes** Sat, Sun 17:00
Winter: **Opens** Sat, Sun 11:00, **Closes** Sat, Sun 17:00
Other: Closed during November.
Location:
Nearest Town/Village: Cleethorpes   **Main Road:** Kings Road   **Bus:** 9X, 17   **Mainline**
Station: Cleethorpes

Contact(s):
● **General Manager:** Mr Chris Shaw
Journeys Available At This Railway:

Lakeside to Kingsway
Features: Views of Open Fields, Urbanisation, Water.
Bridges: 1 'over'   **Level Crossings:** 7   **Signal Boxes:** 2   **Rivers:** 1   **Viaducts:** 1   **Journey Length:** 1 mile(s)
Price: £1.50 (Adult Standard) £1.20 (Child Standard)
Stations On This Journey:

Station Name	St	Al	Bd	Tl	DT	PA	CP	Ph	Mu	WR	Sh	VS	WS	VW	SB	VSB
Lakeside	✔	✔		✔					✔	✔	✔	✔	✔	✔	✔	
Halfway Halt	✔															
Kingsway	✔	✔		✔	✔					✔						

COLNE VALLEY RAILWAY

COLNE VALLEY RAILWAY PRESERVATION SOCIETY Castle Hedingham Station, Yeldham Rd, Castle Hedingham, Halstead, **ESSEX,** CO9 3DZ, **ENGLAND**.
(T) 01787 461174
(W) www.cvr.org.uk
Affiliated Bodies: Heritage Railway Association, Transport Trust
Year Opened: 1972
Type of Complex: Railway Station, Operational Railway Line, Restoration Site
Stock Overview:
No. Steam Locos: 10
No. Diesel Locos: 5
Facilities: Café, Ticket office, Waiting room, Driver footplate experience, Santa Special, 'Thomas' event, Enthusiast galas, Souvenir shop, Main credit cards taken, Facilities for hire, Trains for hire.
Opening/Closing Times:
Spring: **Opens** Sun 12:00, **Closes** Sun 16:00
Summer: **Opens** Sun 12:00, **Closes** Sun 16:00
Autumn: **Opens** Sun 12:00, **Closes** Sun 16:00
Other: Contact for additional opening times during the summer holidays.
Location:
Nearest Town/Village: Braintree   **Main Road:** A1017   **Mainline Station:** Braintree
Contact(s):
● **General Manager:** Mr Dick Hymas
Journeys Available At This Railway:

Castle Hedingham to Castle Hedingham (round trip)
Track Type: Single
Features: Views of Open Fields, Water, Woods.
Signal Boxes: 3   **Rivers:** 1   **Journey Length:** 1 mile(s)
Price: £6.00 (Adult Standard) £3.00 (Child Standard)
Stations On This Journey:

Station Name	St	Al	Bd	Tl	DT	PA	CP	Ph	Mu	WR	Sh	VS	WS	VW	SB	VSB
Castle Hedingham	✔	✔	✔	✔	✔		✔			✔		✔		✔	✔	

CONWY VALLEY

CONWY VALLEY RAILWAY MUSEUM Old Goods Yard, Betws-y-Coed, **CONWY,** LL24 0AL, **WALES**.
(T) 01690 710568   **(F)** 01690 710132
Affiliated Bodies: Heritage Railway Association
Complex Size: 5 Acres   **Year Opened:** 1978
Type of Organisation: Limited Company
Gauge: Narrow

Key: *St* = Stops   *Al* = Alight   *Bd* = Board   *Tl* = Toilets   *DT* = Disabled Toilets   *PA* = Kids Play Area   *CP* = Free Car Park   *Ph* = Pay Phone   *Mu* = Museum
        WR = Waiting Room   *Sh* = Sheds   *VS* = Can Visit Sheds   *WS* = Workshops   *VW* = Can Visit Workshops   *SB* = Signal Box   *VSB* = Can Visit Signal Box

<u>Stock Overview</u>:
No. Steam Locos: 2
No. Diesel Locos: 1
Facilities: Buffet, Disabled access, Santa Special, Souvenir shop, Books for sale, Videos for sale, Paintings/drawings for sale, Camera film for sale, CD's for sale, Tapes for sale, Models for sale, Main credit cards taken, Children's events.
Entry Fees: Adults: £1.00   **Children:** £1.00
<u>Opening/Closing Times</u>:
Spring: **Opens** Sat, Sun 10:00, **Closes** Sat, Sun 17:30
Summer: **Opens** Mon - Sun 10:00, **Closes** Mon - Sun 17:30
Autumn: **Opens** Sat, Sun 10:00, **Closes** Sat, Sun 17:00
Winter: **Opens** Sat, Sun 10:00, **Closes** Sat, Sun 16:00
<u>Location</u>:
Nearest Town/Village: Llanrwst   **Main Road:** A5   **Taxi:** Glyn Joned   **Mainline Station:** Llandudno Junction   **Hotel:** Royal Oak
<u>Contact(s)</u>:
- **For Bookings:** Mrs M Turner
- **Owner:** Mr C M Cartwright
- **Technical Info:** Mr C M Cartwright

CORRIS RAILWAY MUSEUM

CORRIS RAILWAY MUSEUM Corris Railway Museum, Station Yard, Corris, Machynlleth, **POWYS,** SY20 9SH, **WALES**.
(T) 01654 761303
(W) www.corris.co.uk
Affiliated Bodies: Heritage Railway Association
Type of Complex: Operational Railway Line, Museum
Gauge: Narrow
Background: The track is not yet open to the public. Please contact for details.
Facilities: Café, Disabled access, Souvenir shop, Videos for sale, Models for sale, During August Bank Holidays at Machynlleth Model Railway Exhibition, the Society President Christopher Awdry reads from the 'Thomas' books written by his father and himself.
<u>Opening/Closing Times</u>:
Other: Open May - September and during school holidays. Contact for opening times.
<u>Location</u>:
Nearest Town/Village: Machynlleth   **Main Road:** A487
<u>Contact(s)</u>:
- **Chairman:** Mr D K Coleman   **(E)** david@corris.co.uk
- **Curator:** Mr R T E Perfitt   **(E)** richardp@corris.co.uk
- **Press Officer:** Mr R S Greenhough   **(E)** richardg@corris.co.uk
<u>Journeys Available At This Railway</u>:

Corris to Maespaeth
<u>Stations On This Journey</u>:

Station Name	St	Al	Bd	Tl	DT	PA	CP	Ph	Mu	WR	Sh	VS	WS	VW	SB	VSB
Corris							✔		✔							
Maespaeth				✔										✔		

DARLINGTON RAILWAY CENTRE

DARLINGTON RAILWAY CENTRE & MUSEUM North Rd Station, Station Rd, Darlington, **COUNTY DURHAM,** DL3 6ST, **ENGLAND**.

(T) 01325 460532/483606

(E) museum@darlington.gov.uk

(W) www.drcm.org.uk

Affiliated Bodies: Heritage Railway Association

Complex Size: 2 Acres   **Year Opened:** 1980

Type of Complex: Operational Railway Line, Museum

Type of Organisation: Charity, Trust, Limited Company, Volunteer

Gauge: Narrow & Standard   **No. Volunteers:** 60

Stock Overview:

No. Steam Locos: 1

Facilities: Café, Disabled access, Photo line side permit available, Guided tours available, Santa Special, 'Thomas' event, History lectures, Enthusiast galas, Souvenir shop, Books for sale, Videos for sale, Main credit cards taken, Children's events, Facilities for hire.

Entry Fees: Adults: £2.10   **Children:** £1.05

Opening/Closing Times:

Spring: **Opens** Mon - Sun 10:00, **Closes** Mon - Sun 17:00
Summer: **Opens** Mon - Sun 10:00, **Closes** Mon - Sun 17:00
Autumn: **Opens** Mon - Sun 10:00, **Closes** Mon - Sun 17:00
Winter: **Opens** Mon - Sun 10:00, **Closes** Mon - Sun 17:00
Other: Closed on Christmas Day, Boxing Day and New Years Day. Steaming days are usually weekends only, contact for details.

Location:

Main Road: A167

Contact(s):

- **Curator:** Mr John Wilks
- **Education Officer:** Ms Janine Taylor
- **For Donations:** Mr Keith Walshaw   **(T)** 01325 463733

Alternative Contact Details:

- Chairman, 26 Westauckland Rd, Darlington, County Durham, DL3 9EP, England**(T)** 01325 466042

DARTMOOR RAILWAY

DARTMOOR RAILWAY LTD (THE) Meldon Quarry, Okehampton, **DEVON,** EX20 4LT, **ENGLAND**.

(T) 01837 55637   **(F)** 01837 54588

(E) info@dartmoorrailway.co.uk

(W) www.dartmoorrailway.co.uk

Affiliated Bodies: Heritage Railway Association

Stock Overview:

No. Diesel Locos: 1

Facilities: Buffet, Santa Special, Main credit cards taken.

Location:

Nearest Town/Village: Okehampton   **Main Road:** A30   **Mainline Station:** Exeter

Journeys Available At This Railway:

Okehampton to Sampford Courtenay
Features: Views of Open Fields, Woods. Views of ruins of Okehampton Castle. Maximum gradient of 1 in 77.
Tunnels: 1   **Viaducts:** 1
Price: £6.50 (Adult Standard)

Stations On This Journey:

Station Name	St	Al	Bd	TI	DT	PA	CP	Ph	Mu	WR	Sh	VS	WS	VW	SB	VSB
Okehampton	✓	✓														
Meldon	✓	✓														
Sampford Courtenay																

DEAN FOREST RAILWAY

DEAN FOREST RAILWAY Norchard, Forest Rd, Lydney, **GLOUCESTERSHIRE,** GL15 4ET, **ENGLAND**.
(T) 01594 843423
(E) commercial@deanforestrailway.co.uk
(W) www.deanforestrailway.co.uk
Affiliated Bodies: Heritage Railway Association, Transport Trust
Type of Complex: Railway Station, Operational Railway Line, Museum, Restoration Site
Stock Overview:
No. Steam Locos: 4
No. Diesel Locos: 2
Facilities: Restaurant, Ticket office, Disabled access, Advanced booking available, Driver footplate experience, Santa Special, 'Thomas' event, Enthusiast galas, Courses on how to drive Locos, Souvenir shop, Books for sale, Videos for sale, Main credit cards taken, Facilities for hire, Dining car service.
Opening/Closing Times:
Spring: **Opens** Sat, Sun 11:00, **Closes** Sat, Sun 16:00
Summer: **Opens** Mon - Sun 11:00, **Closes** Mon - Sun 16:00
Autumn: **Opens** Sat, Sun 11:00, **Closes** Sat, Sun 16:00
Winter: **Opens** Sat, Sun 11:00, **Closes** Sat, Sun 16:00
Location:
Nearest Town/Village: Lydney   Main Road: B4234   Mainline Station: Lydney
Contact(s):
● **Chairman:** Mr Denis Westerberg
● **Finance Director:** Mr Malcolm Harding
Journeys Available At This Railway:

Norchard to Parkend
Track Type: Single
Features: Views of Open Fields, Urbanisation, Woods.
Level Crossings: 3 **Signal Boxes:** 2 **Journey Length:** 2 mile(s)
Price: £5.50 (Adult Standard) £2.50 (Child Standard)
Stations On This Journey:

Station Name	St	Al	Bd	TI	DT	PA	CP	Ph	Mu	WR	Sh	VS	WS	VW	SB	VSB
Norchard	✓	✓		✓	✓		✓		✓	✓	✓		✓		✓	
Lydney Town	✓	✓														
St Marys Halt	✓	✓														
Lydney Junction	✓	✓		✓	✓									✓		
Whitecroft																
Parkend																

DERBY INDUSTRIAL MUSEUM

DERBY INDUSTRIAL MUSEUM Full St, Derby, **DERBYSHIRE,** DE1 3AR, **ENGLAND**.
(T) 01332 255308   **(F)** 01332 716670
Affiliated Bodies: Transport Trust
Type of Complex: Museum
Stock Overview:
No. Steam Locos: 1
Background: A Museum of Industry specialising in Aero Engines, Railways, Textiles and other aspects of Derby's Heritage.

Facilities: Disabled access, Souvenir shop.

Opening/Closing Times:

Spring:	**Opens** Mon 11:00, Tues - Sat 10:00, Sun 14:00, **Closes** Mon - Sun 17:00
Summer:	**Opens** Mon 11:00, Tues - Sat 10:00, Sun 14:00, **Closes** Mon - Sun 17:00
Autumn:	**Opens** Mon 11:00, Tues - Sat 10:00, Sun 14:00, **Closes** Mon - Sun 17:00
Winter:	**Opens** Mon 11:00, Tues - Sat 10:00, Sun 14:00, **Closes** Mon - Sun 17:00

DERWENT VALLEY

DERWENT VALLEY LIGHT RAILWAY Yorkshire Museum of Farming, Murton, York, **YORKSHIRE (NORTH),** YO19 5UF, **ENGLAND**.

(T) 01904 489966

(W) www.dvlrs.murton.btinternet.co.uk

Affiliated Bodies: Transport Trust

Type of Complex: Operational Railway Line, Museum

Gauge: Standard

Stock Overview:

No. Steam Locos: 2

No. Diesel Locos: 6

Facilities: Ticket office, Disabled access, Waiting room, Santa Special, Souvenir shop, Main credit cards taken, Children's events.

Entry Fees: Adults: £3.60   **Children:** £1.80

Opening/Closing Times:

Spring:	**Opens** Sun 11:00, **Closes** Sun 16:00
Summer:	**Opens** Sun 11:00, **Closes** Sun 16:00
Autumn:	**Opens** Sun 11:00, **Closes** Sun 16:00
Other:	Open Bank Holidays and during December weekends for Santa Specials.

Location:

Nearest Town/Village: York   **Main Road:** A64   **Mainline Station:** York

Contact(s):

● **Railway Historian:** Mr Mark Waudby **(T)** 01904 652556   **(E)** cllrmarkwaudby@hotmail.com

Journeys Available At This Railway:

Murton Park to Murton Park (round trip)
Track Type: Single
Features: Views of Open Fields, Urbanisation.
Bridges: 1 'under'   **Signal Boxes:** 1   **Journey Length:** 1 mile(s)

Stations On This Journey:

Station Name	St	Al	Bd	Tl	DT	PA	CP	Ph	Mu	WR	Sh	VS	WS	VW	SB	VSB
Murton Park	✔	✔							✔			✔			✔	✔

DEVON RAILWAY CENTRE

DEVON RAILWAY CENTRE The Station, Bickleigh, Tiverton, **DEVON,** EX16 8RG, **ENGLAND**.

(T) 01884 855671

(W) www.devonrailcentre.co.uk

Type of Complex: Railway Station, Museum

Gauge: Narrow

Stock Overview:

No. Diesel Locos: 6 (1 Pre-Group)

Location:

Nearest Town/Village: Tiverton   **Main Road:** A396

Journeys Available At This Railway:

Price: £3.25 (Adult Standard) £2.25 (Child Standard)

Key: *St* = Stops   *Al* = Alight   *Bd* = Board   *Tl* = Toilets   *DT* = Disabled Toilets   *PA* = Kids Play Area   *CP* = Free Car Park   *Ph* = Pay Phone   *Mu* = Museum
WR = Waiting Room   *Sh* = Sheds   *VS* = Can Visit Sheds   *WS* = Workshops   *VW* = Can Visit Workshops   *SB* = Signal Box   *VSB* = Can Visit Signal Box

A-Z STEAM RAILWAYS

Derby Industrial Museum — Devon Railway Centre

DIDCOT RAILWAY CENTRE

GREAT WESTERN SOCIETY LTD Station Rd, Didcot, **OXFORDSHIRE,** OX11 7NJ, **ENGLAND**.
(T) 01235 817200   **(F)** 01235 510621
(E) didrlyc@globalnet.co.uk
(W) www.didcotrailwaycentre.org.uk
Affiliated Bodies: Heritage Railway Association, Transport Trust
Complex Size: 16 Acres   **Year Opened:** 1968
Type of Complex: Railway Station, Operational Railway Line, Museum, Restoration Site
Type of Organisation: Charity, Limited Company, Volunteer
Gauge: Standard   **No. Staff:** 10
<u>**Stock Overview:**</u>
No. Steam Locos: 25 (14 Pre-Group, 5 Pre-Nationalisation)
No. Diesel Locos: 2
TV/Film Appearances: Camomile Lawn, Inspector Morse.
Background: The railway recreates the golden age of the Great Western Railway, based around the
Engine Shed with a reconstruction of Brunel's broad gauge railway.
Facilities: Café, Restaurant, Ticket office, Function room, Through ticketing available, Advanced
booking available, Guided tours available, Driver footplate experience, Santa Special, 'Thomas' event,
Enthusiast galas, Souvenir shop, Books for sale, Videos for sale, Photos for sale, Paintings/drawings
for sale, Camera film for sale, CD's for sale, Models for sale, Main credit cards taken, Children's events,
Facilities for hire, Trains for hire.
<u>**Opening/Closing Times:**</u>
Spring: **Opens** Mon - Sun 10:00, **Closes** Mon - Sun 17:00
Summer: **Opens** Mon - Sun 10:00, **Closes** Mon - Sun 17:00
Autumn: **Opens** Mon - Sun 10:00, **Closes** Mon - Sun 17:00
Winter: **Opens** Sat, Sun 10:00, **Closes** Sat, Sun 16:00
<u>**Location:**</u>
Nearest Town/Village: Didcot   **Main Road:** M4   **Mainline Station:** Didcot Parkway
<u>**Contact(s):**</u>
● **For Bookings:** Mrs Pat Bosley
● **General Manager:** Mr Michael Dean
● **Marketing Executive:** Ms Jeanette Howse
<u>**Journeys Available At This Railway:**</u>

Didcot Halt to Burlescombe
Track Type: Single   Direction: South to North
Price: £6.50 (Adult Standard) £4.50 (Child Standard) £7.50 (Adult Special) £7.50 (Child Special)
<u>**Stations On This Journey:**</u>

Station Name	St	Al	Bd	Tl	DT	PA	CP	Ph	Mu	WR	Sh	VS	WS	VW	SB	VSB
Didcot Halt	✔	✔	✔	✔	✔			✔	✔	✔	✔	✔	✔	✔	✔	✔
Burlescombe	✔	✔	✔							✔					✔	

DINGLES STEAM VILLAGE

DINGLES STEAM VILLAGE Milford, Lifton, **DEVON,** PL16 0AT, **ENGLAND**.
(T) 01566 783425   **(F)** 01566 783584
(W) www.dinglesteam.co.uk
Complex Size: 200 Acres   **Year Opened:** 1995
Type of Complex: Museum
Type of Organisation: Heritage Project, Non-Profit, Sole Partnership
No. Staff: 4   **No. Volunteers:** 10
Background: Museum of road, steam and industrial heritage.
Facilities: Café, Disabled access, Courses on how to drive Locos, Souvenir shop, Books for sale,
Videos for sale, Camera film for sale, Main credit cards taken.
Entry Fees: Adults: £6.00   **Children:** £4.50
<u>**Opening/Closing Times:**</u>

Summer: **Opens** 10:30, **Closes** 17:30
Autumn: **Opens** 10:30, **Closes** 17:30
Other: Closed Fridays.
Location:
Nearest Town/Village: Launceston   **Main Road:** A30   **Bus:** X10   **Mainline Station:** Exeter
Hotel: Thatched Cottage   **Restaurant:** Harris Arms
Contact(s):
- **Owner:** Mr Richard Sandercock   **(E)** richard@dinglesteam.co.uk

DONEGAL RAILWAY HERITAGE CTRE

COUNTY DONEGAL RAILWAY RESTORATION SOCIETY The Old Station Hse, Tyrconnell St, Donegal,
COUNTY DONEGAL, IRELAND.
(T) 073 22655
Affiliated Bodies: Heritage Railway Association
Type of Complex: Museum
Type of Organisation: Heritage Project
Gauge: Narrow
Stock Overview:
No. Steam Locos: 1
Facilities: Souvenir shop.
Opening/Closing Times:
Spring: **Opens** Mon - Sun 10:00, **Closes** Mon - Sun 17:00
Summer: **Opens** Mon - Sun 09:00, **Closes** Mon - Sun 17:00
Autumn: **Opens** Mon - Sun 09:00, **Closes** Mon - Sun 17:00
Winter: **Opens** Mon - Fri 10:00, **Closes** Mon - Fri 17:00
Location:
Nearest Town/Village: Donegal   **Main Road:** N15
Contact(s):
- **Chairman:** Mr Owen Howells

DOWNPATRICK & ARDGLASS

DOWNPATRICK & ARDGLASS RAILWAY & CO LTD Downpatrick Station, Market St, Downpatrick,
COUNTY DOWN, BT30 6LZ, **NORTHERN IRELAND**.
(T) 02844 615779
(E) drm@icom43.net
(W) www.downrail.icom43.net
Affiliated Bodies: Heritage Railway Association
Year Opened: 1985
Type of Complex: Operational Railway Line, Museum
Gauge: Standard
Stock Overview:
No. Steam Locos: 2
No. Diesel Locos: 2
Facilities: Café, Ticket office, Disabled access, Guided tours available, Driver footplate experience,
Santa Special, Souvenir shop, Books for sale, Videos for sale, Children's events, Facilities for hire,
Trains for hire.
Opening/Closing Times:
Spring: **Opens** Mon - Fri 11:00, **Closes** Mon - Fri 14:00
Summer: **Opens** Mon - Fri 11:00, **Closes** Mon - Fri 14:00
Autumn: **Opens** Mon - Fri 11:00, **Closes** Mon - Fri 14:00
Winter: **Opens** Mon - Fri 11:00, **Closes** Mon - Fri 14:00
Other: Contact for railway operation days.
Location:
Nearest Town/Village: Downpatrick   **Mainline Station:** Belfast
Contact(s):

Key: *St* = Stops   *Al* = Alight   *Bd* = Board   *Tl* = Toilets   *DT* = Disabled Toilets   *PA* = Kids Play Area   *CP* = Free Car Park   *Ph* = Pay Phone   *Mu* = Museum
     WR = Waiting Room   *Sh* = Sheds   *VS* = Can Visit Sheds   *WS* = Workshops   *VW* = Can Visit Workshops   *SB* = Signal Box   *VSB* = Can Visit Signal Box

- **General Manager:** Mr Edwin Gray
- **Secretary:** Mrs Patricia Magrath

Journeys Available At This Railway:

Downpatrick to Kirs Magnas Halt
Price: £3.00 (Adult Standard) £2.00 (Child Standard)

Stations On This Journey:

Station Name	St	Al	Bd	Tl	DT	PA	CP	Ph	Mu	WR	Sh	VS	WS	VW	SB	VSB
Downpatrick	✔	✔		✔	✔				✔			✔	✔	✔	✔	✔
Loop Line Platform	✔	✔														
Kirs Magnas Halt	✔	✔														

EAST ANGLIA TRANSPORT MUSEUM

EAST ANGLIA TRANSPORT MUSEUM Chapel Rd, Carlton Colville, Lowestoft, **SUFFOLK,** NR33 8BL, **ENGLAND**.

(T) 01502 518459   **(F)** 01502 584658

(W) www.eatm.org.uk

Affiliated Bodies: Heritage Railway Association, Transport Trust

Type of Complex: Museum

Gauge: Narrow

Stock Overview:

No. Diesel Locos: 4

Background: Visitors can view and ride on public transport from the earlier part of the 20th century. There is also a period street - complete with genuine street furniture. The museum collection gives an oppurtunity to view many vehicles, and see how these are being restored to their former glory.

Facilities: Café, Souvenir shop, Books for sale, Picnic area.

EAST ANGLIAN RAILWAY MUSEUM

EAST ANGLIAN RAILWAY MUSEUM Chappel Station, Colchester, **ESSEX,** CO6 2DS, **ENGLAND**.

(T) 01206 242524   **(F)** 0870 1258315

(E) info@earm.co.uk

(W) www.earm.co.uk

Affiliated Bodies: Heritage Railway Association, Transport Trust

Type of Complex: Museum, Restoration Site

Type of Organisation: Charity

Stock Overview:

No. Steam Locos: 9

No. Diesel Locos: 4

Facilities: Ticket office, Waiting room, Driver footplate experience, Santa Special, 'Thomas' event, Slide shows, Souvenir shop, Books for sale, Main credit cards taken.

Opening/Closing Times:

Spring: Opens Mon - Sun 10:00, **Closes** Mon - Sun 17:00
Summer: Opens Mon - Sun 10:00, **Closes** Mon - Sun 17:00
Autumn: Opens Mon - Sun 10:00, **Closes** Mon - Sun 17:00
Winter: Opens Mon - Sun 10:00, **Closes** Mon - Sun 17:00

Location:

Main Road: A1124   **Hotel:** Rosebank

Contact(s):

- **Owner:** Mr Dave Reeve   **(T)** 01206 793923

EAST KENT LIGHT RAILWAY

EAST KENT LIGHT RAILWAY SOCIETY Station Rd, Shepherdswell, Dover, **KENT,** CT15 7PD, **ENGLAND.**
(T) 01304 832042
Affiliated Bodies: Heritage Railway Association
Complex Size: 3 Acres   **Year Opened:** 1994
Type of Complex: Operational Railway Line, Museum, Restoration Site
Type of Organisation: Charity, Trust, Volunteer, Non-Profit
Gauge: Standard   **No. Volunteers:** 40
Stock Overview:
No. Steam Locos: 3
No. Diesel Locos: 4
Facilities: Buffet, Ticket office, Waiting room, Advanced booking available, Guided tours available, Driver footplate experience, Santa Special, Training courses, Enthusiast galas, Courses on how to drive Locos, Souvenir shop, Books for sale, Videos for sale, Photos for sale, Paintings/drawings for sale, Tapes for sale, Models for sale, Children's events, Facilities for hire, Trains for hire.
Opening/Closing Times:
Spring: **Opens** 10:00, **Closes** 16:00
Summer: **Opens** 10:00, **Closes** 17:30
Autumn: **Opens** 10:00, **Closes** 16:00
Winter: **Opens** 10:00, **Closes** 16:00
Contact(s):
• **For Bookings:** C Wallace (T) 01634 856228
• **General Manager:** Mr D Harris   (T) 01303 893320
Journeys Available At This Railway:

Shepherdswell to Eythorne
Track Type: Single   Direction: West to East
Features: Views of Open Fields. Maximum gradient of 1 in 73 (For 100 metres).
Tunnels: 1 **Signal Boxes:** 2   **Journey Duration:** 15 mins   **Journey Length:** 2 mile(s)
Price: £4.00 (Adult Standard) £2.00 (Child Standard) £5.00 (Adult Special) £2.50 (Child Special)
Stations On This Journey:

Station Name	St	Al	Bd	Tl	DT	PA	CP	Ph	Mu	WR	Sh	VS	WS	VW	SB	VSB
Shepherdswell	✔			✔			✔	✔	✔	✔					✔	
Eythorne	✔					✔				✔					✔	

EAST LANCASHIRE RAILWAY

EAST LANCASHIRE RAILWAY CO LTD Bolton St Station, Bolton St, Bury, **LANCASHIRE,** B09 0EY, **ENGLAND.**
(T) 0161 7647790   (F) 0161 7634408
Affiliated Bodies: Heritage Railway Association, Transport Trust
Year Opened: 1987
Type of Complex: Railway Station, Operational Railway Line, Museum, Restoration Site
Gauge: Standard
Stock Overview:
No. Steam Locos: 1
Facilities: Café, Disabled access, Platform tickets, Driver footplate experience, Santa Special, 'Thomas' event, Courses on how to drive Locos, Trains for hire, Dining train available.
Opening/Closing Times:
Spring: **Opens** Sat, Sun 10:00, **Closes** Sat, Sun 17:00
Summer: **Opens** Fri - Sun 10:00, **Closes** Fri - Sun 17:00
Autumn: **Opens** Sat, Sun 10:00, **Closes** Sat, Sun 17:00
Winter: **Opens** Sat, Sun 10:00, **Closes** Sat, Sun 17:00
Location:
Nearest Town/Village: Bury   **Main Road:** A58   **Mainline Station:** Bolton

Key: *St* = Stops   *Al* = Alight   *Bd* = Board   *Tl* = Toilets   *DT* = Disabled Toilets   *PA* = Kids Play Area   *CP* = Free Car Park   *Ph* = Pay Phone   *Mu* = Museum
WR = Waiting Room   *Sh* = Sheds   *VS* = Can Visit Sheds   *WS* = Workshops   *VW* = Can Visit Workshops   *SB* = Signal Box   *VSB* = Can Visit Signal Box

Contact(s):
- **General Manager:** Mr David Wright
- **Technical Info:** Mr N Parkinton

Journeys Available At This Railway:

Bury to Rawtenstall
Track Type: Single
Features: Views of Open Fields, Water.
Signal Boxes: 4　**Rivers:** 1　**Journey Length:** 8 mile(s)
Price: £4.00 (Adult Standard)　£3.00 (Child Standard)
Available on Journey: Refreshments, Drinks, Alcohol, Buffet.

Stations On This Journey:

Station Name	St	Al	Bd	Tl	DT	PA	CP	Ph	Mu	WR	Sh	VS	WS	VW	SB	VSB
Bury	✔	✔		✔	✔				✔	✔				✔		
Summer Seat	✔	✔														
Ramsbottom	✔	✔		✔	✔					✔						
Irwell Vale	✔	✔														
Rawtenstall	✔	✔		✔	✔					✔					✔	

EAST SOMERSET RAILWAY

EAST SOMERSET RAILWAY Cranmore Railway Station, Cranmore, Shepton Mallet, **SOMERSET,** BA4 4QP, **ENGLAND**.
(T) 01749 880417　　**(F)** 01749 880764
(E) info@eastsomersetrailway.org
(W) www.eastsomersetrailway.org
Affiliated Bodies: Transport Trust
Type of Complex: Railway Station, Operational Railway Line, Museum
Type of Organisation: Charity, Heritage Project, Volunteer, Non-Profit
Gauge: Standard
Stock Overview:
No. Steam Locos: 7
No. Diesel Locos: 1
TV/Film Appearances: Canterville Ghost (1986), Hanover St (1975)
Facilities: Restaurant, Ticket office, Disabled access, Waiting room, Platform tickets, Advanced booking available, Driver footplate experience, Santa Special, 'Thomas' event, Enthusiast galas, Souvenir shop, Books for sale, Videos for sale, Photos for sale, Paintings/drawings for sale, Camera film for sale, Models for sale, Main credit cards taken, Children's events, Facilities for hire, Trains for hire.

Opening/Closing Times:
Spring:　**Opens** 10:00, **Closes** 16:00
Summer:　**Opens** 10:00, **Closes** 16:00
Autumn:　**Opens** 10:00, **Closes** 16:00
Winter:　**Opens** 10:00, **Closes** 16:00
Other:　Steam days are on weekends and school holidays, 10:00 - 17:30.

Location:
Nearest Town/Village: Shepton Mallet　　**Main Road:** A361

Contact(s):
- **For Bookings:** Mrs Jackie Hopkins
- **President:** Mr David Shepherd
- **Technical Info:** Mr L Hopkins **(T)** 01749 880777

Journeys Available At This Railway:

Cranmore to Mendip Vale
Track Type: Single
Features: Views of Hills, Open Fields, Urbanisation, Woods. Maximum gradient of 1 in 56.
Bridges: 1 'over', 2 'under'　**Signal Boxes:** 1　**Journey Length:** 3 mile(s)
Price: £5.75 (Adult Standard)　£3.75 (Child Standard)
Stations On This Journey:

Station Name	St	Al	Bd	Tl	DT	PA	CP	Ph	Mu	WR	Sh	VS	WS	VW	SB	VSB
Cranmore	✔	✔		✔	✔	✔	✔		✔	✔					✔	✔
Cranmore West	✔	✔	✔								✔	✔	✔			
Merryfield Lane	✔	✔														
Mendip Vale	✔	✔														

EASTLEIGH LAKESIDE RAILWAY

EASTLEIGH LAKESIDE RAILWAY LTD Lakeside Country Pk, Wide Lane, Eastleigh, **HAMPSHIRE,** SO50 5PE, **ENGLAND**.

(T) 023 80636612   **(F)** 023 80227038

(W) www.steamtrain.co.uk

Affiliated Bodies: Britains Great Little Railways

Year Opened: 1991

Type of Complex: Railway Station, Operational Railway Line

Type of Organisation: Limited Company

Stock Overview:

No. Steam Locos: 5

No. Diesel Locos: 2

Facilities: Buffet, Ticket office, Driver footplate experience, Santa Special, 'Thomas' event, Training courses, Courses on how to drive Locos, Souvenir shop, Videos for sale, Photos for sale, Paintings/drawings for sale, CD's for sale, Models for sale, Main credit cards taken.

Opening/Closing Times:

Spring: **Opens** Sat, Sun 10:30, **Closes** Sat, Sun 16:30

Summer: **Opens** Mon, Sun 10:30, **Closes** Mon, Sun 16:30

Autumn: **Opens** Sat, Sun 10:30, **Closes** Sat, Sun 16:30

Winter: **Opens** Sat, Sun 10:30, **Closes** Sat, Sun 16:30

Location:

Nearest Town/Village: Eastleigh   **Main Road:** Wide Lane   **Mainline Station:** Southampton Airport Parkway

Contact(s):

● **For Bookings:** Mr Clive Upton   **(E)** clive@steamtrain.co.uk

● **For Donations:** Mr Clive Upton   **(E)** clive@steamtrain.co.uk

● **General Manager:** Mr Clive Upton   **(E)** clive@steamtrain.co.uk

● **Technical Info:** Mr Clive Upton   **(E)** clive@steamtrain.co.uk

Alternative Contact Details:

● Fletchwood Hse, Quayside Rd, Bitterne Manor, Southampton, Hampshire, SO18 1DP, England

Journeys Available At This Railway:

Eastleigh Parkway to Eastleigh Parkway (round trip)
Price: £0.80 (Adult Standard)

Stations On This Journey:

Station Name	St	Al	Bd	Tl	DT	PA	CP	Ph	Mu	WR	Sh	VS	WS	VW	SB	VSB
Eastleigh Parkway	✔	✔		✔	✔		✔				✔		✔			
Monks Brook Halt	✔	✔			✔											

ELSECAR HERITAGE CENTRE

ELSECAR HERITAGE CENTRE Wath Rd, Elsecar, Barnsley, **YORKSHIRE (SOUTH),** S74 8HJ, **ENGLAND**.

(T) 01226 740203   **(F)** 01226 350239

Year Opened: 1993

Type of Complex: Operational Railway Line, Restoration Site

Gauge: Standard

Key: *St* = Stops   *Al* = Alight   Bd = Board   *Tl* = Toilets   *DT* = Disabled Toilets   *PA* = Kids Play Area   *CP* = Free Car Park   *Ph* = Pay Phone   *Mu* = Museum
WR = Waiting Room   *Sh* = Sheds   *VS* = Can Visit Sheds   *WS* = Workshops   *VW* = Can Visit Workshops   *SB* = Signal Box   *VSB* = Can Visit Signal Box

Stock Overview:

No. Steam Locos: 1

No. Diesel Locos: 1

Facilities: Café, Disabled access, Guided tours available, Santa Special, 'Thomas' event, Souvenir shop, Children's events.

Opening/Closing Times:

Spring: **Opens** Mon - Sun 10:00, **Closes** Mon - Sun 17:00

Summer: **Opens** Mon - Sun 10:00, **Closes** Mon - Sun 17:00

Autumn: **Opens** Mon - Sun 10:00, **Closes** Mon - Sun 17:00

Winter: **Opens** Mon - Sun 10:00, **Closes** Mon - Sun 17:00

Other: The railway is open on Sundays March - October. The Heritage Centre is closed over Christmas.

Location:

Nearest Town/Village: Hoyland   **Main Road:** B6097   **Mainline Station:** Elsecar

Contact(s):

● **Assistant Manager:** Mr Alan Bates

Journeys Available At This Railway:

Rockingham to Rockingham (round trip)

Track Type: Single

Features: Views of Open Fields, Water.

Bridges: 1 'under'   **Level Crossings:** 1   **Journey Length:** 1 mile(s)

Price: £2.50 (Adult Standard) £1.00 (Child Standard)

Stations On This Journey:

Station Name	St	Al	Bd	Tl	DT	PA	CP	Ph	Mu	WR	Sh	VS	WS	VW	SB	VSB
Rockingham St	✔	✔				✔	✔			✔		✔				
Hemingfield Basin																

EMBSAY & BOLTON ABBEY RLWY

YORKSHIRE DALES RAILWAY MUSEUM TRUST Bolton Abbey Station, Skipton, **YORKSHIRE (NORTH)**, BD23 6AF, **ENGLAND**.

(T) 01756 710614   **(F)** 01756 795189

(E) enquiries@embsayboltonabbeyrailway.org.uk

Affiliated Bodies: Heritage Railway Association, Transport Trust

Stock Overview:

No. Steam Locos: 19

No. Diesel Locos: 11

Facilities: Disabled access, Santa Special, 'Thomas' event, Souvenir shop, Books for sale, Models for sale.

Location:

Nearest Town/Village: Skipton   **Main Road:** A59   **Taxi:** Star Taxis - 01756 794748   **Mainline Station:** Skipton

Journeys Available At This Railway:

Embsay to Bolton Abbey

Price: £5.00 (Adult Standard) £2.50 (Child Standard)

Stations On This Journey:

Station Name	St	Al	Bd	Tl	DT	PA	CP	Ph	Mu	WR	Sh	VS	WS	VW	SB	VSB
Embsay	✔	✔														
Bolton Abbey	✔	✔				✔										

EXMOOR STEAM RAILWAY

EXMOOR STEAM RAILWAY Cape Of Good Hope Farm, Bratton Fleming, Barnstaple, **DEVON,** EX32 7JN, **ENGLAND**.

(T) 01598 710711   **(F)** 01598 710711

Year Opened: 1990

Gauge: Narrow

Stock Overview:

No. Steam Locos: 7

No. Diesel Locos: 1

Background: Situated on the edge of Exmoor National Park.

Facilities: Café, Souvenir shop, Main credit cards taken.

Location:

Instructions: Situated on the A399, midway between South Molton and Combe Martin.

Nearest Town/Village: Barnstaple   **Main Road:** A399

FAIRBOURNE & BARMOUTH

NORTH WALES COAST LIGHT RAILWAY LTD Beach Rd, Fairbourne, **GWYNEDD,** LL38 2PZ, **WALES**.

(T) 01341 250362   **(F)** 01341 250240

(E) enquiries@fairbourne-railway.co.uk

(W) www.fairbourne-railway.co.uk

Affiliated Bodies: Britains Great Little Railways

Complex Size: 15 Acres   **Year Opened:** 1895

Type of Organisation: Limited Company

Gauge: Narrow   **No. Staff:** 4   **No. Volunteers:** 6

Stock Overview:

No. Steam Locos: 4

Background: Originally built in 1895 as a horse drawn tramway, but converted to steam in 1916. Rebuilt in 1985 to a new gauge of 12.25". Now features replicas of famous narrow gauge locomotives. At Golf Halt there is the station with the longest name in the world, which is entered in the Guinness Book of Records, 'GORSAFAWDDACHAIDRAIGODANHEDDOGLEDDOLLONPENRHYNAREURDRAETHCEREDIGION'.

Facilities: Café, Driver footplate experience, Santa Special, 'Thomas' event, Souvenir shop, Books for sale, Videos for sale, Main credit cards taken, Free entry to Rowen Indoor Nature Centre.

Opening/Closing Times:

Summer: **Opens** Mon - Sun 10:30, **Closes** Mon - Sun 17:00

Autumn: **Opens** Mon - Sun 11:00, **Closes** Mon - Sun 16:30

Other: Also open Easter and October half term.

Location:

Instructions: Located between Dolgellau and Tywyn on the Mid Wales coast.

Nearest Town/Village: Barmouth   **Main Road:** A493   **Bus:** 28   **Taxi:** Tywyn Cabs   **Mainline Station:** Fairbourne   **Hotel:** Fairbourne Hotel   **Restaurant:** Fairbourne Hotel

Contact(s):

● **For Bookings:** Mr Colin Jepson

● **General Manager:** Mr Michael Messer

● **Owner:** Ms Maureen Atkinson   **(T)** 01722 415026   **(E)** chimaeron@dial.pipex.com

Journeys Available At This Railway:

Fairbourne to Penrhyn Point

Track Type: Single

Features: Views of Hills, Open Fields, Sea, Water. Views of Mawddach Estuary and Cader Idris Mountain Range. Maximum gradient of 1 in 60 (For 30 metres).

Tunnels: 1   **Level Crossings:** 2   **Signal Boxes:** 1   **Journey Length:** 2.5 mile(s)

Price: £5.50 (Adult Standard) £3.40 (Child Standard) £5.50 (Adult Special) £3.40 (Child Special)

Available on Journey: Refreshments, Drinks, Restaurant.

Stations On This Journey:

Key: *St* = Stops   *Al* = Alight   *Bd* = Board   *Tl* = Toilets   *DT* = Disabled Toilets   *PA* = Kids Play Area   *CP* = Free Car Park   *Ph* = Pay Phone   *Mu* = Museum
         WR = Waiting Room   *Sh* = Sheds   *VS* = Can Visit Sheds   *WS* = Workshops   *VW* = Can Visit Workshops   *SB* = Signal Box   *VSB* = Can Visit Signal Box

Station Name	St	Al	Bd	Tl	DT	PA	CP	Ph	Mu	WR	Sh	VS	WS	VW	SB	VSB
Fairbourne				✔					✔	✔	✔			✔		
Beach Halt	✔															
Golf Halt	✔															
Penrityn Point				✔												

FFESTINIOG RAILWAY

FFESTINIOG RAILWAY Harbour Station, Porthmadog, **GWYNEDD,** LL49 9NS, **WALES**.

(T) 01766 516073   **(F)** 01766 516006

(E) info@festrail.co.uk

(W) www.festrail.co.uk

Affiliated Bodies: Heritage Railway Association

Year Opened: 1836

Type of Complex: Railway Station, Operational Railway Line, Museum, Restoration Site

Stock Overview:

No. Steam Locos: 8

No. Diesel Locos: 7

TV/Film Appearances: Holiday, Rivers of Wales

Facilities: Café, Restaurant, Disabled access, Driver footplate experience, Santa Special, Enthusiast galas, Courses on how to drive Locos, Souvenir shop, Books for sale, Videos for sale, Photos for sale, Main credit cards taken, Children's events, Facilities for hire, Trains for hire.

Opening/Closing Times:

Spring: **Opens** Mon - Sun 09:00, **Closes** Mon - Sun 18:00
Summer: **Opens** Mon - Sun 09:00, **Closes** Mon - Sun 18:00
Autumn: **Opens** Mon - Sun 09:00, **Closes** Mon - Sun 18:00
Winter: **Opens** Mon - Sun 09:00, **Closes** Mon - Sun 18:00
Other: Contact for information on steaming days.

Location:

Nearest Town/Village: Porthmadog   **Mainline Station:** Porthmadog

Contact(s):

● **Managing Director:** Mr Ken Allen

Journeys Available At This Railway:

Porthmadog to Blaenauffest
Track Type: Single
Features: Views of Hills, Open Fields, Sea, Urbanisation, Water, Woods. Maximum gradient of 1 in 60.
Bridges: 4 'over', 3 'under'   Tunnels: 2   Level Crossings: 3   Signal Boxes: 2   Rivers: 1   Journey Length: 13.5 mile(s)
Price: £14.00 (Adult Standard)

Stations On This Journey:

Station Name	St	Al	Bd	Tl	DT	PA	CP	Ph	Mu	WR	Sh	VS	WS	VW	SB	VSB
Porthmadog	✔	✔		✔	✔				✔	✔						
Boston Lodge Halt											✔		✔			
Minfford	✔	✔					✔				✔					
Penrhyn	✔	✔														
Plas Halt											✔					
Tan-y-Bwelch							✔				✔			✔		
Campbells Platform	✔	✔	✔								✔					
Dduallt											✔					
Tanygrisau							✔							✔		
Blaenauffest	✔	✔		✔	✔						✔					

FINTOWN & GLENTIES RAILWAY

FINTOWN & GLENTIES RAILWAY Fintown Railway Station, Fintown, Glenties, **COUNTY DONEGAL, IRELAND**.

(T) 00353 46280

Year Opened: 1995

Type of Complex: Operational Railway Line

Gauge: Narrow

Facilities: Café, Santa Special, Children's events.

Opening/Closing Times:

Other: Open June - September.

Contact(s):

- **Manager:** Ms Anne-Marie Bonner

FORNCETT INDUSTRIAL MUSEUM

FORNCETT INDUSTRIAL STEAM MUSEUM Low Rd, Forncett St. Mary, Norwich, **NORFOLK,** NR16 1JJ, **ENGLAND**.

(T) 01508 488277

Type of Complex: Museum

Background: A collection of industrial steam engines including the pumping engine which was originally used to open Tower Bridge in London.

Facilities: Café, Disabled access, Facilities for hire.

Entry Fees: Adults: £4.00

Opening/Closing Times:

Other: Open on the first Sunday of the month May - November.

Location:

Nearest Town/Village: Norwich   **Main Road:** A140   **Mainline Station:** Windham

Contact(s):

- **Owner:** Dr R Francis
- **Owner:** Mrs J Francis

FOXFIELD STEAM RAILWAY

FOXFIELD STEAM RAILWAY Caverswall Rd Station, Blythe Bridge, Stoke-on-Trent, **STAFFORDSHIRE,** ST11 9BG, **ENGLAND**.

(T) 01782 396210   **(F)** 01782 396210

(E) enquiries@foxfieldrailway.co.uk

(W) www.foxfieldrailway.co.uk

Affiliated Bodies: Heritage Railway Association

Complex Size: 5 Acres   **Year Opened:** 1967

Type of Complex: Railway Station, Operational Railway Line, Museum, Restoration Site

Type of Organisation: Heritage Project, Volunteer, Non-Profit

Gauge: Standard   **No. Volunteers:** 70

Stock Overview:

No. Steam Locos: 19 (14 Pre-Group, 7 Pre-Nationalisation)

No. Diesel Locos: 12 (1 Pre-Group)

Facilities: Café, Buffet, Ticket office, Disabled access, Lecture room, Guided tours available, Santa Special, 'Thomas' event, Enthusiast galas, Slide shows, Souvenir shop, Videos for sale, Camera film for sale, Models for sale, Main credit cards taken, Children's events, Facilities for hire, Trains for hire.

Opening/Closing Times:

Spring: **Opens** Sunday 11:00, **Closes** Sun 17:00

Summer: **Opens** Sunday 11:00, **Closes** Sun 17:00

Autumn: **Opens** Sunday 11:00, **Closes** Sun 17:00

Winter: **Opens** Sunday 11:00, **Closes** Sun 17:00

Other: Open April - September every Sunday and Bank Holiday. Contact for Saturday opening

---

Key: *St* = Stops   *Al* = Alight   *Bd* = Board   *Tl* = Toilets   *DT* = Disabled Toilets   *PA* = Kids Play Area   *CP* = Free Car Park   *Ph* = Pay Phone   *Mu* = Museum
WR = Waiting Room   *Sh* = Sheds   *VS* = Can Visit Sheds   *WS* = Workshops   *VW* = Can Visit Workshops   *SB* = Signal Box   *VSB* = Can Visit Signal Box

times.

Location:
Instructions: Sign posted from A50.

Nearest Town/Village: Blythe Bridge   **Main Road:** A50   **Mainline Station:** Blythe Bridge Station

Contact(s):
- **For Bookings:** Ms Dorothy Ailwood
- **For Bookings:** Mr John Ailwood
- **For Donations:** Mr Jon Beardmore   (T) 02476 687088
- **Press Officer:** Mr Dave Scragg

Alternative Contact Details:
- PO Box 1967, Stoke-on-Trent, Staffordshire, ST4 8YT, England

Journeys Available At This Railway:

Caverswall Rd Station to Dilhorne Park Station
Track Type: Single
Features: Views of Hills, Open Fields, Woods. Maximum gradient of 1 in 33 (For 200 metres).
Level Crossings: 1   **Signal Boxes:** 1   **Journey Duration:** 15 mins   **Journey Length:** 2.5 mile(s)
Price: £4.00 (Adult Standard) £2.00 (Child Standard) £4.80 (Adult Special) £2.80 (Child Special)

Stations On This Journey:

Station Name	St	Al	Bd	Tl	DT	PA	CP	Ph	Mu	WR	Sh	VS	WS	VW	SB	VSB
Caverswall Rd Station	✔	✔		✔	✔		✔		✔		✔	✔	✔		✔	
Dilhorne Park Station	✔	✔														

FOYLE VALLEY RAILWAY CENTRE

NORTH WEST OF IRELAND RAILWAY SOCIETY Foyle Rd, Londonderry, **COUNTY LONDONDERRY,** BT48 6SQ, **NORTHERN IRELAND**.

(T) 028 71265234

Affiliated Bodies: Heritage Railway Association

Type of Complex: Operational Railway Line, Museum

Stock Overview:
No. Steam Locos: 2

Facilities: Ticket office, Disabled access, Santa Special, Main credit cards taken, Children's events.

Opening/Closing Times:
Spring: **Opens** Tues - Sat 09:00, **Closes** Tues - Sat 17:15
Summer: **Opens** Tues - Sat 09:00, **Closes** Tues - Sat 17:15
Autumn: **Opens** Tues - Sat 09:00, **Closes** Tues - Sat 17:15
Winter: **Opens** Tues - Sat 09:00, **Closes** Tues - Sat 17:15

Location:
Instructions: Located near to Craigavon Bridge.

Contact(s):
- **Museum Programme Organiser:** Mr Dermot Francis
- **Technical Info:** Mr Jim McBride   (T) 028 71318856
- **Volunteer:** Mr Jim McBride   (T) 028 71318856

GARTELL LIGHT RAILWAY

GARTELL LIGHT RAILWAY Common Lane, Yenston, Templecombe, **SOMERSET,** BA8 0NB, **ENGLAND**.

(T) 01963 370752

(W) www.gartell-light-railway.co.uk

Stock Overview:
No. Steam Locos: 1

Facilities: Café, Picnic area.

Contact(s):
- **General Manager:** Mr John Gartell

GIANTS CAUSEWAY & BUSHMILLS

GIANTS CAUSEWAY & BUSHMILLS RAILWAY LTD Giants Causeway Station, Runkerry Rd, Bushmills, **COUNTY ANTRIM,** BT57 8SZ, **NORTHERN IRELAND**.

(T) 028 20732844   **(F)** 028 20732844

Year Opened: 2002

Type of Complex: Railway Station, Operational Railway Line, Restoration Site

Type of Organisation: Charity, Heritage Project, Conservation Project, Limited Company, Non-Profit

Gauge: Narrow   **No. Staff:** 3

Stock Overview:

No. Steam Locos: 2

No. Diesel Locos: 1

Background: Combines the former Shanes Castle Railway with the site of the Causeway Tram. It follows the original route of the world's first hydro-electric tram (1883 - 1949).

Facilities: Ticket office, Disabled access, Waiting room, Advanced booking available, Guided tours available, Souvenir shop, Books for sale, Videos for sale, Photos for sale, Main credit cards taken, Trains for hire.

Opening/Closing Times:

Spring: **Opens** 09:00, **Closes** 17:00
Summer: **Opens** 09:00, **Closes** 18:00
Autumn: **Opens** 09:00, **Closes** 18:00
Winter: **Opens** 09:00, **Closes** 17:00
Other: Railway due to open Easter 2002.

Location:

Instructions: Located between Causeway and Bushmills.

Nearest Town/Village: Coleraine   **Mainline Station:** Coleraine   **Hotel:** Causeway Hotel

Contact(s):

- **For Bookings:** Ms Sharon Kirk
- **For Donations:** Ms Sharon Kirk
- **General Manager:** Mr Mark Parker
- **General Manager:** Mr David Laing

Associated Businesses:

- Heritage Railway Association, Turnpike Hse, Maidstone Rd, Marden, Tonbridge, Kent, TN12 9AB, England**(M)** john.c.oakley

Journeys Available At This Railway:

Giants Causeway to Bushmills

Track Type: Single

Features: Views of Hills, Open Fields, Sea, Water, Woods. Seaside views. Maximum gradient of 1 in 40 (For 200 metres).

Bridges: 3 'over'   **Level Crossings:** 12   **Rivers:** 3   **Journey Duration:** 20 mins   **Journey Length:** 2 mile(s)

Price: £3.50 (Adult Standard)   £2.00 (Child Standard)

Stations On This Journey:

Station Name	St	Al	Bd	Tl	DT	PA	CP	Ph	Mu	WR	Sh	VS	WS	VW	SB	VSB
Giants Causeway	✔		✔	✔	✔		✔	✔		✔	✔		✔			
Bushmills	✔					✔				✔						

GLASGOW MUSEUM OF TRANSPORT

GLASGOW MUSEUM OF TRANSPORT Kelvin Hall, 1 Bunhouse Rd, Glasgow, **GLASGOW (CITY OF),** G3 8DP, **SCOTLAND**.

(T) 0141 287720   **(F)** 0141 2872692

Type of Complex: Museum

Background: A museum of the history of transport on land and sea.

Facilities: Café, Disabled access, Guided tours available, Souvenir shop, Books for sale, Videos for sale, Models for sale, Main credit cards taken.

Key: St = Stops   Al = Alight   Bd = Board   Tl = Toilets   DT = Disabled Toilets   PA = Kids Play Area   CP = Free Car Park   Ph = Pay Phone   Mu = Museum   WR = Waiting Room   Sh = Sheds   VS = Can Visit Sheds   WS = Workshops   VW = Can Visit Workshops   SB = Signal Box   VSB = Can Visit Signal Box

Opening/Closing Times:
Spring: Opens Mon - Sat 10:00, Sun 11:00, Closes Mon - Sun 17:00
Summer: Opens Mon - Sat 10:00, Sun 11:00, Closes Mon - Sun 17:00
Autumn: Opens Mon - Sat 10:00, Sun 11:00, Closes Mon - Sun 17:00
Winter: Opens Mon - Sat 10:00, Sun 11:00, Closes Mon - Sun 17:00

Location:
Nearest Town/Village: Glasgow   Main Road: A814

Contact(s):
- Curator: Mr Alistair Smith (T) 0141 2872656
- Museum Officer: Ms Ann Devlin

GLENFINNAN STATION MUSEUM

GLENFINNAN STATION MUSEUM TRUST Glenfinnan Railway Station, Station Rd, Glenfinnan,
HIGHLANDS, PH37 4LT, SCOTLAND.
(T) 01397 722295   (F) 01397 701292
(W) www.road-to-the-isles.org.uk
Type of Complex: Railway Station, Operational Railway Line, Museum
Gauge: Standard
Facilities: Restaurant, Souvenir shop, Books for sale, Videos for sale.
Opening/Closing Times:
Summer: Opens Mon - Sun 09:30, Closes Mon - Sun 16:30
Location:
Main Road: A890
Contact(s):
- Manager: Mr John Barnes
Journeys Available At This Railway:

Fort William to Mallaig
Track Type: Single
Features: Views of Hills, Open Fields, Water. 21 arch Glenfinnan viaduct.
Stations On This Journey:

Station Name	St	Al	Bd	Tl	DT	PA	CP	Ph	Mu	WR	Sh	VS	WS	VW	SB	VSB
Fort William	✔	✔	✔													
Glenfinnan																
Mallaig	✔	✔	✔													

GLOUCESTERSHIRE WARWICKSHIRE

GLOUCESTERSHIRE WARWICKSHIRE STEAM RAILWAY PLC The Railway Station, Toddington,
Cheltenham, GLOUCESTERSHIRE, GL54 5DT, ENGLAND.
(T) 01242 621405
(E) enquiries@gwsr.plc.uk
(W) www.gwsr.plc.uk
Affiliated Bodies: English Tourism Council, Heart of England Tourist Board, Heritage
Railway Association
Year Opened: 1984
Type of Complex: Railway Station, Operational Railway Line, Restoration Site
Type of Organisation: Heritage Project, Limited Company, Volunteer
Gauge: Narrow & Standard   No. Volunteers: 130
Stock Overview:
No. Steam Locos: 8 (1 Pre-Group, 1 Pre-Nationalisation)
No. Diesel Locos: 7
TV/Film Appearances: Disney Adventures (1993), Jeeves & Wooster (1996)
Background: A long term volunteer project to rebuild a 15 mile section of the 'Honeybourne Line'
between Cheltenham Racecourse and Broadway. There are plans to extend from Gotherington to
Cheltenham Racecourse, making the operational line 10 miles long, then attention will be focused on

the Toddington to Broadway section.

Facilities: Café, Ticket office, Disabled access, Waiting room, Platform tickets, Photo line side permit available, Guided tours available, Driver footplate experience, Santa Special, 'Thomas' event, Enthusiast galas, Slide shows, Courses on how to drive Locos, Souvenir shop, Books for sale, Videos for sale, Photos for sale, Paintings/drawings for sale, Camera film for sale, Models for sale, Main credit cards taken, Children's events, Facilities for hire, Trains for hire.

Opening/Closing Times:

Spring:	**Opens** Sat, Sun 10:00, **Closes** Sat, Sun 18:00
Summer:	**Opens** Sat, Sun 10:00, **Closes** Sat, Sun 18:00
Autumn:	**Opens** Sat, Sun 10:00, **Closes** Sat, Sun 18:00
Winter:	**Opens** Sat, Sun 10:00, **Closes** Sat, Sun 17:00
Other:	Open extra days during the school holidays. Contact to confirm opening times.

Location:

Instructions: Toddington Station is 10 miles east of M5 junction 9, near to the junction of B4077 and B4632.

Nearest Town/Village: Broadway   **Main Road:** M5   **Mainline Station:** Cheltenham Spa

Hotel: White Hart   **Restaurant:** Pheasant Inn

Contact(s):

● **Chairman:** Mr Garry Owen   (E) chairman@gwsr.plc.uk
● **Secretary:** Mr Bill Hillier   (E) billhillier@iee.org.uk
● **Shop manager:** Mr David Mee

Journeys Available At This Railway:

Toddington to Gotherington
Track Type: Single   Direction: North to South
Features: Views of Hills, Open Fields, Woods. Views of the Vale of Evesham.
Bridges: 8 'over', 4 'under'   **Tunnels:** 1   **Signal Boxes:** 3   **Journey Duration:** 30 mins   **Journey Length:** 13 mile(s)
Price: £7.00 (Adult Standard) £4.00 (Child Standard)
Available on Journey: Refreshments, Drinks.

Stations On This Journey:

Station Name	St	Al	Bd	Tl	DT	PA	CP	Ph	Mu	WR	Sh	VS	WS	VW	SB	VSB
Toddington	✔	✔		✔	✔		✔			✔				✔		
Winchcombe	✔	✔		✔		✔	✔			✔					✔	✔
Gotherington	✔															

GOLDEN VALLEY LIGHT RAILWAY

GOLDEN VALLEY LIGHT RAILWAY Butterley Station, Ripley, **DENBIGHSHIRE,** DE5 3QZ, **WALES**.
(T) 01773 747674   **(F)** 01773 570721
(E) nbrumpus@lineone.net
Year Opened: 1987
Type of Complex: Railway Station, Operational Railway Line
Gauge: Narrow
Background: Shares site with Midland Railway Centre.
Facilities: Café, Ticket office, Guided tours available, 'Thomas' event, Enthusiast galas, Souvenir shop, Books for sale, Videos for sale, CD's for sale, Tapes for sale, Models for sale, Main credit cards taken, Children's events, Facilities for hire, Trains for hire.

Opening/Closing Times:

Spring:	**Opens** Sat, Sun 10:00, **Closes** Sat, Sun 16:00
Summer:	**Opens** Sat, Sun 10:00, **Closes** Sat, Sun 16:00
Autumn:	**Opens** Sat, Sun 10:00, **Closes** Sat, Sun 16:00
Other:	Contact for additional opening days in Summer.

Location:

Nearest Town/Village: Ripley   **Main Road:** B6179   **Bus:** 91, 92

Contact(s):

● **Development Officer:** Mr Alan Calladine
● **General Manager:** Mr John Hett

Key: St = Stops   Al = Alight   Bd = Board   Tl = Toilets   DT = Disabled Toilets   PA = Kids Play Area   CP = Free Car Park   Ph = Pay Phone   Mu = Museum
WR = Waiting Room   Sh = Sheds   VS = Can Visit Sheds   WS = Workshops   VW = Can Visit Workshops   SB = Signal Box   VSB = Can Visit Signal Box

(side margin) A-Z STEAM RAILWAYS   Gloucestershire Warwickshire — Golden Valley Light Railway

Journeys Available At This Railway:

Butterley Park to Newlands End
Features: Maximum gradient of 1 in 50.
Bridges: 2 'over'   **Level Crossings:** 1   **Journey Length:** 1 mile(s)
Price: £1.00 (Adult Standard) £0.50 (Child Standard)

Stations On This Journey:

Station Name	St	Al	Bd	Tl	DT	PA	CP	Ph	Mu	WR	Sh	VS	WS	VW	SB	VSB
Butterley Park	✔	✔		✔	✔	✔	✔	✔	✔		✔		✔			
Brands Sidings	✔	✔		✔	✔		✔									
Newlands End	✔	✔														

GORSE BLOSSOM MINIATURE

GORSE BLOSSOM MINIATURE RAILWAY Bickington, Newton Abbot, **DEVON**, TQ12 6JD, **ENGLAND**.
(T) 01626 821361
(W) www.gorseblossom.com
Year Opened: 1984
Type of Complex: Operational Railway Line
Gauge: Narrow
Facilities: Café, Santa Special, Paintings/drawings for sale, Models for sale, Main credit cards taken, Children's events, All trains are electric.

Opening/Closing Times:
Spring: **Opens** 10:30, **Closes** 17:00
Summer: **Opens** 10:30, **Closes** 17:00
Autumn: **Opens** 10:30, **Closes** 17:00
Other: Open April - September. Contact for opening days.

Location:
Instructions: Follow signs from A38 or Drumbridges roundabout.
Main Road: A38

Contact(s):
- **Owner:** Mrs Belinda Gottlieb
- **Owner:** Mr Michael Gottlieb

Journeys Available At This Railway:
Price: £5.00 (Adult Standard) 4.00 (Child Standard)

GREAT CENTRAL RAILWAY

GREAT CENTRAL RAILWAY PLC Great Central Station, Great Central Rd, Loughborough,
LEICESTERSHIRE, LE11 1RW, **ENGLAND**.
(T) 01509 230726   **(F)** 01509 239791
(E) bookingoffice@gcrailway.co.uk
(W) www.gcrailway.co.uk
Affiliated Bodies: Heritage Railway Association, Transport Trust
Type of Complex: Railway Station, Operational Railway Line, Museum, Restoration Site
Gauge: Standard
Stock Overview:
No. Steam Locos: 12
No. Diesel Locos: 15
TV/Film Appearances: Shadowlands (1993)
Background: Winner of the Heritage Railway Association Award 2000. Rothley Station is officially a haunted site.
Facilities: Café, Ticket office, Disabled access, Platform tickets, Line permit needed, Advanced booking available, Driver footplate experience, Santa Special, 'Thomas' event, Enthusiast galas, Souvenir shop, Books for sale, Videos for sale, Dining train, Murder Mystery, gift vouchers.

Opening/Closing Times:
Spring: **Opens** 09:00, **Closes** 17:30
Summer: **Opens** 09:00, **Closes** 17:30

Autumn: **Opens** 09:00, **Closes** 17:30
Winter: **Opens** 09:00, **Closes** 17:30
Other: Train service every weekend 09:15 - 17:15. Train service open daily May - September.
Museum open daily.

Location:

Nearest Town/Village: Loughborough   **Main Road:** A6   **Mainline Station:** Loughborough Station

Contact(s):

- **Commercial Manager:** Mr John Looker
- **Locomotive Manager:** Mr Tom Tighe
- **Sales Development Manager:** Mr Jonathan Dul

Journeys Available At This Railway:

Loughborough Central to Leicester North
Track Type: Single
Features: Views of Open Fields, Urbanisation, Woods. Maximum gradient of 1 in 176.
Bridges: 9 'over', 16 'under' **Signal Boxes:** 4 **Rivers:** 3 **Viaducts:** 2 **Journey Duration:** 30 mins **Journey Length:** 7.75 mile(s)
Price: £9.80 (Adult Standard) £6.50 (Child Standard)
Available on Journey: Refreshments, Drinks, Alcohol, Restaurant.

Stations On This Journey:

Station Name	St	Al	Bd	Tl	DT	PA	CP	Ph	Mu	WR	Sh	VS	WS	VW	SB	VSB
Loughborough Central	✔	✔	✔	✔		✔		✔	✔	✔	✔			✔	✔	
Quorn and Woodhouse	✔	✔	✔	✔	✔	✔	✔		✔				✔			
Rothley	✔	✔	✔	✔	✔	✔	✔		✔			✔		✔		
Leicester North				✔		✔			✔							

GREAT COCKCROW RAILWAY

GREAT COCKCROW RAILWAY (THE) Hardwick Lane Line, Chertsey, **LONDON (GREATER), ENGLAND**.
(T) 01932 255500
Type of Complex: Operational Railway Line
Gauge: Narrow
Facilities: Café, Ticket office, Souvenir shop, Books for sale, Videos for sale.

Opening/Closing Times:

Spring: **Opens** Sun 14:00, **Closes** Sun 17:30
Summer: **Opens** Sun 14:00, **Closes** Sun 17:30
Autumn: **Opens** Sun 14:00, **Closes** Sun 17:30

Location:

Nearest Town/Village: Chertsey   **Mainline Station:** Chertsey

Contact(s):

- **Chairman:** Mr Ian Allan

Journeys Available At This Railway:

Hardwick Central to Hardwick Central (round trip)
Price: £2.00 (Adult Standard)

Stations On This Journey:

Station Name	St	Al	Bd	Tl	DT	PA	CP	Ph	Mu	WR	Sh	VS	WS	VW	SB	VSB
Hardwick Central	✔	✔		✔	✔	✔	✔			✔		✔		✔		
Everglades Junction												✔				
Cockcrow Hill												✔				
Green Lane																

Key: *St* = Stops   *Al* = Alight   *Bd* = Board   *Tl* = Toilets   *DT* = Disabled Toilets   *PA* = Kids Play Area   *CP* = Free Car Park   *Ph* = Pay Phone   *Mu* = Museum
WR = Waiting Room   *Sh* = Sheds   *VS* = Can Visit Sheds   *WS* = Workshops   *VW* = Can Visit Workshops   *SB* = Signal Box   *VSB* = Can Visit Signal Box

GREAT WESTERN RAILWAY MUSEUM

GREAT WESTERN RAILWAY MUSEUM (COLEFORD) The Old Railway Station, Railway Drive, Coleford, **GLOUCESTERSHIRE,** GL16 8RH, **ENGLAND**.

(T) 01594 833569

Type of Complex: Museum

Stock Overview:

No. Steam Locos: 5

Background: The museum is housed on the original site of Coleford Railway Yard, in one of the last remaining permanent railway buildings in the Forest of Dean. It is the original GWR Goods Station of 1883. A 7 1/4" gauge Miniature Passenger Electric Loco is on site.

Entry Fees: Adults: £2.00   **Children:** £1.00

Opening/Closing Times:

Other: Open Saturday afternoons. Small groups by appointment only on weekdays. Miniature Steam Loco rides some Bank Holidays.

Location:

Instructions: The museum is situated in the Coleford main free car park.

Nearest Town/Village: Monmouth   **Main Road:** B4228   **Hotel:** Beaufort Hotel

GREAT WHIPSNADE RAILWAY

GREAT WHIPSNADE RAILWAY (THE) Whipsnade Wild Animal Pk, Whipsnade, Dunstable, **BEDFORDSHIRE,** LU6 2LF, **ENGLAND**.

(T) 01582 872171   **(F)** 01582 872649

Affiliated Bodies: Heritage Railway Association

Complex Size: 600 Acres   **Year Opened:** 1970

Type of Complex: Railway Station, Operational Railway Line

Type of Organisation: Charity

Gauge: Narrow   **No. Staff:** 3

Stock Overview:

No. Steam Locos: 3

No. Diesel Locos: 4

Facilities: Café, Restaurant, Ticket office, Disabled access, Function room, Platform tickets, Advanced booking available, Main credit cards taken.

Opening/Closing Times:

Spring: **Opens** Mon - Sun 10:00, **Closes** Mon - Sun 17:00

Summer: **Opens** Mon - Sun 10:00, **Closes** Mon - Sun 17:00

Autumn: **Opens** Mon - Sun 10:00, **Closes** Mon - Sun 17:00

Winter: **Opens** Mon - Sun 10:00, **Closes** Mon - Sun 16:00

Other: Closed Christmas Day.

Location:

Nearest Town/Village: Dunstable   **Main Road:** B4550   **Bus:** 43, 60, 61   **Mainline Station:** Luton

Hotel: Horse and Jockey

Contact(s):

● **General Manager:** Ms Linda Hughes   **(T)** 01582 871332

● **General Manager:** Mr Graham Tyler   **(T)** 01582 871332

Journeys Available At This Railway:

Whipsnade Central to Whipsnade Central (round trip)

Track Type: Single

Features: Views of Open Fields. Train travels through paddocks with free roaming animals such as camels, yaks, deer and antelope. Maximum gradient of 1 in 30.

Tunnels: 1   **Level Crossings:** 4   **Signal Boxes:** 2   **Journey Duration:** 15 mins   **Journey Length:** 2 mile(s)

Price: £2.00 (Adult Standard)   £1.50 (Child Standard)

GRIFFITHSTOWN RAILWAY MUSEUM

GRIFFITHSTOWN RAILWAY MUSEUM Station Rd, Griffithstown, Pontypool, **TORFAEN,** NP4 5JH, **WALES**.

(T) 01495 762908

Year Opened: 2001
Type of Complex: Museum
Type of Organisation: Trust
No. Staff: 1
Facilities: Café, Disabled access, Function room.
Opening/Closing Times:
Spring: **Opens** 10:00, **Closes** 16:00
Summer: **Opens** 10:00, **Closes** 17:30
Autumn: **Opens** 10:00, **Closes** 16:30
Winter: **Opens** 10:00, **Closes** 16:00
Location:
Nearest Town/Village: Cwmbran   **Mainline Station:** Cwmbran
Contact(s):
● **Owner:** Mr Martin Fay

GROUDLE GLEN RAILWAY

GROUDLE GLEN RAILWAY LTD Groudle Glen, Onchan, Douglas, **ISLE OF MAN, ENGLAND**.
Year Opened: 1896
Type of Complex: Railway Station, Operational Railway Line
Type of Organisation: Charity, Limited Company, Volunteer
Gauge: Narrow   **No. Volunteers:** 10
Stock Overview:
No. Steam Locos: 2
No. Diesel Locos: 2
Background: Originally built in 1896, its purpose was to take Victorian holiday makers to the zoo on the coastal headland. Closed in 1939. Partially reopened after the Second World War and closed again in 1962. Restoration began in 1982 and sections of the line reopened (final section in 1992). Operates with original 1896 steam locomotive.
Facilities: Ticket office, Waiting room, Line permit needed, Photo line side permit available, Guided tours available, Santa Special, Enthusiast galas, Souvenir shop, Books for sale, Videos for sale, Photos for sale, Camera film for sale.
Opening/Closing Times:
Other: Open May - December. Also open at Easter and Christmas.
Location:
Instructions: Situated within Groudle Glen.
Nearest Town/Village: Douglas   **Main Road:** King Edward Road   **Hotel:** Douglas Promenade
Restaurant: Groudle Hotel
Contact(s):
● **For Bookings:** Mr Tony Beard
● **For Donations:** Mr Tony Beard
● **General Manager:** Mr Tony Beard   (T) 01624 622138
Alternative Contact Details:
● 29 Hawarden Ave, Douglas, Isle of Man, IM1 4BP, England
Journeys Available At This Railway:

Groudle Lhen Coan to Sea Lion Rocks
Track Type: Single   Direction: East
Features: Views of Hills, Open Fields, Sea, Woods. Picturesque glen and headland coastline. Maximum gradient of 1 in 35.
Journey Duration: 5 mins   **Journey Length:** 0.75 mile(s)
Price: £2.00 (Adult Standard) £1.00 (Child Standard) £2.00 (Adult Special) £1.00 (Child Special)
Available on Journey: Refreshments, Drinks.
Stations On This Journey:

A-Z STEAM RAILWAYS

Griffithstown Railway Museum — Groudle Glen Railway

Key: St = Stops   Al = Alight   Bd = Board   Tl = Toilets   DT = Disabled Toilets   PA = Kids Play Area   CP = Free Car Park   Ph = Pay Phone   Mu = Museum
          WR = Waiting Room   Sh = Sheds   VS = Can Visit Sheds   WS = Workshops   VW = Can Visit Workshops   SB = Signal Box   VSB = Can Visit Signal Box

Station Name	St	Al	Bd	Tl	DT	PA	CP	Ph	Mu	WR	Sh	VS	WS	VW	SB	VSB
Groudle Lhen Coan			✔								✔	✔				
Lime Kiln Halt	✔	✔			✔											
Sea Lion Rocks		✔														

GWILI RAILWAY

GWILI RAILWAY CO Bronwydd Arms Railway Station, Carmarthen, **CARMARTHENSHIRE,** SA33 6HT, **WALES**.

(T) 01267 230666
(E) gwili@talk21.com
(W) www.gwili-railway.co.uk
Affiliated Bodies: Heritage Railway Association, Transport Trust
Type of Complex: Railway Station, Operational Railway Line
Type of Organisation: Volunteer
Gauge: Standard   **No. Volunteers:** 150
Stock Overview:
No. Steam Locos: 6
No. Diesel Locos: 7
TV/Film Appearances: Y Gynddeiriog, Y Cleddraucoll, Y Palmant Aur, Twrio, Heno, Dechrau Canu Dechrau Canmol

Facilities: Buffet, Ticket office, Disabled access, Driver footplate experience, Santa Special, 'Thomas' event, Souvenir shop, Books for sale, Videos for sale, Photos for sale, Children's events, Trains for hire.

Opening/Closing Times:
Spring: Opens 11:00, **Closes** 17:30
Summer: Opens 11:00, **Closes** 17:30
Autumn: Opens 11:00, **Closes** 17:30
Winter: Opens 11:00, **Closes** 17:30

Location:
Instructions: Take the A484 Carmarthen to Cardigan Road. Turn into Bronwydd village 3 miles north of Carmarthen.

Nearest Town/Village: Carmarthen   **Main Road:** A484, A40   **Mainline Station:** Carmarthen

Contact(s):
- **Chairman:** Mr Chris King **(T)** 01792 232603
- **For Bookings:** Mr Chris Jones   **(T)** 01656 653385

Alternative Contact Details:
- Publicity Manager, Frondeg, Peniel, Carmarthen, Carmarthenshire, SA32 7DH, Wales **(T)** 01267 236291

Journeys Available At This Railway:

Bronwydd Arms to Danycoed Halt
Track Type: Single   Direction: South to North
Features: Views of Hills, Open Fields, Water, Woods. Interesting wildlife. Route follows Gwili River Valley. Maximum gradient of 1 in 40 (For 40 metres).
Bridges: 1 'over', 1 'under'   **Signal Boxes:** 1   **Rivers:** 1   **Journey Length:** 2.5 mile(s)
Price: £4.50 (Adult Standard) £3.00 (Child Standard)
Available on Journey: Refreshments, Drinks, Alcohol.

Stations On This Journey:

Station Name	St	Al	Bd	Tl	DT	PA	CP	Ph	Mu	WR	Sh	VS	WS	VW	SB	VSB
Bronwydd Arms	✔	✔	✔	✔	✔			✔						✔	✔	
Llwyfan Cerrig	✔	✔		✔	✔						✔					
Danycoed Halt	✔	✔														

HEATHERSLAW LIGHT RAILWAY

HEATHERSLAW LIGHT RAILWAY CO LTD Ford Forge, Heatherslaw, Cornhill-on-Tweed,
NORTHUMBERLAND, TD12 4TP, **ENGLAND**.

(T) 01890 820244   **(F)** 01890 820317

Complex Size: 2 Acres   **Year Opened:** 1989

Type of Complex: Railway Station, Operational Railway Line

Type of Organisation: Limited Company

Gauge: Narrow

Stock Overview:

No. Steam Locos: 1

No. Diesel Locos: 1

Background: There is also a working water mill and a railway room with model railway on site.

Facilities: Café, Waiting room, Advanced booking available, Driver footplate experience, Santa Special, Training courses, Courses on how to drive Locos, Souvenir shop, Books for sale, Children's events, Facilities for hire.

Opening/Closing Times:

Spring: **Opens** 10:30, **Closes** 16:30

Summer: **Opens** 10:30, **Closes** 17:30

Autumn: **Opens** 10:30, **Closes** 16:30

Location:

Nearest Town/Village: Coldstream   **Main Road:** A697   **Mainline Station:** Berwick

Restaurant: Blue Bell Inn

Contact(s):

- **For Bookings:** Mrs D B Smith
- **Owner:** Mr N C Smith   **(T)** 01890 820317

Journeys Available At This Railway:

Heatherslaw to Etal Castle

Track Type: Single   Direction: South to North

Features: Views of Hills, Open Fields, Water, Woods. The river and the surrounding wildlife. Etal Castle. Maximum gradient of 1 in 35 (For 100 metres).

Journey Duration: 15 mins   **Journey Length:** 1.9 mile(s)

Price: £4.00 (Adult Standard) £2.50 (Child Standard)

Stations On This Journey:

Station Name	St	Al	Bd	Tl	DT	PA	CP	Ph	Mu	WR	Sh	VS	WS	VW	SB	VSB
Heatherslaw	✔	✔		✔	✔		✔			✔	✔		✔			
Etal Castle	✔	✔		✔		✔										

HILCOTE VALLEY RAILWAY

HILCOTE VALLEY RAILWAY Fletchers Garden Ctre, Bridge Farm, Stone Rd, Eccleshall, Stafford,
STAFFORDSHIRE, ST21 6JY, **ENGLAND**.

(T) 01785 284553

(E) info@hilcote.co.uk

(W) www.hilcote.co.uk

Type of Complex: Operational Railway Line

Gauge: Narrow

Background: Visiting locomotives can be seen in mid-June and August.

Facilities: Café, Ticket office, Disabled access, Souvenir shop.

Opening/Closing Times:

Spring: **Opens** Sat, Sun 11:30, **Closes** Sat, Sun 17:00

Summer: **Opens** Sat, Sun 11:30, **Closes** Sat, Sun 17:00

Autumn: **Opens** Sat, Sun 11:30, **Closes** Sat, Sun 17:00

Other: Open school and Bank Holidays 13:30 - 16:30. Also open every other Sunday from November - Easter. Contact for details.

Key: *St* = Stops   *Al* = Alight   *Bd* = Board   *Tl* = Toilets   *DT* = Disabled Toilets   *PA* = Kids Play Area   *CP* = Free Car Park   *Ph* = Pay Phone   *Mu* = Museum
WR = Waiting Room   *Sh* = Sheds   *VS* = Can Visit Sheds   *WS* = Workshops   *VW* = Can Visit Workshops   *SB* = Signal Box   *VSB* = Can Visit Signal Box

Location:
Nearest Town/Village: Stone   **Main Road:** B5026   **Mainline Station:** Stafford
Contact(s):
● **Owner:** Mr Roger Greatrex
Journeys Available At This Railway:
Features: Views of Open Fields, Water.
Bridges: 1 'over'   **Tunnels:** 1   **Journey Length:** 1 mile(s)
Price: £0.80 (Adult Standard) £0.80 (Child Standard)

HOLLYBUSH GARDEN CENTRE

LEISURERAIL LTD Warstone Rd, Shareshill, Wolverhampton, **MIDLANDS (WEST),** WV10 7LX, **ENGLAND**.
(T) 01922 418050   **(F)** 01922 701028
(W) www.hollybush-garden.com
Complex Size: 12 Acres   **Year Opened:** 1996
Type of Organisation: Limited Company
Gauge: Narrow   **No. Staff:** 1   **No. Volunteers:** 2
Stock Overview:
No. Steam Locos: 2
No. Diesel Locos: 2
Facilities: Café, Restaurant, Disabled access, Platform tickets.
Opening/Closing Times:
Other: Open April - September daily (except Thursdays) and October - March at weekends only.
Location:
Instructions: Located on the A462, approximately 500 yards from junction 11 of the M6. Follow brown
tourist signs.
Nearest Town/Village: Cannock   **Main Road:** A462   **Mainline Station:** Landywood
Hotel: Roman Way
Contact(s):
● **For Bookings:** Ms Emma Martin
● **Owner:** Mr Tim Porter   **(E)** tim@hollybush-garden.com
Journeys Available At This Railway:

Hollybush Central to Hollybush Central (round trip)
Features: Views of Open Fields, Water, Woods.
Bridges: 1 'over'   **Tunnels:** 1   **Journey Duration:** 8 mins   **Journey Length:** 1 mile(s)
Price: £0.90 (Adult Standard) £0.60 (Child Standard)
Stations On This Journey:

Station Name	St	Al	Bd	Tl	DT	PA	CP	Ph	Mu	WR	Sh	VS	WS	VW	SB	VSB
Hollybush Central	✔	✔	✔	✔	✔		✔	✔								

HOLLYCOMBE STEAM COLLECTION

HOLLYCOMBE WORKING STEAM MUSEUM LTD Iron Hill, Liphook, **HAMPSHIRE,** GU30 7LP,
ENGLAND.
(T) 01428 724900   **(F)** 01428 723682
(W) www.hollycombe.co.uk
Affiliated Bodies: Heritage Railway Association, Transport Trust
Complex Size: 20 Acres   **Year Opened:** 1970
Type of Complex: Museum
Type of Organisation: Charity, Trust, Volunteer, Non-Profit
Gauge: Narrow & Standard   **No. Staff:** 2   **No. Volunteers:** 40
Stock Overview:
No. Steam Locos: 5 (1 Pre-Group, 2 Pre-Nationalisation)
No. Diesel Locos: 1 (1 Pre-Group)
TV/Film Appearances: Southern Steam (2001)
Background: A working steam museum with Edwardian steam fairground, railways, road rolling,
agricultural machinery, sawmill and paddle steam engines.
Facilities: Café, Ticket office, Disabled access, Cinema, Guided tours available, Souvenir shop,

Books for sale, Videos for sale, Photos for sale, Camera film for sale, Models for sale, Main credit cards taken, Children's events, Facilities for hire.

Opening/Closing Times:
Spring: **Opens** Sun 12:00, **Closes** Sun 17:00
Summer: **Opens** Mon - Sun 12:00, **Closes** Mon - Sun 17:00
Autumn: **Opens** Sun 12:00, **Closes** Sun 17:00

Location:
Instructions: Situated on Midhurst Road, 1 mile from Liphook.
Nearest Town/Village: Liphook   **Mainline Station:** Liphook

Contact(s):
- **For Bookings:** Mr Chris Hooker
- **General Manager:** Mr Chris Hooker
- **Technical Info:** Mr Chris Hooker

Journeys Available At This Railway:

Hollycoombe to Hollycombe
Features: Views of Hills, Open Fields, Woods. Maximum gradient of 1 in 37 (For 200 metres).
Level Crossings: 1   **Signal Boxes:** 1   **Journey Duration:** 10 mins   **Journey Length:** 1.5 mile(s)
Price: £7.50 (Adult Standard) £6.00 (Child Standard) £7.50 (Adult Special) £6.00 (Child Special)
Available on Journey: Refreshments, Entertainment.

Stations On This Journey:

Station Name	St	Al	Bd	Tl	DT	PA	CP	Ph	Mu	WR	Sh	VS	WS	VW	SB	VSB
Hollycombe	✔	✔	✔	✔		✔	✔		✔		✔		✔		✔	✔

INDUSTRIAL RAILWAY MUSEUM

PENRHYN CASTLE INDUSTRIAL RAILWAY MUSEUM The National Trust, Penrhyn Castle, Bangor, **GWYNEDD,** LL57 4HN, **WALES**.

(T) 01248 353084
Affiliated Bodies: Heritage Railway Association
Type of Complex: Museum, Restoration Site
Type of Organisation: Charity, Trust, Conservation Project, Volunteer, Non-Profit
Gauge: Narrow & Standard   **No. Staff:** 1   **No. Volunteers:** 3

Stock Overview:
No. Steam Locos: 8
No. Diesel Locos: 1
Facilities: Café, Disabled access, Souvenir shop.

Opening/Closing Times:
Spring: **Opens** Mon, Wed - Sun 11:00, **Closes** Mon, Wed - Sun 17:00
Summer: **Opens** Mon, Wed - Sun 10:00, **Closes** Mon, Wed - Sun 17:00

Location:
Nearest Town/Village: Bangor   **Main Road:** A5   **Mainline Station:** Bangor

Journeys Available At This Railway:
Features: Views of Hills, Open Fields, Sea, Woods.
Price: £6.00 (Adult Standard) £3.00 (Child Standard)
Available on Journey: Refreshments.

IRCHESTER NARROW GAUGE MUSEUM

IRCHESTER NARROW GAUGE RAILWAY TRUST (THE) Irchester Country Pk, Wellingborough, **HAMPSHIRE, ENGLAND**.

(T) 01234 750469
(E) irchester@kingstonray.freeserve.co.uk
(W) www.ingrt.freeuk.com
Affiliated Bodies: Heritage Railway Association
Type of Complex: Museum

Stock Overview:

Key: St = Stops   Al = Alight   Bd = Board   Tl = Toilets   DT = Disabled Toilets   PA = Kids Play Area   CP = Free Car Park   Ph = Pay Phone   Mu = Museum
WR = Waiting Room   Sh = Sheds   VS = Can Visit Sheds   WS = Workshops   VW = Can Visit Workshops   SB = Signal Box   VSB = Can Visit Signal Box

No. Steam Locos: 4
No. Diesel Locos: 4
Background: Museum with 250 metres of demonstration line.
Facilities: Disabled access, Souvenir shop, Books for sale, Videos for sale.

Opening/Closing Times:

Spring: **Opens** Sun 10:00, **Closes** Sun 17:00
Summer: **Opens** Sun 10:00, **Closes** Sun 17:00
Autumn: **Opens** Sun 10:00, **Closes** Sun 17:00
Winter: **Opens** Sun 10:00, **Closes** Sun 16:00
Other: Contact to confirm demonstration days.

Location:

Instructions: Situated in Irchester Country Park.
Nearest Town/Village: Wellingborough   **Main Road:** A509

Contact(s):
● **Secretary:** Mr Ray Kingston

Alternative Contact Details:
● 71 Bedford Rd, Cranfield, Bedford, Bedfordshire, MK43 0EX, England

IRISH STEAM PRESERVATION SOC

IRISH STEAM PRESERVATION SOCIETY LTD Stradbally Hall, Stradbally, **COUNTY LOAIS, IRELAND**.
(T) 050 225444   **(F)** 050 225154
(W) www.irishsteam.ie
Affiliated Bodies: Heritage Railway Association
Type of Complex: Operational Railway Line, Museum
Gauge: Narrow

Stock Overview:
No. Steam Locos: 1
No. Diesel Locos: 2
Facilities: Disabled access, Souvenir shop, Children's events.

Opening/Closing Times:
Other: Open during Bank Holiday Sundays and Mondays only.

Location:
Nearest Town/Village: Stradbally   **Main Road:** N80   **Mainline Station:** Port Laoise

Contact(s):
● **Hon Secretary:** Mr Clifton Flewitt

Journeys Available At This Railway:

Stradbally to Stradbally (round trip)
Features: Views of Open Fields, Woods.

Stations On This Journey:

Station Name	St	Al	Bd	Tl	DT	PA	CP	Ph	Mu	WR	Sh	VS	WS	VW	SB	VSB
Stradbally	✔	✔					✔				✔	✔				

IRISH TRACTION GROUP

IRISH TRACTION GROUP The Old Goods Store, Carrick-on-Suir, **COUNTY TIPPERARY, IRELAND**.
Affiliated Bodies: Heritage Railway Association
Type of Complex: Museum
Background: Not open to public.

Contact(s):
● **Membership Secretary:** Mr Andy Carey

Alternative Contact Details:
● 31 Hayfield Rd, Bredbury, Stockport, Cheshire, SK6 1DE, England

ISLE OF MAN RAILWAY

ISLE OF MAN RAILWAY Isle of Man Transport, Banks Circus, Douglas, **ISLE OF MAN,** IM1 5PT, **ENGLAND**.

(T) 01624 663366   **(F)** 01624 663637

Year Opened: 1873

Type of Complex: Operational Railway Line

Gauge: Narrow

Stock Overview:

No. Steam Locos: 5

Facilities: Café, Ticket office, Disabled access, Waiting room, Advanced booking available, Main credit cards taken, Trains for hire.

Opening/Closing Times:

Summer: **Opens** Mon - Sun 10:00, **Closes** Mon - Sun 18:00
Autumn: **Opens** Mon - Sun 10:00, **Closes** Mon - Sun 18:00

Location:

Nearest Town/Village: Douglas

Journeys Available At This Railway:

Douglas to Port Erin
Direction: South
Features: Views of Hills, Open Fields, Sea, Urbanisation, Water, Woods. Maximum gradient of 1 in 40.
Journey Duration: 60 mins   **Journey Length:** 15.5 mile(s)

Stations On This Journey:

Station Name	St	Al	Bd	Tl	DT	PA	CP	Ph	Mu	WR	Sh	VS	WS	VW	SB	VSB
Douglas	✔	✔		✔		✔				✔	✔			✔		
Santon	✔	✔								✔						
Ballasalla	✔	✔	✔		✔					✔						
Castletown	✔	✔	✔		✔					✔						
Colby	✔	✔														
Port St Mary	✔	✔	✔													
Port Erin	✔	✔	✔		✔					✔	✔					

ISLE OF WIGHT STEAM RAILWAY

ISLE OF WIGHT RAILWAY CO LTD The Railway Station, Havenstreet, Ryde, **ISLE OF WIGHT,** PO33 4DS, **ENGLAND**.

(T) 01983 882204   **(F)** 01983 884515

(E) info@iwsteamrailway.co.uk

(W) www.iwsteamrailway.co.uk

Affiliated Bodies: Heritage Railway Association, Transport Trust

Complex Size: 2 Acres   **Year Opened:** 1971

Type of Complex: Railway Station, Operational Railway Line, Museum

Type of Organisation: Charity, Heritage Project, Limited Company, Volunteer, Non-Profit

Gauge: Standard   **No. Staff:** 12   **No. Volunteers:** 200

Stock Overview:

No. Steam Locos: 5 (3 Pre-Group, 3 Pre-Nationalisation)

No. Diesel Locos: 2

Facilities: Café, Ticket office, Waiting room, Platform tickets, Santa Special, 'Thomas' event, Enthusiast galas, Souvenir shop, Books for sale, Videos for sale, Paintings/drawings for sale, Trains for hire.

Opening/Closing Times:

Spring: **Opens** 10:00, **Closes** 16:00

Key:	St = Stops	Al = Alight	Bd = Board	Tl = Toilets	DT = Disabled Toilets	PA = Kids Play Area	CP = Free Car Park	Ph = Pay Phone	Mu = Museum
	WR = Waiting Room	Sh = Sheds	VS = Can Visit Sheds	WS = Workshops	VW = Can Visit Workshops	SB = Signal Box	VSB = Can Visit Signal Box		

Summer: **Opens** 10:00, **Closes** 16:00
Autumn: **Opens** 10:00, **Closes** 16:00

Location:
Nearest Town/Village: Ryde   **Mainline Station:** Smallbrook Junction

Contact(s):
- **For Bookings:** Mr Jim Loe
- **For Donations:** Ms Di Aters
- **General Manager:** Mr Hugh Boynton
- **Technical Info:** Mr Ron Lee

Journeys Available At This Railway:

Havenstreet to Havenstreet (round trip)
Track Type: Single   Direction: East to West
Features: Views of Hills, Open Fields, Woods. Maximum gradient of 1 in 66.
Bridges: 1 'over', 3 'under'   **Level Crossings:** 2   **Signal Boxes:** 1   **Journey Duration:** 50 mins   **Journey Length:** 5 mile(s)
Price: £7.00 (Adult Standard)   £4.00 (Child Standard)

Stations On This Journey:

Station Name	St	Al	Bd	Tl	DT	PA	CP	Ph	Mu	WR	Sh	VS	WS	VW	SB	VSB
Havenstreet	✔	✔	✔	✔		✔	✔	✔	✔	✔	✔		✔		✔	
Wootton	✔	✔		✔			✔									
Smallbrook	✔	✔		✔												
Ashey																

KEIGHLEY & WORTH VALLEY

KEIGHLEY & WORTH VALLEY RAILWAY The Railway Station, Haworth, Keighley, **YORKSHIRE (WEST),** BD22 8NJ, **ENGLAND**.
(T) 01535 645214   **(F)** 01535 647317
(E) kwvr@dockroyd.co.uk
(W) www.kwvr.co.uk

Affiliated Bodies: Heritage Railway Association
Type of Complex: Railway Station, Operational Railway Line, Museum
Type of Organisation: Trust

Stock Overview:
No. Steam Locos: 23
No. Diesel Locos: 12

TV/Film Appearances: Railway Children
Facilities: Ticket office, Disabled access, Santa Special, 'Thomas' event, Souvenir shop, Main credit cards taken, Children's events.

Location:
Main Road: B6142   **Hotel:** Woodlands Grange Hotel   **Restaurant:** Chaplins Bistro

Contact(s):
- **Secretary:** Mr Ken Cook

Journeys Available At This Railway:

Keighley to Oxenhope
Price: £6.00 (Adult Standard)

Stations On This Journey:

Station Name	St	Al	Bd	Tl	DT	PA	CP	Ph	Mu	WR	Sh	VS	WS	VW	SB	VSB
Keighley	✔	✔	✔	✔		✔			✔							
Ingrow (West)	✔	✔	✔	✔		✔	✔									
Damens	✔	✔	✔	✔					✔				✔			
Oakworth	✔	✔	✔	✔		✔										
Haworth	✔	✔	✔	✔												
Oxenhope	✔	✔	✔				✔									

KEITH & DUFFTOWN RAILWAY

KEITH & DUFFTOWN RAILWAY (THE) Dufftown Station, Dufftown, Keith, **MORAY,** AB55 4BA, **SCOTLAND**.

(T) 01340 821181   **(F)** 01340 820011

(W) www.keith-dufftown.org.uk

Affiliated Bodies: Heritage Railway Association

Year Opened: 2000

Type of Complex: Railway Station, Operational Railway Line, Restoration Site

Gauge: Standard

Stock Overview:

No. Diesel Locos: 4

Facilities: Café, Ticket office, Disabled access, Santa Special, Souvenir shop, Books for sale, Models for sale, Facilities for hire, Trains for hire.

Opening/Closing Times:

Other: Open weekends from Easter - October.

Location:

Nearest Town/Village: Keith   **Main Road:** A96   **Mainline Station:** Keith

Contact(s):

- **Administrator:** Mr Noel Fitzgerald   **(T)** 01340 810389
- **Chairman:** Ms Maureen Webster **(T)** 01261 861212
- **For Donations:** Ms Maureen Webster   **(T)** 01261 861212
- **Technical Info:** Mr Peter Bradley **(T)** 01261 861212

Journeys Available At This Railway:

Dufftown to Keith Town

Features: Views of Open Fields, Water, Woods. Views of Drummuir Castle. Maximum gradient of 1 in 60.

Bridges: 11 'over', 31 'under'   **Level Crossings:** 1   **Rivers:** 1   **Viaducts:** 1   **Journey Length:** 10.25 mile(s)

Price: £5.00 (Adult Standard) £2.50 (Child Standard)

Stations On This Journey:

Station Name	St	Al	Bd	Tl	DT	PA	CP	Ph	Mu	WR	Sh	VS	WS	VW	SB	VSB
Dufftown	✔	✔		✔	✔		✔			✔		✔				
Drummuir	✔	✔		✔						✔						
Keith Town	✔	✔		✔	✔		✔									

KENT & EAST SUSSEX RAILWAY

TENTERDEN RAILWAY COMPANY LTD (THE) Tenterden Town Station, Station Rd, Tenterden, **KENT,** TN30 6HE, **ENGLAND**.

(T) 01580 765155   **(F)** 01580 765654

(E) kesroffice@aol.com

(W) www.kesr.org.uk

Affiliated Bodies: Heritage Railway Association, Transport Trust

Year Opened: 1974

Type of Complex: Railway Station, Museum

Type of Organisation: Charity, Heritage Project, Limited Company, Volunteer, Non-Profit

Gauge: Standard   **No. Staff:** 23   **No. Volunteers:** 240

Stock Overview:

No. Steam Locos: 14 (1 Pre-Nationalisation)

No. Diesel Locos: 10

TV/Film Appearances: Southern Steam, Art Attack, Darling Buds of May, On The Record (BBC), Off The Rails

Facilities: Café, Ticket office, Disabled access, Cinema, Platform tickets, Line permit needed, Photo line side permit available, Advanced booking available, Guided tours available, Driver footplate

Key:	St = Stops	Al = Alight	Bd = Board	Tl = Toilets	DT = Disabled Toilets	PA = Kids Play Area	CP = Free Car Park	Ph = Pay Phone	Mu = Museum
	WR = Waiting Room	Sh = Sheds	VS = Can Visit Sheds	WS = Workshops	VW = Can Visit Workshops	SB = Signal Box	VSB = Can Visit Signal Box		

experience, Santa Special, 'Thomas' event, Training courses, History lectures, Enthusiast galas, Courses on how to drive Locos, Souvenir shop, Books for sale, Videos for sale, Camera film for sale, Models for sale, Main credit cards taken, Children's events, Facilities for hire, Trains for hire.

Opening/Closing Times:
Spring: **Opens** Sat, Sun 10:00, **Closes** Sat, Sun 17:30
Summer: **Opens** Sat, Sun, Tues - Thurs 10:00, **Closes** Sat, Sun, Tues - Thurs 17:30
Autumn: **Opens** Sat, Sun 10:00, **Closes** Sat, Sun 17:30
Other: Also open at half term school holidays for Thomas events and at Easter, Bank Holidays, and December for Santa specials. Open daily in August.

Location:
Nearest Town/Village: Tenterden   **Main Road:** A28   **Mainline Station:** Headcorn   **Hotel:** White Lion

Contact(s):
● **For Bookings:** Ms Sally Russell
● **For Bookings:** Mr Graham Syvier
● **For Bookings:** Ms Lin Batt
● **General Manager:** Ms Sandra Marsh

Journeys Available At This Railway:

Tenterden Town to Bodiam
Track Type: Single   Direction: East to West
Features: Views of Open Fields, Water, Woods. Maximum gradient of 1 in 12.
Bridges: 3 'over'   **Level Crossings:** 6   **Signal Boxes:** 4   **Rivers:** 3   **Journey Duration:** 50 mins   **Journey Length:** 10.5 mile(s)
Price: £7.50 (Adult Standard) £3.75 (Child Standard)
Available on Journey: Refreshments, Drinks, Alcohol, Restaurant.

Stations On This Journey:

Station Name	St	Al	Bd	Tl	DT	PA	CP	Ph	Mu	WR	Sh	VS	WS	VW	SB	VSB
Tenterden	✔	✔	✔	✔	✔	✔	✔	✔	✔		✔		✔		✔	✔
Rolvenden	✔	✔	✔									✔		✔		
Wittersham	✔	✔	✔	✔		✔	✔			✔					✔	✔
Northiam	✔	✔	✔	✔	✔	✔	✔			✔					✔	✔
Bodiam	✔	✔	✔	✔	✔	✔					✔					

KERR MINIATURE RAILWAY

KERR MINIATURE RAILWAY West Links Pk, Arbroath, **ANGUS, SCOTLAND**.
(T) 01241 879249
(W) www.geocities.com/kmr_scotland
Year Opened: 1935
Type of Complex: Operational Railway Line
Gauge: Narrow
Stock Overview:
No. Steam Locos: 1
TV/Film Appearances: Miniature Railway Memories
Background: The 6th oldest miniature railway in Great Britain, and the oldest small gauge railway in the world.
Facilities: Disabled access.
Location:
Nearest Town/Village: Arbroath   **Main Road:** A92   **Mainline Station:** Arbroath
Contact(s):
● **Owner:** Mr Matthew Kerr
Alternative Contact Details:
● 12 Kinghorne St, Arbroath, Angus, DD11 2LZ, Scotland
Journeys Available At This Railway:

Westlinks to Hospital Field Halt
Price: £0.60 (Adult Standard) £0.60 (Child Standard)
Stations On This Journey:

Station Name	St	Al	Bd	Tl	DT	PA	CP	Ph	Mu	WR	Sh	VS	WS	VW	SB	VSB
Westlinks	✔	✔														
Hospital Field Halt	✔															

KEW BRIDGE STEAM MUSEUM

KEW BRIDGE ENGINES TRUST Green Dragon Lane, Brentford, **LONDON (GREATER),** TW8 0EN, **ENGLAND**.

(T) 020 85684757   **(F)** 020 85699978

(E) info@kbsm.org

(W) www.kbsm.org

Complex Size: 4 Acres   **Year Opened:** 1975

Type of Complex: Museum

Type of Organisation: Charity, Heritage Project, Limited Company, Volunteer

Gauge: Narrow   **No. Staff:** 4   **No. Volunteers:** 55

Stock Overview:

No. Steam Locos: 2 (2 Pre-Group)

No. Diesel Locos: 1

Background: The museum is housed within a Victorian water pumping station and contains most of the original steam pumping engines. The railway is intended to illustrate a typical waterworks railway.

Facilities: Café, Disabled access, Function room, Guided tours available, Souvenir shop, Books for sale, Paintings/drawings for sale, Camera film for sale, Models for sale, Main credit cards taken, Children's events, Facilities for hire.

Opening/Closing Times:

Spring: **Opens** Mon - Sun 11:00, **Closes** Mon - Sun 17:00
Summer: **Opens** Mon - Sun 11:00, **Closes** Mon - Sun 17:00
Autumn: **Opens** Mon - Sun 11:00, **Closes** Mon - Sun 17:00
Winter: **Opens** Mon - Sun 11:00, **Closes** Mon - Sun 17:00

Location:

Main Road: M4 Junction 2   **Bus:** 65, 237, 267, 391   **Taxi:** Kew Cars   **Mainline Station:** Kew Bridge

Hotel: Coach & Horses

Contact(s):

- For Bookings: Ms Jo Willis   **(E)** jo@kbsm.org
- For Donations: Mrs Lesley Bossine   **(E)** lesley@kbsm.org
- General Manager: Mrs Lesley Bossine   **(E)** lesley@kbsm.org

KIDDERMINSTER RAILWAY MUSEUM

KIDDERMINSTER RAILWAY MUSEUM Station Approach, Comberton Hill, Kidderminster, **WORCESTERSHIRE,** DY10 1QX, **ENGLAND**.

(T) 01562 825316   **(F)** 01562 861039

(E) krm@krm.org.uk

(W) www.krm.org.uk

Type of Complex: Museum

Facilities: Café, Disabled access, Souvenir shop.

Opening/Closing Times:

Spring: **Opens** Sat - Sun 10:00, **Closes** Sat - Sun 18:00
Summer: **Opens** Mon - Sun 10:30, **Closes** Mon - Sun 18:00
Autumn: **Opens** Sat - Sun 10:00, **Closes** Sat - Sun 18:00
Winter: **Opens** Sat - Sun 10:00, **Closes** Sat - Sun 17:00
Other: Contact to confirm opening times.

Location:

Instructions: Take A442 from Bromsgrove or A449 from Worcester. Located opposite to the Severn Valley Railway Station.

Bus: X92   **Mainline Station:** Kidderminster

Key:	*St* = Stops	*Al* = Alight	*Bd* = Board	*Tl* = Toilets	*DT* = Disabled Toilets	*PA* = Kids Play Area	*CP* = Free Car Park	*Ph* = Pay Phone	*Mu* = Museum
	WR = Waiting Room	*Sh* = Sheds	*VS* = Can Visit Sheds	*WS* = Workshops	*VW* = Can Visit Workshops	*SB* = Signal Box	*VSB* = Can Visit Signal Box		

Contact(s):
- **General Manager:** Mr David Postle

KIRKLEES LIGHT RAILWAY

KIRKLEES LIGHT RAILWAY CO LTD Park Mill Way, Clayton West, Huddersfield, **YORKSHIRE (WEST),** HD8 9JX, **ENGLAND**.

(T) 01484 865727 **(F)** 01484 865727

(W) www.kirkleeslightrailway.com

Affiliated Bodies: Heritage Railway Association

Complex Size: 10 Acres **Year Opened:** 1991

Type of Complex: Railway Station, Operational Railway Line

Type of Organisation: Limited Company

Gauge: Narrow **No. Staff:** 3 **No. Volunteers:** 20

Stock Overview:

No. Steam Locos: 4

No. Diesel Locos: 2

Facilities: Café, Ticket office, Disabled access, Waiting room, Driver footplate experience, Santa Special, 'Thomas' event, Souvenir shop, Books for sale, Videos for sale, Photos for sale, Models for sale, Main credit cards taken, Children's events, Facilities for hire, Trains for hire.

Opening/Closing Times:
Spring: **Opens** Mon - Sun 11:00, **Closes** Mon - Sun 16:00
Summer: **Opens** Mon - Sun 11:00, **Closes** Mon - Sun 16:00
Autumn: **Opens** Sat - Sun 11:00, **Closes** Sat - Sun 15:00
Winter: **Opens** Sat - Sun 11:00, **Closes** Sat - Sun 15:00

Location:
Instructions: Clayton West is situated midway between Wakefield, Barnsley, Holmfirth and Huddersfield.

Nearest Town/Village: Huddersfield **Main Road:** A636 **Bus:** 235, 484 **Mainline Station:** Wakefield Westgate **Hotel:** Bagden Hall

Contact(s):
- **For Bookings:** Mr Brian Caldwell
- **For Bookings:** Ms Doreen Taylor
- **General Manager:** Mr Brian Caldwell
- **Owner:** Mr Brian Taylor
- **Technical Info:** Mr Brian Taylor

Journeys Available At This Railway:

Clayton West to Shelley
Track Type: Single Direction: East to West
Features: Views of Hills, Open Fields, Water, Woods. Maximum gradient of 1 in 68 (For 825 metres).
Bridges: 12 'over', 3 'under' **Tunnels:** 1 **Rivers:** 1 **Journey Duration:** 20 mins **Journey Length:** 4 mile(s)
Price: £4.50 (Adult Standard) £3.50 (Child Standard) £5.00 (Adult Special) £4.00 (Child Special)

Stations On This Journey:

Station Name	St	Al	Bd	Tl	DT	PA	CP	Ph	Mu	WR	Sh	VS	WS	VW	SB	VSB
Clayton West	✔	✔			✔	✔	✔	✔				✔	✔	✔	✔	
Skelmanthorpe	✔	✔														
Cuckoos Nest	✔	✔									✔					
Shelley	✔	✔														

LAKESIDE & HAVERTHWAITE RLWY

LAKESIDE & HAVERTHWAITE RAILWAY CO LTD Haverthwaite Station, Ulverston, **CUMBRIA,** LA12 8AL, **ENGLAND**.

(T) 01539 531594

Affiliated Bodies: Heritage Railway Association, Transport Trust

Stock Overview:

No. Steam Locos: 11

No. Diesel Locos: 5

TV/Film Appearances: Out and About (BBC)

Facilities: Café, Restaurant, Driver footplate experience, Santa Special, Souvenir shop, picnic area. There is an aquarium located at Lakeside.

Opening/Closing Times:

Other: Open daily May - October.

Location:

Instructions: From junction 36 of the M6, follow the A590 west to Haverthwaite.

Main Road: A590   **Mainline Station:** Ulverston

Journeys Available At This Railway:

Haverthwaite to Lakeside

Features: Views of Open Fields, Water. View of Lake Windermere.

Tunnels: 1   **Signal Boxes:** 2   **Rivers:** 1   **Journey Length:** 3.5 mile(s)

Stations On This Journey:

Station Name	St	Al	Bd	Tl	DT	PA	CP	Ph	Mu	WR	Sh	VS	WS	VW	SB	VSB
Haverthwaite	✓	✓	✓	✓	✓								✓		✓	
Newby Bridge	✓	✓	✓													
Lakeside	✓	✓	✓	✓							✓				✓	

LAPPA VALLEY STEAM RAILWAY

LAPPA VALLEY STEAM RAILWAY Barn Acres, St Newlyn East, Newquay, **CORNWALL**, TR8 5HZ, **ENGLAND**.

(T) 01872 510317

(E) info@lappavalley.co.uk

(W) www.lappa-railway.co.uk

Affiliated Bodies: Transport Trust

Year Opened: 1974

Type of Complex: Railway Station, Operational Railway Line

Type of Organisation: Conservation Project

Gauge: Narrow

Stock Overview:

No. Steam Locos: 2

No. Diesel Locos: 2

Facilities: Café, Ticket office, Disabled access, Santa Special, Souvenir shop, Books for sale, Videos for sale, Main credit cards taken.

Opening/Closing Times:

Spring: **Opens** 10:00, **Closes** 18:00

Summer: **Opens** 10:00, **Closes** 18:00

Autumn: **Opens** 10:00, **Closes** 17:00

Winter: **Opens** 10:00, **Closes** 17:00

Other: Open April - late October (closed some days in October, contact for further details).

Location:

Instructions: Signposted on both the A30 and A3075.

Nearest Town/Village: Newquay   **Main Road:** A30   **Mainline Station:** Truro

Contact(s):

● **General Manager:** Ms Amanda Booth

Journeys Available At This Railway:

Benny Halt to East Wheal Rose

Features: Views of Open Fields, Water, Woods.

Bridges: 1 'under'   **Tunnels:** 1   **Rivers:** 1   **Journey Length:** 1 mile(s)

Price: £6.00 (Adult Standard) £4.00 (Child Standard)

Stations On This Journey:

Key: *St* = Stops   *Al* = Alight   *Bd* = Board   *Tl* = Toilets   *DT* = Disabled Toilets   *PA* = Kids Play Area   *CP* = Free Car Park   *Ph* = Pay Phone   *Mu* = Museum
  WR = Waiting Room   *Sh* = Sheds   *VS* = Can Visit Sheds   *WS* = Workshops   *VW* = Can Visit Workshops   *SB* = Signal Box   *VSB* = Can Visit Signal Box

Station Name	St	Al	Bd	Tl	DT	PA	CP	Ph	Mu	WR	Sh	VS	WS	VW	SB	VSB
Benny Halt	✔	✔		✔	✔		✔						✔			
East Wheal Rose	✔				✔	✔	✔									

LAUNCESTON STEAM RAILWAY

LAUNCESTON STEAM RAILWAY St. Thomas Rd, Launceston, **CORNWALL,** PL15 8DA, **ENGLAND**.
(T) 01566 775665
Affiliated Bodies: Heritage Railway Association, Transport Trust
Year Opened: 1993
Type of Complex: Operational Railway Line, Museum
Type of Organisation: Limited Company
Gauge: Narrow   **No. Volunteers:** 0
Stock Overview:
No. Steam Locos: 5
No. Diesel Locos: 2
Facilities: Café, Buffet, Ticket office, Disabled access, Waiting room, Souvenir shop, Books for sale, Videos for sale, Photos for sale, Paintings/drawings for sale, Camera film for sale, Tapes for sale, Models for sale.
Opening/Closing Times:
Other: Open during Easter, Spring Bank Holiday, half terms and daily in Summer (except Saturdays).
Location:
Nearest Town/Village: Launceston   **Main Road:** A30
Contact(s):
● **General Manager:** Mr Nigel Bowman
Journeys Available At This Railway:

Launceston to Newmills
Track Type: Single   Direction: West
Features: Views of Hills, Open Fields. Maximum gradient of 1 in 80 (For 805 metres).
Journey Duration: 13 mins   **Journey Length:** 2.5 mile(s)
Price: £5.50 (Adult Standard) £3.70 (Child Standard)
Stations On This Journey:

Station Name	St	Al	Bd	Tl	DT	PA	CP	Ph	Mu	WR	Sh	VS	WS	VW	SB	VSB
Launceston	✔	✔	✔	✔			✔	✔	✔	✔	✔	✔	✔	✔		
Newmills	✔	✔	✔	✔		✔			✔							

LAVENDER LINE

LAVENDER LINE PRESERVATION SOCIETY Isfield Station, Isfield, Uckfield, **SUSSEX (EAST),** TN22 5XB, **ENGLAND**.
(T) 01825 750515
Affiliated Bodies: Heritage Railway Association
Type of Complex: Railway Station, Operational Railway Line, Restoration Site
Stock Overview:
No. Steam Locos: 2
No. Diesel Locos: 6
Facilities: Buffet, Disabled access, Platform tickets, Driver footplate experience, Santa Special, Souvenir shop, Books for sale, Videos for sale, Models for sale, Main credit cards taken, Children's events, Facilities for hire, Trains for hire, Play area and model railway are to be completed in 2002.
Opening/Closing Times:
Spring: **Opens** Sun 11:00, **Closes** Sun 16:30
Summer: **Opens** Sat, Sun 11:00, **Closes** Sat, Sun 16:30
Autumn: **Opens** Sun 11:00, **Closes** Sun 16:30
Winter: **Opens** Sun 11:00, **Closes** Sun 16:30

Other: Open on Saturdays in December.
Location:
Nearest Town/Village: Uckfield   **Main Road:** A26   **Mainline Station:** Uckfield
Contact(s):
- **Chairman:** Mr B Monk
- **Trustee:** Ms Jennifer Crawford

Journeys Available At This Railway:

Isfield to Isfield (round trip)
Track Type: Single
Features: Views of Open Fields.
Bridges: 1 'under'   **Signal Boxes:** 1   **Journey Length:** 1 mile(s)
Price: £3.80 (Adult Standard) £2.30 (Child Standard)
Stations On This Journey:

Station Name	St	Al	Bd	Tl	DT	PA	CP	Ph	Mu	WR	Sh	VS	WS	VW	SB	VSB
Isfield	✔	✔	✔	✔	✔		✔				✔	✔	✔	✔	✔	✔

LEADHILLS & WANLOCKHEAD

LEADHILLS & WANLOCKHEAD RAILWAY The Station, Leadhills, Biggar, **LANARKSHIRE,** ML12 6XP, **SCOTLAND**.

(E) info@leadhillsrailway.co.uk

(W) www.leadhillsrailway.co.uk

Affiliated Bodies: Heritage Railway Association

Year Opened: 1988

Gauge: Narrow

Stock Overview:

No. Steam Locos: 1

No. Diesel Locos: 5

Background: Britains highest adhesion railway at 1500 ft above sea level.

Facilities: Disabled access, Enthusiast galas, Souvenir shop, Books for sale, Models for sale.

Opening/Closing Times:

Summer: **Opens** Sat - Sun 11:00, **Closes** Sat - Sun 17:00

Other: Open on Bank Holidays and during Easter.

Location:

Instructions: Access from the M74 from junction 13 and the B797.

Nearest Town/Village: Sanquhar   **Main Road:** B797   **Mainline Station:** Sanquhar

Hotel: Hopetown Arms Hotel

Contact(s):

- **Chairman:** Mr Alastair Ireland   **(T)** 01573 223691
- **Secretary:** Mr Mark Andrew   **(T)** 01555 820778   **(E)** secretary@leadhillsrailway.co.uk

Journeys Available At This Railway:

Leadhills to Glengonnar Halt
Track Type: Single
Features: Maximum gradient of 1 in 40.
Level Crossings: 3   **Signal Boxes:** 1   **Journey Length:** 1 mile(s)
Price: £2.00 (Adult Standard) £1.00 (Child Standard)
Stations On This Journey:

Station Name	St	Al	Bd	Tl	DT	PA	CP	Ph	Mu	WR	Sh	VS	WS	VW	SB	VSB
Leadhills	✔	✔			✔				✔				✔			
Glengonnar Halt	✔															

LEIGHTON BUZZARD RAILWAY

LEIGHTON BUZZARD RAILWAY LTD Page's Park Station, Billington Rd, Leighton Buzzard, **BEDFORDSHIRE,** LU7 4TN, **ENGLAND**.

(T) 01525 373888   **(F)** 01525 377814

(E) info@buzzrail.co.uk

(W) www.buzzrail.co.uk

Affiliated Bodies: Heritage Railway Association, Transport Trust

Year Opened: 1968

Type of Complex: Railway Station, Operational Railway Line, Museum, Restoration Site

Type of Organisation: Charity, Heritage Project, Limited Company, Volunteer, Non-Profit

Gauge: Narrow   **No. Volunteers:** 50

Stock Overview:

No. Steam Locos: 12

No. Diesel Locos: 43

TV/Film Appearances: Off The Rails (Discovery Channel), Classic Trains (Channel 4)

Background: An authentic narrow gauge railway built in 1919 to serve the local sand industry, using World War 1 materials and equipment.

Facilities: Café, Ticket office, Disabled access, Waiting room, Platform tickets, Advanced booking available, Guided tours available, Santa Special, Enthusiast galas, Souvenir shop, Books for sale, Videos for sale, Photos for sale, Paintings/drawings for sale, Camera film for sale, CD's for sale, Tapes for sale, Models for sale, Main credit cards taken, Children's events, Facilities for hire, Trains for hire.

Opening/Closing Times:

Spring: **Opens** Sun 11:15, **Closes** Sun 16:30

Summer: **Opens** Sun 11:15, **Closes** Sun 16:30

Autumn: **Opens** Sun 11:15, **Closes** Sun 16:30

Winter: **Opens** Sun 11:15, **Closes** Sun 15:30

Other: Open March - October, static displays during winter. Contact for details for opening times during school holidays.

Location:

Instructions: Located on the edge of Leighton Buzzard, on the A4146 towards Hemel Hempstead.

Main Road: A4146

Contact(s):

● **Chairman:** Mr Alfred Fisher

● **For Bookings:** Mr Derek Trevelion

● **General Manager:** Mr Joe Horsley

● **PR Manager:** Mr Mervyn Leah

Journeys Available At This Railway:

Page's Park to Stonehenge Works

Track Type: Single   Direction: North to North

Features: Views of Open Fields, Urbanisation. Maximum gradient of 1 in 25 (For 100 metres).

Bridges: 1 'over'   **Level Crossings:** 6   **Rivers:** 1   **Journey Duration:** 25 mins   **Journey Length:** 2.85 mile(s)

Price: £5.00 (Adult Standard) £2.00 (Child Standard) £5.00 (Adult Special) £2.00 (Child Special)

Stations On This Journey:

Station Name	St	Al	Bd	Tl	DT	PA	CP	Ph	Mu	WR	Sh	VS	WS	VW	SB	VSB
Page's Park	✓			✓	✓		✓			✓	✓		✓			
Stonehenge Works	✓			✓					✓					✓		

LINCOLNSHIRE WOLDS RAILWAY

LINCOLNSHIRE WOLDS RAILWAY (THE) The Railway Station, Station Rd, Ludborough, Grimsby, **LINCOLNSHIRE (NORTH EAST),** DN36 5SQ, **ENGLAND**.

(T) 01507 363881

(W) www.louthnet.com

Affiliated Bodies: Heritage Railway Association

Year Opened: 1998

Type of Complex: Railway Station, Operational Railway Line, Museum, Restoration Site
Type of Organisation: Heritage Project, Limited Company, Volunteer, Non-Profit
Gauge: Standard
Facilities: Buffet, Ticket office, Disabled access, Waiting room, Photo line side permit available, Guided tours available, Santa Special, Souvenir shop, Books for sale, Videos for sale, Paintings/drawings for sale, Models for sale, Facilities for hire, Trains for hire, Hoping to open new track in 2002.

Opening/Closing Times:
Spring: **Opens** Tues, Sat, Sun 10:00, **Closes** Tues, Sat, Sun 17:00
Summer: **Opens** Tues, Sat, Sun 10:00, **Closes** Tues, Sat, Sun 17:00
Autumn: **Opens** Tues, Sat, Sun 10:00, **Closes** Tues, Sat, Sun 17:00
Winter: **Opens** Tues, Sat, Sun 10:00, **Closes** Tues, Sat, Sun 15:00
Other: Open Tuesdays, Saturdays and Sundays for static displays. Contact for details of steaming days held throughout the year.

Location:
Instructions: Turn right from A16 (Louth to Grimsby Road) at turning for Fulstow.
Nearest Town/Village: Louth **Main Road:** A16 **Mainline Station:** Grimsby
Hotel: Brackenborough Arms **Restaurant:** Cross Keys

Contact(s):
- **Chairman:** Mr Frank Street (T) 01777 706657
- **General Manager:** Mr Neil Brown (T) 01472 250562
- **Publicity Manager:** Mr David Ambler
- **Secretary:** Mr John Mimmack (T) 01472 351621
- **Technical Info:** Mr Tony Jones
- **Treasurer:** Mr Neil Brown (T) 01472 250562

Journeys Available At This Railway:

Ludborough to Ludborough (round trip)
Track Type: Single Direction: South to North
Features: Views of Hills, Open Fields.
Level Crossings: 1 **Journey Duration:** 5 mins **Journey Length:** 0.75 mile(s)
Price: £2.00 (Adult Standard) £1.00 (Child Standard) £2.00 (Adult Special) £1.00 (Child Special)

Stations On This Journey:

Station Name	*St*	*Al*	*Bd*	*Tl*	*DT*	*PA*	*CP*	*Ph*	*Mu*	*WR*	*Sh*	*VS*	*WS*	*VW*	*SB*	*VSB*
Ludborough				✔			✔		✔	✔	✔	✔	✔	✔	✔	✔

LITTLEHAMPTON MINIATURE RLWY

LITTLEHAMPTON MINIATURE RAILWAY Mewsbrook Pk, Hendon Ave, Rustington, Littlehampton, **SUSSEX (WEST),** BN16 2LX, **ENGLAND**.
(T) 01903 716127
Year Opened: 1948
Gauge: Narrow
Facilities: Disabled access.

Opening/Closing Times:
Spring: **Opens** Sat, Sun 10:00, **Closes** Sat, Sun 18:00
Summer: **Opens** Mon - Sun 10:00, **Closes** Mon - Sun 18:00
Autumn: **Opens** Sat, Sun 10:00, **Closes** Sat, Sun 18:00
Winter: **Opens** Sat, Sun 10:00, **Closes** Sat, Sun 18:00

Location:
Nearest Town/Village: Littlehampton **Mainline Station:** Littlehampton

Contact(s):
- **Owner:** Mr Colin Evans (T) 01243 544984

Journeys Available At This Railway:

Mewsbrook to Mewsbrook (round trip)
Track Type: Single
Features: Views of Open Fields, Sea.
Bridges: 1 'under' **Tunnels:** 1 **Level Crossings:** 2 **Journey Length:** 0.75 mile(s)

Key: *St* = Stops *Al* = Alight Bd = Board *Tl* = Toilets *DT* = Disabled Toilets *PA* = Kids Play Area *CP* = Free Car Park *Ph* = Pay Phone *Mu* = Museum *WR* = Waiting Room *Sh* = Sheds *VS* = Can Visit Sheds *WS* = Workshops *VW* = Can Visit Workshops *SB* = Signal Box *VSB* = Can Visit Signal Box

Price: £0.80 (Adult Standard) £0.80 (Child Standard)

Stations On This Journey:

Station Name	St	Al	Bd	Tl	DT	PA	CP	Ph	Mu	WR	Sh	VS	WS	VW	SB	VSB
Mewsbrook Park	✓	✓									✓		✓			
Norfolk Gardens	✓	✓														

LLANBERIS LAKE RAILWAY

RHEILFFORDD LLYN PADARN CYF Gilfach Ddu, Llanberis, Caernarfon, **GWYNEDD,** LL55 4TY, **WALES.**

(T) 01286 870549   **(F)** 01286 870549

(E) info@lake-railway.co.uk

(W) www.lake-railway.co.uk

Affiliated Bodies: Heritage Railway Association

Year Opened: 1970

Type of Complex: Operational Railway Line

Type of Organisation: Limited Company

Gauge: Narrow   **No. Staff:** 7   **No. Volunteers:** 0

Stock Overview:

No. Steam Locos: 3

No. Diesel Locos: 4

Background: Built on the trackbed of the former Padarn Railway after the closure of Dinorwic Slate Quarries. Primarily a way of employing local people in an area of high unemployment.

Facilities: Café, Ticket office, Disabled access, Waiting room, Line permit needed, Advanced booking available, Souvenir shop, Books for sale, Videos for sale, Main credit cards taken, Trains for hire.

Opening/Closing Times:

Spring: **Opens** 11:00, **Closes** 16:00
Summer: **Opens** 11:00, **Closes** 16:30
Autumn: **Opens** 11:00, **Closes** 16:00
Other: Contact for opening days.

Location:

Nearest Town/Village: Caernarfon   **Main Road:** A4086   **Mainline Station:** Bangor

Contact(s):

● **General Manager:** Mr Bruce Yarborough

Journeys Available At This Railway:

Gilfach Ddu to Penllyn
Track Type: Single   Direction: East to West
Features: Views of Hills, Open Fields, Water, Woods. Views of Snowdonia and Padarn Lake.
Bridges: 1 'under'   **Journey Duration:** 15 mins   **Journey Length:** 2 mile(s)
Price: £4.50 (Adult Standard) £3.00 (Child Standard)

Stations On This Journey:

Station Name	St	Al	Bd	Tl	DT	PA	CP	Ph	Mu	WR	Sh	VS	WS	VW	SB	VSB
Gilfach Ddu	✓		✓	✓				✓		✓	✓	✓				
Cei Llydan	✓			✓	✓		✓									
Penllyn	✓															

LLANGOLLEN RAILWAY

LLANGOLLEN RAILWAY PLC The Station, Abbey Rd, Llangollen, **DENBIGHSHIRE,** LL20 8SN, **WALES**.

(T) 01978 860979　　**(F)** 01978 869247

(E) office@llangollen-railway.co.uk

(W) www.llangollen-railway.co.uk

Affiliated Bodies: Heritage Railway Association, Transport Trust

Year Opened: 1980

Type of Complex: Railway Station, Operational Railway Line

Type of Organisation: Heritage Project, Limited Company

Gauge: Standard　　**No. Staff:** 19　　**No. Volunteers:** 100

Stock Overview:

No. Steam Locos: 5

No. Diesel Locos: 4

Background: Part of the GWR - Ruabon to Barmouth junction line. It reopened 1980 and boasts a riverside location.

Facilities: Café, Ticket office, Disabled access, Waiting room, Driver footplate experience, Santa Special, 'Thomas' event, Enthusiast galas, Courses on how to drive Locos, Souvenir shop, Books for sale, Videos for sale, Camera film for sale, Main credit cards taken, Trains for hire.

Opening/Closing Times:

Other:　　Contact for opening information.

Location:

Nearest Town/Village: Ruabon　　**Bus:** 94　　**Taxi:** Central Taxis　　**Mainline Station:** Ruabon

Hotel: The Hand

Contact(s):

● **For Bookings:** Ms Carol Edwards

● **General Manager:** Mr Paul Gettings

Journeys Available At This Railway:

Llangollen to Carrog

Track Type: Single　Direction: East to West

Features: Views of Open Fields, Water, Woods. Maximum gradient of 1 in 80 (For 800 metres).

Bridges: 2 'over'　**Tunnels:** 1　**Level Crossings:** 1　**Signal Boxes:** 5　**Rivers:** 1　**Viaducts:** 1　**Journey Duration:** 30 mins　**Journey Length:** 8 mile(s)

Price: £8.00 (Adult Standard)　£3.80 (Child Standard)

Stations On This Journey:

Station Name	St	Al	Bd	Tl	DT	PA	CP	Ph	Mu	WR	Sh	VS	WS	VW	SB	VSB
Llangollen	✔	✔	✔	✔	✔		✔			✔	✔		✔		✔	
Berwyn	✔	✔		✔						✔						
Deeside Halt															✔	
Glyndyfrdwy	✔	✔		✔	✔	✔				✔					✔	
Carrog	✔	✔		✔	✔					✔					✔	

LONDON TRANSPORT MUSEUM

LONDON TRANSPORT MUSEUM Convent Garden Piazza, London, **LONDON (GREATER),** WC2E 7BB, **ENGLAND**.

(T) 020 73796344　　**(F)** 020 75657254

(E) contact@ltmuseum.co.uk

(W) www.ltmuseum.co.uk

Affiliated Bodies: Heritage Railway Association, Transport Trust

Year Opened: 1980

Type of Complex: Museum

Stock Overview:

Key:　St = Stops　Al = Alight　Bd = Board　Tl = Toilets　DT = Disabled Toilets　PA = Kids Play Area　CP = Free Car Park　Ph = Pay Phone　Mu = Museum
　　WR = Waiting Room　Sh = Sheds　VS = Can Visit Sheds　WS = Workshops　VW = Can Visit Workshops　SB = Signal Box　VSB = Can Visit Signal Box

No. Steam Locos: 1

Background: The museum documents over 200 years of transport in the capital from trains to trams and buses.

Facilities: Disabled access, Souvenir shop.

Entry Fees: Adults: £5.95   **Children:** £3.95

Opening/Closing Times:

Spring: **Opens** Mon - Thurs, Sat, Sun 10:00, Fri 11:00, **Closes** Mon - Sun 18:00
Summer: **Opens** Mon - Thurs, Sat, Sun 10:00, Fri 11:00, **Closes** Mon - Sun 18:00
Autumn: **Opens** Mon - Thurs, Sat, Sun 10:00, Fri 11:00, **Closes** Mon - Sun 18:00
Winter: **Opens** Mon - Thurs, Sat, Sun 10:00, Fri 11:00, **Closes** Mon - Sun 18:00
Other: Closed on December 24th, 25th and 26th.

Location:

Mainline Station: Charing Cross

Contact(s):
● **Director:** Mr Sam Mullins
● **Head of Collections:** Mr Oliver Green

LYNTON & BARNSTAPLE RAILWAY

LYNTON & BARNSTAPLE RAILWAY Woody Bay Station, Martinhoe Cross, Parracombe, Barnstaple, **DEVON,** EX31 4RA, **ENGLAND**.

(T) 01598 763487

Type of Complex: Operational Railway Line

Background: Due to open to the public in 2002. Contact for details.

Facilities: Disabled access, Souvenir shop.

Location:

Nearest Town/Village: Barnstaple   **Main Road:** A39   **Bus:** 309, 310   **Mainline Station:** Barnstaple

Contact(s):
● **Publicity Manager:** Mr Jim Panels

Alternative Contact Details:
● 14 Ruden Way, Epsom, Surrey, KT17 3LN, England

Journeys Available At This Railway:

Woody Bay to Woody Bay (round trip)
Stations On This Journey:

Station Name	St	Al	Bd	Tl	DT	PA	CP	Ph	Mu	WR	Sh	VS	WS	VW	SB	VSB
Woody Bay	✔	✔		✔	✔		✔								✔	✔

MANGAPPS RAILWAY MUSEUM

MANGAPPS RAILWAY MUSEUM Mangapps Farm, Burnham-on-Crouch, **ESSEX,** CM0 8QQ, **ENGLAND**.

(T) 01621 784898   **(F)** 01621 783833

(W) www.mangapps.co.uk

Affiliated Bodies: Heritage Railway Association

Complex Size: 20 Acres   **Year Opened:** 1989

Type of Complex: Railway Station, Operational Railway Line, Museum, Restoration Site

Type of Organisation: Sole Partnership

Gauge: Standard   **No. Staff:** 2   **No. Volunteers:** 30

Stock Overview:

No. Steam Locos: 5

No. Diesel Locos: 6

Facilities: Café, Ticket office, Santa Special, 'Thomas' event, Souvenir shop, Camera film for sale, Facilities for hire, Trains for hire.

Opening/Closing Times:

Other: Open weekends and bank holidays. Contact for details.

Location:

Nearest Town/Village: Burnham-on-Crouch   **Mainline Station:** Burnham

Contact(s):
- **Owner:** Mr John Jolly

Journeys Available At This Railway:

Mangapps Station to Mangapps Station (round trip)
Track Type: Single   Direction: East to North
Features: Views of Open Fields. Maximum gradient of 1 in 45 (For 150 metres).
Signal Boxes: 2   **Journey Duration:** 7 mins   **Journey Length:** 0.75 mile(s)

MARDYKE MINIATURE RAILWAY

MARDYKE MINIATURE RAILWAY LTD Units 1-3 Lambs Lane Ind Est, Lambs Lane North, Rainham, **ESSEX**, RM13 9XL, **ENGLAND**.
(T) 01708 520264   **(F)** 01708 553395

Type of Organisation: Limited Company

Background: Manufacturer of miniature railway equipment.

Opening/Closing Times:
Spring: **Opens** Mon - Fri 09:00, **Closes** Mon - Fri 16:00
Summer: **Opens** Mon - Fri 09:00, **Closes** Mon - Fri 16:00
Autumn: **Opens** Mon - Fri 09:00, **Closes** Mon - Fri 16:00
Winter: **Opens** Mon - Fri 09:00, **Closes** Mon - Fri 16:00

Location:
Nearest Town/Village: Dagenham   **Main Road:** A1306

Contact(s):
- **Director:** Mrs Beryl De Smedt

MARKEATON PARK LIGHT RAILWAY

MARKEATON PARK LIGHT RAILWAY Markeaton Pk, Off Queensway, Derby, **DERBYSHIRE, ENGLAND**.**(M)** 07961 360812

Year Opened: 1996

Type of Complex: Operational Railway Line

Gauge: Narrow

Stock Overview:
No. Steam Locos: 1

No. Diesel Locos: 2

Facilities: Café, Restaurant, Disabled access, Santa Special.

Opening/Closing Times:
Spring: **Opens** Sat, Sun 11:00, **Closes** Sat, Sun 18:00
Summer: **Opens** Sat, Sun 11:00, **Closes** Sat, Sun 18:00
Autumn: **Opens** Sat, Sun 11:00, **Closes** Sat, Sun 15:30
Winter: **Opens** Sat, Sun 11:00, **Closes** Sat, Sun 15:30
Other: Contact for school holiday opening times.

Location:
Nearest Town/Village: Derby   **Main Road:** A38

Contact(s):
- **Owner:** Mr J Bull

Alternative Contact Details:
- 23 Beck Lane, Skegby, Sutton-in-Ashfield, Nottinghamshire, NG17 3AH, England

Journeys Available At This Railway:

Markeaton St to Mundy Halt
Track Type: Single
Features: Views of Open Fields, Urbanisation, Water, Woods.
Bridges: 2 'over'   **Level Crossings:** 1   **Journey Length:** 0.8 mile(s)
Price: £0.60 (Adult Standard) £0.60 (Child Standard)

Stations On This Journey:

Key: *St* = Stops   *Al* = Alight   *Bd* = Board   *Tl* = Toilets   *DT* = Disabled Toilets   *PA* = Kids Play Area   *CP* = Free Car Park   *Ph* = Pay Phone   *Mu* = Museum
        WR = Waiting Room   *Sh* = Sheds   *VS* = Can Visit Sheds   *WS* = Workshops   *VW* = Can Visit Workshops   *SB* = Signal Box   *VSB* = Can Visit Signal Box

A-Z STEAM RAILWAYS

Markeaton Park Light Railway — Midland Railway Centre

Station Name	St	Al	Bd	Tl	DT	PA	CP	Ph	Mu	WR	Sh	VS	WS	VW	SB	VSB
Markeaton St	✓	✓														
Mundy Halt	✓	✓														

MIDDLETON RAILWAY

MIDDLETON RAILWAY The Station, Moor Rd, Leeds, **YORKSHIRE (WEST),** LS10 2JQ, **ENGLAND**.
(T) 0113 2710320
(E) info@middletonrailway.org.uk
(W) www.middletonrailway.org.uk
Affiliated Bodies: Heritage Railway Association
Type of Complex: Operational Railway Line
Type of Organisation: Trust, Volunteer
Gauge: Standard
Stock Overview:
No. Steam Locos: 15
No. Diesel Locos: 9
Background: The oldest railway in the world.
Facilities: Santa Special, 'Thomas' event, Enthusiast galas, Souvenir shop, Main credit cards taken, Children's events, Trains for hire.
Opening/Closing Times:
Spring: **Opens** Sat - Sun 11:00, **Closes** Sat - Sun 16:30
Summer: **Opens** Sat - Sun 11:00, **Closes** Sat - Sun 16:30
Autumn: **Opens** Sat - Sun 11:00, **Closes** Sat - Sun 16:30
Winter: **Opens** Sat - Sun 11:00, **Closes** Sat - Sun 16:30
Other: Open Sundays only during October.
Location:
Instructions: Located adjacent to junction 5 of the M621.
Main Road: A61   **Mainline Station:** Leeds City Station
Contact(s):
● **Marketing Officer:** Mr Emmanuel Lanne (**T**) 07768 013406
Journeys Available At This Railway:

Middleton to Middleton (round trip)
Features: Maximum gradient of 1 in 43.
Tunnels: 1   **Journey Length:** 1.5 mile(s)
Price: £2.50 (Adult Standard) £1.50 (Child Standard)
Stations On This Journey:

Station Name	St	Al	Bd	Tl	DT	PA	CP	Ph	Mu	WR	Sh	VS	WS	VW	SB	VSB
Middleton	✓	✓		✓	✓				✓	✓	✓	✓				

MIDLAND RAILWAY CENTRE

MIDLAND RAILWAY CENTRE Butterley Station, Ripley, **DERBYSHIRE,** DE5 3QZ, **ENGLAND**.
(T) 01773 747674   **(F)** 01773 570721
(E) info@midlandrailwaycentre.co.uk
Affiliated Bodies: Heritage Railway Association, Transport Trust
Year Opened: 1981
Type of Complex: Operational Railway Line, Museum
Gauge: Standard
Stock Overview:
No. Steam Locos: 24 (10 Pre-Group, 1 Pre-Nationalisation)
No. Diesel Locos: 37
Facilities: Café, Ticket office, Disabled access, Guided tours available, Driver footplate experience, Santa Special, 'Thomas' event, Enthusiast galas, Souvenir shop, Books for sale, Videos for sale, CD's for sale, Tapes for sale, Models for sale, Main credit cards taken, Children's events, Facilities for hire,

Trains for hire.

Opening/Closing Times:

Spring: **Opens** Mon - Sun 10:00, **Closes** Mon - Sun 16:00
Summer: **Opens** Mon - Sun 10:00, **Closes** Mon - Sun 16:00
Autumn: **Opens** Mon - Sun 10:00, **Closes** Mon - Sun 16:00
Winter: **Opens** Mon - Sun 10:00, **Closes** Mon - Sun 16:00

Location:

Instructions: Take junction 28 of the M1, go along the A38 and onto the B6179.
Nearest Town/Village: Ripley   **Main Road:** B6179   **Bus:** 91, 92

Contact(s):

- **Development Officer:** Mr Allan Calladine
- **General Manager:** Mr John Hett

Journeys Available At This Railway:

Butterley to Hammersmith
Features: Views of Open Fields, Water, Woods. Viaduct over the reservoir. Maximum gradient of 1 in 93.
Bridges: 4 'over', 3 'under'   **Signal Boxes:** 4   **Rivers:** 1   **Viaducts:** 1   **Journey Length:** 3.5 mile(s)
Price: £7.95 (Adult Standard)

Stations On This Journey:

Station Name	St	Al	Bd	Tl	DT	PA	CP	Ph	Mu	WR	Sh	VS	WS	VW	SB	VSB
Butterley	✔	✔		✔	✔		✔	✔		✔			✔		✔	
Swanwick Junction	✔	✔		✔	✔	✔	✔	✔	✔	✔	✔	✔	✔		✔	✔
Hammersmith	✔	✔													✔	

MID-NORFOLK RAILWAY

MID-NORFOLK RAILWAY Dereham Station, Station Rd, Dereham, **NORFOLK,** NR19 1DF, **ENGLAND**.

(T) 01362 690633   **(F)** 01362 698487

(E) info@mnr.org.uk

(W) www.mnr.org.uk

Affiliated Bodies: Heritage Railway Association

Complex Size: 6 Acres   **Year Opened:** 1997

Type of Complex: Railway Station, Operational Railway Line, Museum, Restoration Site

Type of Organisation: Charity, Trust, Heritage Project, Limited Company, Volunteer, Non-Profit

Gauge: Standard   **No. Volunteers:** 40

Stock Overview:

No. Diesel Locos: 9

Facilities: Café, Buffet, Ticket office, Platform tickets, Santa Special, Souvenir shop, Books for sale, Videos for sale, Photos for sale, Paintings/drawings for sale, Models for sale, Main credit cards taken, Children's events, Facilities for hire, Trains for hire.

Opening/Closing Times:

Spring: **Opens** Sun 11:00, **Closes** Sun 17:00
Summer: **Opens** Sun 11:00, **Closes** Sun 17:00
Autumn: **Opens** Sun 11:00, **Closes** Sun 17:00
Winter: **Opens** Sun 11:00, **Closes** Sun 17:00
Other: Closed during January. Contact for extra opening days.

Location:

Nearest Town/Village: Dereham   **Main Road:** A47   **Mainline Station:** Wymondham

Contact(s):

- **Membership Secretary:** Mr Stuart Maye (**T**) 01920 467132

Journeys Available At This Railway:

Dereham to Wymondham Abbey
Track Type: Single   Direction: North to South
Features: Views of Open Fields, Water. Maximum gradient of 1 in 141 (For 400 metres).
Bridges: 10 'over', 9 'under'   **Level Crossings:** 6   **Signal Boxes:** 1   **Rivers:** 6   **Journey Duration:** 38 mins
Journey Length: 11 mile(s)

Key: *St* = Stops   *Al* = Alight   *Bd* = Board   *Tl* = Toilets   *DT* = Disabled Toilets   *PA* = Kids Play Area   *CP* = Free Car Park   *Ph* = Pay Phone   *Mu* = Museum
     WR = Waiting Room   *Sh* = Sheds   *VS* = Can Visit Sheds   *WS* = Workshops   *VW* = Can Visit Workshops   *SB* = Signal Box   *VSB* = Can Visit Signal Box

Price: £5.00 (Adult Standard) £2.50 (Child Standard)

Stations On This Journey:

Station Name	St	Al	Bd	Tl	DT	PA	CP	Ph	Mu	WR	Sh	VS	WS	VW	SB	VSB
Dereham	✔	✔		✔	✔		✔		✔						✔	
Yaxham	✔	✔														
Thuxton	✔	✔														
Wymondham Abbey	✔	✔														

MID-SUFFOLK LIGHT RAILWAY

MID-SUFFOLK LIGHT RAILWAY Brockford Station, Wetheringsett, Stowmarket, **SUFFOLK,** IP14 5PW, **ENGLAND**.

(T) 01449 766899

(W) www.mslr.org.uk

Affiliated Bodies: Heritage Railway Association

Type of Complex: Museum

Gauge: Standard

Stock Overview:

No. Steam Locos: 1

No. Diesel Locos: 1

Background: 2002 will see the steam celebration for the anniversary of the opening and closure of the railway (1902 - 1952).

Facilities: Café, Disabled access, Enthusiast galas, Souvenir shop, Books for sale, Children's events, Trackbed walk, picnic area.

Opening/Closing Times:

Summer: **Opens** Sun 11:00, **Closes** Sun 17:00

Other: Open Sundays only between Easter and September.

Location:

Instructions: Follow signs from the Park Green turning on the A140. Turn left at the next T junction and the museum is on the right after 1 mile.

Nearest Town/Village: Stowmarket   **Main Road:** A140   **Mainline Station:** Stowmarket

Contact(s):

● **Publicity Manager:** Mr Andrew Cullum   **(E)** cullumandrew@hotmail.com

● **Vice Chairman:** Mr Andrew Cullum   **(E)** cullumandrew@hotmail.com

MONKWEARMOUTH STATION MUSEUM

MONKWEARMOUTH STATION MUSEUM North Bridge St, Sunderland, **TYNE AND WEAR,** SR5 1AP, **ENGLAND**.

(T) 0191 5677075

Year Opened: 1973

Type of Complex: Museum

Background: The station was built in the 1840s and has an Edwardian ticket office.

Facilities: Ticket office, Disabled access, History lectures, Souvenir shop, Main credit cards taken.

Entry Fees: Adults: £0.00   **Children:** £0.00

Opening/Closing Times:

Spring: **Opens** Mon - Sat 10:00, Sun 14:00, **Closes** Mon 16:00, Tues - Sun 17:00

Summer: **Opens** Mon - Sat 10:00, Sun 14:00, **Closes** Mon 16:00, Tues - Sun 17:00

Autumn: **Opens** Mon - Sat 10:00, Sun 14:00, **Closes** Mon 16:00, Tues - Sun 17:00

Winter: **Opens** Mon - Sat 10:00, Sun 14:00, **Closes** Mon 16:00, Tues - Sun 17:00

Other: Closed Christmas Day and Boxing Day.

Location:

Nearest Town/Village: Sunderland   **Main Road:** A19   **Mainline Station:** Sunderland

Contact(s):

● **Assistant Keeper of Social History:** Mr Martin Routledge

● **Curator:** Ms Juliet Horsley

MOORS VALLEY RAILWAY

NAROGAUGE LTD Moors Valley Country Pk, Horton Rd, Ashley Heath, Ringwood, **HAMPSHIRE,** BH24 2ET, **ENGLAND**.

(T) 01425 471415

(W) www.moorsvalleyrailway.co.uk

Complex Size: 10 Acres   **Year Opened:** 1986

Type of Complex: Railway Station, Operational Railway Line, Restoration Site

Type of Organisation: Limited Company

Gauge: Narrow   **No. Staff:** 2   **No. Volunteers:** 15

Stock Overview:

No. Steam Locos: 14

No. Diesel Locos: 1

Facilities: Buffet, Ticket office, Disabled access, Waiting room, Driver footplate experience, Santa Special, Enthusiast galas, Courses on how to drive Locos, Souvenir shop, Books for sale, Videos for sale, Photos for sale, Camera film for sale, Models for sale, Main credit cards taken, Children's events, Facilities for hire, Trains for hire, Picnic area.

Opening/Closing Times:

Spring: **Opens** Mon - Sun 10:45, **Closes** Mon - Sun 17:00

Summer: **Opens** Mon - Sun 10:45, **Closes** Mon - Sun 17:00

Autumn: **Opens** Sat, Sun 10:45, **Closes** Sat, Sun 17:00

Winter: **Opens** Sat, Sun 10:45, **Closes** Sat, Sun 17:00

Other: Open during winter school holidays.

Location:

Instructions: Situated in Moors Valley Country Park.

Nearest Town/Village: Ringwood   **Main Road:** A31   **Bus:** X2   **Mainline Station:** Bournemouth

Hotel: St Leonards   **Restaurant:** Little Chef

Contact(s):

● **For Bookings:** Ms Mary Culver

● **Owner:** Mr Jim Haylock

Journeys Available At This Railway:

Kingsmere to Lakeside

Direction: South to North

Features: Views of Open Fields, Water, Woods. Maximum gradient of 1 in 50 (For 50 metres).

Bridges: 1 'over', 1 'under'   **Tunnels:** 4   **Level Crossings:** 2   **Signal Boxes:** 2   **Journey Duration:** 7 mins   **Journey Length:** 1 mile(s)

Price: £2.25 (Adult Standard) £1.50 (Child Standard) £5.50 (Adult Special) £5.50 (Child Special)

Stations On This Journey:

Station Name	St	Al	Bd	Tl	DT	PA	CP	Ph	Mu	WR	Sh	VS	WS	VW	SB	VSB
Kingsmere	✔	✔		✔	✔					✔	✔		✔		✔	
Lakeside	✔	✔		✔	✔	✔										

MOSELEY RAILWAY TRUST

MOSELEY RAILWAY TRUST 11 Ashwood Rd, Disley, Nr Hazel Gr, Stockport, **CHESHIRE,** SK12 2EL, **ENGLAND**.

(T) 01663 766992

Background: Is a storage site for engines. No site as yet for a museum or a railway.

Opening/Closing Times:

Other: Open at weekends by prior arrangement.

Contact(s):

● **Publicity Manager:** Mr David Hall

Key: *St* = Stops   *Al* = Alight   *Bd* = Board   *Tl* = Toilets   *DT* = Disabled Toilets   *PA* = Kids Play Area   *CP* = Free Car Park   *Ph* = Pay Phone   *Mu* = Museum
     WR = Waiting Room   *Sh* = Sheds   *VS* = Can Visit Sheds   *WS* = Workshops   *VW* = Can Visit Workshops   *SB* = Signal Box   *VSB* = Can Visit Signal Box

MULL RAILWAY

MULL & WEST HIGHLAND NARROW GAUGE RAILWAY CO LTD Old Pier Station, Craignure, Isle of Mull, **ARGYLL AND BUTE,** PA65 6AY, **SCOTLAND**.

(T) 01680 812494   **(F)** 01680 300595

(W) www.holidaymull.org/rail

Affiliated Bodies: Heritage Railway Association, Transport Trust

Year Opened: 1983

Type of Complex: Operational Railway Line

Type of Organisation: Limited Company

Gauge: Narrow   **No. Staff:** 6   **No. Volunteers:** 2

Stock Overview:

No. Steam Locos: 3

No. Diesel Locos: 3

TV/Film Appearances: Clarissa and the Country Man (BBC2)

Facilities: Ticket office, Through ticketing available, Advanced booking available, Guided tours available, Souvenir shop, Books for sale, Videos for sale, Photos for sale, Paintings/drawings for sale, Camera film for sale, Main credit cards taken, Trains for hire.

Location:

Nearest Town/Village: Oban   **Mainline Station:** Oban   **Hotel:** Isle of Mull Hotel

Restaurant: Craignure Inn

Contact(s):

- **For Donations:** Mr David Crombie
- **General Manager:** Mr Graham Ellis
- **Technical Info:** Mr David Moseley

Alternative Contact Details:

- 1 Mulberry Drive, Dunfermline, Fife, KY11 8BZ, Scotland**(T)** 01383 728652

Journeys Available At This Railway:

Craignure to Torosay

Track Type: Single   Direction: North West to East South

Features: Views of Hills, Sea, Water, Woods. Views of Ben Nevis, Glencoe Hills, Ben Croacham and the Island of Lismore. Maximum gradient of 1 in 52 (For 100 metres).

Level Crossings: 2   **Journey Duration:** 20 mins   **Journey Length:** 1.25 mile(s)

Price: £3.50 (Adult Standard) £2.50 (Child Standard)

Stations On This Journey:

Station Name	St	Al	Bd	Tl	DT	PA	CP	Ph	Mu	WR	Sh	VS	WS	VW	SB	VSB
Craignure	✔		✔				✔			✔						
Torosay	✔			✔	✔							✔	✔			

MUSEUM OF ARMY TRANSPORT

MUSEUM OF ARMY TRANSPORT Flemingate, Beverley, **YORKSHIRE (EAST),** HU17 0NG, **ENGLAND**.

(T) 01482 860445   **(F)** 01482 872767

Affiliated Bodies: Transport Trust

Type of Complex: Museum

Stock Overview:

No. Steam Locos: 2

No. Diesel Locos: 1

Facilities: Café, Disabled access, Souvenir shop, Books for sale, Models for sale.

Entry Fees: Adults: £4.50   **Children:** £3.00

Opening/Closing Times:

Spring: **Opens** Mon - Sun 10:00, **Closes** Mon - Sun 17:00

Summer: **Opens** Mon - Sun 10:00, **Closes** Mon - Sun 17:00

Autumn: **Opens** Mon - Sun 10:00, **Closes** Mon - Sun 17:00

Winter: **Opens** Mon - Sun 10:00, **Closes** Mon - Sun 17:00

Location:

Instructions: On arrival at Beverley take the Old Hull Road. The museum is on the site of the old

tannery and is close to Beverley Minister.

Nearest Town/Village: Beverley   **Mainline Station:** Beverley

<u>Contact(s):</u>
- **General Manager:** Mrs Hilary Cole

MUSEUM OF SCIENCE & INDUSTRY

MUSEUM OF SCIENCE & INDUSTRY IN MANCHESTER (THE) Liverpool Rd, Castlefield, Manchester, **MANCHESTER (GREATER),** M3 4FP, **ENGLAND**.

(T) 0161 8322244

Type of Complex: Museum

<u>Stock Overview:</u>

No. Steam Locos: 4

Facilities: Restaurant, Disabled access, Guided tours available, Souvenir shop, Books for sale, Videos for sale, Photos for sale, Main credit cards taken, Facilities for hire.

<u>Opening/Closing Times:</u>

Spring:	**Opens** Mon - Sun 10:00, **Closes** Mon - Sun 17:00
Summer:	**Opens** Mon - Sun 10:00, **Closes** Mon - Sun 17:00
Autumn:	**Opens** Mon - Sun 10:00, **Closes** Mon - Sun 17:00
Winter:	**Opens** Mon - Sun 10:00, **Closes** Mon - Sun 17:00

<u>Location:</u>

Instructions: Located in Castlefield.

Nearest Town/Village: Manchester   **Main Road:** Liverpool Rd   **Bus:** 33   **Mainline Station:** Deansgate Metro

<u>Contact(s):</u>
- **Curator:** Mr Nick Forder **(E)** n.forder@msim.org.uk

NARROW GAUGE RAILWAY MUSEUM

NARROW GAUGE RAILWAY MUSEUM (THE) Wharf Station, Tywyn, **GWYNEDD,** LL36 9EY, **WALES**.

(T) 01654 710472

(E) chris.white@messages.co.uk

(W) www.talyllyn.co.uk/ngrm/

Year Opened: 1956

Type of Complex: Museum

Type of Organisation: Charity, Trust, Volunteer, Non-Profit

Gauge: Narrow   **No. Volunteers:** 12

<u>Stock Overview:</u>

No. Steam Locos: 6

Background: Collection of items from narrow gauge railways of the UK and Ireland. The collection ranges from items such as tickets and nameplates to signalling equipment and locomotives.

Facilities: Café, Ticket office, Disabled access, Platform tickets, Guided tours available, Souvenir shop, Books for sale, Paintings/drawings for sale, Models for sale, Main credit cards taken, Children's events.

Entry Fees: Adults: £0.50   **Children:** £0.20

<u>Opening/Closing Times:</u>

Spring:	**Opens** Mon - Sun 09:30, **Closes** Mon - Sun 17:00
Summer:	**Opens** Mon - Sun 08:30, **Closes** Mon - Sun 18:00
Autumn:	**Opens** Mon - Sun 09:30, **Closes** Mon - Sun 17:00
Winter:	**Opens** Mon - Fri 09:30, **Closes** Mon - Fri 17:00
Other:	Steam trains run from April - November. Contact for details of Winter Steaming days.

<u>Location:</u>

Nearest Town/Village: Tywyn   **Bus:** 28, 29, 30   **Mainline Station:** Tywyn

<u>Associated Businesses:</u>
- Talyllyn Railway Co, Tywyn, Gwynedd, Wales

Key: *St* = Stops   *Al* = Alight   *Bd* = Board   *Tl* = Toilets   *DT* = Disabled Toilets   *PA* = Kids Play Area   *CP* = Free Car Park   *Ph* = Pay Phone   *Mu* = Museum
WR = Waiting Room   *Sh* = Sheds   *VS* = Can Visit Sheds   *WS* = Workshops   *VW* = Can Visit Workshops   *SB* = Signal Box   *VSB* = Can Visit Signal Box

NATIONAL RAILWAY MUSEUM

NATIONAL RAILWAY MUSEUM Leeman Rd, York, **YORKSHIRE (NORTH),** YO26 4XJ, **ENGLAND**.
(T) 01904 621261   **(F)** 01904 611112
(E) nrm@nmsi.ac.uk
(W) www.nrm.org.uk
Affiliated Bodies: Heritage Railway Association, Transport Trust
Type of Complex: Museum

Stock Overview:
No. Steam Locos: 81 (2 Pre-Group, 16 Pre-Nationalisation)
No. Diesel Locos: 2
Background: Home to a wide range of railway stock and memorabilia, from Mallard - the world's
fastest steam engine - to a lock of Stephenson's hair.

Facilities: Café, Restaurant, Disabled access, Guided tours available, Souvenir shop, Books for sale,
Videos for sale, Facilities for hire.
Opening/Closing Times:
Spring:	**Opens** Mon - Sun 10:00, **Closes** Mon - Sun 18:00
Summer:	**Opens** Mon - Sun 10:00, **Closes** Mon - Sun 18:00
Autumn:	**Opens** Mon - Sun 10:00, **Closes** Mon - Sun 18:00
Winter:	**Opens** Mon - Sun 10:00, **Closes** Mon - Sun 18:00

NATIONAL TRAMWAY MUSEUM

NATIONAL TRAMWAY MUSEUM Crich, Matlock, **DERBYSHIRE,** DE4 5DP, **ENGLAND**.
(T) 01773 852565
(W) www.tramway.co.uk
Affiliated Bodies: Heritage Railway Association, Transport Trust
Type of Complex: Museum
Stock Overview:
No. Steam Locos: 1
No. Diesel Locos: 3
Facilities: Restaurant, Disabled access, Cinema, Souvenir shop, Books for sale, Drive a vintage tram
experience. Picnic area.
Entry Fees: Adults: £7.00   **Children:** £3.50
Opening/Closing Times:
Spring:	**Opens** Sun - Mon 10:30, **Closes** Sun - Mon 16:00
Summer:	**Opens** Mon - Sun 10:00, **Closes** Mon - Sun 17:30
Autumn:	**Opens** Mon - Sun 10:00, **Closes** Mon - Sun 17:30
Winter:	**Opens** Sun - Mon 10:30, **Closes** Sun - Mon 16:00
Location:
Nearest Town/Village: Matlock   **Main Road:** A38   **Mainline Station:** Whatstandwell
Contact(s):
● **Manager:** Mr John Miller

NATIONAL WATERWAYS MUSEUM

NATIONAL WATERWAYS MUSEUM Llanthony Warehouse, Gloucester Docks, Gloucester,
GLOUCESTERSHIRE, GL1 2EH, **ENGLAND**.
(T) 01452 318054   **(F)** 01452 318066
(E) info@nwm.org.uk
(W) www.nwm.org.uk
Affiliated Bodies: Heritage Railway Association
Type of Complex: Museum
Facilities: Café, Disabled access, Books for sale.
Entry Fees: Adults: £4.95   **Children:** £3.95
Opening/Closing Times:

Spring: **Opens** Mon - Sun 10:00, **Closes** Mon - Sun 17:00
Summer: **Opens** Mon - Sun 10:00, **Closes** Mon - Sun 17:00
Autumn: **Opens** Mon - Sun 10:00, **Closes** Mon - Sun 17:00
Winter: **Opens** Mon - Sun 10:00, **Closes** Mon - Sun 17:00

Location:

Mainline Station: Gloucester

Contact(s):
● **Co-ordinator:** Mr David McDougall

NENE VALLEY RAILWAY

NENE VALLEY RAILWAY LTD Wansford Station, Stibbington, Peterborough, **CAMBRIDGESHIRE,** PE8 6LR, **ENGLAND**.

(T) 01780 784444　　**(F)** 01780 784440
(E) nvrorg@aol.com
(W) www.nvr.org.uk

Affiliated Bodies: Heritage Railway Association, Transport Trust
Year Opened: 1977
Type of Complex: Railway Station, Operational Railway Line, Museum, Restoration Site
Type of Organisation: Charity
No. Staff: 10　　**No. Volunteers:** 220

Stock Overview:

No. Steam Locos: 14 (2 Pre-Group)
No. Diesel Locos: 6

TV/Film Appearances: Octopussy (1982), Goldeneye (1995), Dirty Dozen - Next Mission (1984), Last Days of Patton (1985), London's Burning (1989 & 1997)

Facilities: Café, Ticket office, Disabled access, Function room, Waiting room, Platform tickets, Photo line side permit available, Guided tours available, Driver footplate experience, Santa Special, 'Thomas' event, History lectures, Enthusiast galas, Souvenir shop, Books for sale, Videos for sale, Photos for sale, Paintings/drawings for sale, Camera film for sale, CD's for sale, Tapes for sale, Main credit cards taken, Children's events, Facilities for hire, Trains for hire.

Opening/Closing Times:

Spring: **Opens** Mon - Sun 10:00, **Closes** Mon - Sun 16:00
Summer: **Opens** Mon - Sun 09:00, **Closes** Mon - Sun 17:00
Autumn: **Opens** Mon - Sun 10:00, **Closes** Mon - Sun 16:00
Winter: **Opens** Mon - Sun 09:00, **Closes** Mon - Sun 16:00
Other: Open every day for static displays. Closed Christmas Day and Boxing Day. Contact for details of steaming days.

Location:

Nearest Town/Village: Peterborough　　**Main Road:** A1　　**Taxi:** Reg Cunnington - 01780 782895
Mainline Station: Peterborough　　**Hotel:** Haycock　　**Restaurant:** Stibbington Diner

Contact(s):
● **General Manager:** M A Warrington

Journeys Available At This Railway:

Wansford to Peterborough
Track Type: Single
Features: Views of Open Fields, Urbanisation, Water, Woods. The Railway passes along the banks of the River Nene.
Bridges: 4 'under'　**Tunnels:** 1　**Level Crossings:** 2　**Signal Boxes:** 3　**Rivers:** 1　**Viaducts:** 2　**Journey Duration:** 30 mins　**Journey Length:** 7.5 mile(s)
Price: £10.00 (Adult Standard) £4.00 (Child Standard)
Available on Journey: Drinks, Alcohol.

Stations On This Journey:

Station Name	St	Al	Bd	Tl	DT	PA	CP	Ph	Mu	WR	Sh	VS	WS	VW	SB	VSB
Wansford	✔	✔	✔	✔	✔		✔	✔	✔	✔	✔		✔		✔	✔
Ferry Meadows	✔	✔	✔	✔					✔							
Orton Mere	✔	✔	✔	✔			✔			✔					✔	
Peterborough	✔	✔	✔	✔						✔					✔	

NIRT

NORTHAMPTONSHIRE IRONSTONE RAILWAY TRUST Hunsbury Hill Country Pk, Hunsbury Hill Rd, Northampton, **NORTHAMPTONSHIRE,** NN4 9UW, **ENGLAND**.

(T) 01604 702031   **(F)** 01604 702031

Affiliated Bodies: Heritage Railway Association

Year Opened: 1974

Type of Complex: Operational Railway Line, Museum, Restoration Site

Type of Organisation: Charity, Trust, Heritage Project, Non-Profit

Gauge: Standard   **No. Volunteers:** 22

Stock Overview:

No. Steam Locos: 3

No. Diesel Locos: 8

Facilities: Buffet, Disabled access, Advanced booking available, Guided tours available, Driver footplate experience, Santa Special, Courses on how to drive Locos, Children's events, Facilities for hire, Trains for hire.

Opening/Closing Times:

Spring: **Opens** 10:00, **Closes** 16:00

Summer: **Opens** 10:00, **Closes** 16:00

Autumn: **Opens** 10:00, **Closes** 16:00

Location:

Nearest Town/Village: Northampton   **Main Road:** A45   **Bus:** 23   **Taxi:** City Cars   **Mainline Station:** Northampton   **Hotel:** Queen Eleanor

Contact(s):

- **Chairman:** Mr Ian Cave
- **For Bookings:** Mr Kevin Smith
- **General Manager:** Mr Nick Robinson
- **Owner:** Mr William Nile   **(T)** 01604 757481
- **Treasurer:** Andris Dauksta

Journeys Available At This Railway:

Museum to Tunnel

Direction: West to East

Features: Views of Open Fields. Maximum gradient of 1 in 6 (For 30 metres).

Level Crossings: 3   Journey Duration: 20 mins

Price: £3.00 (Adult Standard) £1.50 (Child Standard) £3.00 (Adult Special) £7.00 (Child Special)

Stations On This Journey:

Station Name	St	Al	Bd	Tl	DT	PA	CP	Ph	Mu	WR	Sh	VS	WS	VW	SB	VSB
Museum	✔	✔		✔	✔	✔	✔		✔		✔		✔			
Tunnel	✔	✔														

NORTH GLOUCESTERSHIRE RAILWAY

NORTH GLOUCESTERSHIRE RAILWAY (THE) The Railway Station, Cheltenham, **GLOUCESTERSHIRE,** GL54 5DT, **ENGLAND**.

(T) 01452 539062

Type of Complex: Operational Railway Line

Gauge: Narrow

Stock Overview:

No. Steam Locos: 5 (2 Pre-Group, 3 Pre-Nationalisation)

No. Diesel Locos: 4 (2 Pre-Group)

Background: Shares a site with Gloucestershire & Warwickshire Railway. Currently extending the track by half a mile, completion expected by 2003.

Opening/Closing Times:

Spring:	**Opens** 10:45, **Closes** 16:30
Summer:	**Opens** 10:45, **Closes** 16:30
Autumn:	**Opens** 10:45, **Closes** 16:30
Winter:	**Opens** 10:45, **Closes** 16:30
Other:	Open various Sundays and Bank Holidays throughout the year, contact for details.

Location:

Nearest Town/Village: Broadway　　**Mainline Station:** Cheltenham Spa

Contact(s):

● **Chairman:** Mr Robert Hickman

Journeys Available At This Railway:

Toddington Halt to Toddington Halt (round trip)

Stations On This Journey:

Station Name	St	Al	Bd	Tl	DT	PA	CP	Ph	Mu	WR	Sh	VS	WS	VW	SB	VSB
Toddington Halt	✔	✔	✔												✔	✔
Calafernia Crossing																

NORTH NORFOLK RAILWAY

NORTH NORFOLK RAILWAY PLC The Station, Sheringham, **NORFOLK,** NR26 8RA, **ENGLAND**.

(T) 01263 820800　　**(F)** 01263 820801

(E) enquiries@nnrailway.co.uk

(W) www.nnrail.co.uk

Affiliated Bodies: Heritage Railway Association, Transport Trust

Year Opened: 1970

Type of Complex: Railway Station, Operational Railway Line, Restoration Site

Type of Organisation: Charity, Trust, Heritage Project, Limited Company, Volunteer, Non-Profit

Gauge: Standard　　**No. Staff:** 16　　**No. Volunteers:** 150

Stock Overview:

No. Steam Locos: 9 (2 Pre-Group, 1 Pre-Nationalisation)

No. Diesel Locos: 11

TV/Film Appearances: Love on a Branch Line (1993), Dad's Army (1973), All the Kings Men (1999), Sherlock Holmes Murder Rooms (2001)

Facilities: Buffet, Ticket office, Disabled access, Waiting room, Platform tickets, Photo line side permit available, Advanced booking available, Driver footplate experience, Santa Special, 'Thomas' event, Training courses, Enthusiast galas, Courses on how to drive Locos, Souvenir shop, Books for sale, Videos for sale, Photos for sale, Paintings/drawings for sale, Camera film for sale, Models for sale, Main credit cards taken, Children's events, Facilities for hire, Trains for hire.

Opening/Closing Times:

Spring:	**Opens** Mon - Sun 10:00, **Closes** Mon - Sun 16:00
Summer:	**Opens** Mon - Sun 10:00, **Closes** Mon - Sun 16:00
Autumn:	**Opens** Mon - Sun 10:00, **Closes** Mon - Sun 16:00
Winter:	**Opens** Mon - Sun 10:00, **Closes** Mon - Sun 16:00
Other:	Closed throughout January. Steam days held during summer and weekends in March, November and December.

Location:

Nearest Town/Village: Sheringham　　**Main Road:** A148　　**Bus:** 50, 50A, X50　　**Mainline Station:** Sheringham

Contact(s):

● **General Manager:** Mr Geoff Gowing

Journeys Available At This Railway:

A-Z STEAM RAILWAYS

North Gloucestershire Railway — North Norfolk Railway

Key:　St = Stops　　Al = Alight　　Bd = Board　　Tl = Toilets　　DT = Disabled Toilets　　PA = Kids Play Area　　CP = Free Car Park　　Ph = Pay Phone　　Mu = Museum
WR = Waiting Room　　Sh = Sheds　　VS = Can Visit Sheds　　WS = Workshops　　VW = Can Visit Workshops　　SB = Signal Box　　VSB = Can Visit Signal Box

Sheringham to Holt
Track Type: Single   Direction: East to West
Features: Views of Open Fields, Sea, Woods. Views of Weybourne Village & Sea. Maximum gradient of 1 in 80 (For 1500 metres).
Bridges: 2 'over', 4 'under'   **Level Crossings:** 3   **Signal Boxes:** 3   **Journey Duration:** 23 mins   **Journey Length:** 5.25 mile(s)
Price: £7.50 (Adult Standard) £4.00 (Child Standard) £8.50 (Adult Special) £5.00 (Child Special)
Available on Journey: Refreshments, Drinks, Alcohol.

Stations On This Journey:

Station Name	St	Al	Bd	Tl	DT	PA	CP	Ph	Mu	WR	Sh	VS	WS	VW	SB	VSB
Sheringham	✔	✔							✔	✔					✔	✔
Weybourne	✔	✔		✔	✔		✔			✔	✔		✔		✔	✔
Kelling Heath Park Halt	✔	✔														
Holt ✔		✔			✔		✔	✔								

NORTH TYNESIDE STEAM RAILWAY

NORTH TYNESIDE STEAM RAILWAY ASSOCIATION & STEPHENSON RAILWAY MUSEUM Middle Engine Lane, West Chirton, North Shields, **TYNE AND WEAR,** NE29 8DX, **ENGLAND**.
(T) 0191 2007146
Affiliated Bodies: Heritage Railway Association
Type of Complex: Museum
Gauge: Standard
Facilities: Café, Disabled access, Santa Special, Children's events.
Opening/Closing Times:
Summer: **Opens** Tues – Thurs, Sat, Sun 11:00, **Closes** Tues – Thurs 15:00, Sat, Sun 16:00
Other: Open May – September. Contact for information on steaming days.
Location:
Instructions: Situated adjacent to Silver Link Retail Park.
Nearest Town/Village: Newcastle upon Tyne   **Main Road:** A19   **Bus:** 300, 303, 313, 337, 339.
Contact(s):
● **Chairman:** Mr Malcolm Dunlavey
● **Secretary:** Mr Bob Stapley
● **Technical Info:** Mr Lewis Lycett
Journeys Available At This Railway:

Museum Station to Percy Main
Features: Views of Open Fields, Urbanisation.
Bridges: 1 'over', 4 'under'   **Level Crossings:** 1   **Journey Length:** 1.75 mile(s)
Price: £2.00 (Adult Standard) £1.00 (Child Standard)
Stations On This Journey:

Station Name	St	Al	Bd	Tl	DT	PA	CP	Ph	Mu	WR	Sh	VS	WS	VW	SB	VSB
Museum Station	✔	✔							✔		✔	✔	✔	✔		
Percy Main	✔	✔														

NORTH YORKSHIRE MOORS RAILWAY

NORTH YORKSHIRE MOORS RAILWAY CHARITABLE TRUST Pickering Station, Pickering, **YORKSHIRE (NORTH),** YO18 7AJ, **ENGLAND**.
(T) 01751 472508   **(F)** 01751 476970
(E) admin@nymrpickering.fsnet.co.uk
(W) www.northyorkshiremoorsrailway.com
Affiliated Bodies: Heritage Railway Association, Transport Trust
Year Opened: 1973
Type of Complex: Railway Station, Operational Railway Line
Type of Organisation: Charity
Stock Overview:

No. Steam Locos: 21 (11 Pre-Group, 4 Pre-Nationalisation)
No. Diesel Locos: 15 (1 Pre-Group)
TV/Film Appearances: All Creatures Great and Small, Casualty, Poirot, Sherlock Holmes, Heartbeat, Harry Potter
Facilities: Café, Restaurant, Ticket office, Disabled access, Platform tickets, Photo line side permit available, Through ticketing available, Advanced booking available, Driver footplate experience, Santa Special, 'Thomas' event, Enthusiast galas, Courses on how to drive Locos, Souvenir shop, Books for sale, Videos for sale, Photos for sale, Paintings/drawings for sale, Camera film for sale, CD's for sale, Tapes for sale, Models for sale, Main credit cards taken, Children's events, Facilities for hire, Trains for hire.

Contact(s):
- **For Bookings:** Ms Rosie Owsten
- **For Donations:** Ms Sue Lovell

Journeys Available At This Railway:

Pickering to Grosmont
Features: Maximum gradient of 1 in 49.
Journey Length: 18 mile(s)

Stations On This Journey:

Station Name	St	Al	Bd	Tl	DT	PA	CP	Ph	Mu	WR	Sh	VS	WS	VW	SB	VSB
Pickering	✔		✔	✔	✔		✔									
Levisham	✔			✔			✔									
Newton Dale			✔													
Goathland	✔			✔		✔										
Grosmont	✔		✔	✔		✔						✔				

NORTHAMPTON & LAMPORT RAILWAY

NORTHAMPTON STEAM RAILWAY LTD T/A NORTHAMPTON & LAMPORT RAILWAY Pitsford & Brampton Station, Pitsford Rd, Chapel Brampton, Northampton, **NORTHAMPTONSHIRE,** NN6 8BA, **ENGLAND**.
(T) 01604 820327
(W) www.nlr.org.uk
Affiliated Bodies: Heritage Railway Association
Type of Complex: Operational Railway Line

Stock Overview:
No. Steam Locos: 5
No. Diesel Locos: 14
Facilities: Buffet, Ticket office, Disabled access, Santa Special, 'Thomas' event, Souvenir shop, Books for sale, Main credit cards taken, Children's events, Facilities for hire, Trains for hire.

Opening/Closing Times:
Spring: **Opens** Sun 10:00, **Closes** Sun 17:00
Summer: **Opens** Sun 10:00, **Closes** Sun 17:00
Autumn: **Opens** Sun 10:00, **Closes** Sun 17:00
Winter: **Opens** Sun 10:00, **Closes** Sun 17:00
Other: Contact for information on steaming days.

Location:
Nearest Town/Village: Northampton   **Main Road:** A5149   **Mainline Station:** Northampton

Contact(s):
- **Chairman:** Dr Colin Watson
- **Secretary:** Mr Tim Parker

Journeys Available At This Railway:

Pitsford & Brampton to Pitsford & Brampton (round trip)
Features: Views of Open Fields, Water.
Bridges: 1 'under'   **Signal Boxes:** 5   **Rivers:** 1   **Journey Length:** 1 mile(s)

Stations On This Journey:

Key:	St = Stops	Al = Alight	Bd = Board	Tl = Toilets	DT = Disabled Toilets	PA = Kids Play Area	CP = Free Car Park	Ph = Pay Phone	Mu = Museum
	WR = Waiting Room	Sh = Sheds	VS = Can Visit Sheds	WS = Workshops	VW = Can Visit Workshops	SB = Signal Box	VSB = Can Visit Signal Box		

Station Name	St	Al	Bd	Tl	DT	PA	CP	Ph	Mu	WR	Sh	VS	WS	VW	SB	VSB
Pitsford & Brampton	✔	✔		✔			✔			✔				✔		

NOTTINGHAM TRANSPORT CTRE

NOTTINGHAM TRANSPORT HERITAGE CENTRE Mere Way, Ruddington, **NOTTINGHAMSHIRE,** NG11 6NX, **ENGLAND**.

(T) 0115 9405705   **(F)** 0115 9405905

(E) ken-phethean@supanet.com

(W) www.nthc.org.uk

Affiliated Bodies: Heritage Railway Association

Stock Overview:

No. Steam Locos: 6

No. Diesel Locos: 5

Facilities: Santa Special, Enthusiast galas.

Opening/Closing Times:

Other: Open every Sunday during summer and at various times during winter. Contact for further details.

Location:

Nearest Town/Village: Nottingham   **Main Road:** A60   **Bus:** 10   **Mainline Station:** Nottingham Midland

OLD KILN LIGHT RAILWAY

OLD KILN LIGHT RAILWAY Rural Life Ctre, Tilford, Farnham, **SURREY,** GU10 2DL, **ENGLAND**.

(T) 01252 795571

Type of Complex: Operational Railway Line, Museum, Restoration Site

Type of Organisation: Volunteer

Gauge: Narrow

Stock Overview:

No. Steam Locos: 2

Facilities: Café, Buffet, Disabled access, Lecture room, Function room, Waiting room, Guided tours available, Santa Special, History lectures, Enthusiast galas, Souvenir shop, Books for sale, Videos for sale, Photos for sale, Paintings/drawings for sale.

Opening/Closing Times:

Summer: **Opens** Sun 11:00, **Closes** Sun 16:00

Other: Contact for information concerning additional opening days.

Location:

Nearest Town/Village: Farnham   **Main Road:** Reeds Road   **Mainline Station:** Farnham

Journeys Available At This Railway:

Old Kiln Halt, Tilford to Oatlands Station, Tilford

Features: Maximum gradient of 1 in 60.

Journey Duration: 5 mins   **Journey Length:** 0.33 mile(s)

Price: £0.50 (Adult Standard) £0.50 (Child Standard) £1.00 (Adult Special) £0.50 (Child Special)

Stations On This Journey:

Station Name	St	Al	Bd	Tl	DT	PA	CP	Ph	Mu	WR	Sh	VS	WS	VW	SB	VSB
Old Kiln Halt	✔	✔		✔	✔	✔	✔			✔	✔	✔	✔	✔	✔	

OLD STATION MUSEUM

NORTH WOOLWICH OLD STATION MUSEUM Pier Rd, North Woolwich, London, **LONDON (GREATER),** E16 2JJ, **ENGLAND**.

(T) 020 74747244   **(F)** 020 74736065

(W) www.newham.gov.uk/leisure/museums/moldstn.htm

Year Opened: 1984

Type of Complex: Museum

Facilities: Disabled access, Souvenir shop, Books for sale, Videos for sale, Children's events, Facilities for hire, Trains for hire.

Opening/Closing Times:

Spring: **Opens** Sat, Sun 13:00, **Closes** Sat, Sun 17:00
Summer: **Opens** Mon - Sun 13:00, **Closes** Mon - Sun 17:00
Autumn: **Opens** Sat, Sun 13:00, **Closes** Sat, Sun 17:00
Winter: **Opens** Sat, Sun 13:00, **Closes** Sat, Sun 17:00
Other: Closed during December. Contact for details on steaming days.

Location:

Nearest Town/Village: London   **Bus:** 101, 473   **Mainline Station:** North Woolwich

Contact(s):
- **General Manager:** Mr Charlie Harris

PAIGNTON & DARTMOUTH RAILWAY

DART VALLEY RAILWAY PLC Queens Park Station, Torbay Rd, Paignton, **DEVON,** TQ4 6AF, **ENGLAND.**
(T) 01803 555872   **(F)** 01803 664313
Year Opened: 1973
Type of Complex: Operational Railway Line
Type of Organisation: Limited Company
Gauge: Standard
Stock Overview:
No. Steam Locos: 5 (4 Pre-Group)
No. Diesel Locos: 3
TV/Film Appearances: French Lieutenant's Woman
Facilities: Café, Ticket office, Disabled access, Santa Special, 'Thomas' event, Souvenir shop, Books for sale, Videos for sale, Dining service available.

Opening/Closing Times:

Summer: **Opens** Mon - Sun 10:30, **Closes** Mon - Sun 17:30
Other: Open selected days April - October and daily during May - September. Contact for details.

Contact(s):
- **For Bookings:** Miss S Houghton **(T)** 01803 553760
- **General Manager:** Mr J B Cogar **(T)** 01803 553760
- **Technical Info:** Mr P Roach   **(T)** 01803 845732

Journeys Available At This Railway:

Paignton to Kingswear
Track Type: Single   Direction: North to South
Features: Views of Open Fields, Sea, Water, Woods. Views across Torbay, English Channel, River Dart Estuary and Dartmouth. Maximum gradient of 1 in 60 (For 3218 metres).
Bridges: 1 'over', 7 'under'   **Tunnels:** 1   **Level Crossings:** 3   **Signal Boxes:** 1   **Rivers:** 1   **Viaducts:** 3   **Journey Duration:** 30 mins   **Journey Length:** 7 mile(s)
Price: £6.40 (Adult Standard) £4.40 (Child Standard)

Stations On This Journey:

Station Name	St	Al	Bd	Tl	DT	PA	CP	Ph	Mu	WR	Sh	VS	WS	VW	SB	VSB
Paignton	✔	✔	✔	✔	✔					✔	✔					
Goodrington	✔	✔	✔													
Churston	✔	✔	✔	✔			✔			✔		✔				
Kingswear	✔	✔	✔	✔												

PALLOT STEAM MUSEUM

L C PALLOT TRUST Rue de Bechet, Trinity, Jersey, **CHANNEL ISLANDS,** JE3 5BE, **ENGLAND.**
(T) 01534 865307   **(F)** 01534 864248
Type of Complex: Operational Railway Line, Museum
Type of Organisation: Trust
Gauge: Narrow & Standard   **No. Staff:** 2   **No. Volunteers:** 0

Key: St = Stops   Al = Alight   Bd = Board   Tl = Toilets   DT = Disabled Toilets   PA = Kids Play Area   CP = Free Car Park   Ph = Pay Phone   Mu = Museum   WR = Waiting Room   Sh = Sheds   VS = Can Visit Sheds   WS = Workshops   VW = Can Visit Workshops   SB = Signal Box   VSB = Can Visit Signal Box

Stock Overview:

No. Steam Locos: 4

Facilities: Disabled access, Waiting room, Souvenir shop, Books for sale, Museum moving into purpose built premises in April 2002. Official opening time expected May 9th 2002.

Opening/Closing Times:

Spring: **Opens** Mon - Sat 10:00, **Closes** Mon - Sat 17:00
Summer: **Opens** Mon - Sat 10:00, **Closes** Mon - Sat 17:00
Autumn: **Opens** Mon - Sat 10:00, **Closes** Mon - Sat 17:00
Other: Open April 1st - 31st October.

Contact(s):

- **Administrator:** Ms Elizabeth Pallot
- **Manager:** Mr Sam Pallot
- **Manager:** Mr Trevor Pallot   (T) 07797 711861
- **Secretary:** Ms Liz Vivian
- **Trustee:** Ms Liz Vivian
- **Trustee:** Mr Sam Pallot

Journeys Available At This Railway:

Victorian Station to Victorian Station (round trip)
Track Type: Single
Price: £1.00 (Adult Standard) £1.00 (Child Standard)

PEAK RAIL

PEAK RAIL LTD Matlock Station, Matlock, **DERBYSHIRE,** DE4 3NA, **ENGLAND**.

(T) 01629 580381   **(F)** 01629 760645

(E) peakrail@peakrail.co.uk

(W) www.peakrail.co.uk

Affiliated Bodies: Heritage Railway Association

Complex Size: 28 Acres   **Year Opened:** 1991

Type of Complex: Operational Railway Line

Type of Organisation: Limited Company, Volunteer

No. Staff: 5

Stock Overview:

No. Steam Locos: 5

No. Diesel Locos: 7

TV/Film Appearances: Peak Practice, Tweenies

Facilities: Restaurant, Buffet, Ticket office, Disabled access, Line permit needed, Advanced booking available, Guided tours available, Driver footplate experience, Santa Special, Enthusiast galas, Souvenir shop, Books for sale, Videos for sale, Photos for sale, Paintings/drawings for sale, Camera film for sale, CD's for sale, Tapes for sale, Models for sale, Main credit cards taken, Children's events, Facilities for hire, Trains for hire.

Opening/Closing Times:

Spring: **Opens** Sat, Sun 11:00, **Closes** Sat, Sun 17:15
Summer: **Opens** Sat, Sun 11:00, **Closes** Sat, Sun 17:15
Autumn: **Opens** Sat, Sun 11:00, **Closes** Sat, Sun 17:15
Winter: **Opens** Sun 11:00, **Closes** Sun 16:00
Other: Open Sundays only in November, January and March. Open Saturdays and Sundays in December, and mid week in June, July and August.

Location:

Nearest Town/Village: Matlock   **Main Road:** A6   **Mainline Station:** Matlock

Contact(s):

- **For Bookings:** Mrs K Baxter
- **General Manager:** Mr J Clegg
- **General Manager:** Mrs J T Statham

Journeys Available At This Railway:

Rowsley South Station to Matlock Riverside
Track Type: Single   Direction: South to North
Features: Views of Hills, Open Fields, Water. Views of Valley in Derbyshire Dales.
Journey Length: 8 mile(s)

Price: £6.00 (Adult Standard) £3.00 (Child Standard)
Available on Journey: Refreshments, Drinks, Alcohol, Commentary.

Stations On This Journey:

Station Name	St	Al	Bd	Tl	DT	PA	CP	Ph	Mu	WR	Sh	VS	WS	VW	SB	VSB
Rowsley South	✔	✔	✔	✔		✔	✔			✔	✔					
Darley Dale	✔	✔		✔	✔		✔						✔		✔	✔
Matlock Riverside																

PERRYGROVE RAILWAY

PERRYGROVE RAILWAY Coleford, **GLOUCESTERSHIRE,** GL16 8QB, **ENGLAND**.
(T) 01594 834991
(E) mkc@perrygrove.com
(W) www.perrygrove.co.uk
Affiliated Bodies: Britains Great Little Railways
Complex Size: 22 Acres   **Year Opened:** 1996
Type of Complex: Operational Railway Line, Restoration Site
Type of Organisation: Heritage Project, Conservation Project, Limited Company
Gauge: Narrow   **No. Staff:** 2   **No. Volunteers:** 2

Stock Overview:
No. Steam Locos: 2
No. Diesel Locos: 1

TV/Film Appearances: Collectors Lot (1998), Central News (1996 & 2001)

Background: A narrow gauge line built according to the minimum gauge principles of Sir Arthur Heywood. There is a railway treasure hunt for children.

Facilities: Café, Buffet, Ticket office, Disabled access, Waiting room, Guided tours available, Driver footplate experience, Santa Special, Training courses, History lectures, Courses on how to drive Locos, Souvenir shop, Books for sale, Photos for sale, Children's events, Trains for hire.

Opening/Closing Times:
Spring: **Opens** 11:00, **Closes** 16:15
Summer: **Opens** 11:00, **Closes** 16:15
Autumn: **Opens** 11:00, **Closes** 16:15
Winter: **Opens** 11:00, **Closes** 16:15
Other: Open 5 days a week during School holidays, also open on selected days throughout the year, Please contact for details.

Location:
Instructions: Situated on B4228, about 0.5 mile south of Coleford.
Nearest Town/Village: Coleford   **Main Road:** B4228   **Bus:** F31, 722   **Taxi:** JR - 07703 372106
Mainline Station: Lydney   **Hotel:** Lambsquay Hotel

Contact(s):
● **For Bookings:** Mr M Crofts
● **For Donations:** Mr M Crofts
● **Owner:** Mr M Crofts
● **Technical Info:** Mr M Crofts

Journeys Available At This Railway:

Perrygrove to Oakiron
Track Type: Single   Direction: South to North
Features: Views of Hills, Open Fields, Woods. Maximum gradient of 1 in 30 (For 200 metres).
Bridges: 1 'under'   **Level Crossings:** 1   **Journey Duration:** 9 mins   **Journey Length:** 0.75 mile(s)
Price: £3.30 (Adult Standard) £2.30 (Child Standard)

Stations On This Journey:

Station Name	St	Al	Bd	Tl	DT	PA	CP	Ph	Mu	WR	Sh	VS	WS	VW	SB	VSB
Perrygrove	✔	✔	✔	✔	✔	✔	✔				✔	✔	✔	✔		
Rookwood	✔	✔	✔								✔					
Heywood	✔	✔	✔								✔					
Oakiron	✔										✔					

PLYM VALLEY RAILWAY

PLYM VALLEY RAILWAY Marsh Mills Station, Coypool Rd, Plymouth, **DEVON,** PL7 4TB, **ENGLAND**.

(E) plymvalrwy@btinternet.com

(W) www.plymrail.co.uk

Affiliated Bodies: Heritage Railway Association

Year Opened: 2001

Type of Complex: Railway Station, Operational Railway Line

Type of Organisation: Volunteer

Gauge: Standard

Stock Overview:

No. Steam Locos: 1

No. Diesel Locos: 6

Facilities: Café, Disabled access, Souvenir shop.

Opening/Closing Times:

Spring: **Opens** Sun 10:00, **Closes** Sun 18:00

Summer: **Opens** Sun 10:00, **Closes** Sun 18:00

Autumn: **Opens** Sun 10:00, **Closes** Sun 18:00

Other: Some Sundays may be closed, contact for further details.

Location:

Instructions: Follow signs for Coypool Park & Ride car park which is situated opposite the railway.

Nearest Town/Village: Plymouth   **Main Road:** A38

Contact(s):

- ● **For Bookings:** Mr John Netherton
- ● **General Manager:** Mr Malcolm Stead
- ● **Volunteer:** Mr Bernard Mills

Journeys Available At This Railway:

Marsh Mills to Marsh Mills (round trip)

Track Type: Single

Features: Views of Water, Woods.

Journey Length: 0.5 mile(s)

Price: £1.00 (Adult Standard) £1.00 (Child Standard)

Stations On This Journey:

Station Name	St	Al	Bd	Tl	DT	PA	CP	Ph	Mu	WR	Sh	VS	WS	VW	SB	VSB
Marsh Mills	✔	✔	✔				✔			✔			✔	✔		

PONTYPOOL & BLAENAVON RAILWAY

PONTYPOOL & BLAENAVON RAILWAY COMPANY (1983) LTD C/O Council Offices, 101 High St, Blaenavon, **TORFAEN,** NP4 7EF, **WALES**.

(E) railway@pontypoolandblaenavon.freeserve.co.uk

(W) www.pontypool-and-blaenavon.co.uk

Affiliated Bodies: Heritage Railway Association

Year Opened: 1984

Type of Complex: Operational Railway Line, Restoration Site

Type of Organisation: Charity, Limited Company, Volunteer

Gauge: Standard   **No. Volunteers:** 50

Stock Overview:

No. Steam Locos: 4
No. Diesel Locos: 5
Facilities: Ticket office, Santa Special, 'Thomas' event.

Opening/Closing Times:

Spring: **Opens** Sat 11:30, **Closes** Sat 16:30
Summer: **Opens** Sat 11:30, **Closes** Sat 16:30
Other: Open throughout September for diesel. Contact for details of steaming days.

Location:

Instructions: Located just off the B4248.
Nearest Town/Village: Blaenavon **Main Road:** B4248 **Bus:** 30 **Mainline Station:** Abergavenny
Restaurant: Whistle Inn

Journeys Available At This Railway:

Furnace Sidings Platform to Whistle Inn Halt
Track Type: Single
Features: Views of Hills, Open Fields, Water. Highest preserved standard gauge railway in Wales.
Journey Duration: 4 mins **Journey Length:** 0.75 mile(s)
Price: £2.40 (Adult Standard) £1.20 (Child Standard)
Available on Journey: Refreshments, Drinks.

Stations On This Journey:

Station Name	St	Al	Bd	Tl	DT	PA	CP	Ph	Mu	WR	Sh	VS	WS	VW	SB	VSB
Furnace Sidings Platform	✔	✔	✔			✔				✔	✔		✔			
Whistle Inn Halt	✔	✔			✔					✔						

PRESTONGRANGE INDUSTRIAL

PRESTONGRANGE INDUSTRIAL HERITAGE MUSEUM Morrison's Haven, Prestonpans, **LOTHIAN (EAST),** EH32 9RX, **SCOTLAND**.
(T) 0131 6532904 **(F)** 01620 828201
Type of Complex: Museum
Type of Organisation: Heritage Project
Background: Coal was mined for centuries in this area and now this former colliery has been converted into a Heritage Centre.
Facilities: Disabled access.

Opening/Closing Times:

Other: Contact for details of steaming days.

Location:

Nearest Town/Village: Musselburgh **Main Road:** B1348

RAILWAY AGE

CREWE HERITAGE TRUST Vernon Way, Crewe, **CHESHIRE,** CW1 2DB, **ENGLAND**.
(T) 01270 212130 **(F)** 01270 256410
(W) www.therailwayage.co.uk
Type of Complex: Museum
Gauge: Standard

Stock Overview:

No. Steam Locos: 1
Facilities: Disabled access, Souvenir shop, Children's events, Facilities for hire.
Entry Fees: Adults: £3.50 **Children:** £2.00

Opening/Closing Times:

Spring: **Opens** Mon - Sun 10:00, **Closes** Mon - Sun 16:00
Summer: **Opens** Mon - Sun 10:00, **Closes** Mon - Sun 16:00
Autumn: **Opens** Mon - Sun 10:00, **Closes** Mon - Sun 16:00
Other: Open Mid February - October.

Location:

Nearest Town/Village: Crewe **Main Road:** M6 **Mainline Station:** Crewe

---

Key: *St* = Stops *Al* = Alight *Bd* = Board *Tl* = Toilets *DT* = Disabled Toilets *PA* = Kids Play Area *CP* = Free Car Park *Ph* = Pay Phone *Mu* = Museum
WR = Waiting Room *Sh* = Sheds *VS* = Can Visit Sheds *WS* = Workshops *VW* = Can Visit Workshops *SB* = Signal Box *VSB* = Can Visit Signal Box

Contact(s):
- **Chairman:** Mr John Williams

RAILWORLD

RAILWORLDOundle Rd, Peterborough, **CAMBRIDGESHIRE,** PE2 9NR, **ENGLAND**.

(T) 01733 344240   **(F)** 01733 344240

(E) info@railworld.net

(W) www.railworld.com

Affiliated Bodies: Heritage Railway Association

Complex Size: 12 Acres   **Year Opened:** 1993

Type of Complex: Museum

Type of Organisation: Charity, Volunteer, Non-Profit

No. Volunteers: 20

Stock Overview:

No. Steam Locos: 1

No. Diesel Locos: 1

Background: An exhibition centre and museum, Railworld operates model trains and has 'hands-on' exhibits. The centre shows the need for sustainable integrated transport.

Facilities: Buffet, Disabled access, Cinema, Lecture room, Guided tours available, History lectures, Souvenir shop, Facilities for hire.

Entry Fees: Adults: £2.50   **Children:** £1.50

Opening/Closing Times:

Spring: **Opens** Mon - Sun 11:00, **Closes** Mon - Sun 16:00
Summer: **Opens** Mon - Sun 11:00, **Closes** Mon - Sun 16:00
Autumn: **Opens** Mon - Sun 11:00, **Closes** Mon - Sun 16:00
Winter: **Opens** Mon - Fri 11:00, **Closes** Mon - Fri 16:00

Location:

Nearest Town/Village: Peterborough   **Main Road:** A605, Oundle Road   **Mainline Station:** Peterborough

Contact(s):
- **For Bookings:** Mr Richard Paten
- **For Donations:** Mr Richard Paten
- **General Manager:** Mr Richard Paten
- **Technical Info:** Mr Richard Paten
- **Trustee:** Mr Roman Falinski
- **Vice Chairman:** Mr Brian Pearce

RAVENGLASS & ESKDALE

RAVENGLASS & ESKDALE RAILWAY Ravenglass, **CUMBRIA,** CA18 1SW, **ENGLAND**.

(T) 01229 717171   **(F)** 01229 717011

(E) rer@netcomuk.co.uk

(W) www.ravenglass-railway.co.uk

Affiliated Bodies: Heritage Railway Association

Year Opened: 1960

Type of Complex: Operational Railway Line

Type of Organisation: Limited Company

Gauge: Narrow   **No. Staff:** 18

Stock Overview:

No. Steam Locos: 5

No. Diesel Locos: 1

Facilities: Café, Ticket office, Disabled access, Cinema, Through ticketing available, Santa Special, 'Thomas' event, Enthusiast galas, Souvenir shop, Videos for sale, Photos for sale, Paintings/drawings for sale, Camera film for sale, Main credit cards taken, Children's events, Facilities for hire, Trains for hire.

Opening/Closing Times:

Spring: **Opens** Mon - Sun 08:00, **Closes** Mon - Sun 17:00

Summer: **Opens** Mon - Sun 08:00, **Closes** Mon - Sun 19:00
Autumn: **Opens** Mon - Sun 08:00, **Closes** Mon - Sun 17:00
Other: Opening times are for the station, contact for details of steaming days and Winter open days.

Location:
Nearest Town/Village: Whitehaven

Contact(s):
● **General Manager:** Mr Trevor Stockton

Journeys Available At This Railway:

Ravenglass to Eskdale (Dalegarth)
Track Type: Single   Direction: West to East
Features: Views of Hills, Open Fields, Sea, Water, Woods. Views of Western Lake District. Maximum gradient of 1 in 36 (For 300 metres).
Bridges: 2 'over', 6 'under'   **Level Crossings:** 2   **Signal Boxes:** 1   **Journey Duration:** 40 mins   **Journey Length:** 7 mile(s)
Price: £7.00 (Adult Standard) £3.50 (Child Standard)

Stations On This Journey:

Station Name	St	Al	Bd	Tl	DT	PA	CP	Ph	Mu	WR	Sh	VS	WS	VW	SB	VSB
Ravenglass	✔	✔	✔	✔	✔	✔		✔	✔		✔	✔	✔		✔	✔
Muncaster Mill	✔	✔	✔	✔	✔		✔		✔							
Irton Road	✔	✔	✔	✔	✔		✔		✔							
The Green	✔	✔	✔	✔	✔		✔		✔							
Eskdale (Dalegarth)	✔	✔	✔	✔	✔	✔	✔									

RHYL MINIATURE RAILWAY

RHYL MINIATURE RAILWAY Marine Lake, Rhyl, **DENBIGHSHIRE, WALES**.
(T) 01352 759109
Type of Complex: Operational Railway Line
Gauge: Narrow

Stock Overview:
No. Steam Locos: 1
No. Diesel Locos: 3
Facilities: Disabled access.

Location:
Instructions: The railway is situated on the western outskirts of Rhyl behind the promenade.
Nearest Town/Village: Rhyl   **Main Road:** A648

Contact(s):
● **Chairman:** Mr Simon Townsend
● **For Bookings:** Mr Simon Townsend
● **President:** Rev Alan Cliff
● **Treasurer:** Mr Justin Bell

Alternative Contact Details:
● Secretary, 22 River St, Rhyl, Denbighshire, LL18 1PT, Wales

Journeys Available At This Railway:

Marine Lake to Marine Lake (round trip)
Track Type: Single
Features: Views of Water.
Level Crossings: 3   **Journey Length:** 1 mile(s)
Price: £1.00 (Adult Standard) £1.00 (Child Standard)

Key:	*St* = Stops *Al* = Alight *Bd* = Board *Tl* = Toilets *DT* = Disabled Toilets *PA* = Kids Play Area *CP* = Free Car Park *Ph* = Pay Phone *Mu* = Museum
	WR = Waiting Room *Sh* = Sheds *VS* = Can Visit Sheds *WS* = Workshops *VW* = Can Visit Workshops *SB* = Signal Box *VSB* = Can Visit Signal Box

ROMNEY HYTHE & DYMCHURCH

ROMNEY HYTHE & DYMCHURCH RAILWAY 2 Littlestone Rd, Littlestone, New Romney, **KENT,** TN28 8PL, **ENGLAND.**

(T) 01797 362353   **(F)** 01797 363591

(E) rhdr@dels.demon.co.uk

(W) www.rhdr.demon.co.uk

Affiliated Bodies: Heritage Railway Association

Year Opened: 1927

Type of Complex: Operational Railway Line

Gauge: Narrow

Stock Overview:

No. Steam Locos: 10

No. Diesel Locos: 2

Background: The Railway celebrates its 75th Anniversary on July 14th 2002.

Facilities: Café, Disabled access, Platform tickets, Santa Special, 'Thomas' event, Enthusiast galas, Courses on how to drive Locos, Souvenir shop, Books for sale, Videos for sale, Camera film for sale, Main credit cards taken, Parties available.

Opening/Closing Times:

Spring: **Opens** Mon - Sun 10.30, **Closes** Mon - Sun 18.30

Summer: **Opens** Mon - Sun 10.30, **Closes** Mon - Sun 18.30

Other: Open weekends March 2nd - 17th, October 5th - 20th and daily February 9th - 17th and October 26th - November 3rd. Open on selected days in December for Santa Specials and New Year service. Thomas days will be held June 23rd, July 21st and September 7th.

Location:

Nearest Town/Village: New Romney

Contact(s):

● **Chief Mechanical Engineer:** Mr Fred Sargent

● **Marketing Manager:** Mr Derek Smith

Journeys Available At This Railway:

Hythe to Dungeness
Price: £6.30 (Adult Standard)
Available on Journey: Refreshments, Drinks, Alcohol.

Stations On This Journey:

Station Name	St	Al	Bd	Tl	DT	PA	CP	Ph	Mu	WR	Sh	VS	WS	VW	SB	VSB
Hythe	✓	✓	✓	✓	✓					✓						
Dymchurch	✓	✓		✓	✓					✓						
St Marys Bay	✓	✓														
New Romney	✓	✓		✓	✓	✓						✓	✓			
Romney Sands	✓	✓														
Dungeness	✓	✓		✓	✓					✓						

ROTHER VALLEY RAILWAY

ROTHER VALLEY RAILWAY (EAST SUSSEX) Station Rd, Robertsbridge, **SUSSEX (EAST),** TN32 5DA, **ENGLAND.**

(T) 01424 436168

(E) info.rvr@wizo.co.uk

(W) www.wizo.com/rvr/

Affiliated Bodies: Heritage Railway Association

Year Opened: 1993

Type of Complex: Operational Railway Line, Museum, Restoration Site

Gauge: Standard

Facilities: Buffet, Disabled access, Souvenir shop.

Opening/Closing Times:

Spring: **Opens** Sun 09:30, **Closes** Sun 17:00
Summer: **Opens** Sun 09:30, **Closes** Sun 17:00
Autumn: **Opens** Sun 09:30, **Closes** Sun 17:00
Winter: **Opens** Sun 09:30, **Closes** Sun 17:00

Location:

Nearest Town/Village: Tunbridge Wells   **Main Road:** A21   **Mainline Station:** Robertsbridge

Contact(s):

● **General Manager:** Helen Brett   **(T)** 01424 436138

Alternative Contact Details:

● 12 Lobat Nead, Beds Hill Rd, St. Leonards-on-Sea, Sussex (East), TN38 8EH, England

ROYAL VICTORIA RAILWAY

ROYAL VICTORIA RAILWAY Royal Victoria County Pk, Netley, Southampton, **HAMPSHIRE,** SO31 5GA, **ENGLAND**.

(T) 02380 456246   **(F)** 01344 621286

(E) steamyhbm@hotmail.com

Complex Size: 4 Acres   **Year Opened:** 1995

Type of Complex: Railway Station, Operational Railway Line

Type of Organisation: Volunteer, Non-Profit

Gauge: Narrow   **No. Staff:** 1   **No. Volunteers:** 6

Stock Overview:

No. Steam Locos: 3

No. Diesel Locos: 3

Background: There is also a 10.25'' miniature railway on the site of the L&S Western track bed that served the hospital. The hospital was demolished in 1966 and the site turned into a country park (270 acres in all).

Facilities: Café, Ticket office, Disabled access, Function room, Through ticketing available, Advanced booking available, Driver footplate experience, Santa Special, Enthusiast galas, Souvenir shop, Paintings/drawings for sale, Children's events.

Opening/Closing Times:

Spring: **Opens** Sat, Sun 11:00, **Closes** Sat, Sun 16:30
Summer: **Opens** Sat, Sun 11:00, **Closes** Sat, Sun 16:30
Autumn: **Opens** Sat, Sun 11:00, **Closes** Sat, Sun 16:30
Winter: **Opens** Sat, Sun 11:00, **Closes** Sat, Sun 16:30
Other: Open every weekend and school holidays.

Location:

Nearest Town/Village: Southampton   **Main Road:** M27   **Mainline Station:** Netley   **Hotel:** Victoria Hotel   **Restaurant:** Prince Consort

Contact(s):

● **For Bookings:** Ms Sonia Bowers
● **For Bookings:** Ms Helen Allenby
● **For Donations:** Mr Peter Bowers
● **General Manager:** Ms Helen Allenby
● **Owner:** Mr Peter Bowers
● **Technical Info:** Mr Peter Bowers

Associated Businesses:

● Bowers of Sunningdale, Station Lodge, Priory Rd, Sunningdale, Hampshire, SL5 0EN, England

Journeys Available At This Railway:

Chapel Road to Chapel Road (round trip)
Track Type: Single   Direction: South to East
Features: Views of Sea, Woods. Maximum gradient of 1 in 60 (For 100 metres).
Level Crossings: 2   **Journey Duration:** 10 mins   **Journey Length:** 1 mile(s)
Price: £1.50 (Adult Standard) £1.50 (Child Standard) £2.50 (Adult Special) £2.50 (Child Special)

Stations On This Journey:

Key: *St* = Stops   *Al* = Alight   *Bd* = Board   *Tl* = Toilets   *DT* = Disabled Toilets   *PA* = Kids Play Area   *CP* = Free Car Park   *Ph* = Pay Phone   *Mu* = Museum
        WR = Waiting Room   *Sh* = Sheds   *VS* = Can Visit Sheds   *WS* = Workshops   *VW* = Can Visit Workshops   *SB* = Signal Box   *VSB* = Can Visit Signal Box

A-Z STEAM RAILWAYS

Royal Victoria Railway — Rudyard Lake Railway

Station Name	St	Al	Bd	Tl	DT	PA	CP	Ph	Mu	WR	Sh	VS	WS	VW	SB	VSB
Chapel Road	✔	✔		✔												
Piccadilly	✔	✔		✔							✔		✔			

RPSI

RAILWAY PRESERVATION SOCIETY OF IRELAND (THE) The Tarry, RPSI Whitehead Depot, Whitehead, **COUNTY ANTRIM, NORTHERN IRELAND**.

(E) rpsitrains@hotmail.com
(W) www.rpsi-online.org
Affiliated Bodies: Heritage Railway Association, Transport Trust
Year Opened: 1964
Type of Complex: Restoration Site
Type of Organisation: Charity
Stock Overview:
No. Steam Locos: 9
TV/Film Appearances: Michael Collins, First Great Train Robbery
Background: Operate Steam train excursions on mainline track.
Facilities: Buffet, Santa Special, Children's events, Facilities for hire, Trains for hire.
Opening/Closing Times:
Spring: Opens Mon - Fri 09:30, **Closes** Mon - Fri 13:30
Summer: Opens Mon - Fri 09:30, **Closes** Mon - Fri 13:30
Autumn: Opens Mon - Fri 09:30, **Closes** Mon - Fri 13:30
Winter: Opens Mon - Fri 09:30, **Closes** Mon - Fri 13:30
Contact(s):
● **Operations Manager:** Mr Phil Lockett
Alternative Contact Details:
● PO Box 171, Larne, County Antrim, BT40 1UU, Northern Ireland **(T)** 028 28260803

RUDYARD LAKE RAILWAY

RUDYARD LAKE STEAM RAILWAY LTD Rudyard Station, Rudyard, Leek, **STAFFORDSHIRE,** ST13 8PF, **ENGLAND**.

(T) 01995 672280   **(F)** 01995 672280
Year Opened: 1983
Type of Complex: Railway Station, Operational Railway Line
Type of Organisation: Limited Company, Volunteer
Gauge: Narrow   **No. Staff:** 2   **No. Volunteers:** 15
Stock Overview:
No. Steam Locos: 2
No. Diesel Locos: 2
Facilities: Driver footplate experience, Santa Special, Enthusiast galas, Courses on how to drive Locos, Children's events.
Opening/Closing Times:
Spring: Opens Sun 11:00, **Closes** Sun 16:30
Summer: Opens Sat, Sun 11:00, **Closes** Sat, Sun 16:30
Autumn: Opens Sun 11:00, **Closes** Sun 16:30
Location:
Instructions: Situated on B5223, about half a mile from A523.
Nearest Town/Village: Leek   **Main Road:** A523   **Mainline Station:** Macclesfield   **Hotel:** Hotel Rudyard
Contact(s):
● **General Manager:** Ms Eileen Turpin
● **Owner:** Mr Mike Hanson
Alternative Contact Details:
● Flonora, Blackpool Old Rd, Little Eccleston, Garstang, Lancashire, PR3 0YQ, England **(T)** 01995

672280
Journeys Available At This Railway:

Rudyard Station to Hunthouse Wood
Track Type: Single   Direction: South to North
Features: Views of Hills, Water, Woods. Maximum gradient of 1 in 100.
Bridges: 1 'over'   **Level Crossings:** 1   **Journey Duration:** 15 mins   **Journey Length:** 1.5 mile(s)
Price: £2.50 (Adult Standard) £1.00 (Child Standard)
Available on Journey: Refreshments.
Stations On This Journey:

Station Name	St	Al	Bd	Tl	DT	PA	CP	Ph	Mu	WR	Sh	VS	WS	VW	SB	VSB
Rudyard	✔	✔					✔				✔		✔			
The Dam	✔	✔		✔	✔											
Lakeside	✔	✔														
Hunthouse Wood	✔	✔														

RUISLIP LIDO RAILWAY

RUISLIP LIDO RAILWAY SOCIETY LTD Reservoir Rd, Ruislip, **LONDON (GREATER),** HA4 7TY, **ENGLAND**.
(T) 01895 622595
Affiliated Bodies: Heritage Railway Association
Year Opened: 1945
Type of Complex: Railway Station, Operational Railway Line
Gauge: Narrow
Stock Overview:
No. Steam Locos: 1
No. Diesel Locos: 3
Facilities: Café, Ticket office, Disabled access, Santa Special, Enthusiast galas, Souvenir shop, Books for sale, Children's events.
Opening/Closing Times:
Spring: **Opens** Sat 13:00, Sun 11:40, **Closes** Sat 16:20, Sun 17:00
Summer: **Opens** Mon - Sat 13:00, Sun 11:40, **Closes** Mon - Sat 16:20, Sun 17:00
Autumn: **Opens** Sat 13:00, Sun 11:40, **Closes** Sat 16:20, Sun 17:00
Winter: **Opens** Sat 13:00, Sun 11:40, **Closes** Sat 16:20, Sun 17:00
Other: Also open Tuesdays, Wednesdays and Thursdays April - May and September - October.
Location:
Instructions: Located in North West London, just north of Ruislip.
Nearest Town/Village: Ruislip   **Main Road:** A4180   **Bus:** H13
Contact(s):
● **Secretary:** Mr Stan Simmons **(T)** 020 88669654
Journeys Available At This Railway:

Ruislip Lido to Woody Bay
Track Type: Single
Features: Views of Open Fields, Woods.
Level Crossings: 1   **Journey Length:** 1.25 mile(s)
Price: £1.10 (Adult Standard) £0.90 (Child Standard)
Stations On This Journey:

Station Name	St	Al	Bd	Tl	DT	PA	CP	Ph	Mu	WR	Sh	VS	WS	VW	SB	VSB
Ruislip Lido	✔	✔	✔			✔			✔							
Woody Bay	✔	✔		✔	✔	✔				✔	✔		✔			

RUSHDEN HISTORICAL TNSPRT SOC

RUSHDEN HISTORICAL TRANSPORT SOCIETY The Old Railway Station, Station Approach, Rushden, **NORTHAMPTONSHIRE,** NN10 0AW, **ENGLAND**.

Key: *St* = Stops   *Al* = Alight   *Bd* = Board   *Tl* = Toilets   *DT* = Disabled Toilets   *PA* = Kids Play Area   *CP* = Free Car Park   *Ph* = Pay Phone   *Mu* = Museum
     WR = Waiting Room   *Sh* = Sheds   *VS* = Can Visit Sheds   *WS* = Workshops   *VW* = Can Visit Workshops   *SB* = Signal Box   *VSB* = Can Visit Signal Box

A-Z STEAM RAILWAYS

Rushden Historical Tnsprt Soc — Scottish Railway Centre

(T) 01933 318988
(E) info@rhts.co.uk
(W) www.rhts.co.uk
Type of Complex: Operational Railway Line, Museum
Location:
Main Road: A6   **Mainline Station:** Wellingborough
Contact(s):
- **Chairman:** Mr Richard Woodcock   **(T)** 01933 350287   **(E)** richard@rhts.co.uk
- **Secretary:** Mr John Sugars   **(T)** 01933 350415   **(E)** john@rhts.co.uk

RUTLAND RAILWAY MUSEUM

RUTLAND RAILWAY MUSEUM Ashwell Rd, Cottesmore, Oakham, **RUTLAND,** LE15 7BX, **ENGLAND**.
(T) 01572 813203
Affiliated Bodies: Heritage Railway Association
Type of Complex: Operational Railway Line, Museum
Type of Organisation: Volunteer
Facilities: Santa Special, Souvenir shop, Books for sale, Videos for sale, Children's events, Picnic area and line side walk available.
Opening/Closing Times:
Spring: Opens Sat, Sun 11:00, **Closes** Sat, Sun 17:00
Summer: Opens Sat, Sun 11:00, **Closes** Sat, Sun 17:00
Autumn: Opens Sat, Sun 11:00, **Closes** Sat, Sun 17:00
Winter: Opens Sat, Sun 11:00, **Closes** Sat, Sun 17:00
Other: Open most weekends. Contact to confirm opening times.
Location:
Instructions: Museum is located between Ashwell & Cottesmore.
Nearest Town/Village: Oakham   **Main Road:** B668   **Mainline Station:** Oakham
Contact(s):
- **Secretary:** Mr Stuart Geeson

SCIENCE MUSEUM

SCIENCE MUSEUM Exhibition Rd, Kensington, **LONDON (GREATER),** SW7 2DD, **ENGLAND**.
(T) 020 79424000
(W) www.sciencemuseum.org.uk
Type of Complex: Museum
Background: The museum has oppurtunities that allow the visitor to see and touch exhibits tha show the major scientific advances of the last 300 years. The Museum is the largest of its kind in the world.
Facilities: Café, Books for sale, Picnic area.
Opening/Closing Times:
Spring: Opens Mon - Sun 10:00, **Closes** Mon - Sun 18:00
Summer: Opens Mon - Sun 10:00, **Closes** Mon - Sun 18:00
Autumn: Opens Mon - Sun 10:00, **Closes** Mon - Sun 18:00
Winter: Opens Mon - Sun 10:00, **Closes** Mon - Sun 18:00
Other: Closed from 24th December - 26th December.
Location:
Mainline Station: South Kensington Underground

SCOTTISH RAILWAY CENTRE

AYRSHIRE RAILWAY PRESERVATION GROUP Minnivey Colliery, Dalmellington, Ayr, **AYRSHIRE,** KA6 7PU, **SCOTLAND**.
(T) 01292 531144
(W) www.arpg.org.uk
Affiliated Bodies: Heritage Railway Association, Transport Trust
Type of Complex: Operational Railway Line
Gauge: Narrow & Standard
Stock Overview:

No. Steam Locos: 1
No. Diesel Locos: 4
Facilities: Café, Disabled access, Souvenir shop, Books for sale, Videos for sale, Paintings/drawings for sale, Models for sale, Main credit cards taken.

Opening/Closing Times:
Summer: **Opens** Sat 11:00, **Closes** Sat 16:00
Other: Open Saturdays for static displays. Contact for details of steaming days.

Location:
Instructions: From Ayr take the A713 to Dalmellington. Turn left at Burnton turn off just before Dalmellington. Turn left at the next T junction. Situated half a mile from A713.
Main Road: A713   **Bus:** 51   **Mainline Station:** Ayr

Contact(s):
● **Secretary:** Mr Gordon Thomson

Journeys Available At This Railway:

Minnivey to Minnivey (round trip)
Price: £2.50 (Adult Standard) £1.50 (Child Standard)

Stations On This Journey:

Station Name	St	Al	Bd	Tl	DT	PA	CP	Ph	Mu	WR	Sh	VS	WS	VW	SB	VSB
Minnivey	✓	✓	✓			✓			✓		✓	✓				

SEVERN VALLEY RAILWAY

SEVERN VALLEY RAILWAY (HOLDINGS) PLC The Railway Station, Bewdley, **WORCESTERSHIRE,** DY12 1BG, **ENGLAND**.
(T) 01299 403816   **(F)** 01299 400839
(W) www.svr.co.uk
Affiliated Bodies: Heritage Railway Association, Transport Trust
Year Opened: 1970
Type of Complex: Railway Station, Operational Railway Line, Museum, Restoration Site
Type of Organisation: Limited Company
Gauge: Standard   **No. Staff:** 72   **No. Volunteers:** 1200
Stock Overview:
No. Steam Locos: 24 (15 Pre-Group, 1 Pre-Nationalisation)
No. Diesel Locos: 17
Facilities: Café, Restaurant, Buffet, Ticket office, Disabled access, Lecture room, Function room, Waiting room, Line permit needed, Photo line side permit available, Through ticketing available, Advanced booking available, Guided tours available, Driver footplate experience, Santa Special, 'Thomas' event, Enthusiast galas, Slide shows, Movie shows, Souvenir shop, Books for sale, Videos for sale, Photos for sale, Paintings/drawings for sale, Camera film for sale, CD's for sale, Tapes for sale, Models for sale, Main credit cards taken, Children's events, Facilities for hire, Trains for hire, Dining car service, Murder Mystery, gift vouchers.

Opening/Closing Times:
Spring: **Opens** Sat - Sun 10:45, **Closes** Sat - Sun 17:00
Summer: **Opens** Mon - Sun 10:30, **Closes** Mon - Sun 18:00
Autumn: **Opens** Sat - Sun 10:45, **Closes** Sat - Sun 17:00
Winter: **Opens** Sat - Sun 10:45, **Closes** Sat - Sun 17:00
Other: Also open during school holidays and extra days in December for Santa specials.

Location:
Nearest Town/Village: Kidderminster   **Main Road:** A456   **Bus:** 192   **Mainline**
Station: Kidderminster   **Hotel:** Collingdale Hotel

Contact(s):
● **General Manager:** Mr Alun Rees
● **Marketing Manager:** Mr John Leech

Journeys Available At This Railway:

Kidderminster to Bridgnorth
Track Type: Single   Direction: South to North

Key:	St = Stops	Al = Alight	Bd = Board	Tl = Toilets	DT = Disabled Toilets	PA = Kids Play Area	CP = Free Car Park	Ph = Pay Phone	Mu = Museum
	WR = Waiting Room	Sh = Sheds	VS = Can Visit Sheds	WS = Workshops	VW = Can Visit Workshops	SB = Signal Box	VSB = Can Visit Signal Box		

Features: Views of Hills, Open Fields, Urbanisation, Water, Woods. Views of the River Severn. Maximum gradient of 1 in 100.

Bridges: 9 'over', 5 'under'　**Tunnels:** 2　**Level Crossings:** 1　**Signal Boxes:** 7　**Rivers:** 2　**Viaducts:** 5　**Journey Duration:** 70 mins　**Journey Length:** 16 mile(s)

Price: £10.00 (Adult Standard)　£5.00 (Child Standard)

Available on Journey: Refreshments, Drinks, Alcohol, Buffet, Restaurant.

Stations On This Journey:

Station Name	St	Al	Bd	Tl	DT	PA	CP	Ph	Mu	WR	Sh	VS	WS	VW	SB	VSB
Kidderminster	✓	✓	✓	✓	✓		✓	✓	✓	✓	✓		✓		✓	
Bewdley	✓	✓	✓	✓			✓			✓			✓		✓	
Arley	✓	✓	✓	✓			✓			✓					✓	
Highley	✓	✓	✓	✓			✓			✓					✓	
Hampton Loade	✓	✓	✓	✓			✓			✓					✓	
Bridgnorth	✓	✓	✓	✓	✓		✓	✓			✓	✓	✓	✓	✓	

SITTINGBOURNE & KEMSLEY

SITTINGBOURNE & KEMSLEY LIGHT RAILWAY PO Box 300, Sittingbourne, **KENT,** ME10 2DZ, **ENGLAND**.

(T) 01795 424899

(E) sklr@talk21.com

(W) www.sklr.net

Affiliated Bodies: Heritage Railway Association, Transport Trust

Type of Complex: Operational Railway Line

Type of Organisation: Charity, Non-Profit

Gauge: Narrow

Stock Overview:

No. Steam Locos: 8

No. Diesel Locos: 2

Facilities: Café, Driver footplate experience, Santa Special, Enthusiast galas, Courses on how to drive Locos, Souvenir shop, Parties available.

Opening/Closing Times:

Spring:　Opens Sun 12:00, **Closes** Sun 16:00

Summer:　Opens Sun 12:00, **Closes** Sun 16:00

Other:　Also open Easter, Bank Holidays 11:00 - 16:00, and selected Wednesdays and Saturdays in Summer. Open in December for Santa specials.

Location:

Nearest Town/Village: Sittingbourne　**Main Road:** A2　**Mainline Station:** Sittingbourne Main Line

Journeys Available At This Railway:

Sittingbourne Viaduct to Kemsley Down

Price: £3.50 (Adult Standard)　£2.00 (Child Standard)

Stations On This Journey:

Station Name	St	Al	Bd	Tl	DT	PA	CP	Ph	Mu	WR	Sh	VS	WS	VW	SB	VSB
Sittingbourne Viaduct	✓	✓	✓				✓									
Milton Regis	✓															
Burley Crossing																
Kemsley Down	✓	✓	✓												✓	

SNAEFELL MOUNTAIN RAILWAY

SNAEFELL MOUNTAIN RAILWAY Banks Circus, Douglas, **ISLE OF MAN,** IM1 5PT, **ENGLAND**.

(T) 01624 663366　　**(F)** 01624 663637

Year Opened: 1895

Type of Complex: Operational Railway Line

Background: Still operating with its six original tramcars, the Snaefell Mountain Railway climbs 2036 ft from Laxey to the summit of Snaefell Mountain, the highest point on the Isle of Man.

Opening/Closing Times:

Other: Open daily from Mid April to October.

Journeys Available At This Railway:

Laxey to Summit

Features: Views of Hills, Open Fields, Water. View the islands largest glacial valley and Sulby reservoir. Maximum gradient of 1 in 12.

Journey Length: 4 mile(s)

Stations On This Journey:

Station Name	St	Al	Bd	Tl	DT	PA	CP	Ph	Mu	WR	Sh	VS	WS	VW	SB	VSB
Laxey Station	✔	✔														
Bungalow	✔	✔														
Summit	✔	✔														

SNIBSTON DISCOVERY PARK

SNIBSTON DISCOVERY PARK Ashby Rd, Coalville, **LEICESTERSHIRE,** LE67 3LN, **ENGLAND**.

(T) 01530 278444   **(F)** 01530 813301

(E) snibston@leics.gov.uk

Affiliated Bodies: Transport Trust

Background: The museum houses a collection exhibits telling the story of transport, mining and quarrying, engineering and the fashion industry.

Facilities: Café, Disabled access, Guided tours available, Souvenir shop, Books for sale.

Entry Fees: Adults: £4.75   **Children:** £2.95

Opening/Closing Times:

Spring: **Opens** Mon - Sun 10:00, **Closes** Mon - Sun 17:00
Summer: **Opens** Mon - Sun 10:00, **Closes** Mon - Sun 17:00
Autumn: **Opens** Mon - Sun 10:00, **Closes** Mon - Sun 17:00
Winter: **Opens** Mon - Sun 10:00, **Closes** Mon - Sun 17:00

Location:

Nearest Town/Village: Coalville   **Main Road:** A511

Contact(s):

● **Curator:** Mr S Mastonif

SNOWDON MOUNTAIN RAILWAY

SNOWDON MOUNTAIN RAILWAY Llanberis, Caernarfon, **GWYNEDD,** LL55 4TY, **WALES**.

(T) 0870 4580033   **(F)** 01286 872518

(E) info@snowdonrailway.co.uk

(W) www.snowdonrailway.co.uk

Affiliated Bodies: Heritage Railway Association

Type of Complex: Operational Railway Line

Type of Organisation: Limited Company

Gauge: Narrow

Stock Overview:

No. Steam Locos: 7

No. Diesel Locos: 4

Background: Climbs 1085 metres to the peak of Snowdon. Is the only Rack & Pinion railway in Britain.

Facilities: Café, Disabled access, Souvenir shop, Main credit cards taken.

Opening/Closing Times:

Summer: **Opens** Mon - Sun 09:00, **Closes** Mon - Sun 17:00
Other: Open March - November.

Key:	St = Stops Al = Alight Bd = Board Tl = Toilets DT = Disabled Toilets PA = Kids Play Area CP = Free Car Park Ph = Pay Phone Mu = Museum
	WR = Waiting Room Sh = Sheds VS = Can Visit Sheds WS = Workshops VW = Can Visit Workshops SB = Signal Box VSB = Can Visit Signal Box

Location:
Nearest Town/Village: Carnarvon   **Main Road:** A4086
Contact(s):
● **Commercial Manager:** Mr Dince Hughes
Journeys Available At This Railway:

Llanberis to Summit
Features: Views of Hills, Open Fields, Water. Maximum gradient of 1 in 6.
Signal Boxes: 5   **Viaducts:** 1   **Journey Length:** 4.5 mile(s)
Price: £11.90 (Adult Standard) £8.90 (Child Standard)
Stations On This Journey:

Station Name	St	Al	Bd	Tl	DT	PA	CP	Ph	Mu	WR	Sh	VS	WS	VW	SB	VSB
Llanberis	✓	✓		✓	✓						✓			✓		
Clogwyn	✓	✓														
Summit	✓	✓		✓	✓											

SOMERSET & DORSET RAILWAY

SOMERSET & DORSET RAILWAY TRUST Washford Station, Watchet, **SOMERSET,** TA23 0PP, **ENGLAND.**
(T) 01984 640869
(E) enquiries@sdrt.org
(W) www.sdrt.org.uk
Affiliated Bodies: Heritage Railway Association
Year Opened: 1975
Type of Complex: Museum, Restoration Site
Gauge: Standard
Stock Overview:
No. Steam Locos: 2
Background: The trust is dedicated to keeping alive the memory of the Somerset and Devon railway and regularly hosts meetings and events. There is a signal box that can be visited at the restored Washford Station.
Facilities: Disabled access, 'Thomas' event, Souvenir shop, Books for sale, Videos for sale.
Opening/Closing Times:
Summer: **Opens** 10:00, **Closes** 16:30
Other: Open for Gala Days and Bank Holidays. Contact for details. Closed November to March.
Location:
Nearest Town/Village: Minehead   **Main Road:** A39   **Mainline Station:** Taunton
Contact(s):
● **Chairman:** Mr Peter Cattermole   **(T)** 01458 210330
● **Station Master:** Mr Ray Pidman   **(T)** 01278 683574
Journeys Available At This Railway:
Price: £1.00 (Adult Standard) £0.50 (Child Standard)
Stations On This Journey:

Station Name	St	Al	Bd	Tl	DT	PA	CP	Ph	Mu	WR	Sh	VS	WS	VW	SB	VSB

SOUTH DEVON RAILWAY

SOUTH DEVON RAILWAY The Station, Buckfastleigh, **DEVON,** TQ11 0DZ, **ENGLAND.**
(T) 01364 642338   **(F)** 01364 642170
(W) www.southdevonrailway.org
Affiliated Bodies: Heritage Railway Association, Transport Trust
Type of Complex: Operational Railway Line
Gauge: Standard
Stock Overview:
No. Steam Locos: 16

A-Z STEAM RAILWAYS

Facilities: Santa Special, 'Thomas' event, Courses on how to drive Locos, Souvenir shop, Books for sale, Models for sale.

Location:

Instructions: Located between Exeter and Plymouth on A38.

Main Road: A38   **Bus:** X80, 165   **Hotel:** The Old Forge

Contact(s):

- **General Manager:** Mr Richard Elliot   **(E)** richardelliot@southdevonrailway.org
- **Workshop Manager:** Mr Rob LeChavalier

Journeys Available At This Railway:

Buckfastleigh to Totnes
Price: £6.80 (Adult Standard) £4.00 (Child Standard)

Stations On This Journey:

Station Name	St	Al	Bd	Tl	DT	PA	CP	Ph	Mu	WR	Sh	VS	WS	VW	SB	VSB
Buckfastleigh	✔	✔	✔			✔										
Staverton	✔	✔	✔			✔								✔		
Totnes	✔	✔	✔													

SOUTH DOWNS LIGHT RAILWAY

SOUTH DOWNS LIGHT RAILWAY SOCIETY Wyevale Garden Centre, Stopham Rd, Pulborough, **SUSSEX (WEST),** RH20 1DS, **ENGLAND**.**(F)** 01273 304819

(W) www.sdlrs.com

Affiliated Bodies: Britains Great Little Railways, Southern Federation of Model Engineering

Complex Size: 10 Acres   **Year Opened:** 2000

Type of Complex: Operational Railway Line

Type of Organisation: Volunteer, Non-Profit

No. Volunteers: 25

Stock Overview:

No. Steam Locos: 10 (6 Pre-Group)

No. Diesel Locos: 3

Background: Comprises the largest collection of 10.25'' gauge locomotives in the UK.

Facilities: Restaurant, Disabled access, Santa Special, 'Thomas' event, Enthusiast galas, Books for sale.

Opening/Closing Times:

Spring: **Opens** Sat, Sun 11:00, **Closes** Sat, Sun 16:00

Summer: **Opens** Sat, Sun 11:00, **Closes** Sat, Sun 16:00

Other: Operates from April - September (weekends only), and December (weekends only).

Location:

Instructions: Railway is located within the Wyevale Garden Centre, 0.5 mile West of Pulborough Town Centre on A283 to Petworth.

Main Road: A283   **Mainline Station:** Pulborough

Contact(s):

- **Hon Secretary:** Mr Chris English **(T)** 07711 717470   **(E)** chris@cjenglish.demon.co.uk

Alternative Contact Details:

- 16 Wanderdown Way, Ovingdean, Brighton, Sussex (East), BN2 7BX, England**(M)** chris

Journeys Available At This Railway:

Stopham Road Station to Stopham Road Station (round trip)
Track Type: Single   Direction: West to North
Features: Views of Open Fields, Woods. Constantly changing views throughout journey. Maximum gradient of 1 in 60 (For 100 metres).
Bridges: 1 'over'   **Level Crossings:** 2   **Signal Boxes:** 1   **Journey Length:** 0.5 mile(s)
Price: £0.80 (Adult Standard) £0.50 (Child Standard) £1.20 (Adult Special) £0.80 (Child Special)

Stations On This Journey:

South Devon Railway — South Downs Light Railway

Key:	St = Stops	Al = Alight	Bd = Board	Tl = Toilets	DT = Disabled Toilets	PA = Kids Play Area	CP = Free Car Park	Ph = Pay Phone	Mu = Museum
	WR = Waiting Room	Sh = Sheds	VS = Can Visit Sheds	WS = Workshops	VW = Can Visit Workshops	SB = Signal Box	VSB = Can Visit Signal Box		

Station Name	St	Al	Bd	Tl	DT	PA	CP	Ph	Mu	WR	Sh	VS	WS	VW	SB	VSB
Stopham Road	✔	✔	✔	✔	✔		✔				✔	✔	✔		✔	✔

SOUTH TYNEDALE RAILWAY

SOUTH TYNEDALE RAILWAY PRESERVATION SOCIETY (THE) The Railway Station, Alston, **CUMBRIA,** CA9 3JB, **ENGLAND**.

(T) 01434 381696
(E) mail@strps.org.uk
(W) www.strps.org.uk
Affiliated Bodies: Heritage Railway Association
Year Opened: 1983
Type of Complex: Railway Station, Operational Railway Line, Restoration Site
Type of Organisation: Charity, Trust, Limited Company, Volunteer, Non-Profit
Gauge: Narrow   **No. Volunteers:** 50
Stock Overview:
No. Steam Locos: 6
No. Diesel Locos: 8
Background: England's highest Narrow Gauge Railway.
Facilities: Café, Ticket office, Disabled access, Platform tickets, Driver footplate experience, Santa Special, 'Thomas' event, Enthusiast galas, Souvenir shop, Books for sale, Videos for sale, Photos for sale, Paintings/drawings for sale, Camera film for sale, Children's events, Trains for hire.
Opening/Closing Times:
Other: Open from April - October.
Location:
Nearest Town/Village: Alston   **Main Road:** A686   **Taxi:** Henderson's Garage   **Mainline Station:** Haltwhistle   **Hotel:** Lowbyer Manor
Contact(s):
● **For Bookings:** Mr Ivan Ward
● **For Donations:** Mr Mike Ryan   **(T)** 01768 865418
● **Technical Info:** Mr Alan Blackburn   **(T)** 01388 517272
Journeys Available At This Railway:

Alston to Kirkhaugh
Track Type: Single   Direction: South to North
Features: Views of Hills, Open Fields, Water, Woods. Maximum gradient of 1 in 60 (For 100 metres).
Bridges: 2 'under'   **Level Crossings:** 1   **Signal Boxes:** 1   **Rivers:** 1   **Viaducts:** 3   **Journey Duration:** 15 mins
Journey Length: 2.25 mile(s)
Price: £4.00 (Adult Standard) £2.00 (Child Standard) £5.00 (Adult Special) £4.50 (Child Special)
Stations On This Journey:

Station Name	St	Al	Bd	Tl	DT	PA	CP	Ph	Mu	WR	Sh	VS	WS	VW	SB	VSB
Alston	✔	✔	✔	✔	✔	✔	✔			✔		✔			✔	✔
Kirkhaugh	✔	✔														

SOUTH YORKSHIRE RAILWAY

SOUTH YORKSHIRE RAILWAY Barrow Rd Railway, Meadowhall, Sheffield, **YORKSHIRE (SOUTH),** S9 1HN, **ENGLAND**.

(T) 0114 2424405
Affiliated Bodies: Heritage Railway Association
Type of Complex: Restoration Site
Stock Overview:
No. Diesel Locos: 12
Contact(s):
● **General Manager:** Mr John Wade
● **Membership Secretary:** Mr G Barnes

SPA VALLEY RAILWAY

WEALDEN RAILWAY CO LTD West Station, Nevill Trce, Tunbridge Wells, **KENT,** TN2 5QY, **ENGLAND**.
(T) 01892 537715
(E) spavalleyrailway@email.com
(W) www.spavalleyrailway.co.uk
Affiliated Bodies: Heritage Railway Association
Year Opened: 1996
Type of Complex: Operational Railway Line, Museum, Restoration Site
Type of Organisation: Charity, Volunteer
Gauge: Standard
Stock Overview:
No. Steam Locos: 5 (1 Pre-Group)
No. Diesel Locos: 3
TV/Film Appearances: Southern Steam, Country Ways
Background: Closed by British Rail in 1985, this railway reopened in stages since 1996. The headquarters are in a restored Victorian engine shed.
Facilities: Buffet, Ticket office, Disabled access, Waiting room, Platform tickets, Guided tours available, Santa Special, 'Thomas' event, Enthusiast galas, Souvenir shop, Books for sale, Videos for sale, Main credit cards taken, Trains for hire.
Opening/Closing Times:
Spring: **Opens** Sat - Sun 10:30, **Closes** Sat - Sun 17:15
Summer: **Opens** Mon - Sun 11:00, **Closes** Mon - Sun 16:30
Autumn: **Opens** Sat - Sun 10:30, **Closes** Sat - Sun 17:15
Other: Also open during school holidays and in December for Santa specials.
Location:
Instructions: From London - leave M25 at J5 and follow A21 to Southborough leaving onto A26. Follow through Tunbridge Wells until a signpost for 'Union House Public Car Park' on left. Situated next to Sainsburys Superstore.
Nearest Town/Village: Tunbridge Wells   **Main Road:** A26   **Mainline Station:** Tunbridge Wells
Hotel: Swan Hotel
Contact(s):
- **Chairman:** Mr Jon Nye
- **Engineering Director:** Mr Bob Ashbee
- **Finance Director:** Mr Stephen Woolven
- **For Bookings:** Ms Val Ashbee
Journeys Available At This Railway:

Tunbridge Wells West to Groombridge
Track Type: Single   Direction: East to West
Features: Views of Hills, Open Fields, Urbanisation, Woods. Maximum gradient of 1 in 88.
Bridges: 6 'over', 4 'under'   **Level Crossings:** 1   **Signal Boxes:** 1   **Journey Duration:** 15 mins   **Journey Length:** 3 mile(s)
Price: £3.50 (Adult Standard) £2.50 (Child Standard)
Available on Journey: Refreshments, Drinks, Alcohol, Buffet.
Stations On This Journey:

Station Name	St	Al	Bd	Tl	DT	PA	CP	Ph	Mu	WR	Sh	VS	WS	VW	SB	VSB
Tunbridge Wells West	✔	✔	✔	✔	✔				✔	✔	✔	✔	✔		✔	
High Rocks		✔	✔	✔	✔	✔		✔								
Groombridge	✔	✔	✔	✔	✔	✔		✔		✔						

ST ANDREWS

ST ANDREWS PRESERVATION TRUST MUSEUM 12 North St, St. Andrews, **FIFE,** KY16 9PW, **SCOTLAND**.
(T) 01334 477152

Key: St = Stops Al = Alight Bd = Board Tl = Toilets DT = Disabled Toilets PA = Kids Play Area CP = Free Car Park Ph = Pay Phone Mu = Museum WR = Waiting Room Sh = Sheds VS = Can Visit Sheds WS = Workshops VW = Can Visit Workshops SB = Signal Box VSB = Can Visit Signal Box

(W) www.standrewspreservationtrust.co.uk

Type of Complex: Museum

Background: The museum houses a large number of artefacts and displays illustrating aspects of life in St Andrews in days gone by. In addition to permanent displays, major exhibitions are put on regularly.

Facilities: Guided tours available, History lectures.

Opening/Closing Times:

Other: Contact for opening days.

ST ANNES MINI RAILWAY

ST ANNES MINI RAILWAY South Promenade, Lytham St. Annes, **LANCASHIRE, ENGLAND**.

(T) 01772 864875   **(F)** 01772 864875

Year Opened: 1972

Type of Complex: Operational Railway Line

Gauge: Narrow

Facilities: Disabled access.

Opening/Closing Times:

Spring: Opens Mon - Sun 11:00, **Closes** Mon - Sun 17:00
Summer: Opens Mon - Sun 11:00, **Closes** Mon - Sun 17:00
Autumn: Opens Mon - Sun 11:00, **Closes** Mon - Sun 17:00

Location:

Nearest Town/Village: St Annes   **Main Road:** Promenade, St Annes   **Mainline Station:** St Annes

Contact(s):

● **Owner:** Mr G Leeming

Alternative Contact Details:

● 8 Carnoustie Cl, Fulwood, Preston, Lancashire, PR2 7ER, England

Journeys Available At This Railway:

Price: £1.00 (Adult Standard) £1.00 (Child Standard)

STEAM

STEAM - MUSEUM OF THE GREAT WESTERN RAILWAY Kemble Drive, Swindon, **WILTSHIRE,** SN2 2TA, **ENGLAND**.

(T) 01793 466646   **(F)** 01793 466615

(E) steampostbox@swindon.gov.uk

(W) www.steam-museum.org.uk

Affiliated Bodies: Heritage Railway Association, Swindon Borough Council

Year Opened: 2000

Type of Complex: Museum

Type of Organisation: Non-Profit

Stock Overview:

No. Steam Locos: 7 (7 Pre-Group, 1 Pre-Nationalisation)

No. Diesel Locos: 1 (1 Pre-Group)

Facilities: Café, Disabled access, Lecture room, Function room, 'Thomas' event, Souvenir shop, Books for sale, Videos for sale, Paintings/drawings for sale, Models for sale, Main credit cards taken, Children's events, Facilities for hire.

Entry Fees: Adults: £5.70   **Children:** £3.60

Opening/Closing Times:

Spring: Opens Mon - Sat 10:00, Sun 11:00, **Closes** Mon - Sat 17:00, Sun 17:00
Summer: Opens Mon - Sat 10:00, Sun 11:00, **Closes** Mon - Sat 17:00, Sun 17:00
Autumn: Opens Mon - Sat 10:00, Sun 11:00, **Closes** Mon - Sat 17:00, Sun 17:00
Winter: Opens Mon - Sat 10:00, Sun 11:00, **Closes** Mon - Sat 17:00, Sun 17:00
Other: Closed Christmas Day and New Years Day.

Location:

Nearest Town/Village: Swindon   **Mainline Station:** Swindon

Contact(s):

● **For Bookings:** Ms Kirsten Norris

● **For Donations:** Mr Tim Bryan

● **General Manager:** Mr Andrew Lovett

STRATHSPEY RAILWAY

STRATHSPEY RAILWAY CO LTD Aviemore Station, Dalfaber Rd, Aviemore, **HIGHLANDS,** PH22 1PY, **SCOTLAND**.

(T) 01479 810725

(E) information@strathspeyrailway.co.uk

(W) www.strathspeyrailway.co.uk

Affiliated Bodies: Heritage Railway Association, Transport Trust

Year Opened: 1978

Type of Complex: Operational Railway Line

Type of Organisation: Heritage Project, Limited Company, Volunteer, Non-Profit

Gauge: Standard   **No. Staff:** 5   **No. Volunteers:** 6

Stock Overview:

No. Steam Locos: 5 (3 Pre-Group, 1 Pre-Nationalisation)

No. Diesel Locos: 3

TV/Film Appearances: Monarch of the Glen (1999 & 2000)

Background: Part of the original Highland Railway (Perth - Inverness). Closed in 1965, it was acquired in 1972.

Facilities: Ticket office, Disabled access, Waiting room, Platform tickets, Line permit needed, Photo line side permit available, Advanced booking available, Driver footplate experience, Santa Special, 'Thomas' event, Training courses, Souvenir shop, Books for sale, Videos for sale, Camera film for sale, Main credit cards taken, Children's events, Facilities for hire, Trains for hire.

Opening/Closing Times:

Summer: **Opens** Mon - Sun 10:00, **Closes** Mon - Sun 16:30

Other: Open selected days in Spring, Autumn and Winter. Contact for further details.

Location:

Nearest Town/Village: City of Inverness   **Main Road:** A9   **Mainline Station:** Aviemore

Contact(s):

● **Director:** Mr Ron Black   (T) 01389 752214

● **For Bookings:** Mr Laurence Grant

● **For Donations:** Mr Douglas Norris

● **General Manager:** Mr Laurence Grant

● **Technical Info:** Mr Eric Cooper

Journeys Available At This Railway:

Aviemore to Broomhill (For Nethy Bridge)

Track Type: Single   Direction: South to North

Features: Views of Hills, Open Fields, Urbanisation, Water, Woods. Views of Cairngorm Mountain Range. Broomhill Station opens in 2002. Aviemore shed is a working area and is not open to the public.

Bridges: 2 'over', 2 'under'   **Level Crossings:** 1   **Signal Boxes:** 3   **Rivers:** 1   **Journey Duration:** 40 mins   **Journey Length:** 9.5 mile(s)

Price: £8.00 (Adult Standard)   £4.00 (Child Standard)   £8.00 (Adult Special)   £4.00 (Child Special)

Available on Journey: Refreshments, Drinks, Alcohol, Buffet, Restaurant.

Stations On This Journey:

Station Name	St	Al	Bd	Tl	DT	PA	CP	Ph	Mu	WR	Sh	VS	WS	VW	SB	VSB
Aviemore	✔	✔	✔	✔	✔		✔			✔	✔					
Aviemore (Speyside) - Closed											✔	✔	✔			
Boat of Garten	✔	✔	✔	✔			✔		✔	✔				✔		
Broomhill		✔		✔			✔			✔						

SUMMERLEE HERITAGE PK

SUMMERLEE HERITAGE PK Heritage Way, Coatbridge, **LANARKSHIRE (NORTH),** ML5 1QD, **SCOTLAND**.

(T) 01236 431261   **(F)** 01236 440429

| Key: | *St* = Stops   *Al* = Alight   *Bd* = Board   *Tl* = Toilets   *DT* = Disabled Toilets   *PA* = Kids Play Area   *CP* = Free Car Park   *Ph* = Pay Phone   *Mu* = Museum |
| | *WR* = Waiting Room   *Sh* = Sheds   *VS* = Can Visit Sheds   *WS* = Workshops   *VW* = Can Visit Workshops   *SB* = Signal Box   *VSB* = Can Visit Signal Box |

(Side margin text: A-Z STEAM RAILWAYS   STEAM — Summerlee Heritage Pk)

Complex Size: 22 Acres   **Year Opened:** 1980

Type of Complex: Museum

Background: Indoor and outdoor heritage exhibits including Scotland's only working electric tramway, recreated mines and miners cottages.

Facilities: Café, Disabled access, Souvenir shop, Books for sale, Children's events, Facilities for hire, Picnic area, play area.

Opening/Closing Times:

Spring: **Opens** Mon - Sun 10:00, **Closes** Mon - Sun 17:00

Summer: **Opens** Mon - Sun 10:00, **Closes** Mon - Sun 17:00

Autumn: **Opens** Mon - Sun 10:00, **Closes** Mon - Sun 17:00

Winter: **Opens** Mon - Sun 10:00, **Closes** Mon - Sun 16:00

Other: Closed during Christmas and New Year.

Location:

Nearest Town/Village: Coatbridge   **Main Road:** A8   **Mainline Station:** Coatbridge Central

Contact(s):

- **Assistant Manager:** Miss Isabel McDonald
- **Assistant Manager:** Ms Kate Dargie
- **Tours Officer:** Mr Trevor Rees

SWANAGE RAILWAY

SWANAGE RAILWAY Station Hse, Swanage, **DORSET,** BH19 1HB, **ENGLAND**.

(T) 01929 425800   **(F)** 01929 426680

(E) general@swanrail.freeserve.co.uk

(W) www.swanagerailway.co.uk

Affiliated Bodies: Heritage Railway Association

Year Opened: 1975

Type of Complex: Railway Station, Operational Railway Line

Stock Overview:

No. Steam Locos: 5

No. Diesel Locos: 3

Facilities: Restaurant, Ticket office, Disabled access, Driver footplate experience, Santa Special, 'Thomas' event, Enthusiast galas, Souvenir shop, Books for sale, Videos for sale, Main credit cards taken, Children's events.

Opening/Closing Times:

Spring: **Opens** Mon - Sun 10:30, **Closes** Mon - Sun 16:00

Summer: **Opens** Mon - Sun 10:30, **Closes** Mon - Sun 16:00

Autumn: **Opens** Mon - Sun 10:30, **Closes** Mon - Sun 16:00

Winter: **Opens** Sat - Sun 10:30, **Closes** Sat - Sun 16:00

Other: Closed during January.

Location:

Main Road: A351   **Bus:** 142, 143, 144, 150.   **Mainline Station:** Wareham   **Hotel:** Bankes Hotel

Contact(s):

- **Membership Secretary:** Ms Sue Payne
- **Operations Manager:** Mr Paul McDonald
- **Passenger Services Manager:** Mr David Green

Journeys Available At This Railway:

Swanage to Norden

Features: Views of Hills, Open Fields. Views of the ruins of Corfe Castle. Maximum gradient of 1 in 80.

Bridges: 2 'under' **Level Crossings:** 2 **Signal Boxes:** 2 **Viaducts:** 1   **Journey Length:** 6 mile(s)

Price: £6.00 (Adult Standard) £4.00 (Child Standard)

Stations On This Journey:

Station Name	St	Al	Bd	Tl	DT	PA	CP	Ph	Mu	WR	Sh	VS	WS	VW	SB	VSB
Swanage	✓	✓		✓						✓	✓		✓		✓	
Harmans Cross	✓	✓									✓					
Corfe Castle	✓	✓		✓				✓	✓							
Norden	✓	✓			✓	✓	✓	✓			✓					

SWANSEA INDUSTRIAL MUSEUM

SWANSEA MARITIME & INDUSTRIAL MUSEUM Museum Sq, Maritime Quarter, Swansea, **SWANSEA,** SA1 1SN, **WALES**.

(T) 01792 650351

Complex Size: 1977 Acres

Type of Complex: Museum

Background: The Tramshed Annexe is open from April to September and visitors can see the last remains of a Mumbles Railway tram and a restored Swansea town tram.

Facilities: Disabled access, Cafe available during summer.

Opening/Closing Times:

Spring:	**Opens** Tues - Sun 10:00, **Closes** Tues - Sun 17:00
Summer:	**Opens** Tues - Sun 10:00, **Closes** Tues - Sun 17:00
Autumn:	**Opens** Tues - Sun 10:00, **Closes** Tues - Sun 17:00
Winter:	**Opens** Tues - Sun 10:00, **Closes** Tues - Sun 17:00
Other:	Closed 25th - 27th December and 1st January.

SWANSEA VALE RAILWAY

SWANSEA VALE RAILWAY Upper Bank Works, Swansea, **SWANSEA,** SA1 7DB, **WALES**.

(T) 01792 461000

Affiliated Bodies: Heritage Railway Association

Year Opened: 1985

Type of Complex: Operational Railway Line

Gauge: Standard

Stock Overview:

No. Steam Locos: 4

No. Diesel Locos: 6

Background: The only preserved railway whose track passes under a mainline track on the national network.

Facilities: Café, Disabled access, Driver footplate experience, Santa Special, Souvenir shop, Children's events, Facilities for hire, Trains for hire.

Opening/Closing Times:

Spring:	**Opens** Sat, Sun 08:00, **Closes** Sat, Sun 17:00
Summer:	**Opens** Sat, Sun 08:00, **Closes** Sat, Sun 17:00
Autumn:	**Opens** Sat, Sun 08:00, **Closes** Sat, Sun 17:00
Winter:	**Opens** Sat, Sun 08:00, **Closes** Sat, Sun 17:00
Other:	Open every weekend for static displays. Contact for details of steaming days.

Location:

Instructions: Railway is located at Bonymaen, to the north east of Swansea City Centre and is on the edge of the city's enterprise zone.

Nearest Town/Village: Swansea   **Main Road:** M4, J45   **Bus:** 31a, 31b   **Mainline Station:** Swansea

Contact(s):

● **Chairman:** Mr Robert Vayle

Journeys Available At This Railway:

Six Pit to Six Pit (round trip)
Price: £3.00 (Adult Standard) £2.00 (Child Standard)

Stations On This Journey:

Station Name	St	Al	Bd	Tl	DT	PA	CP	Ph	Mu	WR	Sh	VS	WS	VW	SB	VSB
Six Pit	✔	✔	✔			✔										

Key: *St* = Stops   *Al* = Alight   *Bd* = Board   *Tl* = Toilets   *DT* = Disabled Toilets   *PA* = Kids Play Area   *CP* = Free Car Park   *Ph* = Pay Phone   *Mu* = Museum
WR = Waiting Room   *Sh* = Sheds   *VS* = Can Visit Sheds   *WS* = Workshops   *VW* = Can Visit Workshops   *SB* = Signal Box   *VSB* = Can Visit Signal Box

SWINDON & CRICKLADE RAILWAY

SWINDON & CRICKLADE RAILWAY Blunsdon Station, Tadpole Lane, Blunsdon, Swindon, **WILTSHIRE,** SN25 2DA, **ENGLAND**.

(T) 01793 771615

(W) www.swindon-cricklade-railway.org

Affiliated Bodies: Heritage Railway Association, Transport Trust

Year Opened: 1984

Type of Complex: Operational Railway Line, Restoration Site

Type of Organisation: Charity

Gauge: Standard

<u>Stock Overview:</u>

No. Steam Locos: 8

No. Diesel Locos: 3

<u>Facilities:</u> Café, Ticket office, Disabled access, Driver footplate experience, Santa Special, 'Thomas' event, Enthusiast galas, Souvenir shop, Children's events, Facilities for hire, Trains for hire, Picnic area.

<u>Opening/Closing Times:</u>

Spring: **Opens** Sat 10:00, Sun 11:00, **Closes** Sat, Sun 16:00
Summer: **Opens** Sat 10:00, Sun 11:00, **Closes** Sat, Sun 16:00
Autumn: **Opens** Sat 10:00, Sun 11:00, **Closes** Sat, Sun 16:00
Winter: **Opens** Sat 10:00, Sun 11:00, **Closes** Sat, Sun 16:00

<u>Location:</u>

Instructions: Leave the A419 at the top of Blunsdon Hill, just north of Swindon, where there is a junction controlled by traffic lights. Take the westwards crossroad for Blunsdon and Purton and the railway is about 2 miles on. There is a small roundabout, followed by a road junction, shortly after leaving the A419. In both cases, bear right.

Nearest Town/Village: Swindon   **Main Road:** A419   **Mainline Station:** Swindon

<u>Contact(s):</u>

● **Trustee:** Mr Russel Weir

<u>Journeys Available At This Railway:</u>

Blunsdon to Hayes Knoll
Track Type: Single
Features: Views of Open Fields.
Signal Boxes: 2
Price: £2.00 (Adult Standard) £1.00 (Child Standard)

<u>Stations On This Journey:</u>

Station Name	St	Al	Bd	Tl	DT	PA	CP	Ph	Mu	WR	Sh	VS	WS	VW	SB	VSB
Blunsdon	✔	✔		✔	✔		✔			✔					✔	✔
Hayes Knoll	✔	✔									✔	✔	✔		✔	

TALYLLYN RAILWAY

TALYLLYN RAILWAY CO Wharf Station, Tywyn, **GWYNEDD,** LL36 9EY, **WALES**.

(T) 01654 710472   **(F)** 01654 711755

(E) enquiries@talyllyn.co.uk

(W) www.talyllyn.co.uk

Affiliated Bodies: Heritage Railway Association, Transport Trust

Year Opened: 1866

Type of Complex: Operational Railway Line

Gauge: Narrow   **No. Staff:** 13   **No. Volunteers:** 300

<u>Stock Overview:</u>

No. Steam Locos: 6 (2 Pre-Nationalisation)

No. Diesel Locos: 4

<u>TV/Film Appearances:</u> Railway with a Heart of Gold (1953)

<u>Background:</u> The first preserved railway in the world. Still using some of the original locomotives and coaches.

Facilities: Café, Ticket office, Disabled access, Waiting room, Photo line side permit available, Advanced booking available, Driver footplate experience, Santa Special, Enthusiast galas, Souvenir shop, Books for sale, Videos for sale, Photos for sale, Paintings/drawings for sale, Camera film for sale, Models for sale, Main credit cards taken, Children's events, Trains for hire.

Location:
Nearest Town/Village: Tywyn **Main Road:** A493 **Bus:** 28, 29 **Mainline Station:** Tywyn

Contact(s):
- **For Bookings:** Mr David Leech
- **General Manager:** Mr David Mitchell

Journeys Available At This Railway:

Tywyn Wharf to Nant Gwernol
Track Type: Single   Direction: West to East
Features: Views of Hills, Open Fields, Woods. Maximum gradient of 1 in 77 (For 250 metres).
Bridges: 7 'under' **Level Crossings:** 3 **Signal Boxes:** 4 **Viaducts:** 1 **Journey Duration:** 55 mins **Journey Length:** 7.25 mile(s)
Price: £9.50 (Adult Standard) £4.75 (Child Standard)

Stations On This Journey:

Station Name	St	Al	Bd	Tl	DT	PA	CP	Ph	Mu	WR	Sh	VS	WS	VW	SB	VSB
Tywyn Wharf	✔	✔		✔	✔				✔	✔						
Pendre	✔	✔								✔	✔	✔				
Rhydyronen	✔	✔								✔						
Brynglas	✔	✔								✔						
Dolgoch	✔	✔		✔	✔		✔			✔						
Abergynolwyn	✔	✔		✔	✔	✔	✔	✔		✔				✔		
Nant Gwernol	✔	✔								✔						

TANFIELD RAILWAY

TANFIELD RAILWAY (THE) Marley Hill Engine Shed, Old Marley Hill, Gateshead, **COUNTY DURHAM,** NE16 5ET, **ENGLAND**.
(T) 0191 3887545   **(F)** 0191 3874784
(W) www.tanfield-railway.co.uk
Affiliated Bodies: Heritage Railway Association
Type of Complex: Railway Station, Operational Railway Line, Museum, Restoration Site
Gauge: Standard

Stock Overview:
No. Steam Locos: 10
No. Diesel Locos: 1
Facilities: Café, Disabled access, Santa Special, Enthusiast galas, Souvenir shop, Children's events, Evening wine and dine facilities.

Opening/Closing Times:
Summer: **Opens** 11:00, **Closes** 16:00
Other: Open every Sunday.

Location:
Nearest Town/Village: Gateshead   **Main Road:** A6076

Contact(s):
- **Commercial Manager:** Mr Tommy Knocks

Alternative Contact Details:
- 22 Coverley, Great Lumley, Chester Le Street, County Durham, DH3 4LS, England

Journeys Available At This Railway:

Sunniside to East Tanfield
Features: Views of Woods. Railway runs alongside Causey Arch (The first arched railway bridge). Maximum gradient of 1 in 32.
Bridges: 2 'over', 1 'under' **Signal Boxes:** 1 **Journey Duration:** 25 mins **Journey Length:** 2.8 mile(s)
Price: £4.00 (Adult Standard) £2.00 (Child Standard)

Key:	St = Stops	Al = Alight	Bd = Board	Tl = Toilets	DT = Disabled Toilets	PA = Kids Play Area	CP = Free Car Park	Ph = Pay Phone	Mu = Museum
	WR = Waiting Room	Sh = Sheds	VS = Can Visit Sheds	WS = Workshops	VW = Can Visit Workshops	SB = Signal Box	VSB = Can Visit Signal Box		

Stations On This Journey:

Station Name	St	Al	Bd	Tl	DT	PA	CP	Ph	Mu	WR	Sh	VS	WS	VW	SB	VSB
Sunniside	✔	✔	✔													
Andrews House	✔	✔	✔	✔	✔				✔		✔	✔	✔	✔	✔	
Causey Arch	✔	✔	✔	✔												
East Tanfield	✔	✔	✔													

TEESIDE SMALL GAUGE RAILWAY

TEESIDE SMALL GAUGE RAILWAY Preston Pk, Yarm Rd, Stockton-on-Tees, **CLEVELAND,** TS18 3RH, **ENGLAND**.

Year Opened: 1993

Type of Complex: Operational Railway Line

Gauge: Narrow

Facilities: Disabled access.

Opening/Closing Times:

Spring: **Opens** Sun 13:00, **Closes** Sun 16:00

Summer: **Opens** Sun 13:00, **Closes** Sun 16:00

Autumn: **Opens** Sun 13:00, **Closes** Sun 16:00

Location:

Instructions: Situated in the grounds of the Preston Hall Museum Park.

Nearest Town/Village: Stockton-on-Tees   **Main Road:** A19   **Mainline Station:** Eagles Cliffe

Contact(s):

● **Secretary:** Mr William Foster **(T)** 01642 710198

Alternative Contact Details:

● Secretary, 44 The Holme, Great Broughton, Middlesbrough, Tyne and Wear, TS9 7HF, England

Journeys Available At This Railway:

Price: £0.50 (Adult Standard) £0.50 (Child Standard)

TEIFI VALLEY RAILWAY

TEIFI VALLEY RAILWAY (THE) Station Yard, Henllan, Newcastle Emlyn, **CARMARTHENSHIRE,** SA44 5TD, **WALES**.

(T) 01559 371077   **(F)** 01559 371077

(W) www.teifivr.f9.co.uk

Affiliated Bodies: Heritage Railway Association

Year Opened: 1982

Type of Complex: Railway Station, Operational Railway Line, Museum

Gauge: Narrow

Stock Overview:

No. Steam Locos: 2

No. Diesel Locos: 2

Facilities: Café, Disabled access, Driver footplate experience, Santa Special, Courses on how to drive Locos, Souvenir shop, Videos for sale, Models for sale, Main credit cards taken, Children's events, Trains for hire.

Location:

Nearest Town/Village: Newcastle Emlyn   **Main Road:** A484   **Mainline Station:** Camarthen

Contact(s):

● **Director:** Mr Michael Martin

Journeys Available At This Railway:

Henllan to Llandyfriog

Track Type: Single

Features: Views of Water, Woods. 80 foot high bridge over waterfalls. Maximum gradient of 1 in 40.

Bridges: 3 'over'   **Journey Length:** 1.25 mile(s)

Stations On This Journey:

Station Name	St	Al	Bd	Tl	DT	PA	CP	Ph	Mu	WR	Sh	VS	WS	VW	SB	VSB
Henllan	✔	✔		✔	✔	✔	✔					✔		✔		
Pontprenshity	✔	✔														
Llandyfriog																

TELFORD STEAM RAILWAY

TELFORD (HORSEHAY) STEAM TRUST The Old Loco Shed, Bridge Rd, Horsehay, Telford, **SHROPSHIRE,** TF4 2NF, **ENGLAND**.**(M)** 07765 858348

(W) www.thad.demon.co.uk/tsr

Affiliated Bodies: Heritage Railway Association

Year Opened: 1976

Type of Complex: Railway Station, Operational Railway Line, Museum, Restoration Site

Type of Organisation: Charity, Heritage Project, Volunteer, Non-Profit

Gauge: Narrow & Standard   **No. Volunteers:** 170

Stock Overview:

No. Steam Locos: 4 (1 Pre-Group)

Background: An original Great Western Railway line. Horsehay site was started for the Ironworks. Telford Steam Railway started in 1976 and is continually expanding.

Facilities: Café, Ticket office, Disabled access, Waiting room, Line permit needed, Photo line side permit available, Guided tours available, Driver footplate experience, Santa Special, 'Thomas' event, Training courses, Enthusiast galas, Souvenir shop, Books for sale, Videos for sale, Photos for sale, Paintings/drawings for sale, Camera film for sale, Main credit cards taken, Children's events, Facilities for hire, Trains for hire.

Opening/Closing Times:

Spring: **Opens** Sat, Sun 11:00, **Closes** Sat, Sun 17:00

Summer: **Opens** Sat, Sun 11:00, **Closes** Sat, Sun 17:00

Autumn: **Opens** Sat, Sun 11:00, **Closes** Sat, Sun 17:00

Winter: **Opens** Sat 11:00, **Closes** Sat 17:00

Other: Open for static displays only in Winter, except in December when open Saturdays and Sundays for Santa Specials.

Location:

Nearest Town/Village: Telford   **Main Road:** M54   **Taxi:** Central Cabs   **Mainline Station:** Telford Central

Contact(s):

● **Marketing Executive:** Mr Dave Angell   **(T)** 07968 975867

Journeys Available At This Railway:

Spring Village to Horsehay & Dawley

Track Type: Single   Direction: South to North

Features: Views of Woods. Steep pulling gradient. Maximum gradient of 1 in 39 (For 500 metres).

Tunnels: 1   **Signal Boxes:** 1   **Journey Duration:** 10 mins   **Journey Length:** 1 mile(s)

Price: £3.50 (Adult Standard) £2.50 (Child Standard)

Available on Journey: Refreshments, Drinks, Buffet.

Stations On This Journey:

Station Name	St	Al	Bd	Tl	DT	PA	CP	Ph	Mu	WR	Sh	VS	WS	VW	SB	VSB
Spring Village	✔	✔	✔			✔	✔		✔	✔	✔	✔	✔	✔		
Horsehay & Dawley	✔	✔	✔						✔						✔	

TIMOTHY HACKWORTH

TIMOTHY HACKWORTH VICTORIAN & RAILWAY MUSEUM Soho Cottages, Hackworth Cl, Shildon, **COUNTY DURHAM,** DL4 1PQ, **ENGLAND**.

(T) 01388 777999   **(F)** 01388 777999

(W) www.hackworthmuseum.co.uk

Year Opened: 1975

Type of Complex: Operational Railway Line, Museum

Gauge: Standard

Stock Overview:

No. Steam Locos: 3

TV/Film Appearances: Songs of Praise (1999), Fred Dibnah (1999)

Facilities: Lecture room, Function room, Advanced booking available, Guided tours available, Santa Special, Souvenir shop, Books for sale, Paintings/drawings for sale, Models for sale, Children's events, Facilities for hire, Trains for hire.

Entry Fees: Adults: £2.00   **Children:** £1.00

Opening/Closing Times:

Spring: **Opens** Wed - Sun 10:00, **Closes** Wed - Sun 17:00

Summer: **Opens** Wed - Sun 10:00, **Closes** Wed - Sun 17:00

Autumn: **Opens** Wed - Sun 10:00, **Closes** Wed - Sun 17:00

Other: Also open Bank Holidays. Contact for steaming days.

Location:

Instructions: Located just off the B6282.

Nearest Town/Village: Shildon   **Main Road:** A6072   **Mainline Station:** Shildon

Contact(s):

● **General Manager:** Mr Alan Pearce

TRALEE & DINGLE RAILWAY

TRALEE & DINGLE RAILWAY Ballyard Station, Dingle Rd, Tralee, **COUNTY KERRY, IRELAND**.

(T) 066 7121064

Year Opened: 1991

Type of Complex: Operational Railway Line, Museum

Gauge: Narrow

Stock Overview:

No. Steam Locos: 1

Background: Europes most westerly line.

Facilities: Disabled access, Souvenir shop, Facilities are located in Blennerville Windmill.

Location:

Nearest Town/Village: Tralee   **Main Road:** N86   **Mainline Station:** Enroad

Contact(s):

● **General Manager:** Mr John Griffin

Journeys Available At This Railway:

Ballyard to Blennerville

Stations On This Journey:

Station Name	St	Al	Bd	Tl	DT	PA	CP	Ph	Mu	WR	Sh	VS	WS	VW	SB	VSB
Ballyard	✔	✔														
Blennerville	✔	✔														

TYSELEY LOCOMOTIVE WORKS

TYSELEY LOCOMOTIVE WORKS670 Warwick Rd, Tyseley, Birmingham, **MIDLANDS (WEST),** B11 2HL, **ENGLAND**.

(T) 0121 7074696

(E) office@vintagetrains.co.uk

(W) www.vintagetrains.co.uk

Type of Complex: Museum

Gauge: Standard

Background: Formerly Birmingham Railway Museum.

Facilities: Restaurant, Driver footplate experience, Souvenir shop, Books for sale, Videos for sale.

Entry Fees: Adults: £2.50   **Children:** £1.25

Opening/Closing Times:

Spring:	**Opens** Sat, Sun 10:00,	**Closes** Sat, Sun 16:00
Summer:	**Opens** Sat, Sun 10:00,	**Closes** Sat, Sun 16:00
Autumn:	**Opens** Sat, Sun 10:00,	**Closes** Sat, Sun 16:00
Winter:	**Opens** Sat, Sun 10:00,	**Closes** Sat, Sun 16:00

Location:

Instructions: From Junction 5 of M42 follow A41 towards Birmingham.

Nearest Town/Village: Birmingham   **Main Road:** A41   **Mainline Station:** Tyseley

Contact(s):

● **Marketing Manager:** Mr Will Atkin

ULSTER FOLK & TRANSPORT

ULSTER FOLK & TRANSPORT MUSEUM Cultra, Holywood, **COUNTY DOWN**, BT18 0EU, **NORTHERN IRELAND**.

(T) 028 90428428   **(F)** 028 90428728

(W) www.nidex.com/uftm

Complex Size: 190 Acres   **Year Opened:** 1955

Type of Complex: Museum

Gauge: Narrow & Standard   **No. Staff:** 150

Stock Overview:

No. Steam Locos: 10

No. Diesel Locos: 2

TV/Film Appearances: Spike Milligan's Puckoon (2001)

Facilities: Café, Restaurant, Ticket office, Disabled access, Lecture room, Function room, Advanced booking available, Souvenir shop, Books for sale, Videos for sale, Main credit cards taken.

Location:

Nearest Town/Village: Holywood   **Main Road:** A2   **Mainline Station:** Cultra   **Hotel:** Culloden Hotel

Contact(s):

● **For Bookings:** Mrs Lauriane Lindsay

VALE OF GLAMORGAN RAILWAY

VALE OF GLAMORGAN RAILWAY COMPANY LTD (THE) Barry Island Station, Station Approach Rd, Barry, **GLAMORGAN (VALE OF)**, CF62 5TH, **WALES**.

(T) 01446 748816   **(F)** 01446 749018

(E) valeglamrail@netscapeonline.co.uk

Affiliated Bodies: Heritage Railway Association

Year Opened: 1997

Type of Complex: Railway Station, Operational Railway Line, Museum, Restoration Site

Type of Organisation: Charity, Heritage Project, Limited Company, Volunteer

Gauge: Standard   **No. Staff:** 1   **No. Volunteers:** 30

Stock Overview:

No. Steam Locos: 3

No. Diesel Locos: 1

Facilities: Buffet, Ticket office, Disabled access, Lecture room, Guided tours available, Driver footplate experience, Santa Special, Souvenir shop, Books for sale, Videos for sale.

Location:

Nearest Town/Village: Barry   **Taxi:** New Harbour Cars   **Mainline Station:** Barry Island

Hotel: Mount Sorrel   **Restaurant:** Fortes

A-Z STEAM RAILWAYS

Tyseley Locomotive Works — Vale of Glamorgan Railway

Key: *St* = Stops   *Al* = Alight   *Bd* = Board   *Tl* = Toilets   *DT* = Disabled Toilets   *PA* = Kids Play Area   *CP* = Free Car Park   *Ph* = Pay Phone   *Mu* = Museum
WR = Waiting Room   *Sh* = Sheds   *VS* = Can Visit Sheds   *WS* = Workshops   *VW* = Can Visit Workshops   *SB* = Signal Box   *VSB* = Can Visit Signal Box

Contact(s):
- **For Bookings:** Ms Tania Webster
- **For Donations:** Mr Alan Wales
- **General Manager:** Mr John Hayes

Journeys Available At This Railway:

Barry Island to Hood Road
Track Type: Single
Features: Views of Open Fields, Sea. Maximum gradient of 1 in 86 (For 70 metres).
Viaducts: 1   **Journey Duration:** 8 mins   **Journey Length:** 3 mile(s)
Price: £3.00 (Adult Standard) £2.00 (Child Standard)

Stations On This Journey:

Station Name	St	Al	Bd	Tl	DT	PA	CP	Ph	Mu	WR	Sh	VS	WS	VW	SB	VSB
Barry Island	✔	✔		✔	✔						✔	✔				
Hood Road	✔	✔			✔											
Plymouth Road	✔	✔											✔	✔		

VALE OF RHEIDOL RAILWAY

VALE OF RHEIDOL RAILWAY Park Ave, Aberystwyth, **CEREDIGION,** SY23 1PG, **WALES**.

(T) 01970 625819   **(F)** 01970 623769

(E) vor@rheidolrailway.co.uk

(W) www.rheidolrailway.co.uk

Affiliated Bodies: Heritage Railway Association

Year Opened: 1902

Type of Complex: Railway Station, Operational Railway Line, Restoration Site

Gauge: Narrow

Stock Overview:

No. Steam Locos: 3

No. Diesel Locos: 1

Facilities: Café, Souvenir shop.

Opening/Closing Times:

Other: Open April - October. Closed certain days during this period. Please contact for details.

Location:

Nearest Town/Village: Aberystwyth   **Mainline Station:** Aberystwyth

Contact(s):

- **General Manager:** Mr N Thompson

Journeys Available At This Railway:

Aberystwyth to Devils Bridge
Track Type: Single
Features: Views of Open Fields, Urbanisation, Woods. Maximum gradient of 1 in 50.
Journey Duration: 60 mins   **Journey Length:** 11.75 mile(s)

Stations On This Journey:

Station Name	St	Al	Bd	Tl	DT	PA	CP	Ph	Mu	WR	Sh	VS	WS	VW	SB	VSB
Aberystwyth	✔	✔	✔	✔	✔						✔		✔			
Devils Bridge	✔	✔	✔	✔												

VINTAGE CARRIAGES TRUST

VINTAGE CARRIAGES TRUST MUSEUM OF RAIL TRAVEL Ingrow Railway Ctre, Keighley, **YORKSHIRE (WEST),** BD22 8NJ, **ENGLAND**.

(T) 01535 680425   **(F)** 01535 610796

(E) vct@mwdjcope.demon.co.uk

(W) www.vintagecarriagestrust.org

Affiliated Bodies: Heritage Railway Association, Transport Trust

Year Opened: 1990

Type of Complex: Museum

Type of Organisation: Charity

Gauge: Standard   **No. Staff:** 2   **No. Volunteers:** 50

Stock Overview:

No. Steam Locos: 1

TV/Film Appearances: Hours (2001), League of Gentlemen (2000), Unknown Soldier (1997), Holiday (1996), Budweiser Beer Commercial (1996), History of British Art (1995), Tomorrow's World (1995), Sherlock Holmes (1988), Railway Children (1968 & 1970)

Facilities: Disabled access, Souvenir shop, Books for sale, Camera film for sale, Main credit cards taken.

Entry Fees: Adults: £1.00   **Children:** £0.75

Opening/Closing Times:

Spring: **Opens** Mon - Sun 11:00, **Closes** Mon - Sun 16:30
Summer: **Opens** Mon - Sun 11:00, **Closes** Mon - Sun 16:30
Autumn: **Opens** Mon - Sun 11:00, **Closes** Mon - Sun 16:30
Winter: **Opens** Mon - Sun 11:00, **Closes** Mon - Sun 16:30
Other: Closed Christmas Day and Boxing Day.

Location:

Instructions: Located adjacent to Ingrow West HWVR Station, on main A629 - Keighley to Halifax Road.

Nearest Town/Village: Keighley   **Main Road:** A629   **Bus:** 500, 502, 663, 664, 665, 697   **Mainline Station:** Keighley

Contact(s):

- Mr Paul Holroyd
- **For Donations:** Ms Jackie Cope
- **Technical Info:** Mr Michael W Cope

Alternative Contact Details:

- c/o Haworth Railway Station, Keighley, Yorkshire (West), BD22 8NJ, England

VINTAGE TRAINS

VINTAGE TRAINS LTD670 Warwick Rd, Tyseley, Birmingham, **MIDLANDS (WEST),** B11 2HL, **ENGLAND**.

(T) 0121 7074696

(E) office@vintagetrains.co.uk

(W) www.vintagetrains.co.uk

Background: Operate Steam train excursions on mainline track.

Facilities: Restaurant, Souvenir shop, Books for sale, Videos for sale.

Opening/Closing Times:

Other: Contact for excursion dates.

Location:

Instructions: From junction 5 of M42 follow A41 towards Birmingham.

Nearest Town/Village: Birmingham   **Main Road:** A41   **Mainline Station:** Tyseley

Contact(s):

- **Marketing Executive:** Mr Will Atkin

Key: *St* = Stops   *Al* = Alight   *Bd* = Board   *Tl* = Toilets   *DT* = Disabled Toilets   *PA* = Kids Play Area   *CP* = Free Car Park   *Ph* = Pay Phone   *Mu* = Museum
         WR = Waiting Room   *Sh* = Sheds   *VS* = Can Visit Sheds   *WS* = Workshops   *VW* = Can Visit Workshops   *SB* = Signal Box   *VSB* = Can Visit Signal Box

WATERCRESS LINE

MID-HANTS RAILWAY PLC (THE) Station Offices, Alresford, **HAMPSHIRE,** SO24 9JG, **ENGLAND**.
(T) 01962 733810　　**(F)** 01962 735448
(E) watercressline@compuserve.com
(W) www.watercressline.co.uk
Affiliated Bodies: Heritage Railway Association
Type of Complex: Railway Station, Operational Railway Line, Restoration Site
Type of Organisation: Limited Company
Gauge: Standard
<u>Stock Overview</u>:
No. Steam Locos: 19 (9 Pre-Group, 2 Pre-Nationalisation)
No. Diesel Locos: 7
<u>**TV/Film Appearances:**</u> Glass, High Heels and Low Lifes, Birds of a Feather, Pie in the Sky, Great Kadinsky
<u>**Background:**</u> Celebrating 25 years of preservation operations in 2002.
<u>**Facilities:**</u> Buffet, Ticket office, Disabled access, Function room, Line permit needed, Photo line side permit available, Through ticketing available, Advanced booking available, Guided tours available, Driver footplate experience, Santa Special, 'Thomas' event, Enthusiast galas, Courses on how to drive Locos, Souvenir shop, Books for sale, Videos for sale, Main credit cards taken, Trains for hire, Traditional goods shed now re-opened as Edward Knight Centre with shop and museum.
<u>Opening/Closing Times</u>:
Spring:　　**Opens** Sat - Sun 10:30, **Closes** Sat - Sun 17:00
Summer:　**Opens** Sat - Sun 10:30, **Closes** Sat - Sun 17:00
Autumn:　**Opens** Sat - Sun 10:30, **Closes** Sat - Sun 17:00
Other:　　Open Sundays only during February. Contact for further details.
<u>Location</u>:
Instructions: Located just off A31 Guildford to Winchester Road.
Main Road: A31　　**Bus:** 64, X64
<u>Contact(s)</u>:
- **Chairman:** Mr David Snow
- **Filming Contact:** Mr Chris Cornell
- **Finance Director:** Mr David Snow
- **For Bookings:** Mr Rod Wicks
- **Sales & Marketing Manager:** Ms Julie Doel
- **Technical Info:** Mr Clive Holliday
<u>Journeys Available At This Railway</u>:

Alresford to Alton
Track Type: Single
Features: Views of Open Fields, Woods. Medstead & Four Marks is one of the highest southern stations.
Bridges: 10 'over', 6 'under'　**Signal Boxes:** 4　**Journey Duration:** 25 mins　**Journey Length:** 10 mile(s)
Price: £9.00 (Adult Standard) £2.00 (Child Standard) £2.00 (Child Special)
Available on Journey: Refreshments, Drinks, Alcohol.
<u>Stations On This Journey</u>:

Station Name	St	Al	Bd	Tl	DT	PA	CP	Ph	Mu	WR	Sh	VS	WS	VV	SB	VSB
Alresford	✔	✔		✔	✔				✔	✔					✔	
Ropley	✔	✔		✔		✔				✔	✔		✔		✔	
Medstead & Four Marks	✔	✔		✔						✔					✔	
Alton	✔	✔														

WELLINGTON COUNTRY PARK

WELLINGTON COUNTRY PARK MINIATURE RAILWAY Odiham Rd, Riseley, Reading, **BERKSHIRE,** RG7 1SP, **ENGLAND**.

(T) 0118 9326444

Type of Complex: Operational Railway Line

Gauge: Narrow

Stock Overview:

No. Diesel Locos: 1

Background: Train rides available at an extra cost. Entry prices reduced during winter.

Facilities: Disabled access, Santa Special, Main credit cards taken, Children's events.

Entry Fees: Adults: £4.30   **Children:** £2.20

Opening/Closing Times:

Spring: **Opens** Mon - Sun 10:00, **Closes** Mon - Sun 17:30
Summer: **Opens** Mon - Sun 10:00, **Closes** Mon - Sun 17:30
Autumn: **Opens** Mon - Sun 10:00, **Closes** Mon - Sun 16:30
Winter: **Opens** Mon - Sun 10:00, **Closes** Mon - Sun 16:30

Location:

Nearest Town/Village: Wokingham   **Main Road:** A33

Contact(s):

- **Manager:** Ms Suzanna Gorings
- **Technical Info:** Mr John Toovy   **(T)** 07931 658669

WELLS & WALSINGHAM

WELLS & WALSINGHAM LIGHT RAILWAY Wells-next-the-Sea, **NORFOLK,** NR23 1QB, **ENGLAND**.

(T) 01328 711630

Affiliated Bodies: Heritage Railway Association, Transport Trust

Year Opened: 1982

Type of Complex: Railway Station, Operational Railway Line

Type of Organisation: Sole Partnership

Gauge: Narrow   **No. Staff:** 3   **No. Volunteers:** 24

Stock Overview:

No. Steam Locos: 1

No. Diesel Locos: 1

Background: The longest 10.25 gauge track in the world.

Facilities: Line permit needed, Advanced booking available, Souvenir shop, Trains for hire.

Opening/Closing Times:

Other: Open April - October.

Location:

Main Road: A149   **Mainline Station:** Kings Lynn   **Hotel:** Crown Hotel

Contact(s):

- **For Bookings:** Mr Roy W Francis
- **For Donations:** Mr Roy W Francis
- **General Manager:** Mr S K Tuck
- **Owner:** Mr Roy W Francis

Journeys Available At This Railway:

Wells-next-the-Sea to Walsingham

Features: Views of Open Fields, Woods. Maximum gradient of 1 in 60 (For 350 metres).

Bridges: 3 'over', 3 'under'   **Level Crossings:** 2   **Signal Boxes:** 1   **Journey Duration:** 30 mins   **Journey Length:** 4 mile(s)

Price: £6.00 (Adult Standard) £4.50 (Child Standard)

Available on Journey: Refreshments, Drinks.

Stations On This Journey:

Key: *St* = Stops   *Al* = Alight   *Bd* = Board   *Tl* = Toilets   *DT* = Disabled Toilets   *PA* = Kids Play Area   *CP* = Free Car Park   *Ph* = Pay Phone   *Mu* = Museum
        WR = Waiting Room   *Sh* = Sheds   *VS* = Can Visit Sheds   *WS* = Workshops   *VW* = Can Visit Workshops   *SB* = Signal Box   *VSB* = Can Visit Signal Box

Station Name	St	Al	Bd	Tl	DT	PA	CP	Ph	Mu	WR	Sh	VS	WS	VW	SB	VSB
Wells-next-the-Sea	✔	✔	✔	✔			✔				✔				✔	
Warham Halt	✔	✔	✔													
Wighton Halt	✔	✔	✔													
Walsingham	✔	✔	✔													

WELSH HIGHLAND RAILWAY

WELSH HIGHLAND RAILWAY LTD Tremadog Rd, Porthmadog, **GWYNEDD**, LL49 9DY, **WALES**.
(T) 0151 6081950   **(F)** 0151 6082696
(W) www.whr.co.uk
Affiliated Bodies: Great Little Trains of Wales, Heritage Railway Association
Complex Size: 10 Acres   **Year Opened:** 1981
Type of Complex: Operational Railway Line, Museum
Type of Organisation: Charity, Heritage Project, Conservation Project, Limited Company, Volunteer, Non-Profit
Gauge: Narrow   **No. Volunteers:** 50
Stock Overview:
No. Steam Locos: 6
No. Diesel Locos: 4
Facilities: Café, Ticket office, Disabled access, Guided tours available, Driver footplate experience, Santa Special, Courses on how to drive Locos, Souvenir shop, Books for sale, Videos for sale, Photos for sale, Models for sale, Main credit cards taken, Trains for hire.
Opening/Closing Times:
Summer: Opens Mon - Sun 11:00, **Closes** Mon - Sun 16:30
Autumn: Opens Thurs - Sun 11:00, **Closes** Thurs - Sun 16:00
Other: Also open during school holidays, and in December for Santa specials. Closed in November. Contact for confirmation of opening times in Autumn.
Location:
Nearest Town/Village: Porthmadog   **Main Road:** Tremadog Rd   **Mainline Station:** Porthmadog
Hotel: Royal Sportsman
Contact(s):
● **For Bookings:** Mr David Allan   **(T)** 0151 327 3576   **(E)** dweallan89@fsnet.co.uk
Journeys Available At This Railway:

Porthmadog to Pen Y Mount
Track Type: Single   Direction: South to North
Features: Views of Hills, Open Fields.
Bridges: 1 'over' **Signal Boxes:** 1   **Journey Length:** 1 mile(s)
Price: £3.00 (Adult Standard) £2.00 (Child Standard)
Stations On This Journey:

Station Name	St	Al	Bd	Tl	DT	PA	CP	Ph	Mu	WR	Sh	VS	WS	VW	SB	VSB
Porthmadog	✔	✔	✔	✔	✔		✔				✔					
Gelerts Farm Halt	✔	✔	✔							✔		✔	✔			
Pen Y Mount	✔	✔	✔													

WELSH HIGHLAND RAILWAY

WELSH HIGHLAND RAILWAY (CAERNARFON) St Helens Rd, Caernarfon, **GWYNEDD, WALES**.
(T) 01766 516073   **(F)** 01766 516006
(W) www.bangor.ac.uk/ml/whr/whr
Affiliated Bodies: Heritage Railway Association
Year Opened: 1997
Type of Complex: Railway Station, Operational Railway Line, Museum, Restoration Site
Gauge: Narrow

Facilities: Ticket office, Disabled access, Waiting room, Santa Special, Souvenir shop, Books for sale, Videos for sale, Main credit cards taken, Children's events.

Opening/Closing Times:

Spring:	**Opens** Mon - Sun 09:00, **Closes** Mon - Sun 18:00
Summer:	**Opens** Mon - Sun 09:00, **Closes** Mon - Sun 18:00
Autumn:	**Opens** Mon - Sun 09:00, **Closes** Mon - Sun 18:00
Winter:	**Opens** Mon - Sun 09:00, **Closes** Mon - Sun 18:00
Other:	Contact for train times. The museum and shop are open 7 days per week.

Location:

Instructions: Follow signs for Caernarfon Castle.

Nearest Town/Village: Caernarfon   **Main Road:** A487   **Mainline Station:** Bangor

Contact(s):

● **Corporate & Public Affairs Manager:** Mr Tim Davies   **(T)** 07769 938384

● **Managing Director:** Mr Ken Allen

Alternative Contact Details:

● Harbour Station, Porthmadog, Gwynedd, LL49 9NS, Wales

Journeys Available At This Railway:

Caernarfon to Waunfawr

Features: Views of Hills, Open Fields, Water, Woods. Maximum gradient of 1 in 40.

Bridges: 3 'over', 7 'under'   **Rivers:** 1   **Journey Length:** 7 mile(s)

Price: £8.00 (Adult Standard)

Stations On This Journey:

Station Name	St	Al	Bd	Tl	DT	PA	CP	Ph	Mu	WR	Sh	VS	WS	VW	SB	VSB
Caernarfon	✔	✔		✔	✔					✔						
Bontnewydd	✔									✔						
Dinas	✔	✔		✔	✔				✔	✔	✔		✔			
Waunfawr	✔	✔		✔	✔					✔						

WELSH SLATE MUSEUM

WELSH SLATE MUSEUM Padarn Country Pk, Llanberis, Caernarfon, **GWYNEDD**, LL55 4TY, **WALES**.

(T) 01286 870630   **(F)** 01286 871906

(E) slate@nmgw.ac.uk

(W) www.nmgw.ac.uk

Year Opened: 1972

Type of Complex: Operational Railway Line, Museum

Background: The track extends out of the museum grounds and onto the Llanberis Lake Railway.

Facilities: Café, Disabled access, Guided tours available, Santa Special, Souvenir shop, Books for sale, Videos for sale, Models for sale, Main credit cards taken, Children's events, Model railway exhibitions and miniature engines.

Opening/Closing Times:

Spring:	**Opens** Mon - Sun 10:00, **Closes** Mon - Sun 17:00
Summer:	**Opens** Mon - Sun 10:00, **Closes** Mon - Sun 17:00
Autumn:	**Opens** Mon - Sun 10:00, **Closes** Mon - Sun 17:00
Winter:	**Opens** Sun - Fri 10:00, **Closes** Sun - Fri 16:00

Location:

Nearest Town/Village: Carnarvon   **Main Road:** A4086   **Mainline Station:** Bangor

Contact(s):

● **Marketing Executive:** Ms Julie Williams

Key: *St* = Stops   *Al* = Alight   *Bd* = Board   *Tl* = Toilets   *DT* = Disabled Toilets   *PA* = Kids Play Area   *CP* = Free Car Park   *Ph* = Pay Phone   *Mu* = Museum
WR = Waiting Room   *Sh* = Sheds   *VS* = Can Visit Sheds   *WS* = Workshops   *VW* = Can Visit Workshops   *SB* = Signal Box   *VSB* = Can Visit Signal Box

WELSHPOOL & LLANFAIR

WELSHPOOL & LLANFAIR LIGHT RAILWAY The Station, Llanfair Caereinion, Welshpool, **POWYS**, SY21 0SF, **WALES**.
(T) 01938 810441　　**(F)** 01938 810861
(E) info@wllr.org.uk
(W) www.wllr.org.uk
Affiliated Bodies: Heritage Railway Association
Year Opened: 1903
Type of Complex: Railway Station, Operational Railway Line, Restoration Site
Type of Organisation: Charity
Gauge: Narrow　　**No. Staff:** 3　　**No. Volunteers:** 200
Stock Overview:
No. Steam Locos: 7 (2 Pre-Nationalisation)
No. Diesel Locos: 3
Facilities: Café, Ticket office, Disabled access, Waiting room, Driver footplate experience, Santa Special, 'Thomas' event, Enthusiast galas, Souvenir shop, Books for sale, Videos for sale, Paintings/drawings for sale, Main credit cards taken, Facilities for hire, Trains for hire.
Opening/Closing Times:
Spring:　**Opens** Sat, Sun 10:00, **Closes** Sat, Sun 17:00
Summer:　**Opens** Mon - Sun 10:00, **Closes** Mon - Sun 17:00
Autumn:　**Opens** Sat, Sun 10:00, **Closes** Sat, Sun 17:00
Location:
Nearest Town/Village: Welshpool　　**Main Road:** A458　　**Mainline Station:** Welshpool
Contact(s):
● **General Manager:** Mr Terry Turner
Journeys Available At This Railway:

Welshpool to Llanfair Caereinion
Track Type: Single　Direction: East to West
Features: Views of Hills, Open Fields, Water, Woods. Maximum gradient of 1 in 29.
Bridges: 5 'over'　**Level Crossings:** 6　**Signal Boxes:** 3　**Rivers:** 2　**Viaducts:** 1　**Journey Duration:** 50 mins
Journey Length: 8 mile(s)
Price: £8.50 (Adult Standard)　£4.25 (Child Standard)
Stations On This Journey:

Station Name	St	Al	Bd	Tl	DT	PA	CP	Ph	Mu	WR	Sh	VS	WS	VW	SB	VSB
Welshpool	✔	✔		✔	✔	✔	✔			✔					✔	
Galfa	✔															
Sylfaen	✔															
Castle Caereinion	✔															
Cyfronydd	✔															
Heniarth	✔															
Llanfair Caereinion	✔	✔		✔	✔	✔	✔			✔	✔	✔	✔		✔	

WEST LANCASHIRE LIGHT RLWY

WEST LANCASHIRE LIGHT RAILWAY Station Rd, Hesketh Bank, Preston, **LANCASHIRE**, PR4 6SP, **ENGLAND**.
(T) 01772 815881
Affiliated Bodies: Heritage Railway Association
Type of Complex: Operational Railway Line
Gauge: Narrow
Stock Overview:
No. Steam Locos: 8
No. Diesel Locos: 16

A-Z STEAM RAILWAYS

Facilities: Santa Special, Souvenir shop, Children's events.

Opening/Closing Times:

Spring: **Opens** Sun 12:00, **Closes** Sun 17:00
Summer: **Opens** Sun 12:00, **Closes** Sun 17:00
Autumn: **Opens** Sun 12:00, **Closes** Sun 17:00

Location:

Nearest Town/Village: Preston   **Main Road:** A59   **Bus:** 102   **Mainline Station:** Preston

Contact(s):

- **Chairman:** Mr Paul Smith
- **Publicity Manager:** Mr Phillip Pacey   **(T)** 01772 729203   **(E)** p.pacey@uclan.ac.uk

Journeys Available At This Railway:

Becconsall to Becconsall (round trip)
Price: £1.50 (Adult Standard) £1.00 (Child Standard)

Stations On This Journey:

Station Name	St	Al	Bd	Tl	DT	PA	CP	Ph	Mu	WR	Sh	VS	WS	VW	SB	VSB
Becconsall	✔	✔	✔		✔					✔	✔	✔	✔			
Delph	✔	✔														

WEST SOMERSET RAILWAY

WEST SOMERSET RAILWAY PLC The Railway Station, Minehead, **SOMERSET,** TA24 5BG, **ENGLAND**.
(T) 01643 704996   **(F)** 01643 706329
(E) info@west-somerset-railway.co.uk
(W) www.west-somerset-railway.co.uk

Affiliated Bodies: Heritage Railway Association, Transport Trust

Year Opened: 1976

Type of Complex: Railway Station, Operational Railway Line, Museum, Restoration Site

Type of Organisation: Limited Company

Gauge: Standard   **No. Staff:** 20   **No. Volunteers:** 300

Stock Overview:

No. Steam Locos: 11 (5 Pre-Group)

No. Diesel Locos: 23

Facilities: Café, Ticket office, Disabled access, Platform tickets, Photo line side permit available, Driver footplate experience, Santa Special, 'Thomas' event, Training courses, Enthusiast galas, Courses on how to drive Locos, Souvenir shop, Books for sale, Videos for sale, Photos for sale, Paintings/drawings for sale, Camera film for sale, CD's for sale, Models for sale, Main credit cards taken, Facilities for hire, Trains for hire.

Opening/Closing Times:

Spring: **Opens** Mon - Sun 09:30, **Closes** Mon - Sun 17:30
Summer: **Opens** Mon - Sun 09:00, **Closes** Mon - Sun 19:00
Autumn: **Opens** Mon - Sun 09:30, **Closes** Mon - Sun 17:30
Winter: **Opens** Mon - Sun 09:30, **Closes** Mon - Sun 17:30
Other: Opening days may be static only, please contact for details of steaming days.

Location:

Instructions: Leave M5 at junction 25 and proceed through Taunton. Follow tourist signs to railway.
Nearest Town/Village: Taunton   **Main Road:** A358   **Bus:** 28, 28A, 928   **Mainline Station:** Taunton

Contact(s):

- **For Donations:** Mr Mark L Smith
- **General Manager:** Mr Mark L Smith
- **Technical Info:** Mr Andrew Forster
- **Tours Officer:** Mr Gavin Duenas

Journeys Available At This Railway:

Minehead to Bishops Lydeard
Direction: North to South
Features: Views of Hills, Open Fields, Sea, Water, Woods. Many places of interest including Dunster Castle and Cleve Abbey. Maximum gradient of 1 in 65 (For 1000 metres).

West Lancashire Light Rlwy — West Somerset Railway

| Key: | *St* = Stops   *Al* = Alight   *Bd* = Board   *Tl* = Toilets   *DT* = Disabled Toilets   *PA* = Kids Play Area   *CP* = Free Car Park   *Ph* = Pay Phone   *Mu* = Museum *WR* = Waiting Room   *Sh* = Sheds   *VS* = Can Visit Sheds   *WS* = Workshops   *VW* = Can Visit Workshops   *SB* = Signal Box   *VSB* = Can Visit Signal Box |

Bridges: 30 'over', 25 'under'   Level Crossings: 7   Signal Boxes: 6   Rivers: 9   Journey Duration: 75 mins
Journey Length: 19.75 mile(s)
Price: £9.80 (Adult Standard) £4.40 (Child Standard) £10.80 (Adult Special) £5.90 (Child Special)
Available on Journey: Refreshments, Drinks, Alcohol, Buffet.

Stations On This Journey:

Station Name	St	Al	Bd	Tl	DT	PA	CP	Ph	Mu	WR	Sh	VS	WS	VW	SB	VSB
Minehead	✓	✓	✓	✓	✓						✓		✓		✓	
Dunster	✓	✓	✓	✓				✓		✓						
Blue Anchor	✓	✓	✓	✓				✓	✓	✓				✓		
Washford	✓	✓	✓	✓				✓		✓				✓	✓	
Watchet	✓	✓	✓	✓				✓		✓						
Doniford Halt	✓	✓	✓							✓						
Williton	✓	✓	✓	✓				✓		✓	✓		✓		✓	
Stogumber	✓	✓	✓	✓	✓	✓	✓			✓						
Crowcombe Heathfield	✓	✓	✓	✓				✓		✓				✓		
Bishops Lydeard	✓			✓	✓				✓		✓		✓		✓	

WESTON PARK RAILWAY

B & J WHALLEY (ENGINEERING) Weston Pk, Weston Under Lizard, Nr Shifnal, Telford, **SHROPSHIRE,**
TF11 8OE, **ENGLAND**.

(T) 01952 850336   **(F)** 01952 850336
(E) info@westonrail.freeserve.co.uk
Year Opened: 1980
Type of Complex: Operational Railway Line
Gauge: Narrow

Stock Overview:
No. Steam Locos: 3
No. Diesel Locos: 1

Facilities: Disabled access, Enthusiast galas.

Opening/Closing Times:
Spring: Opens Sat, Sun 11:00, Closes Sat, Sun 17:00
Summer: Opens Mon, Sun 11:00, Closes Mon, Sun 17:00
Other: The railway operates when the park is open.

Location:
Instructions: Located in the grounds of Weston Park.
Nearest Town/Village: Telford   **Main Road:** A5   **Mainline Station:** Shifnal

Contact(s):
● **General Manager:** Mr Bruce Whalley

Journeys Available At This Railway:

Weston Central to Lakeside
Track Type: Single
Features: Views of Open Fields, Water.
Bridges: 1 'over'   Level Crossings: 2   Signal Boxes: 1   Journey Length: 1.5 mile(s)
Price: £1.50 (Adult Standard) £1.00 (Child Standard)

Stations On This Journey:

Station Name	St	Al	Bd	Tl	DT	PA	CP	Ph	Mu	WR	Sh	VS	WS	VW	SB	VSB
Weston Central	✓	✓										✓		✓		
Lakeside	✓	✓														

WINCHCOMBE RAILWAY

WINCHCOMBE RAILWAY MUSEUM & GARDEN 23 Gloucester St, Winchcombe, Cheltenham,
GLOUCESTERSHIRE, GL54 5LX, **ENGLAND**.

(T) 01242 602257   **(F)** 01242 602507

Year Opened: 1968

Type of Complex: Museum

Background: The museum features a collection of railway equipment and working exhibits including a signal box.

Facilities: Café, Disabled access, Souvenir shop, Books for sale.

Entry Fees: Adults: £2.25   **Children:** £0.50

Opening/Closing Times:

Spring: **Opens** Wed - Sun 13:30, **Closes** Wed - Fri 17:00, Sat - Sun 17:30
Summer: **Opens** Mon - Sun 13:30, **Closes** Mon - Sun 17:30
Autumn: **Opens** Wed - Sun 13:30, **Closes** Wed - Fri 17:00, Sat - Sun 17:30

Location:

Nearest Town/Village: Winchcombe   **Main Road:** B4632   **Mainline Station:** Honeybourne

Contact(s):

● **Curator:** Mr Tim Petty   ● **General Manager:** Mr Tim Petty

WINDMILL FARM RAILWAY

WINDMILL FARM RAILWAYC/O Windmill Animal Farm, Red Cat Lane, Burscough, Ormskirk, **LANCASHIRE,** L40 1UQ, **ENGLAND**.

(T) 01704 892282

(W) www.windmillfarmrailway.freeservers.com

Affiliated Bodies: Heritage Railway Association

Year Opened: 1977

Type of Complex: Museum

Stock Overview:

No. Steam Locos: 4   **No. Diesel Locos:** 9

Facilities: Café, Disabled access, Santa Special, Picnic area.

Opening/Closing Times:

Spring: **Opens** Sat, Sun 10:00, **Closes** Sat, Sun 17:00
Summer: **Opens** Mon - Sun 10:00, **Closes** Mon - Sun 17:00
Autumn: **Opens** Sat, Sun 10:00, **Closes** Sat, Sun 17:00
Winter: **Opens** Sat, Sun 10:00, **Closes** Sat, Sun 17:00

Location:

Instructions: Contact for details before visiting.

Nearest Town/Village: Burscough   **Main Road:** A59

Contact(s):

● **Owner:** Mr Austin Moss

YEOVIL RAILWAY CENTRE

YEOVIL RAILWAY CENTRE Yeovil Junction Station, Stoford, Yeovil, **SOMERSET,** BA22 9UU, **ENGLAND**.

(T) 01935 411003   **(F)** 01935 410904

Affiliated Bodies: Heritage Railway Association

Type of Complex: Operational Railway Line

Stock Overview:

No. Steam Locos: 1

No. Diesel Locos: 1

Background: Steam train rides and shunting demonstrations. Visitors can also see work in progress and interesting artifacts.

Entry Fees: Adults: £2.00   **Children:** £1.50

Opening/Closing Times:

Summer: **Opens** Sun 11:00, **Closes** Sun 16:00
Autumn: **Opens** Sun 11:00, **Closes** Sun 16:00
Other: Open the first and third Sunday of the month, May - September.

Contact(s):

● **Chairman:** Mr Eric Taylor

| Key: | *St* = Stops | *Al* = Alight | *Bd* = Board | *Tl* = Toilets | *DT* = Disabled Toilets | *PA* = Kids Play Area | *CP* = Free Car Park | *Ph* = Pay Phone | *Mu* = Museum |
| | *WR* = Waiting Room | *Sh* = Sheds | *VS* = Can Visit Sheds | *WS* = Workshops | *VW* = Can Visit Workshops | *SB* = Signal Box | *VSB* = Can Visit Signal Box | | |

(T) 01372 802273 (F) 01372 803467
Year Opened: 1949
Type of Complex: Museum

Background: The museum features a collection of steam locomotives and rolling stock and includes a gift shop.

Facilities: Disabled access, Licensed, Car Park, Shop, Gift Shop

Entry Fees: Adults £2.00, Children £0.50

Opening/Closing Times:
Spring: Open Wed-Sun 10.00, Closes Wed-Fri 17.00, Sat-Sun 17.30
Summer: Open Mon-Sun 10.00, Closes 17.30
Autumn: Open Wed-Sun 10.00, Closes Wed-Fri 17.00, Sat-Sun 17.30

Location:
Nearest Town/Village: Whaddon, Main Road: B4021, Mainline Station: Aberystwyth

Contact(s):
• Curator/Chairman: General Manager: Mr T. Perry

WINDMILL FARM RAILWAY

WINDMILL FARM RAILWAY, c/o Windmill Animal Farm, Red Cat Lane, Burscough, Ormskirk,
LANCASHIRE, L40 1UQ, ENGLAND
(T) 01704 892282 (F)
(W) www.windmillanimalfarm.co.uk
Affiliated Bodies: Heritage Railway Association
Year Opened: 1997
Type of Complex: Museum

Stock Overview:
No. Steam Locos: 4   No. Diesel Locos: 2

Facilities: Café, Disabled Access, Gents, Ladies, Picnic Area

Opening/Closing Times:
Spring: Open Sat-Sun 10.00, Closes Sat-Sun 17.00
Summer: Open Mon-Sun 10.00, Closes Mon-Sun 17.00
Autumn: Open Sat-Sun 10.00, Closes Sat-Sun 17.00
Winter: Open Sat-Sun 10.00, Closes Sat-Sun 16.00

Location:
Instructions: Contact for details before visiting
Nearest Town/Village: Burscough, Main Road: A59

Contact(s):
• Owner: Mr Austin More

YEOVIL RAILWAY CENTRE

YEOVIL RAILWAY CENTRE, Yeovil Junction Station, Stoford, Yeovil, SOMERSET, BA22 9UU, ENGLAND
(T) 01935 410063 (F) 01935 410304
Affiliated Bodies: Heritage Railway Association
Type of Complex: Operational Railway Lines

Stock Overview:
No. Steam Locos:
No. Diesel Locos: 1   No. BR:

Background: Steam train rides and shuttle trips on demand. Visitor can also see various preserved locomotives and wagons.

Entry Fees: Adults £2.00, Children £1.50

Opening/Closing Times:
Summer: Open Sun 11.00, Closes Sun 16.00
Autumn: Open Sun 11.00, Closes Sun 16.00
Other: Open from first and third Sunday of the month, May - September

Contact(s):
• Chairman: Mr Paul Foss

A-Z of Steam Railways
and Museums showing the stock
they have available.

SECTION 1B

What information can I find?

An alphabetical listing
of railways/museums
showing name, current number,
type/class, origin, wheel
arrangement, year built, builder,
icons denoting details about the
stock, and additional information.

It is our aim to make the HCC
Steam Railway stock listing the
definitive guide to stock
information for restored railways
throughout the whole of the UK
and Ireland.

To find out how you can help us
achieve this aim, please refer to
the 'Your Involvement' section in
the introduction pages.

ABBEY LIGHT RAILWAY

Leeds, YORKSHIRE (WEST)

Name	Current No.	Type/Class	Origin	Wh.Arr.	Built	Builder			
Loweco	1			0-4-0	1942	Lister Dursley	D	Op	
Atlas	2			0-4-0	1943	Hunslet Engine Co Ltd	D	Op	
Odin	3				1934	Motor Rail Ltd, Simplex	D	Op	
Vulcan	4			0-4-0	1942	Ruston & Hornsby Ltd	D	Op	
	5				1946	Ruston & Hornsby Ltd	D	Op	
Druid	6				1941	Motor Rail Ltd, Simplex	D	Op	
	7			0-4-0	1935	Orenstein, Koppel	D		U
Hudson GoGo	8			0-4-0	1924	Hudson	P		U
Muir Hill	9			0-4-0	1925	Muir Hill	P		U
Owned by Gavin Lowe.									
Baguley	10			0-4-0	1917		P		U
Baguley	11			0-4-0	1917		P		U
Greenbat	12			0-4-0	1957	Greenwood, Batley	E	Op	

ABBEY PUMPING STATION

Leicester, LEICESTERSHIRE

Name	Current No.	Type/Class	Origin	Wh.Arr.	Built	Builder			
—	5260			4wPM	1931	Motor Rail Ltd	P		
—	1776			4wPM	1931	F C Hibberd & Co Ltd	P		
—	223700	DM		4wDM	1944	Ruston & Hornsby Ltd	D	Op	N

ALDERNEY RAILWAY

St. Anne, CHANNEL ISLANDS

Name	Current No.	Type/Class	Origin	Wh.Arr.	Built	Builder		
Elizabeth		DM		0-4-0DM	1949	Vulcan Foundry	D	Op

Built at Newton Le Willows.

ALFORD VALLEY RAILWAY

Alford, ABERDEENSHIRE

Name	Current No.	Type/Class	Origin	Wh.Arr.	Built	Builder			
Saccharine				0-4-2T	1914	John Fowler & Co	S	Op	G
Owned by Alford Valley. Formerly worked in a sugar plantation in South Africa.									
Gordon Highlander				4w	1960		D	Op	
Brawlass				4w	1960		D	Op	
James Gordon					2001		D	Op	

Key: Wh.Arr. = Wheel Arrangement $ = Steam D = Diesel P = Petrol E = Electric C = Coach W = Wagon R = Rolling Stock Op = Operational St = Static O = On Display U = Under Restoration G = Pre Group N = Pre Nationalisation

Steam Railway Directory www.steamrailway.com

Abbey Light Railway — Alford Valley Railway

A-Z SHOWING ROLLING STOCK

©HCC Publishing Ltd

Section 1b. 125

Steam Railway Directory   www.steamrailway.com

Almond Valley Heritage Trust — Amberley Working Museum

ALMOND VALLEY HERITAGE TRUST

Livingston, LOTHIAN (WEST)

Name	Current No.	Type/Class	Origin	Builder	Built	Wh. Arr.			
Oak Bank Oil Company No 2	05/576	DH		Andrew Barclay & Sons	1970	4wDH	D	Op	
	20	BE		Baldwin Locomotive Works	1902	4wBE	E	St O	
In Store.				Brook, Victor	1972	4wBE	E	Op	
	38	BE		Brook, Victor	1972	4wBE	E	Op	
	42	BE		Brook, Victor	1972	4wBE	E	Op	
	13			Greenwood	1940	4wDE	D	St O	
	7330	DM		Hunslet Engine Co Ltd	1940	0-4-0DM	D	Op	
		DM		Hunslet Engine Co Ltd	1973	4wDM	D	Op	
		DM		Simplex	1981	4wDM	D	Op	N

AMBERLEY WORKING MUSEUM

Arundel, SUSSEX (WEST)

Name	Current No.	Type/Class	Origin	Builder	Built	Wh. Arr.			
Polar Bear	1781		Groudle Glen	W G Bagnall	1905	2-4-0T	S		G
Previously served the Groudle Glen Railway (Isle of Man).									
Peter	2067			W G Bagnall	1918	0-4-0ST	S		G
Originally purchased by the Ministry of Munitions and delivered to the Canadian Forestry Corps at Longtown, Cumberland.									
Barbouilleur	1126			Decauville	1947	0-4-0WT	S		N
Built as part of a batch for the Ivory Coast but never delivered.									
Peldon	21295	DM		John Fowler & Co	1936	4wDM	D		
Bought for the construction of Abberton Reservoir, Colchester.									
Townsend Hook	4			Fletcher Jennings	1880	0-4-0T	S		G
Scaldwell	23			Peckett & Sons	1913	0-6-0ST	S		G
				Spence	1921	0-4-0T	S		G
				Decauville	1950	0-4-0T			
Monty	6	DM		Orenstein, Koppel	1936	4wDM	D		
Major (The)	2	DM		Orenstein, Koppel	1937	4wDM	D		
		DM		Ransomes, Rapier	1937	4wDM	D		
		DM		Hudson, Hunslet	1944	4wDM	D	P	
Redland	3101	PM		Motor Rail Ltd	1918	4wPM	D		
		DM		Orenstein, Koppel	1937	4wDM	D		
		PM		R A Lister & Co Ltd	1949	4wPM	D	P	
		PM		Motor Rail Ltd	1918	4wPM	D		
	27	DM		Motor Rail Ltd	1934	4wDM	D		
		DM		Motor Rail Ltd	1949	4wDM	D		
Ibstock		DM		Motor Rail Ltd	1951	4wDM	D		
Burt		DM		Simplex	1959	4wDM	D		
CCSW		DM		F C Hibberd & Co Ltd	1936	4wDM	D		N
Thakeham Tiles No 3		DM		Hudson, Hunslet	1941	4wDM	D		N

Name	Current No.	Type/Class	Origin	Wh. Arr.	Builder	Built			
Thakeham Tiles No 4	4	DM		4wDM	Hudson, Hunslet	1948	D		
—		DM		0-4-0DM	Hudswell, Clarke & Co	1948	D		
Star Construction *Not on public display.*		DM		4wDM	Hudson, Hunslet	1941	D		N
—	18	DM		4wDM	Ruston & Hornsby Ltd	1937	D		
—		DM		4wDM	R A Lister & Co Ltd	1949	D		
—		PM		4wPM	F C Hibberd & Co Ltd	1953	P		
—		BE		4wBE	Wingrove, Rogers	1953	E		
—		BE		4wBE	Wingrove, Rogers	1953	E		N

AMERTON RAILWAY

Stafford, STAFFORDSHIRE

Name	Current No.	Type/Class	Origin	Wh. Arr.	Builder	Built			
Isabel				0-4-0ST	W G Bagnall	1897	S	Op	
Pearl 2 *Built at Uttoxeter. Inverted Tank.*				0-4-2IST		1997	S	Op	G
Yellow Peril	747	DM		4wDM	Simplex	1975	D		N
Dreadnought		DM		0-4-0DM	Motor Rail Ltd	1940	D		
Gordon *Under construction.*		DM		0-4-0DM	Baguley	1939	D		N
—		DH		4wDH	Hunslet Engine Co Ltd	1978	D		
Golspie *Awaiting restoration.*		DM		0-4-0DM	Baguley	1935	D		
18ft in length. Designed by Cassel, Henschel.				0-8-0T	Henschel, Cassel	1916	S	Op	U G
—	746	DM		4wDM	Motor Rail Ltd	1975	D		
8tt in length. Designed by Motor Rail Ltd. Owned by John Strike & Nick Curtis.		DM							
—		DM		4wDM	Ruston & Hornsby Ltd	1943	D		U N
13t in length. Designed by Ruston. Owned by John Strike & Nick Curtis.		DM							
—		DM		4wDM	Ruston & Hornsby Ltd	1964	D		
10ft in length. Designed by Ruston. Owned by L Hodgkinson.									

APPLEBY-FRODINGHAM RAILWAY

Brigg, LINCOLNSHIRE (NORTH)

Name	Current No.	Type/Class	Origin	Wh. Arr.	Builder	Built			
Hutnik *Built at Poland. Imported from Poland.*	3138		PKP, Polish State Railways	0-6-0T	Chrzanow	1950	S	Op	G
—	1438			0-4-0ST	Peckett & Sons	1916	S	Op	G

Key: Wh. Arr. = Wheel Arrangement S = Steam D = Diesel E = Electric P = Petrol R = Rolling Stock W = Wagon C = Coach Op = Operational St = Static O = On Display U = Under Restoration G = Pre Group N = Pre Nationalisation

Steam Railway Directory   www.steamrailway.com

Amberley Working Museum — Appleby-Frodingham Railway

A-Z SHOWING ROLLING STOCK

© HCC Publishing Ltd

Section 1b.   127

ARMLEY MILLS

Leeds, YORKSHIRE (WEST)

Name	Current No.	Type/Class	Origin	Wh. Arr.	Built	Builder			
	865			0-6-0ST	1882	Manning, Wardie & Co	S		
Located at Leeds Industrial Museum.									
Jack	684			0-4-0WT	1898	Hunslet Engine Co Ltd	S	Op	G
Located at Leeds Industrial Museum.									
Coffin		BE		0-4-0BE	1933	Greenwood, Batley	E	St	N
Located at Leeds Industrial Museum. Not on public display.									
Barber	441			0-6-2ST	1908	Thomas Green	S	St	U G
Located at Leeds Industrial Museum.									
Cheetal				0-6-0WT	1923	Fowler	S	St O	
Located at Leeds Industrial Museum.									
Hudson Fordson		DM		4wDM	1928	Hudson	D	Op	
Located at Leeds Industrial Museum.									
Layer		DM		0-4-0	1936	Fowler	D	St	N
Located at Leeds Industrial Museum. Not on public display.									
Hudson Hunslet		DM		4wDM	1944	Hunslet Engine Co Ltd	P	Op	
Located at Leeds Industrial Museum.									
Resin		DM		0-4-0DM	1939	Hunslet Engine Co Ltd	D	St	N
Located at Leeds Industrial Museum.									
Nacob		DM		0-4-0DM	1957	Hunslet Engine Co Ltd	D	St	
Located at Leeds Industrial Museum. Not on public display.									
Ficol		DM		0-4-0DM	1948	Hunslet Engine Co Ltd	D	St	N
Located at Leeds Industrial Museum. Not on public display.									
Pitpo				0-4-0	1955	Hunslet Engine Co Ltd	S	St	
Located at Leeds Industrial Museum. Not on public display.									
Calverton		DM		0-4-0DM	1965	Hudswell, Clarke & Co	D	St	N
Located at Leeds Industrial Museum. Not on public display.									
Junin		DM		2-6-2DM	1930	Hudswell, Clarke & Co	D	St	
Located at Leeds Industrial Museum. Is the first production line diesel.									
Union	D571			0-4-0	1932	Hudswell, Clarke & Co	D	St O	
Located at Leeds Industrial Museum.									
Lord Granby	633			0-4-0ST	1902	Hudswell, Clarke & Co	S	St	G
Located at Leeds Industrial Museum. Not on public display.									
Cement	20685	DM		2-4-0DM	1935	Fowler	D	St	G
Located at Leeds Industrial Museum. Not on public display.									
Lofti		DM		0-6-0DM	1953	Hunslet Engine Co Ltd	D	St	
Located at Leeds Industrial Museum. Not on public display.									
Progress		DM		0-6-0DM	1946	Hudswell, Clarke & Co	D	St	N
Located at Leeds Industrial Museum.									
Festival of Britain	299	DM		0-6-0DM	1951	Hudswell, Clarke & Co	D	St	
Located at Leeds Industrial Museum. Not on public display.									
Hodbarrow				0-4-0ST	1882	Hunslet Engine Co Ltd	S	St	G
Located at Leeds Industrial Museum.									
Capper		DM		0-4-0DM	1938	Fowler	D	St O	N
Located at Leeds Industrial Museum.									
Fort William		DM		0-4-0DM	1940	Fowler	D	St	N
Located at Leeds Industrial Museum. Not on public display.									

Name	Current No.	Type/Class	Origin	Wh.Arr.	Built	Builder				
Trecwn	2390	DM		0-4-0DM	1941	Hunslet Engine Co Ltd	D		St O	N
Located at Leeds Industrial Museum.										
Elizabeth	1888			0-4-0ST	1958	Hudswell, Clarke & Co	S		St O	N
Located at Leeds Industrial Museum. Last loco made by Hudswell, Clarke & Co.										
Southam No 2	D625	DM		0-4-0DM	1942	Hudswell, Clarke & Co	D		St	N
Located at Leeds Industrial Museum. Not on public display.										
Luton	1210	BE		0-4-0BE	1930	Greenwood, Batley	E		St O	N
Located at Leeds Industrial Museum.										
Smithy Wood				0-4-0WE	1955	Greenwood, Batley	E			
Located at Leeds Industrial Museum.										
Pioneer	D634			0-6-0	1946	Hudswell, Clarke & Co	D		St	
Located at Leeds Industrial Museum. The first flame-proof mines locomotive. Not on public display.										
Simplex	1369			0-4-0	1918	Motor Rail Ltd, Tramcar Co	P		St O	
Owned by War Department. Located at Leeds Industrial Museum.										
Hunslet Taylor				0-4-0	1971	Hunslet Engine Co Ltd	E		St O	N
Located at Leeds Industrial Museum. Built as an experimental prototype.										

AVON VALLEY RAILWAY

Bristol, BRISTOL

Name	Current No.	Type/Class	Origin	Wh.Arr.	Built	Builder				
Sir Frederick Pile	34058		SR	4-6-2	1947		S		U	N
BR No. 34058. Designed by O V Bulleid. Built at Brighton.										
—	44123		LMS	0-6-0	1925		S		U	N
Prev. No. 4123. Designed by Fowler.										
—	48173		LMS	2-8-0	1943		S		U	N
BR No. 48173. Prev. No. 8173.										
—	D2994		BR	0-6-0DE	1962	Ruston & Hornsby Ltd	D	Op		
BR No. 07010. Built at Lincoln.										
Meteor	7151			0-6-0T	1944	Robert Stephenson, Hawthorn	S	Op		
Edwin Hulse	2			0-6-0T	1950	Robert Stephenson, Hawthorn	S		U	G
Grumpy	WD70031	DH		0-6-0ST	1918	Avonside Engineering Co	S		U	G
Stored out of use.										
—				0-4-0DM	1941	Drewry Car Co	D			N
—		DH		4wDH	1963	Thomas Hill	D			
Awaiting restoration.										
General Lord Robertson	610	DH		0-8-0DH	1963	Sentinel	D			
Kingswood		DM		0-4-0DM	1959	Andrew Barclay & Sons	D		U	
—		DM		0-4-0DM	1941	Andrew Barclay & Sons	D			N
In store.										
Basil		DM		4wDM	1945	Ruston & Hornsby Ltd	D		U	
—		DM		4wDM	1941	Ruston & Hornsby Ltd	D			N
Chassis only.										
—				4wDM	1947	Ruston & Hornsby Ltd	D			
Chassis only.										
Western Pride	D1171	DM		0-6-0DM	1959	Hudswell, Clarke & Co	D			

Key: Wh.Arr. = Wheel Arrangement   S = Steam   D = Diesel   E = Electric   P = Petrol   C = Coach   W = Wagon   R = Rolling Stock   Op = Operational   St = Static   O = On Display   U = Under Restoration   G = Pre Group   N = Pre Nationalisation

A-Z SHOWING ROLLING STOCK

Steam Railway Directory www.steamrailway.com

Avon Valley Railway — Avon Valley Railway

No.	Description	Type	Year	Builder	P	Op	
In store.							
Engineer No 1	PWM3769	4wPM	1953	Wickham		C	U
In store.							
Littleton No 5		4wPM	1959	Wickham		C	U
		0-6-0ST	1922	Manning, Wardle & Co		C	
3051	First Open		1954			C	
Prev. No. DB977492. Awaiting restoration.							
1867	Restaurant Miniature Buffet		1961			C	
Prev. No. 977752.							
1933	Restaurant Unclassified (Buffet)		1959			C	
In use as part of 'Steam and Cuisine'.							
2599			1959			C	
Dormitory coach for members.							
3089	First Open		1959			C	Op
Prev. No. DB977351. Awaiting restoration.							
3745	Tourist Second Open		1953			C	
In use as part of 'Steam and Cuisine'.							
3746	Tourist Second Open		1953			C	
Awaiting restoration.							
3749	Tourist Second Open		1953			C	
Awaiting restoration.							
3815	Tourist Second Open		1953			C	
Prev. No. AD3305. Awaiting restoration.							
3991	Tourist Second Open		1954			C	
Prev. No. DB977627. Awaiting restoration.							
4035	Tourist Second Open		1956			C	
Seating for buffet, Bitton bears coach.							
4058	Tourist Second Open		1956			C	
Awaiting restoration.							
6839	Brake Composite Corridor		1935			C	
Prev. No. DS70244.							
9208	Brake Second Open		1955			C	
Prev. No. DB977134. In use as part of 'Steam and Cuisine'.							
13231	First Corridor		1959			C	U
Prev. No. DB977132.							
14031	Brake First Corridor		1966			C	
Awaiting restoration.							
25040	Second Corridor		1956			C	
25299	Second Corridor		1957			C	
25735	Second Corridor		1961			C	
Prev. No. DB977635. Awaiting restoration.							
25972	Second Corridor		1962			C	
Prev. No. 99629. Awaiting restoration.							
34111	Brake Second Corridor		1951			C	
Prev. No. AD5318.							
34531	Brake Second Corridor		1955			C	

Prev. No. DB977410. Awaiting restoration.

Current No.	Type/Class	Built	status
35174	Brake Second Corridor		C

Prev. No. AD5319. Awaiting restoration.

| 35255 | Brake Second Corridor | 1958 | C Op |
| 35481 | Brake Second Corridor | 1958 | C |

Prev. No. 99153. | | 1962 | |

BALA LAKE RAILWAY

Bala, GWYNEDD

Name	Current No.	Type/Class	Origin	Wh.Arr.	Built	Builder				
Chilmark	12	DM		4wDM	1940	Ruston & Hornsby Ltd	D	Op	U	N
Meirionnydd	11	DM		Bo-Bo	1973	Severn Lamb	D	Op	U	
Bob Davies				4wDM	1983	Baguley, Drewry	D	Op		
Holy War	3			0-4-0ST	1902	Hunslet Engine Co Ltd	S	Op		
Maid Marian	5			0-4-0ST	1903	Hunslet Engine Co Ltd	S	Op	G	

BARLEYLANDS MINIATURE RAILWAY

Billericay, ESSEX

Name	Current No.	Type/Class	Origin	Wh.Arr.	Built	Builder			
Britannia	70000			4-6-2	1981	J Clarke	S	Op	
Black Prince	92203			2-10-0	1980	J Clarke	S	Op	
Vulcan				2-6-0	1972	J Clarke	S	Op	
Gowrie			North Wales Narrow Gauge	0-6-4T	1989	H Dyson	S	Op	
Maid of Benfleet				4-4-2T	1970	J Clarke	S	St	O
Royal Scot	6100			4-6-0	1985		S	St	O
							R	C	Op
							R	W	Op O
							R	W	Op O

BR No. 70000. 8ft in length. Owned by H R Philpot & Sons. Originally named Duke of Benfleet.
BR No. 92203. 8ft in length. Owned by H R Philpot & Sons. Originally named Benfleet Star.
6ft in length. Owned by H R Philpot & Sons.
Designed by Hunslet Engine Co Ltd. Owned by H R Philpot & Sons.
Owned by H R Philpot & Sons. Originally 4-4-0T.
BR No. 46100. 7ft in length. Owned by H R Philpot & Sons. Non working model. Built mainly of wood.

Nine owned by railway. 8ft in length. Owned by H R Philpot & Sons.

Two owned by railway. 8ft in length. Owned by H R Philpot & Sons.

Owned by H R Philpot & Sons. Converted from passenger coaches.

BARROW HILL ROUNDHOUSE

Chesterfield, DERBYSHIRE

Name	Current No.	Type/Class	Origin	Wh.Arr.	Built	Builder			
	03066	DM /03	BR	0-6-0	1959	BR	D	St	O

Key: Wh.Arr. = Wheel Arrangement   S = Steam   D = Diesel   E = Electric   P = Petrol   R = Rolling Stock   W = Wagon   C = Coach   Op = Operational   St = Static   O = On Display   U = Under Restoration   G = Pre Group   N = Pre Nationalisation

Steam Railway Directory   www.steamrailway.com

©HCC Publishing Ltd

Barrow Hill Roundhouse — Barrow Hill Roundhouse

Steam Railway Directory   www.steamrailway.com

No. / Name	Notes	Orig.	Wheel	Year	Builder		
03094 (DM /03)	*BR No. 03066. Prev. No. D2066. 26ft in length. Owned by T Dean.* / *BR No. 03094. Prev. No. D2094. 26ft in length. Owned by T Dean. Built at Doncaster.*	BR	0-6-0DM	1960	BR	D	U
20056	*BR No. 20056. Prev. No. D8056. 46.75ft in length. Designed by English Electric. Owned by T Dean.*	BR	Bo-Bo	1961	Robert Stephenson, Hawthorn	D	Op
45060 Sherwood Forester	*BR No. D101. Prev. No. D101. Owned by Pioneer Diesel Group.*	BR	Co-Co	1961	BR	D	St
Howe 50023	*BR No. 50023. Prev. No. D423. Designed by English Electric. Built at Newton-Le-Willows.*	BR	Co-Co	1967	English Electric	D	St
2553	*Owned by Marston Brewery. Was originally a 0-4-0ST and was rebuilt in 1955.*		0-4-0	1931	Hawthorn Leslie & Co	D	Op
Harry 2589	*Built at Darlington.*		0-4-0	1956	Robert Stephenson, Hawthorn	D	U
20096	*BR No. 20096. Prev. Nos. 3003, 8255, D8096. 46.75ft in length. Designed by English Electric. Owned by T Dean.*	BR	Bo-Bo	1961	Robert Stephenson, Hawthorn	D	St
20135	*BR No. 20135. Prev. No. D8135. 46.75ft in length. Designed by English Electric. Owned by Class 20 Work Group. Built at Newton-le-Willows.*		Bo-Bo	1966	English Electric	D	Op
25067	*BR No. 25067. Prev. No. D5217. 50.75ft in length. Owned by Martin Sargent. Built at Derby.*		Bo-Bo	1963	BR	D	St
26007	*BR No. 26007. Prev. No. D5300. 50.75ft in length. Built at Birmingham.*		Bo-Bo	1958	Birmingham Carriage & Wagon Co Ltd	D	U
26011	*BR No. 26011. 50.75ft in length. Owned by Martin Sargent. Built at Birmingham.*		Bo-Bo	1958	BRCW	D	St O
E3003	*BR No. 81002. Owned by AC Locomotive Group. Built at Rugby.*	BR	Bo-Bo	1958		E	St O U
82008	*BR No. 82008. Prev. No. E3054. Designed by Beyer, Peacock. Owned by AC Locomotive Group.*		Bo-Bo	1961	Beyer, Peacock	E	St O
E3035	*BR No. 83012. Designed by English Electric. Owned by AC Locomotive Group. Built at Newton-le-Willows.*	BR	Bo-Bo	1961	English Electric	E	St O
E3036	*BR No. 84001. Designed by North British. Owned by AC Locomotive Group.*	BR	Bo-Bo	1960	North British Locomotive Co	E	O U
E3061	*BR No. 85101. Prev. Nos. E3061, 85006. Owned by AC Locomotive Group.*	BR	Bo-Bo	1961	BR		
34699 Brake Second Corridor	*Owned by Deltic Preservation Society. Built at Wolverton.*			1955			C
80212	*63.5ft in length. Owned by A C Locomotive Group. Built at Wolverton.*			1958			C
80257	*Owned by Pioneer Diesel Group.*			1958			C
W94034	*57.75ft in length. Owned by Pioneer Diesel Group.*			1958			C
94058	*Owned by Martin Sargent.*			1958	Pressed Steel Co Ltd		C
95199	*Owned by A C Locomotive Group.*			1972			C
AD975814							C

© HCC Publishing Ltd

Note	Number	Type	Wh.Arr.	Owner	Year	Status
74ft in length. Owned by Pioneer Diesel Group.	B953231	Brake Van		BR	1956	R
Owned by Birmingham Railway Museum.	B954215	Brake Van		BR	1958	R
Owned by M Allcock & M Allen.		Brake Van			1899	R
Owned by 1708 Trust.	DM730687	Brake Van		LMS	1940	R
Owned by M Allcock & M Allen.	DW35403	Guards Van			1942	R
Owned by M Sargent.	ADM40252	Fish Van		LMS	1949	Op O
Owned by P Fox, M Jacob & S Hatton.	DB977241				1960	Op O
Owned by M Sargent.	042227	Ventilated Van			1950	Op
Owned by M Allcock.	99625	Generator Coach			1955	Op
Owned by AC Locomotive Group.	S1874S	Van			1940	Op
Owned by Class 20 Work Group.	1101					W
Owned by BHESS.	1112					W
Owned by BHESS.		Flat Wagon			1941	W
Owned by BHESS.		Flat Wagon				W
Owned by BHESS.		Flat Wagon		MR	1898	W
Owned by BHESS.	DS61976				1928	Op
Capacity 20 tonnes. Owned by BHESS.	DB787287				1963	W
	DB787163		4w		1963	W
Owned by Martin Allen.	DB998017				1959	W
Owned by AC Locomotive Group.						W

Steam Railway Directory   www.steamrailway.com

Barrow Hill Roundhouse — Barrow Hill Roundhouse

Key: Wh.Arr. = Wheel Arrangement   S = Steam   D = Diesel   E = Electric   P = Petrol   R = Rolling Stock   W = Wagon   C = Coach   Op = Operational   St = Static   O = On Display   U = Under Restoration   G = Pre Group   N = Pre Nationalisation

A-Z SHOWING ROLLING STOCK

BATTLEFIELD LINE

Nuneaton, WARWICKSHIRE

Name	Current No.	Type/Class	Origin	Wh. Arr.	Built	Builder				
Sir Gomer	1859			0-6-0ST	1932	Peckett & Sons	s		Op	N
28ft in length. Owned by Shackerstone Railway Society.										
Lamport No 3	2670			0-6-0ST	1942	W G Bagnall	s		Op	N
Owned by Leicester Ind Group.										
Northern Gas Board No 1	2142	ST	Northern Gas Board	0-4-0ST	1953	Peckett & Sons	s		Op	
23ft in length. Owned by Darlington Railway.										
Linda	2648			0-4-0ST	1941	W G Bagnall	s			u N
Owned by Dave Johnson.										
Richard III	3			0-6-0T	1949	Robert Stephenson, Hawthorn	s		St	u
Owned by Dave Prattey.										
William	9599			4wVBT	1956	Sentinel	s		St	u
Owned by Evans.										
	D5518		BR	A1A-A1A	1958	Brush Electrical Engineering	D		Op	
BR No. 31101. Prev. No. D5518. Built at Loughborough. Re engined in 1969, with electrical power unit replacing original mirlees unit.										
	11215	DM /04	BR	0-6-0DM	1956	Robert Stephenson, Hawthorn	D			
BR No. D2245. Prev. No. D2245.										
	06003	DM /06	BR	0-4-0DM	1958	Andrew Barclay & Sons	D			
BR No. 06003. Prev. Nos. 97804, D2420. Built at Kilmarnock.										
Victor	2996			0-6-0ST	1950	W G Bagnall	s			G
Waleswood	11			0-4-0ST	1906	Hudswell, Clarke & Co	s			
				0-4-0ST	1925	Hunslet Engine Co Ltd	s			
Dunlop No 7		DM		0-4-0ST	1951	Peckett & Sons	s			
Toby	10252			4wDM	1945	Ruston & Hornsby Ltd	D		Op	N
Built at Lincoln. Converted to 'Thomas' for Thomas events.										
Jessie	E1104	DH		4wDH	1965	Sentinel	D		c	
Owned by Shackerstone Railway.										

BEAMISH

Stanley, COUNTY DURHAM

Name	Current No.	Type/Class	Origin	Wh. Arr.	Built	Builder				
	876		NER	0-6-0	1889	NER	s		St O	G
BR No. 65033. Prev. Nos. 5033, 876. Designed by Worsdell. Built at Gateshead.										
Twizell	3		Beamish Wagon Way	0-6-0T	1891	Robert Stephenson	s			u G
Located at Tanfield Railway. On long term loan to Tanfield.										
	14			0-4-0ST	1914	Hawthorn Leslie & Co	s		St O	G
South Durham Malleable No 5	5			0-4-0ST	1880	Grange Ironworks	s		St O	G
Rebuilt using Black Hawthorn parts.										
Coffee Pot			Dorking Lime	0-4-0VB	1871	Head Wrightson	s		St O U	
Designed by T Head.										
Lewin	18		Seaham Harbour	0-4-0WT	1877	Stephen Lewin	s		St O U	
Designed by Stephen Lewin.										
			Hetton Colliery	0-4-0VG	1851		s		St O	

Owned by NRM National Coln.												
—	E2		Harton Coal Co	0-4-0	1908	Siemens, Schukert	E		St	O		
Designed by Siemens, Schukert. Overhead wire electric.												
Jacob	680	PM	Jacobs Aintree	0-4-0PM	1916	McEwan, Pratt	P				U	G
—	E1		Consett Iron Co	0-4-0VCT	1887	Black, Hawthorn	S		St			G
In store.												
—			War Department Light Railways	0-4-0	1916		D		Op			
On loan to Imperial War Museum.												
—			Gas Board	0-4-0	1963	Ruston	D		Op			
Locomotion	1		Stockton & Darlington Railway	0-4-0	1825	Robert Stephenson	S		Op	O		G
Designed by G Stephenson. Owned by Locomotion Trust. A replica of the 'Locomotion'.												
Steam Elephant			Wallsend Colliery	0-6-0VCG	1815	Hawks, Wallsend	S		Op	O		G
Designed by Buddle, Chapman.												
—	818				1903			C				
—	118				1913			C				
BR No. E2118.												
—				4	1915	Charles Roberts & Co Ltd		W				
—	44842							W				
—				4+4	1902			W				
—	NER92189			6w	1899	NER		W				
—	NER108635			4		NER		W				
Capacity 15 tonnes.												
—	95861			4	1917			W				
Capacity 10 tonnes.												
—	03938			4	1901			W				
—	1319			4	1902			W				
Capacity 15 tonnes.												
—	46152			4	1903			W				
Capacity 20 tonnes.												
—	64994			4	1900			W				
Capacity 10.5 tonnes.												
—	81			4	1880			W				
Capacity 8 tonnes.												
—	102833			4	1906			W				
Capacity 12 tonnes.												
—	1077			4	1887			W				
Capacity 10.5 tonnes.												
—				4	1870			W				
Capacity 3 tonnes.												

Key: Wh.Arr. = Wheel Arrangement **S** = Steam **D** = Diesel **E** = Electric **P** = Petrol **R** = Rolling Stock **W** = Wagon **C** = Coach **Op** = Operational **St** = Static **O** = On Display **U** = Under Restoration **G** = Pre Group **N** = Pre Nationalisation

©*HCC* Publishing Ltd

BEER HEIGHTS

Seaton, DEVON

Name	Current No.	Type/Class	Wh. Arr.	Built	Origin	Builder	Status
Mr P	7	Op	2-4-2T & Tender			Beer Heights Light Railway	s
Thomas II	4		0-4-2ST & Tender	1979		Roger Marsh & Co	s Op

11ft in length. Designed by John MacDougall.

Dickie	3		0-4-2	1975		D Curwen	s

10ft in length. Designed by Roger Marsh.

Linda	5		2-4-0ST	1983		Don Clarke	Op

10ft in length. Designed by D Curwen.

Gem	8		0-6-0T	1999		Beer Heights Light Railway	s

10ft in length. Designed by Hunslet Engine Co Ltd.
8ft in length. Designed by Roger Marsh, Beer Heights Light Railway.

Jimmy	9		2-4-2	2001		Beer Heights Light Railway	s
	6	DH	4-4wDH	1984		Severn Lamb	D

11ft in length. Designed by John MacDougall. Loco under construction in Beer Heights Light Railway workshops.
9ft in length. Designed by Severn Lamb, Beer Heights Light Railway.

		4 Seat Bogie Open Coaches				Cromar, White, Beer Heights Light Railway	C Op

22 owned by railway. 9ft in length. Designed by Beer Heights Light Railway.

	12		4w	2001		Beer Heights Light Railway	W

12 owned by railway. Designed by Beer Heights Light Railway.

BICTON WOODLAND RAILWAY

Budleigh Salterton, DEVON

Name	Current No.	Type/Class	Wh. Arr.	Built	Origin	Builder	Status
Bicton	2	DM	4wDM	1942		Ruston & Hornsby Ltd	Op D
Clinton	4	DM	0-4-0	1941		Hudson, Hunslet	Op s D
Sir Walter Raleigh			4wDM	2000		Alan Keef Ltd	Op N

BLUEBELL RAILWAY

Uckfield, SUSSEX (EAST)

Name	Current No.	Type/Class	Wh. Arr.	Built	Origin	Builder	Status
Fenchurch	672		0-6-0T	1872	London Brighton & South Coast Railway		Op s
Stepney	55		0-6-0T	1875	London Brighton & South Coast Railway		Op s
Birch Grove	473		0-6-2T	1898	London Brighton & South Coast Railway		Op s

— BR No. 32473. Prev. Nos. B473, 2473.

	592		0-6-0	1902	South Eastern & Chatham Railway	SECR	St O s G

— BR No. 31592. Prev. Nos. A592, 1592, 31592, DS239, 51.5ft in length. Owned by C Class Locomotive Preservation Society.

	27		0-6-0T	1910	South Eastern & Chatham Railway	SECR	s G

— BR No. 31027. Prev. Nos. A27, 1027. Built at Ashford. Dismantled and awaiting overhaul.

	178		0-6-0T	1910	South Eastern & Chatham Railway	SECR	Op G

— BR No. 31178. Prev. Nos. A178, 1178. Built at Ashford. Overhaul in progress.

Bluebell

Name / Details	No.	Railway / Builder	Year	Wh.Arr.	Type	Status	Era
Bluebell — BR No. 31323. Prev. Nos. A323, 1323.	323	South Eastern & Chatham Railway	1910	0-6-0T	S	St O	G
Normandy — BR No. 30583. Prev. Nos. 0488, EKR5, 3488, 30583. Designed by Adams.	488	LSWR / Neilson & Co	1885	4-4-2T	S	St O	N
BR No. 30096. Prev. No. 696. Designed by Adams. (Dock Tank /B4)	96	LSWR	1893	0-4-0T	S	Op	N
Earl of Berkeley — BR No. 9017. Designed by C B Collett. Built at Swindon. Last operational 1987.	3217	GWR	1938	4-4-0	S	St O	N
BR No. 31618. Prev. No. A618. Designed by Maunsell. Built at Brighton.	1618	SR	1928	2-6-0	S	U	N
BR No. 31638. Prev. No. A638. Designed by Maunsell. Built at Ashford.	1638	SR	1931	2-6-0	S	St O	N
BR No. 30847. Designed by Maunsell. Built at Eastleigh.	847	SR	1936	4-6-0	S	U	N
BR No. 30541. Built at Eastleigh.	541	SR	1939	0-6-0	S	St O	N
C1 — BR No. 33001. Designed by O V Bulleid. Built at Brighton.	C1	SR	1942	0-6-0	S	St O	N
BR No. 30064. Prev. No. 64. Awaiting overhaul.	30064	SR	1943	0-6-0T	S	St O	N
Blackmoor Vale — BR No. 21C123. Built at Brighton. BR No. 34023. Designed by O V Bulleid. Built at Brighton.	21C123	SR	1946	4-6-2	S	St O	N
Camelot — Owned by Camelot Locomotive Society.	73082	BR	1955	4-6-0	S	Op	
—	75027	BR	1952	4-6-0	S	Op	
—	78059	BR	1956	2-6-0	S	Op	U
Owned by 80064 Locomotive Fund. Awaiting overhaul.	80064	BR	1953	2-6-4T	S	Op	U
Ex Barry scrapyard condition.	80100	BR	1955	2-6-4T	S	St O	U
Restoration nearing completion.	80151	BR	1957	2-6-4T	S	St	U
—	92240	BR	1958	2-10-0	S	Op	
Baxter — Awaiting 10 year boiler exam.	3		1877	0-4-0T	S	U	
Dismantled and under overhaul.	957	James, Frederick Howard Ltd	1926	4w PM	P	Op	
Stamford — Built at Avonside.	24		1927	0-6-0ST	S	U	
Awaiting Overhaul.	263	South Eastern & Chatham Railway	1905	0-4-4T	S	St O	
Stowe — Prev. No. 30928.	928	SR	1934	4-4-0	S	St O	
Sir Archibald Sinclair — Prev. No. 21C159. Rebuilt in 1960.	34059	SR	1947	4-6-2	S	U	

Key: Wh.Arr. = Wheel Arrangement   S = Steam   D = Diesel   E = Electric   P = Petrol   R = Rolling Stock   W = Wagon   C = Coach   Op = Operational   St = Static   U = Under Restoration   O = On Display   G = Pre Group   N = Pre Nationalisation

Steam Railway Directory   www.steamrailway.com

Bluebell Railway — Bluebell Railway

A-Z SHOWING ROLLING STOCK

©HCC Publishing Ltd

Steam Railway Directory www.steamrailway.com

	No.	Type	Railway	Wheels	Builder	Year	St O
Sharpthorn	4			0-6-0ST	Manning, Wardle & Co	1877	C
Dismantled body only.	35	Second	LBSCR	4w		1856	C
	60	Saloon	LBSCR			1913	C
	328	Third	LBSCR	4w		1890	C
Body only.	661	First	LBSCR	4w		1880	C
Previously 6w.	676	Brake Third	LBSCR	4w		1875	C
Body only.	949	Brake Third	LBSCR	4w		1881	C
Body only.	7598	First	LBSCR			1903	C
	48	Brake Third	LCDR	6w		1894	C
Previously Brake Second.	106	Brake Second	LCDR	4w		1889	C
	5546	Composite	SER			1891	C
Reconstructed by SR in 1927.	33		SER			1891	C
	950	Second Saloon Brake	SECR			1907	C Op
Prev. No. 3582.	971	Third	SECR			1923	C
Prev. No. 1434. 100 seater.	1061	Third Brake	SECR			1909	C
Prev. No. 3334.	1098	Third	SECR			1922	C Op
Prev. No. 1416.	1170	Third Brake	SECR			1912	C
Prev. No. 3410.	3363	Lavatory Brake Third	SECR			1910	C
	320	Lavatory Third	LSWR			1900	C
Prev. Nos. 1228, 288. Rebuilt and lengthened in 1935.	494	Third Corridor	LSWR			1911	C
Prev. No. 673.	1520	Lavatory Brake Third	LSWR			1910	C u
Prev. No. 2975.	368	Composite	MR		Ashbury	1898	C u
Prev. Nos. 515, 9702.	387	Brake Third	MR		Ashbury	1898	C Op
Prev. Nos. 512, 2761.	394	Full Brake	MR		Ashbury	1900	C Op
Prev. Nos. 518, 6702.	412	Composite	MR		Cravens	1900	C u
Prev. Nos. 516, 9705.	43909	Directors Saloon	GNR			1897	C Op

Bluebell Railway — Bluebell Railway

Notes	No.	Description	Region	Year	Status
Prev. Nos. 706, 706E, 942090.	15843	Observation Car	LNWR	1913	C U
Prev. Nos. LNWR 1503, 5316.	806	Semi Royal Saloon	LNWR	1903	C
Prev. Nos. LNWR 74, 5074, LMS 10506, 806..	1309	Third Open	SR	1935	C Op
	1336	Third Open	SR	1933	C
	1365	Dining Third	SR	1927	C
	2356	Third Corridor	SR	1931	C
	3687	Brake Third Corridor	SR	1930	C
	3724	Brake Third Corridor	SR	1933	C
	4441	Unclassed Brake	SR	1933	C
	4444	Unclassed Brake	SR	1939	C
	4922	Travelling Post Office	SR	1930	C
	5644	Composite Corridor	SR	1929	C
	6575	Brake Composite Corridor	SR	1935	C Op
	6686	Brake Composite Corridor	SR	1935	C Op
	7864	Kitchen Buffet	SR	1932	C
Rebuilt in 1947.	1456	Third Open	SR	1947	C
	1464	Third Open	SR	1950	C Op
	1481	Third Open	SR	1950	C Op
	1482	Third Open	SR	1950	C Op
	2515	Semi Open Brake Third	SR	1951	C Op
	2526	Semi Open Brake Third	SR	1951	C
Undergoing overhaul.	4227	Semi Open Brake Third with Coupe	SR	1948	C
	4279	Semi Open Brake Third	SR	1949	C Op
	5768	Composite Corridor	SR	1947	C
	175	Pullman First Kitchen		1924	Op
	229	Pullman Third		1928	Op
	311	Pullman First Kitchen		1960	Op
	398	First Sleeper	LMS	1952	C
Used as volunteer sleeping accomodation.	603	Sleeper /Third Class	LMS	1951	C
Used as volunteer sleeping accomodation.	623	Sleeper /Third Class	LMS	1952	C
Used as volunteer sleeping accomodation.	1818	Restaurant Miniature Buffet	BR	1960	C Op
	1838	Restaurant Miniature Buffet	BR	1959	C Op
	1987	Restaurant Unclassified (Buffet)	BR	1961	C

Key: Wh.Arr. = Wheel Arrangement   **S** = Steam   **D** = Diesel   **E** = Electric   **P** = Petrol   **R** = Rolling Stock   **W** = Wagon   **C** = Coach   **Op** = Operational   **St** = Static   **O** = On Display   **U** = Under Restoration   **G** = Pre Group   **N** = Pre Nationalisation

Steam Railway Directory   www.steamrailway.com

Steam Railway Directory www.steamrailway.com

Notes	No.	Type	Company		Year			
	3116	First Open	BR		1961			C Op
	4941	Second Open	BR		1962			C Op
	4957	Second Open	BR		1962			C Op
	5034	Saloon	BR		1962			C Op
	16210	Composite Corridor	BR		1961			C Op
	16263	Composite Corridor	BR		1963			C
	21271	Brake Composite	BR		1964			C
	25728	Second Corridor	BR		1961			C Op
	25769	Second Corridor	BR		1961			C Op
	35448	Brake Second Corridor	BR		1963			C Op
	153	Passenger Luggage Van	SECR		1922	R		
	270	Milk Van	LBSCR		1908	R		
Prev. Nos. 2178, 1525S.	719	Birdcage Brake Van	SECR		1905	R		
Prev. Nos. 616, 1601S.	5498	Ventilated Luggage Van	LSWR		1920	R		
Prev. Nos. 1584, DS1686.	404	Van	SR	4w	1937	R		Op
	419	Van	SR		1937	R		Op
	2462	Gangwayed Bogie Luggage Van	SR		1910			Op
	4430	Milk Tank	SR	6w	1933			Op
	32975	Brake Gangwayed (Z)	LMS	6w	1938			Op
	5706	Road Van	LSWR		1898			Op
Prev. Nos. 1541, SR 54663. 21ft in length. Capacity 1 tonnes.	11916	Brake Van	SECR		1923		W	
Prev. No. SR 55477.	55490	Brake Van	SECR		1923		W	
Owned by Port Line Group.	17908	Brake Van	GWR		1913		W	
	55993	Brake Van	SR		1930		W	
	56290	Bogie Vacuum Brake Van	SR		1936		W	
	49018	Brake Van	War Department Light Railways		1942		W	
	DS 62864	Shark Ballast Plough	BR		1949		W	
	590	Covered Goods Van	LBSCR				W	
Capacity 8 tonnes.	2773	Covered Goods Van	LSWR				W	
Capacity 10 tonnes.	8112	Covered Goods Van	LSWR		1912		W	
Capacity 10 tonnes.	15750	Covered Goods Van	SECR				W	Op
	44611	Covered Goods Van	SR				W	Op
Capacity 10 tonnes.	47588	Covered Goods Van	SR		1931		W	Op
Capacity 12 tonnes.								

Capacity	Number	Type	Company	Year	Status
Capacity 12 tonnes.	506190	Covered Goods Van	LMS	1935	W
Capacity 12 tonnes.	813	Covered Goods Van	LMS	1945	W
Capacity 10 tonnes. Insulated and heated.	570027	Covered Goods Van	LMS	1946	W
—	402	Covered Goods Van	War Department Light Railways	1940	W
—	B761349	Covered Goods Van	BR	1956	W
—	B772972	Covered Goods Van	BR	1914	W
Capacity 10 tonnes.	3346	Open Goods Wagon	LBSCR		W
Capacity 12 tonnes.	5542	7 Plank Open Wagon	SECR		W
Capacity 12 tonnes.	16358	7 Plank Open Wagon	SECR		W Op
Capacity 12 tonnes.	50899	5 Plank Open High Bar	SECR		W
Capacity 12 tonnes.	59252	7 Plank Open Wagon	SECR		W
Capacity 12 tonnes.	59305	7 Plank Open Wagon	SECR		W
Capacity 12 tonnes.	9604	5 Plank Open	SR		W
Capacity 10 tonnes.	9752	Open High Bar	SR		W
Capacity 12 tonnes.	30004	8 Plank Open Goods	SR		W
Capacity 12 tonnes.	DM411245	6 Plank Open High Bar	LMS	1934	W
Capacity 12 tonnes.	66071	Open High Bar	LMS	1934	W
Capacity 10 tonnes.	87782	5 Plank Open High Bar	GWR		W
Capacity 12 tonnes.	59685	Open Goods Wagon	SR	1933	W
Capacity 14 tonnes.	39617	Open Carriage Truck	SR	1936	W
Capacity 40 tonnes.	57889	Bogie Bolster	SR	1944	W Op
Capacity 40 tonnes.	57949	Bogie Bolster	SR	1928	W Op
Capacity 20 tonnes.	DS 62002	Dropside Engineers Wagon	SR	1937	W
Capacity 12 tonnes.	474558	3 Plank Drop Side Ballast Wagon	LMS		W

Key: Wh.Arr. = Wheel Arrangement   S = Steam   D = Diesel   E = Electric   P = Petrol   R = Rolling Stock   W = Wagon   C = Coach   Op = Operational   St = Static   O = On Display   U = Under Restoration   G = Pre Group   N = Pre Nationalisation

Bluebell Railway — Bluebell Railway

Steam Railway Directory   www.steamrailway.com

Bluebell Railway — Bodmin & Wenford Railway

Current No.	Type/Class	Origin	Built	Builder	Status
Capacity 12 tonnes.					
480222	3 Plank Drop Side Ballast Wagon	LMS	1949		W
Capacity 24 tonnes.					
B458525	Drop Side Ballast Wagon	BR	1951		W Op
B461224	Drop Side Ballast Wagon	Br	1952		W Op
D8983103	Dogfish Ballast Hopper	BR			W Op
Capacity 24 tonnes.					
D8984082	Drop Side Wagon	BR	1957		W Op
D8984506	Drop Side Wagon	BR	1955		W Op
D8986419	Drop Side Wagon	BR	1956		W Op
D8986591	Drop Side Wagon	BR	1956		W Op
D8987403	Drop Side Wagon	BR			W Op
D8988395	Drop Side Wagon	BR			W Op
D8991391	Drop Side Wagon	BR			W Op
D8992780	Dogfish Ballast Hopper	BR	1959		W Op
Capacity 24 tonnes.					
D8993210	Dogfish Ballast Hopper	BR	1957		W Op
Capacity 24 tonnes.					
D8993217	Dogfish Ballast Hopper	BR	1957		W Op
Capacity 24 tonnes.					
D8993348	Dogfish Ballast Hopper	BR	1957		W Op
92	Tool Van	GWR	1922		R
100677	Sleeper Wagon	GWR	1938		W
B904134	Machinery Wagon	BR	1957		W
B900920	Bogie Well Wagon	BR	1960		W
RS1083	Steam Crane	MOWT	1943		R
1748S	Hand Crane	MOWT	1943	Ransomes, Rapier	R Op
1748SM	Match Wagon For Hand Crane	MOWT	1943	Joseph Booth & Sons	R Op

BODMIN & WENFORD RAILWAY

Bodmin, CORNWALL

Name	Current No.	Type/Class	Origin	Wh. Arr.	Built	Builder		
Built at Swindon.	5552			2-6-2T	1928		S	U
Built at Swindon.	3802			2-8-0	1938		S	U
Wadebridge Built at Brighton.	34007			4-6-2	1945		S	U
Swiftsure	2857			0-6-0ST	1943	Hunslet Engine Co Ltd	S	Op
Located at Peak Rail.	7597			0-6-0T	1949		S	Op
Ugly	62			0-6-0ST	1950		S	Op
	2766			0-6-0ST	1944	W G Bagnall	S	St

Built at Darlington.

Built at Derby.

Name	Current No.	Type/Class	Origin	Wh.Arr.	Builder	Built	Power	Status
—	19							
Alfred	3058			0-4-0ST	W G Bagnall	1950	S	Op
	3121			0-4-0ST	W G Bagnall	1953	S	Op
Triumph	500042			0-4-0F	W G Bagnall	1957		St
	D3452					1968	D E	Op
	D3559					1957	D E	Op
						1958	D E	Op
	D6527			Bo-Bo		1960	D E	Op
	D8166			Bo-Bo		1966	D E	Op
	D8197			Bo-Bo		1967	D E	St
Progress	1	DH		0-4-0DH	Fowler	1945	D	Op
Peter	2	DM		0-4-0DM	Fowler	1940	D	Op
Lec	3	DM		4wDM		1960	D	Op
	M52054		BR			1959	D	St
	51947		BR			1960	D	
	DRT80169	Steam Crane		6w		1947	S	Op

Capacity 10 tonnes.

BO'NESS & KINNEIL RAILWAY

Bo'ness, LOTHIAN (WEST)

Name	Current No.	Type/Class	Origin	Wh.Arr.	Builder	Built	Power	Status
Maude	42			0-4-0ST		1887	S	
	673		NBR	0-6-0	Neilson & Co	1891	S	G

BR No. 65243. Prev. Nos. 9673, 5243. Designed by Matthew Holmes.

| | 419 | | | 0-4-4T | | 1907 | S | Op |

BR No. 55189. Prev. No. 15189. Designed by J F Macintosh.

| Morayshire | 246 | | | 4-4-0 | LNER | 1928 | S | U N |

BR No. 62712. Prev. No. 2712. Designed by Gresley. Owned by Royal Scottish Museum. Built at Darlington.

| Sovereign | | | LMS | 4-6-0 | LMS | 1945 | S | Op N |

BR No. 44871. Prev. No. 4871. Designed by W A Stanier. Built at Crewe.

| | 80105 | | | 2-6-4T | | 1955 | S | |

Designed by R A Riddles.

Lord Roberts	19	NCB		0-6-0T	Hunslet Engine Co Ltd	1954	S	
Kelton Fell				0-6-0T		1902	S	
City of Aberdeen				0-4-0ST	Black, Hawthorn	1876	S	
Borrowstowness				0-4-0ST	Andrew Barclay & Sons	1899	S	
Lady Victoria					Andrew Barclay & Sons	1916	S	
Lord King				0-4-0ST	Hawthorn Leslie & Co	1926	S	
Clydesmill				0-4-0ST	Andrew Barclay & Sons	1928	S	
				0-4-0ST	Andrew Barclay & Sons	1937	S	

Key: Wh.Arr. = Wheel Arrangement   **S** = Steam   **D** = Diesel   **E** = Electric   **P** = Petrol   **R** = Rolling Stock   **C** = Coach   **W** = Wagon   **Op** = Operational   **St** = Static   **O** = On Display   **U** = Under Restoration   **G** = Pre Group   **N** = Pre Nationalisation

Steam Railway Directory   www.steamrailway.com

Bodmin & Wenford Railway — Bo'ness & Kinneil Railway

A–Z SHOWING ROLLING STOCK

© HCC Publishing Ltd   **Section 1b.**   143

Steam Railway Directory   www.steamrailway.com   Bo'ness & Kinneil Railway — Bowes Railway

Weymss Coal Company No 20

Name / Notes	Current No.	Type/Class	Origin	Wh. Arr.	Built	Builder	Status
	6	Crane Tank		0-6-0	1939	Andrew Barclay & Sons	s
		NCB		0-6-0T	1942	Andrew Barclay & Sons	s
	7	NCB		0-6-0T	1943	Hunslet Engine Co Ltd	s
		NCB		0-4-0T	1945	W G Bagnall	s
	24	NCB		0-6-0T	1950	Andrew Barclay & Sons	s
		NCB		0-6-0T	1953	Andrew Barclay & Sons	s
	D5351			Bo-Bo	1961	Birmingham Carriage & Wagon Co Ltd	D
	26004			Bo-Bo	1958		D
Owned by 6LDA Group.	D8020			Bo-Bo	1959	Robert Stephenson, Hawthorn	D
	D7585			Bo-Bo	1964		D
Built at Darlington Works.	47643			Bo-Bo	1966		D
Built at Crewe.	14901	DH		0-6-0DH	1964		D
Prev. No. D9524. Built at Swindon. Rodney	50021		BR	Bo-Bo	1968	English Electric	D
Built at Derby.	08443		BR	0-6-0DE	1958		D
Tiger		DH		0-6-0	1941	Andrew Barclay & Sons	D
		DH		0-4-0DH	1954	North British Locomotive Co	D
Kilbaggle		DM		0-4-0DH	1962	Ruston	D
		DH		4wDH	1949	Ruston	D
	P6687			4wDH	1949	Ruston	D
		DM		0-4-0DE	1951	Ruston	D
		DM		4wDM	1952	Ruston	D
				4wDM	1965	John Fowler & Co	D
Built at Leeds.				0-4-0	1958	Ruston	D
				0-4-0DE	1958	Ruston	D

BOWES RAILWAY

Gateshead, TYNE AND WEAR

Name	Current No.	Type/Class	Origin	Wh. Arr.	Built	Builder		
William Stewart Trimble	22	Saddle Tank		0-4-0	1949	Andrew Barclay & Sons	s	Op
Norwood	2361	Saddle Tank		0-4-0	1954	Andrew Barclay & Sons	s	Op
	77	Saddle Tank		0-6-0	1948	Robert Stephenson, Hawthorn	s	St
	101	DM		0-4-0DM	1959	F C Hibberd & Co Ltd	D	Op
	6263	DH		0-4-0DH		Hunslet Engine Co Ltd	D	Op
	613	6 Coupled		0-6-0DH	1977	Andrew Barclay & Sons	D	
	20	DH		Bo-BoDH	1981	Andrew Barclay & Sons	D	

Victoria | 2216 | | | 0-6-0DMF | | Hudswell, Clarke & Co | D

BRECON MOUNTAIN RAILWAY
Merthyr Tydfil, MERTHYR TYDFIL

Name	Current No.	Type/Class	Origin	Wh.Arr.	Built	Builder		
Graf Schwerin-Lowitz		Well Tank		0-6-2	1908	Arn Jung	s	

BREDGAR & WORMSHILL
Sittingbourne, KENT

Name	Current No.	Type/Class	Origin	Wh.Arr.	Built	Builder		
Bronhilde	1			0-4-0	1927	Schartzkopf	s	Op
16ft in length.								
Katie	2			0-6-0	1931	Arn Jung	s	Op
Harrogate	3			0-6-0	1944	Peckett & Sons	s	Op
Armistice	4			0-4-0	1919	W G Bagnall	s	Op
Eigiau	6			0-4-2	1912	Orenstein, Koppel	s	Op
Victory	7			0-4-2	1897	Decauville	s	Op, u
Lady Joan	1			0-4-0	1922	Orenstein, Koppel	s	Op
Owned by R Tolhurst.								
—	6			0-4-0	1929	La Meuse	s	St
Siam	105			0-6-0	1956	Henschel	s	Op
—				0-6-0	1930	Fowler	s	u
—				0-4-2	1912	Fowler	s	u
—	8			0-6-0	1936	Orenstein, Koppel	s	u

BRESSINGHAM STEAM
Diss, NORFOLK

Name	Current No.	Type/Class	Origin	Wh.Arr.	Built	Builder		
Martello	662			0-6-0T	1875		s	St O
Granville	102		LSWR	0-4-0T	1893		s	St O
Royal Scot	6100		LMS	4-6-0	1927		s	St
Peer Gynt	5865		NSB	2-10-0	1944		s	St O
King Haakon VII	377		NSB	2-6-0	1919		s	St O
Beckton No 1				0-4-0ST	1892	Neilson & Co	s	St O
Beckton No 25				0-4-0ST	1896	Neilson & Co	s	St O
William Francis	6841			0-4-0 + 0-4-0T	1937	Hudswell, Clarke & Co	S	St O
Brontlwyd				0-6-0WT	1930	Motor Rail Ltd	s	Op, D
Toby		DM		4wDM	1964		D	Op
Rosenkavalier				4-6-2	1937	Krupp	s	Op
Mannertreu				4-6-2	1937	Krupp	s	
Flying Scotsman	4472			4-6-2	1976	W Stewart	s	Op
Alan Bloom				0-4-0ST	1995		s	Op

Key: Wh.Arr. = Wheel Arrangement   **S** = Steam   **D** = Diesel   **E** = Electric   **P** = Petrol   **R** = Rolling Stock   **W** = Wagon   **C** = Coach   **Op** = Operational   **St** = Static   **O** = On Display   **U** = Under Restoration   **G** = Pre Group   **N** = Pre Nationalisation

Steam Railway Directory   www.steamrailway.com

Bowes Railway — Bressingham Steam

© HCC Publishing Ltd

Section 1b.   145

BRISTOL HARBOUR RAILWAY

Bristol, BRISTOL

Name	Current No.	Type/Class	Origin	Wh. Arr.	Built	Builder				
Henbury	1940	ST /Industrial		0-6-0	1937	Peckett & Sons	s			Op
27ft in length. Designed by Peckett & Sons. Owned by Bristol City Council. Located at Bristol Industrial Museum.										
Portbury	34	ST /Industrial		0-6-0	1917	Avonside Engineering Co	s			Op
27ft in length. Designed by Avonside Engineering Co. Owned by Bristol City Council. Located at Bristol Industrial Museum. Purchased in 1920 by Port of Bristol Authority.										
—	242	ST /Industrial		0-6-0	1874	Fox, Walker & Co	s			Op
25ft in length. Designed by Fox, Walker & Co. Owned by Bristol City Council. Located at Bristol Industrial Museum.										
—		Shunter /Industrial		0-4-0	1958	Ruston	D			Op
Designed by Ruston. Owned by Bristol City Council. Located at Bristol Industrial Museum. Ex Mountain Ash Colliery.										
—		Rail Crane		4W	1951	Coles				Op
Designed by Coles. Owned by Bristol City Council. Located at Bristol Industrial Museum.										
—	17391	Goods Brake Van		4	1941	GWR		W		Op O
Owned by Bristol City Council. Located at Bristol Industrial Museum.										
—	297147	Goods Brake Van	LMS	4	1929	LMS		W	Op	O
Designed by LMS. Owned by Bristol City Council. Located at Bristol Industrial Museum. Ex PBA No1.										
—	700320	Bogie Wagon	LMS	4	1941	LMS		W	Op	O
BR No. DM700320. Two owned by railway. Designed by LMS. Owned by Bristol City Council. Located at Bristol Industrial Museum.										
—	B900910	Bogie Wagon	BR	4	1958	BR		W	Op	O
BR No. B900910. Two owned by railway. Designed by BR. Owned by Bristol City Council. Located at Bristol Industrial Museum.										
—		Van						W	Op	O
Three owned by railway. Owned by Bristol City Council. Located at Bristol Industrial Museum. GW Mogo.										
—		Open Wagon						W	Op	O
14 owned by railway. Owned by Bristol City Council. Located at Bristol Industrial Museum. Include sulphuric acid tank, wagon ex ROF puriton.										

BROOKSIDE MINIATURE

Poynton, CHESHIRE

Name	Current No.	Type/Class	Origin	Wh. Arr.	Built	Builder		
Jane				0-4-2		Exmoor Steam Railway	s	Op
7ft in length. Designed by T Stirland. Owned by D McFarlane.								
Jean				0-4-2	2000	Exmoor Steam Railway	s	Op
7ft in length. Designed by T Stirland. Owned by C Halsall.								
Mighty Max				Bo-Bo	2001	R Greatrex	D	Op
12ft in length. Owned by C Halsall. Petrol - Hydraulic Drive.								
Brookside				Bo-Bo	1997	B Lomas	D	Op
8ft in length. Designed by B Lomas. Owned by C Halsall. Petrol - Hydraulic Drive.								
Thor						B Lomas	D	Op
8ft in length. Owned by D McFarlane.								

BUCKINGHAMSHIRE RLWY CTRE

Aylesbury, BUCKINGHAMSHIRE

Name	Current No.	Type/Class	Origin	Wh. Arr.	Built	Builder

Name	Notes	Number	Type	Railway	Wh.Arr.	Year	Builder	Status
	BR No. 30585. Prev. Nos. E0314, 3314. Designed by Beattie. Rebuilt in 1921.	0314		LSWR	0-4-0T	1898	Beyer, Peacock	S
					2-4-0WT	1874		S, U
Wightwick Hall	BR No. 6989. Designed by Hawksworth. Built at Swindon.	6989		GWR	4-6-0	1948	GWR	S
	BR No. 7200. Designed by C B Collett. First of Class.	7200		GWR	2-8-2T	1934	GWR	S, U
	BR No. 7715. Designed by C B Collett.	7715		GWR	0-6-0PT	1930	Kerr, Stuart & Co Ltd	S, Op, N
	BR No. 9466. Designed by Hawksworth.	9466		GWR	0-6-0PT	1952	RSH	S, Op, N
	BR No. 41298. Designed by Ivatt. Built at Crewe.	41298			2-6-2T	1951	BR	S
	BR No. 41313. Designed by Ivatt. Built at Crewe.	41313			2-6-2T	1952	BR	S, U
	BR No. 46447. Designed by Ivatt. Built at Crewe.	46447		LMS	2-6-0	1950	BR	S
		D2298	DM/04	BR	0-6-0DM	1960	North British Locomotive Co	D
	South African.	3405		SAR	4-8-4	1958		D, St
		51886	Driving Motor Brake Second/115			1960		D
		51899	Driving Motor Brake Second/115			1960		D
		59761	TCL/115			1960		D
Sir Vincent					0-4-0WT	1917	A Porter	S
Blue Circle					2-2-0TG	1926	A Porter	S
Scott					0-4-0ST	1932	W G Bagnall	S
Swanscombe			DM		0-4-0DM	1942	Baguley	S
					0-4-0ST	1891	Andrew Barclay & Sons	D
					0-4-0F	1916	Andrew Barclay & Sons	S
Osram			DM		0-4-0DM	1948	Andrew Barclay & Sons	S
					0-4-0F	1933	Fowler	D
Sir Thomas					0-4-0ST	1928	Hawthorn Leslie & Co	S
					0-6-0T	1918	Hudswell, Clarke & Co	S
					0-4-0ST	1946	Hudswell, Clarke & Co	S
Arthur			DM		0-4-0DM	1940	Hunslet Engine Co Ltd	D
Juno		65			0-6-0ST	1953	Hunslet Engine Co Ltd	S
		66			0-6-0ST	1958	Hunslet Engine Co Ltd	S
		26	DH		0-6-0ST	1964	Hunslet Engine Co Ltd	S
					0-6-0DH	1971	Hunslet Engine Co Ltd	D
Redland			DM		0-4-0DM	1929	Kerr, Stuart & Co Ltd	D
					0-4-0ST	1912	Manning, Wardle & Co	S
Coventry No 1		14			0-6-0ST	1939	Manning, Wardle & Co	S
					0-4-0T	1936	Peckett & Sons	S

Key: Wh.Arr. = Wheel Arrangement   **S** = Steam   **D** = Diesel   **E** = Electric   **P** = Petrol   **C** = Coach   **W** = Wagon   **R** = Rolling Stock   **Op** = Operational   **St** = Static   **O** = On Display   **U** = Under Restoration   **G** = Pre Group   **N** = Pre Nationalisation

Name	Current No.	Type/Class	Wh. Arr.	Built	Builder			
Gibraltar			0-4-0ST	1948	Peckett & Sons	s		c Op
			0-4-0ST	1948	Peckett & Sons	s		c Op
			0-4-0ST	1948	Peckett & Sons	s		U
Tarmac		DM						
	11		4wD	1937	F C Hibberd & Co Ltd	D		
			0-4-0DM	1955	F C Hibberd & Co Ltd	D		
	7		4wVBTG	1945	Sentinel	s		
	9		4wVBTG	1947	Sentinel	s		
			0-6-0ST	1951	Sentinel	s		

Built at Yorkshire.

	Saloon	1880	London, Chatham & Dover Railway
	Ventilated Van	1917	London & South West Railway
	Picnic Saloon	1900	London & North Western Railway

Built at Wolverton.

BURE VALLEY RAILWAY

Norwich, NORFOLK

Name	Current No.	Type/Class	Origin	Wh. Arr.	Built	Builder			
Wroxham Broad	1			2-6-4 T	1992	Winson Engineering	s		Op
Blickling Hall	6			2-6-2	1994	Mark Watkins	s		Op

Designed by Mark Watkins. Based on Indian Railways 2ft 6in.- gauge 'ZB' class.

Name	Current No.	Type/Class	Origin	Wh. Arr.	Built	Builder			
Spitfire				2-6-2	1994	Winson Engineering	s		Op
Thunder				2-6-2	1996	Winson Engineering	s		Op
2nd Air Division USAAF	3	DH		Bo-Bo	1988	John Edwards	D		Op

Designed by John Edwards.

Name	Current No.	Type/Class	Origin	Wh. Arr.	Built	Builder			
Apprentice (The)				4wDH	1996	Hudson, Hurslet			

Rebuilt by the apprentices at Eagit Ltd with a peugeot diesel engine and hydraulic drive. Formerly called 'Volunteer'.

	5	DM						
Little Titan			0-4-0 DM	1952	R A Lister & Co Ltd	D		Op

Converted to a tram engine to resemble 'Toby' for Thomas events.

Little Titan	Steam Crane		1975	Ernest Cheeseman		Op

Complete with match truck and well wagon.

CADEBY LIGHT RAILWAY

Hinckley, LEICESTERSHIRE

Name	Current No.	Type/Class	Origin	Wh. Arr.	Built	Builder			
Pixie	V47			0-4-0 ST	1919	W G Bagnall	s		M
				0-4-0 ST	1941	Peckett & Sons	s	st O	M

Standard gauge.

		PM		0-4-0 PM	1928	Baguley	P		
		PM		4wPM	1931	R A Lister & Co Ltd	P		M
		PM		4wPM	1932	Orenstein, Koppel	P		M
		PM		4wPM	1946	Thakeham	P		

Built at Surrey.

Delta		DM		0-4-0 DM	1930	Deutz	D		
		DM		4wDM	1930	Hudswell, Clarke & Co	D		M

(continued — Cadeby Light Railway)

Current No.	Type/Class	Wh. Arr.	Builder	Built	Status
		4wDM	Motor Rail Ltd, Tramcar Co	1918	D G N
87004		4wDM	Motor Rail Ltd, Tramcar Co	1923	D N
87009		4wPM	Motor Rail Ltd, Tramcar Co	1929	P N
		4wDM	Motor Rail Ltd, Tramcar Co	1930	D N
		4wDM	Motor Rail Ltd	1934	D N

Built for Petrol Loco Hirers.

Current No.	Type/Class	Wh. Arr.	Builder	Built	Status
	DM	4wDM	Motor Rail Ltd	1938	D N
42	DM	4wDM	Motor Rail Ltd	1939	D N
20	DM	4wDM	Motor Rail Ltd	1942	D N
87008	DM	4wDM	Ruston & Hornsby Ltd	1936	D N
87051	DM	4wDM	Ruston & Hornsby Ltd	1957	D
	DM	4wDM	Simplex	1976	D N

CALEDONIAN RAILWAY

Brechin, ANGUS

Name	Current No.	Type/Class	Origin	Wh. Arr.	Built	Builder	Status
Barclay	7			0-4-0 ST	1926	Andrew Barclay & Sons	S Op N
Menelaus	1883			0-6-0 ST	1935	Peckett & Sons	S U
Patricia	68189			0-4-0 ST	1915	Peckett & Sons	S St O G
Uranus				0-4-0	1954	Peckett & Sons	S U
Dewar Highlander		DM		4wDM	1961	Ruston & Hornsby Ltd	D O U
	25083	DE /25	BR	Bo-Bo	1964	BR	D Op
	D5314		BR	Bo-Bo	1958	BRCW	D O U
	26035	DE /26	BR	Bo-Bo	1958	BRCW	D Op
	27024	DE /27	BR	Bo-Bo	1959	BRCW	D O U
Brechin City	D3059	DE /08	BR	0-6-0DE	1954		D Op
Mrs Slocombe	51993		BR	0-4-0ST	1960	Peckett & Sons	S R
Patricia	68189				1915	Peckett & Sons	R
Mr Humphries	52012		BR		1960		U G

Barclay — Prev. No. 63. Owned by Angus Railway Steam Engineers. In lined blue Caledonian Railway livery.

Menelaus — Owned by Angus Railway Steam Engineers.

Patricia — Owned by Steve Pegg.

Uranus — Owned by Steve Pegg.

Dewar Highlander — Owned by K.Joy. In maroon livery.

25083 — BR No. 25083. Prev. No. D5233. Designed by BR. Owned by C R Diesel Group & K.Joy. Built at Derby.

D5314 — BR No. 26014. Prev. No. 26014. Designed by BRCW. Owned by C R Diesel Group & K.Joy. Built at Birmingham.

26035 — BR No. 26035. Prev. No. D5335. Designed by BRCW. Owned by C R Diesel Group & K.Joy. Built at Birmingham.

27024 — BR No. 27024. Prev. Nos. D5370, ADB968028. Designed by BRCW. Owned by C R Diesel Group & K.Joy. Built at Birmingham.

Brechin City — Prev. Nos. 08046, 13059. Painted CR blue.

Cadeby Light Railway — Caledonian Railway

A-Z SHOWING ROLLING STOCK

CAMBRIAN RAILWAY SOCIETY

Oswestry, SHROPSHIRE

Name	Current No.	Type/Class	Wh. Arr.	Built	Builder	Origin		
	8		0-6-0ST	1900	Andrew Barclay & Sons		S	G
Located at Cambrian Railways Society.								
	322	DM	4wDM	1952	Planet		D	
Located at Cambrian Railways Society.								
	3	DH	0-4-0DH		Sentinel		D	
Located at Cambrian Railways Society.								

CAVAN & LEITRIM RAILWAY

Dromod, COUNTY LEITRIM

Name	Current No.	Type/Class	Wh. Arr.	Built	Builder	Origin			
Dromad	3900011		0-4-2T	1916	Kerr, Stuart & Co Ltd			Op	
Rebuilt in 1993 by Alan Keef.									
Dinmor			4w	1946	Fowler			Op	
Built at Leeds.									
	2659		4w	1880	Hudson, Hunslet			Op	
	4202	2 Plank Wagon					W		St O
	19764	2 Plank Wagon					W		St O
	19765	Box Van					R		St O
	20c	Box Van					R		O
	5	Inspection Car	4w	1927	Drewry Car Co		R		St O

CHASEWATER RAILWAY

Walsall, MIDLANDS (WEST)

Name	Current No.	Type/Class	Wh. Arr.	Built	Builder	Origin			
Alfred Paget	11		0-4-0ST	1882	Neilson & Co		S		St O
Sheepbridge No 15			0-6-0T	1885	Hudswell, Clarke & Co		S		St O
Asbestos	6		0-4-0ST	1902	Peckett & Sons		S		
Colin McAndrew	4		0-4-0ST	1909	Hawthorn Leslie & Co		S		St O
Whit No 4	3		0-4-0ST	1911	Andrew Barclay & Sons		S		O
Sentinel	S100		0-6-0T	1949	Hudswell, Clarke & Co		S		
	5		4wVBT	1957	Sentinel				Op
	1	4wPM	4w	1919	Motor Rail Ltd		P		
	21	DM	4wDM	1929	Kent Construction & Eng Co		D		U
Built at Shrewsbury.									
		DM	0-4-0DM	1948	Fowler				U
		DM	0-4-0DM	1952	Ruston & Hornsby Ltd		D		Op
Hem Heath	3D	DM	0-6-0DM	1956	W G Bagnall		D		U
Toad	37	DH	0-4-0DH	1962	Fowler		D		U

Fleet

Fleet No.	Built at	Description	Railway	Builder	Year	Wh.Arr.	Status
7				Ruston & Hornsby Ltd	1963	0-4-0DE	D, Op
W51370		Driving Motor Brake Second	BR	Pressed Steel Co Ltd	1960		Op
W51372		Driving Motor Brake Second	BR	Pressed Steel Co Ltd	1960		Op
W51412		DMS	BR	Pressed Steel Co Ltd	1960		Op
W59444		Tourist Second	BR	BR	1958		Op
W59603	Built at Derby.	Trailer Second Lavatory	BR	Pressed Steel Co Ltd	1959		Op
11		Full Third	M & C	Birmingham Carriage & Wagon Co Ltd	1875	6w	U
68		Passenger Brake			1880	4w	U
44	Built at Derby.	Passenger Brake	GER		1894	6w	U
1470	Built at Stratford.	Composite Brake	MS & L		1898	6w	U
DM01836M	Built at Gorton.		L & NW		1905		C, St O
7080	Built at Wolverton.	Brake Bogie Third			1917		St O
14024	Built at Wolverton.	Brake First Corridor	BR		1962		C, U
35831	Built at Swindon.	4 Plank Open Wagon	GWR		1887		W
		Brake Van			1888		R
15	Built at Swindon.	4 Plank Open Wagon			1897		W
1109		Box Van			1902		R
4	Built at Derby.	Box Van	CCWR		1905		R
		Brake Van	NER		1910		R
100684		Box Van			1910		R
120116	Built at Darlington.	Flat Wagon	LMSR		1927		W
DS169		Staff & Tool Van	SR		1936		R
S1770S	Built at Ashford.	Covered Carriage Truck	SR		1938		R
DS1385	Built at Eastleigh.	Staff & Tool Van	SR		1939		R
35251	Built at Ashford.	Brake Van	GWR		1947		R
S62861	Built at Swindon.	Ballast Plough Van	BR		1948		R
W2336W	Built at Ashford.	Passenger Fruit Van	BR		1952		R
	Built at Swindon.						

Key: Wh.Arr. = Wheel Arrangement S = Steam D = Diesel E = Electric P = Petrol W = Wagon C = Coach Op = Operational St = Static O = On Display R = Rolling Stock G = Pre Group N = Pre Nationalisation U = Under Restoration

Chasewater Railway — Chasewater Railway

Current No.	Type/Class	Origin	Built	Builder	Status
B749678	Tank Wagon	BR	1953		W
B741161	Pipe Wagon	BR	1955		W
B993736	Shark Ballast Plough	BR	1956		R
B274600	Mineral Wagon	NCB	1957		W
94240	Staff & Tool Van	BR	1959		R
B904147	Lowmac	BR	1960		Op
DB993632	Dogfish	BR	1960		R
DB983908	Dogfish	BR	1961		R
B47757	Tank Wagon	BR	1963		W
B316711	Mineral Wagon		1963	Charles Roberts & Co Ltd	W
301580	Pipe Wagon		1972		Op
DS36	Staff & Tool Van	SR	1933		W
DS70278	Flat Wagon	SR	1935		R
B953827	Brake Van	BR	1958		R

Built at Ashford.
Built at Wolverton.
Built at Birmingham C & W.
Built at Shildon.
Built at Ashford.
Built at Eastleigh.
Built at Darlington.

CHINNOR & PRINCES RISBOROUGH

Princes Risborough, OXFORDSHIRE

Name	Current No.	Type/Class	Origin	Wh. Arr.	Built	Builder	Status
	55023				1960	Pressed Steel Co Ltd	D Op
	13018			0-6-0DE	1953	BR	D Op
Clayton	D8568			Bo-BoDE	1964	Clayton Equipment Co	D Op
Iris	459515	DH		0-6-0DH	1961	Ruston & Hornsby Ltd	D C
	1845				1960		C
	4779				1956		C
	7931				1957		C
	35337				1963		C
	80501				1951		C
	13436				1968		C

BR No. W55023. Owned by Chinnor & Princes Risborough Railway.
BR No. 13018. Prev. Nos. D3018, 08011. 29ft in length. Owned by Chinnor & Princes Risborough Railway. Built at Derby.
BR No. D8568. Owned by Diesel Traction Group. Ex Mod.
Built at Wolverton.
Built at York.
Built at Wolverton.
Built at Wolverton.
Built at Derby.
Built at Derby.

Origin	Current No.	Type/Class	Wh. Arr.	Built	Builder		
Built at Swindon.	17424			1940			W
Built at Swindon.	35883			1944			W
Built at Swindon.	076104			1948			W
	WGB4041			1958	Pressed Steel Co Ltd		W
	B503877			1955			W
Built at Derby.	064847						W
	BP060174			1964	Metropolitan Cammell		W
	B945798			1958	Metropolitan Cammell		W
	18798		4w+4w	1960	Coles		R

CHOLSEY & WALLINGFORD RAILWAY — Wallingford, OXFORDSHIRE

Name	Current No.	Type/Class	Origin	Wh. Arr.	Built	Builder		
Lion	08022		BR No. D3030. Built at Derby. Guinness Livery.		1953		D	Op
Unicorn	08060		BR No. D3074. Built at Darlington. Guinness Livery.		1953		D	Op
George Mason	08123		BR No. D3190. Built at Derby.		1955		D	Op
Carpenter	3270	Shunter		0-4-0	1948	F C Hibberd & Co Ltd	D	Op

CHURNET VALLEY RAILWAY — Cheddleton, STAFFORDSHIRE

Name	Current No.	Type/Class	Origin	Wh. Arr.	Built	Builder		
Owned by NRM. Built at Stoke.	2			0-6-2T	1922	NSR	S	St O
	5197				1944		S	Op
Built at Lima, USA.	44422			0-6-0	1927	LMS	S	U
Owned by 4F Fund. Built at Derby.	80136			2-6-4T	1951	BR	S	Op
Owned by Standard Class 4 Trust. Built at Brighton.	48305			2-8-0	1941	LMS	S	U
Josiah Wedgwood	3777			0-6-0T	1952	Hunslet Engine Co Ltd	S	U
Owned by Standard Class 4 Trust.	92134			2-10-0	1957	BR	S	U
Built at Crewe.	D2334	DM/04		0-6-0DM	1961	BR	D	Op

Key: Wh.Arr. = Wheel Arrangement S = Steam D = Diesel E = Electric P = Petrol W = Wagon C = Coach R = Rolling Stock Op = Operational St = Static O = On Display U = Under Restoration G = Pre Group N = Pre Nationalisation

Steam Railway Directory   www.steamrailway.com

Churnet Valley Railway — Colne Valley Railway

	D3420	DE/08		BR	D	Op

BR No. 08350. Prev. No. D3420. Owned by NSR Diesel Group. Built at Crewe.

	08823		0-6-0DE	1957	BR	D	Op

Owned by Churnet Traction & RS Group.

| | D8154 | DE | 0-6-0DE | | BR | D |

Owned by Churnet Traction & RS Group.

Tamworth Castle   D7672   Bo-Bo   1967   BR   D   Op

Owned by NSR Diesel Group. Built at Derby.

Burma Star   33056   Bo-Bo   1961   BRCW   D   Op

Owned by NSR Diesel Group.

| | 33102 | | Bo-Bo | 1960 | BRCW | D |

Owned by NSR Diesel Group.

| | | | 0-4-0DH | | Yorkshire Engine Co | D | Op |
| | | | 0-4-0DH | | Metropolitan Cammell | D | u |

Owned by Churnet Traction & RS Group.

CLEETHORPES LIGHT RAILWAY

Cleethorpes, LINCOLNSHIRE (NORTH EAST)

Name	Current No.	Type/Class	Origin	Wh. Arr.	Built	Builder	
Konigswinter	1	GH		2-8-0GH	1992	R A Lister & Co Ltd	D
Arnold J Rimmer	2			4wDH Tram	1993		D
Cub (The)	6	DM		4w4DM	1995	Stanhope	D
	24			0-4-0VBT	1989	Fairbourne	s

Owned by Sandy River Consortium.

Seabreeze | | | | 4-6-2 | | CCLR | s

Under construction.

COLNE VALLEY RAILWAY

Halstead, ESSEX

Name	Current No.	Type/Class	Origin	Wh. Arr.	Built	Builder	
Blue Star	35010				1942	SR	

Built at Eastleigh.

	45163				1935	Armstrong, Whitworth	s
	45293				1936	Armstrong, Whitworth	s
	68072	Saddle Tank			1945	Vulcan Foundry	s
	WD190				1952	Hunslet Engine Co Ltd	s
Barrington					1921	Avonside Engineering Co	s
	1				1923	Hawthorn Leslie & Co	s
Victory					1945	Andrew Barclay & Sons	s
Jupiter					1951	Robert Stephenson, Hawthorn	s
	40				1954	Robert Stephenson, Hawthorn	s
	D3476				1957		D
	YD43				1943	Ruston & Hornsby Ltd	D

— 4007   F C Hibberd & Co Ltd   1947   D
— 3211   Andrew Barclay & Sons   1941   D
— 281266   Ruston & Hornsby Ltd   D

Built at Lincoln.

CONWY VALLEY

Betws-y-Coed, CONWY

Name	Current No.	Type/Class	Origin	Wh.Arr.	Built	Builder		
Old Rube				2-8-0	1983	Milner Eng	s	Op
Sian				0-4-2T	1989	Humphries	s	Op
Union Pacific				Bo-Bo	1991	R Greatrex	D	Op

DARLINGTON RAILWAY CENTRE

Darlington, COUNTY DURHAM

Name	Current No.	Type/Class	Origin	Wh.Arr.	Built	Builder		
Met		Saddle Tank		0-4-0	1909	Hawthorn Leslie & Co	s	St

Located at Darlington Railway & Museum.

| | | F | | | 1948 | W G Bagnall | | |

Located at Darlington Railway & Museum. Built at Stafford.

DARTMOOR RAILWAY

Okehampton, DEVON

Name	Current No.	Type/Class	Origin	Wh.Arr.	Built	Builder		
	08937		BR	0-6-0DE	1962	BR	D	Op

BR No. 08937. Prev. No. D4167. Built at Darlington.

—	61742		BR		1956			C
—	61743		BR		1956			C
—	69310		BR		1965			C

DEAN FOREST RAILWAY

Lydney, GLOUCESTERSHIRE

Name	Current No.	Type/Class	Origin	Wh.Arr.	Built	Builder		
—	9642	Pannier Tank					s	Op
—	51914						D	Op
—	5541						s	Op
—	9681	Pannier Tank					s	U
Wilbert the Forest Engine	56492						D	U

Recently received a complete repaint.

Colne Valley Railway — Dean Forest Railway

Key: Wh.Arr. = Wheel Arrangement   **S** = Steam   **D** = Diesel   **E** = Electric   **P** = Petrol   **R** = Rolling Stock   **W** = Wagon   **C** = Coach   **Op** = Operational   **St** = Static   **O** = On Display   **U** = Under Restoration   **G** = Pre Group   **N** = Pre Nationalisation

Steam Railway Directory   www.steamrailway.com

A-Z SHOWING ROLLING STOCK

© HCC Publishing Ltd   **Section 1b.**   155

DERBY INDUSTRIAL MUSEUM

Derby, DERBYSHIRE

Name	Current No.	Type/Class	Origin	Wh. Arr.	Built	Builder	Status
Victory				0-4-0ST	1919	Peckett & Sons	S St O
—				4w	1919	Motor Rail Ltd	St O

DERWENT VALLEY

York, YORKSHIRE (NORTH)

Name	Current No.	Type/Class	Origin	Wh. Arr.	Built	Builder	Status
—	8			0-4-0ST	1955	Andrew Barclay & Sons	S Op
—	65			0-6-0T	1929	Hudswell, Clarke & Co	S Op
—	03079	DM/03	BR	0-6-0DM	1960	Drewry Car Co	D Op
—	DS165	DM		0-4-0DM	1953	Ruston & Hornsby Ltd	D Op
Octavius Atkinson	DS88	Shunter		4w	1947	John Fowler & Co	D Op
Churchill		Shunter		0-4-0DM	1948	John Fowler & Co	D Op

Awaiting restoration.

Name	Current No.	Type/Class	Origin	Wh. Arr.	Built	Builder	Status
Jim	DS48	Shunter		4wDM	1959	Ruston & Hornsby Ltd	D C U
—	1214	Compartment Coach	NER		1890		C

Two owned by railway:

Name	Current No.	Type/Class	Origin	Wh. Arr.	Built	Builder	Status
—	1367	Parcels Van			1939		R
—	B951144	Brake Van	BR		1951		R
—	295516	Brake Van	LMS		1933		R
—	W95166	Ventilated Box Van	GWR		1940		R W
—	NE239656	Plate Wagon	LNER		1920		W
—	516537	Bogie Bolster Wagon	GCR		1923		R W
—	NE539249	Box Van			1940		W
—	B291264	Coal Wagon	NCB		1938		W

This tank has a capacity of 4275 gallons.

Name	Current No.	Type/Class	Origin	Wh. Arr.	Built	Builder	Status
—	5081	Tank Wagon					U
—	20055	Steam Crane				Smith, Rodley	

DEVON RAILWAY CENTRE

Tiverton, DEVON

Name	Current No.	Type/Class	Origin	Wh. Arr.	Built	Builder	Status
Ivor		DM		4wDM	1944	Motor Rail Ltd	D Op
Ruston		DM		4wDM	1957	Ruston	D Op
Planet		DM		4wDM	1939	F C Hibberd & Co Ltd	D Op
Lister				4wPM	1935	R A Lister & Co Ltd	P Op
—					1931	Kent Construction & Eng Co	D O
Berryland					1937	F C Hibberd & Co Ltd	D O N

Name	Current No.	Type/Class	Origin	Wh.Arr.	Built	Builder			
Boris *Owned by Works number 3357.*	1	DM		0-4-0DM	1952	Baguley	Op	D	G
Pen-yr-Orsedd		DM		4wDM	1945	Ruston	Op	D	

DIDCOT RAILWAY CENTRE

Didcot, OXFORDSHIRE

Name	Current No.	Type/Class	Origin	Wh.Arr.	Built	Builder			
BR No. 1338. Prev. No. 5.	1338		Cardiff Railway	0-4-0ST	1898	Kitson & Co		s	
Trojan *BR No. 1340. Built at Bristol.*	1340		Alexander Docks & Railway Co	0-4-0ST	1897	Avonside Engineering Co		s	U
BR No. 1363. Built at Swindon.	1363		GWR	0-6-0ST	1910	GWR		s	U G
BR No. 3650. Designed by Churchward. Built at Swindon.	3650		GWR	0-6-0PT	1939	GWR	St	s	
BR No. 3738. Designed by C B Collett. Built at Swindon.	3738		GWR	0-6-0PT	1937	GWR	Op	s	N
BR No. 3822. Designed by C B Collett. Built at Swindon.	3822		GWR	2-8-0	1940	GWR		s	N
Pendennis Castle *BR No. 4079. Designed by C B Collett. Built at Swindon. It was exported to Australia in 1973 and returned to the UK in 1999.*	4079		GWR	4-6-0	1923	GWR		s	N
BR No. 4144. Designed by C B Collett. Built at Swindon.	4144		GWR	2-6-2T	1946	GWR		s	N
BR No. 1466. Prev. No. 4866. Designed by C B Collett. Built at Swindon.	4866		GWR	0-4-2T	1936	GWR		s	U
Lady of Legend *BR No. 4942. Designed by Churchward. Built at Swindon.*	2999		GWR	4-6-0	1929	GWR		s	
Earl Bathurst *BR No. 5051. Designed by C B Collett. Built at Swindon. Occasionally runs as 'Drysllwyn Castle'.*	5051		GWR	2-6-0	1936	GWR	Op	s	N
BR No. 5322. Designed by Churchward. Built at Swindon.	5322		GWR	2-6-2T	1917	GWR	St	s	G
BR No. 5572. Designed by Churchward. Built at Swindon.	5572		GWR	4-6-0	1929	GWR		s	G
Hinderton Hall *BR No. 5900. Built at Swindon.*	5900		GWR	4-6-0	1931	GWR	St	s	N
King Edward II *BR No. 6023. Built at Swindon.*	6023		GWR	4-6-0	1930	GWR	St	s	N
King Edward I *BR No. 6024. Designed by C B Collett. Built at Swindon.*	6024		GWR	4-6-0	1930	GWR	Op	s	N
BR No. 6106. Built at Swindon.	6106		GWR	2-6-2T	1931	GWR		s	N
	6697			0-6-2T	1928	Armstrong, Whitworth		s	N
Burton Agnes Hall *Built at Swindon.*	6998			4-6-0	1949	BR		s	N

Key: Wh.Arr. = Wheel Arrangement   S = Steam   D = Diesel   E = Electric   P = Petrol   C = Coach   W = Wagon   R = Rolling Stock   Op = Operational   St = Static   O = On Display   U = Under Restoration   G = Pre Group   N = Pre Nationalisation

Steam Railway Directory   www.steamrailway.com

Devon Railway Centre — Didcot Railway Centre

A-Z SHOWING ROLLING STOCK

Steam Railway Directory www.steamrailway.com

Didcot Railway Centre — Didcot Railway Centre

Name / No.	Description	Owner / Rlwy	Wheel Arr.	Date	Builder		
7202			2-8-2T	1934	GWR	S	M
BR No. 7202. Prev. No. 5275. Designed by C B Collett. Built at Swindon. Rebuilt from 5277, 2-8-0T.							
Cookham Manor 7808				1938	GWR	S	M
BR No. 7808. Designed by C B Collett. Built at Swindon.							
Bonnie Prince Charlie							
BR No. 7808 Designed by C B Collett. Built at Swindon.							
Pontyberem 1		Bury Port & Gwendraeth Valley Rlwy	0-4-0ST	1949	Robert Stephenson, Hawthorn	S	G
2			0-6-0ST	1900	Avonside Engineering Co	S	G
Shannon 5			0-4-0WT	1857	George England	S	
Built at Bristol.							
Owned by National Railway Museum. Built at London.							
DL26	DM		0-6-0DM	1957	Hunslet Engine Co Ltd	D	
08 604	DE/08	BR	0-6-0DE	1959	BR	D	
Phantom							
Prev. No. D3771. Built at Derby.							
93	Steam Railmotor	GWR	0-4-0VBT	1908	C B Collett	S	U
BR No. 212. Converted to auto trailer in 1935. It is now being returned to it's original railmotor form.							
92	Auto Trailer			1912	G W Churchward	R	
111	Passenger Brake			1934	C B Collett	R	
190	Auto Trailer			1933	C B Collett	R	
231	Auto Trailer			1951	Hawksworth	R	
290	4w Composite			1902	Dean	R	
316	Passenger Brake			1950	Hawksworth	R	
416	BT			1891	Dean	R	
484				1913	G W Churchward	R	
536				1940	C B Collett	R	
565	Covered Carriage Truck			1914		R	
814	Brake Stowage Van			1940	C B Collett	R	
933	Passenger Brake			1898	Dean	R	
975	4w Third			1902	Dean	R	
1111				1938	C B Collett	R	
1184	Passenger Brake			1930	C B Collett	R	
1289				1937	C B Collett	R	
1357				1903	Dean	R	
1941				1901	Dean	R	
2202	Brake Third			1950	Hawksworth	R	
2511				1894	Dean	R	
Siphon G 3299	Bogie Milk Churn Van			1937	G W Churchward	R	
3755	Brake Third			1905	G W Churchward	R	
3756	Brake Third			1921	G W Churchward	R	
4553				1925	C B Collett	R	C
5085				1928	C B Collett	R	
5787	Brake Third			1933	C B Collett	R	
5952				1935	C B Collett	R	
6824	6w Tri Composite			1887	Dean	R	C

Originally built for Broad Gauge.

Name	Number	Description	Year	Builder	Category
Queen Mary	9112	Super Saloon	1932	C B Collett	R
Prince of Wales	9113	Super Saloon	1932	C B Collett	R
Princess Elizabeth	9118	Super Saloon Kitchen	1932	C B Collett	R
Originally Super Saloon. Converted in 1935.					
—	9520	Composite Diner Clerestory	1903	Dean	R
Carried on chassis of 3655.					
—	9635	First Diner	1935	C B Collett	R
—	101	6w Drinking Water Tank Wagon	1946		W
—	263	Mess Van	1905		W
—	752	Special Cattle Van	1952		W
—	2356	Fruit Van	1892		W
—	2671	Fish Van	1926		W
—	2862	Passenger Fruit Van	1938		W
—	3030		1947		W
Carries road tank trailer.					
—	10153	Open Wagon	1900		W
Built for Taff Vale Railway.					
Iron Mink	11152	Iron Bodied Van	1918		W
—	19818	Open Wagon	1881		W
—	32337		1881		W
—	32338		1908		W
Coral A	41723	Well Wagon	1908		W
Crocodile F	41934	Bogie Well Wagon	1917		W
Hydra D	42193	Well Wagon	1917		W
On loan from National Railway Museum.					
Grain	42239	Convertible Hopper Van	1927		W
Loriot L	42271	Well Wagon	1934		W
—	43949	Tank Wagon	1911		W
—	56400	Brake Van	1895		W
—	63066	Coal Wagon	1946		W
—	68684	Brake Van	1924		W
Macaw B	70335	Bogie Bolster Wagon	1939		W
Tevan	79933	Special Traffics Van	1922		W
Originally 'Mica B'. Converted in 1938.					
—	80668	Ballast Wagon	1936		W
—	80789	Ballast Wagon	1937		W
—	92943	China Clay Wagon	1913		W
—	94835	Open Wagon	1920		W
—	100377	Shunter	1923		W
Originally 'Mink A' Van. Converted in 1953.					
—	100682		1939		W
—	101720	Van	1924		W
—	101836	Van	1925		W

Key: Wh.Arr. = Wheel Arrangement **S** = Steam **D** = Diesel **E** = Electric **P** = Petrol **R** = Rolling Stock **W** = Wagon **C** = Coach **Op** = Operational **St** = Static **On** = On Display **U** = Under Restoration **G** = Pre Group **N** = Pre Nationalisation

Steam Railway Directory www.steamrailway.com

Didcot Railway Centre — Didcot Railway Centre

A-Z SHOWING ROLLING STOCK

Steam Railway Directory   www.steamrailway.com

Current No.	Type/Class	Builder	Built	
105599	Banana Van		1929	W
105742	Motor Car Van		1936	W
105860	Meat Van		1925	W
112843	Express Freight Van		1931	W
116954	Motor Car Van		1930	W
117993	Open Wagon		1930	W
145428	Van		1944	W
146366	Van		1948	W

Plywood Body.

Current No.	Type/Class	Builder	Built	
950592	Brake Van		1950	W
1	Tar Tank Wagon	Charles Roberts & Co Ltd	1898	W
18	Open Wagon		1927	W
745	Oil Tank Wagon	Hurst, Nelson & Co Ltd	1912	W
S4409	6w Milk Tank Wagon	SR	1931	W

Built at Lancing.

Current No.	Type/Class	Builder	Built	
516673	Van		1956	R
5267	Coal Wagon		1956	R
5268	Coal Wagon		1981	R
10509	Dormitory Coach			R

Formerly Mark 2 Sleeping Car.

Current No.	Type/Class	Builder	Built	
80224	Support Coach		1960	R

DINGLES STEAM VILLAGE
Lifton, DEVON

Name	Current No.	Type/Class	Origin	Wh. Arr.	Built	Builder	
—							O u

Owned by Mr Dingle. Ex Falmouth Docks steam crane.

DONEGAL RAILWAY HERITAGE CTRE
Donegal, COUNTY DONEGAL

Name	Current No.	Type/Class	Origin	Wh. Arr.	Built	Builder	
Drumbo				2-6-4	1906	Walkers	s u

Built at Wigan.

DOWNPATRICK & ARDGLASS
Downpatrick, COUNTY DOWN

Name	Current No.	Type/Class	Origin	Wh. Arr.	Built	Builder		
	3	Side Tank		0-4-0	1934	Orenstein, Koppel	s	Op
		Saddle Tank		0-4-0	1919	Hudswell, Clarke & Co	s	St
—					1950		D	

Owned by Downpatrick & Ardglass Railway. Built at Leeds.

Owned by Northern Ireland Railways.

Railbus

©HCC Publishing Ltd

EAST ANGLIA TRANSPORT MUSEUM — Lowestoft, SUFFOLK

Name	Current No.	Type/Class	Origin	Wh.Arr.	Built	Builder			
									D
	2	DM		4w	1934	Motor Rail Ltd	D		Op
	4	DM		4w	1936	Ruston & Hornsby Ltd	D		Op
Thorpeness	5	DM		4w	1964	Motor Rail Ltd	D		Op
Ortordness	6	DM		4w	1964	Motor Rail Ltd	D		Op

EAST ANGLIAN RAILWAY MUSEUM — Colchester, ESSEX

Name	Current No.	Type/Class	Origin	Wh.Arr.	Built	Builder			
BR No. 69621.									
Belvoir	79999	Side Tank		0-6-2			s		
Jubilee	11	Saddle Tank		0-6-0	1953	Andrew Barclay & Sons	s		
Alexander		Saddle Tank		0-4-0	1905	Andrew Barclay & Sons	s		
William Murdoch		Saddle Tank		0-4-0	1935	W G Bagnall	s		
Birkenhead		Saddle Tank		0-4-0			s		
Penn Green		Saddle Tank		0-6-0			s		
Jeffrey		Saddle Tank		0-6-0			s		
	37003						D		U
	23	DH		0-4-0	1938	Andrew Barclay & Sons	D		Op
	AMW144	Shunter		0-4-0	1920	Motor Rail Ltd, Simplex	D		St O
	D2279	Shunter		0-6-0		Drewry Car Co	D	P	Op
	19			4w	1878	Birmingham Carriage & Wagon Co Ltd			C
	24082	Buffet Car	LNER						R
	43157	Brake Second			1951				C
	16631	BTO							C
	553	Passenger Brake			1890				Op O
	975496	Brake Second Corridor	BR		1951				St O
	24959	Second Corridor	BR		1959				Op
	3779	Tourist Second Open	BR		1953				Op
	61553				1921				C
	308	Third Brake			1873				U
	13251	Open Third	LNER		1936				U

Key: Wh.Arr. = Wheel Arrangement   S = Steam   D = Diesel   E = Electric   P = Petrol   W = Wagon   C = Coach   R = Rolling Stock   G = Pre Group   N = Pre Nationalisation   St = Static   O = On Display   Op = Operational   U = Under Restoration

Steam Railway Directory   www.steamrailway.com

Downpatrick & Ardglass — East Anglian Railway Museum

A-Z SHOWING ROLLING STOCK

East Anglian Railway Museum — East Kent Light Railway

Steam Railway Directory   www.steamrailway.com

Built at Swindon.	17898	Brake Van		1913		W
	CDM700704	Lowmac		1944	LNER	W
	E765W	Cattle Van		1953		W
	M405032	5 Plank Open		1936	Hurst, Nelson & Co Ltd	W
	32518	Unfitted Van				W
Capacity 10 tonnes.	B68231	Open Mineral Wagon	BR	1951		W
Capacity 16 tonnes.	5474	Oil Tank Wagon		1944	Hurst, Nelson & Co Ltd	W
Two owned by railway.	S1439	Covered Carriage Truck		1952	Lancing Carriage Works	W
Built at Sussex.	055	Flat Bogie Bolster		1895		W
Capacity 12 tonnes.	1152	Miscellaneous Van		1937		W
	159918	Fish Van		1926		W
Capacity 10 tonnes.	2					W
Capacity 15 tonnes.	B91762	Open Hopper	LMS			W
Capacity 13 tonnes.	B745522	Open Sheet Bar Wagon				W
Capacity 20 tonnes.	B951771	Brake Van	BR			W
Capacity 12 tonnes.	B760651	Ventilated Van	BR			W

EAST KENT LIGHT RAILWAY   Dover, KENT

Name	Current No.	Type/Class	Origin	Wh. Arr.	Built	Builder			
Spitfire				0-4-0	1929	Andrew Barclay & Sons			Op
Owned by Kent Colliery Loco Fund.									
Albert					1948	Andrew Barclay & Sons	s		Op
Owned by R Ovenden.									
	33063							D	Op
BR No. 33063. Owned by SELG.									
	33065							D	Op
BR No. 33065. Owned by SELG.									
Snowdown					1953	Fowler		D	Op
Owned by A Larkins.									
St Dunstan				0-6-0	1926	Avonside Engineering Co	s		St 0
Owned by East Kent Light Railway Society.									
Buffs (The)	427			0-6-0	1961	Ruston & Hornsby Ltd		D	Op
Owned by SELG.									

Richborough Castle
Designed by English Electric.

Name / Notes	Current No.	Type/Class	Origin	Wh.Arr.	Built	Builder	Status
Richborough Castle				0-6-0	1967	Vulcan Foundry	Op
BR No. 568001. Owned by EPB PG.	568001		BR				R C
BR No. 5759. Owned by EPB PG.	5759		BR				R C

EAST SOMERSET RAILWAY
Shepton Mallet, SOMERSET

Name / Notes	Current No.	Type/Class	Origin	Wh.Arr.	Built	Builder	Status
Designed by C B Collett.	5637			0-6-2			s
Lord Fisher	1398			0-4-0ST	1915	Andrew Barclay & Sons	s Op
Lady Nan	1719			0-4-0ST	1920	Andrew Barclay & Sons	s Op
	705			0-4-0ST	1937	Andrew Barclay & Sons	s Op
	110			0-6-0T	1877		s U
Burgundy	39				1950	Sentinel	D Op
BR No. 47493. Designed by Fowler. Under repair.	47493	F/3	LMS	0-6-0	1927	Vulcan Foundry	s Op
Built at York.	43289	Brake Second	BR		1955		C U
Built at Doncaster.	9241	Brake Second Open			1955		C
Part of Wine and Dine set.	W4907	Tourist Second Open	BR		1960	BR	C
BR No. 51000. 67ft in length. Coach body made of fibreglass. Built at Eastleigh.	51000		BR		1962	BR	C
BR No. B854907. Generator van for Wine and Dine set.		Shoc Van			1958	BR	W
Used on Wine & Dine and Santa trains.	M81156	Brake Gangwayed			1958	BR, Metro Cammell	C
Built at York. Used on Wine & Dine.	E4641	Tourist Second Open			1957	BR	C
BR No. E4562. Built at York.					1956	BR	C
BR No. E4584. Built at York.					1956	BR	C

EASTLEIGH LAKESIDE RAILWAY
Eastleigh, HAMPSHIRE

Name	Current No.	Type/Class	Origin	Wh.Arr.	Built	Builder	Status
Sandy River	7			2-4-2	1982	A Bimpson, D Smallwood	s Op

Key: Wh.Arr. = Wheel Arrangement   S = Steam   D = Diesel   E = Electric   P = Petrol   R = Rolling Stock   C = Coach   W = Wagon   St = Static   Op = Operational   O = On Display   U = Under Restoration   s = Static   G = Pre Group   N = Pre Nationalisation

Steam Railway Directory   www.steamrailway.com

East Kent Light Railway — East Light Railway   Eastleigh Lakeside Railway

Steam Railway Directory www.steamrailway.com

Eastleigh Lakeside Railway — Embsay & Bolton Abbey Rlwy

				Builder		
7.25" gauge.						
Monarch (The)	1001		4-6-2	1932	HCS Bullock	S	Op
10.25" gauge.						
William Baker	4789		4-4-2	1947		S	Op
7.25" gauge.						
Francis Henry Lloyd	3		4-8-4	1959		S	Op
7.25" gauge.						
Sir Arthur Heywood	10		2-6-2	1984		S	Op
7.25" gauge.						
Eastleigh	1994		B-B		Eastleigh Lakeside Railway	D	Op
7.25" gauge.						
University of Southampton	3221		Bo-Bo	1998	Southampton University, Eastleigh Lakeside Rlwy	E	Op
7.25" gauge.						
Florence	92		0-6-0	2000	Eastleigh Lakeside Railway	D	Op
10.25" gauge.						

ELSECAR HERITAGE CENTRE

Name	Current No.	Type/Class	Origin	Wh. Arr.	Built	Builder		
Earl Fitzwilliam				0-6-0	1924	Ruston	S	U
Countess Fitzwilliam							D	

Barnsley, YORKSHIRE (SOUTH)

Skipton, YORKSHIRE (NORTH)

EMBSAY & BOLTON ABBEY RLWY

Name	Current No.	Type/Class	Origin	Wh. Arr.	Built	Builder		
Monckton No 1					1953	Hunslet Engine Co Ltd	S	
In final stages of overhaul.								
Cranford No 2		Saddle Tank		0-6-0ST	1942	W G Bagnall	S	Op
York No 1				0-4-0	1949	Yorkshire Engine Co	S	
In store - awaiting overhaul.								
BEA No 2		Saddle Tank		0-4-0ST	1959	Robert Stephenson, Hawthorn	S	
Slough Estates No 5					1939	Hudswell, Clarke & Co	S	
In store - awaiting overhaul.								
Ann					1927	Sentinel	S	
Beatrice	2705				1945	Hunslet Engine Co Ltd	S	Op
Under going overhaul.								
	8						S	
Formerly 'Sir Robert Peel'.								
Airedale No 3				0-4-0ST	1923	Hunslet Engine Co Ltd	S	Op
Awaiting restoration.								
Thomas				0-6-0	1922	Hudswell, Clarke & Co	S	
Formerly 'Dorothy'. Undergoing overhaul.								
Awaiting overhaul.				0-4-0ST	1952	Andrew Barclay & Sons	S	
South Hetton No 69					1953	Hunslet Engine Co Ltd	S	
Undergoing cosmetic overhaul.								

Name	Current No.	Type/Class	Origin	Wh.Arr.	Built	Builder		
Revenge								
Formerly 'Spitfire'. Undergoing overhaul.								
Primrose No 2					1942	Hunslet Engine Co Ltd	S	
Wheldale					1952	Hunslet Engine Co Ltd	S	U
—					1944	Hunslet Engine Co Ltd	S	U
—	140			0-6-0T	1948	Hudswell, Clarke & Co	S	Op
—	68005			0-6-0ST	1945	Robert Stephenson, Hawthorn	S	Op
Illingworth					1916	Hudswell, Clarke & Co	S	U
Undergoing overhaul. Also called 'Mitchell'.								
Meaford No 1		Shunter		0-4-0	1957	Andrew Barclay & Sons	D	Op
—	36				1958	Hudswell, Clarke & Co	D	Op
—	38			0-6-0	1964	BR	D	Op
Built at Swindon.								
—	887			0-6-0	1955	Ruston & Hornsby Ltd	D	Op
—	D2203				1952	BR	D	Op
Wickham Trolley								
Built at Wickham.								
H W Robinson		DM		0-4-0DM	1946	Fowler	D	Op
Baby Ruston					1950	Ruston & Hornsby Ltd	D	Op
Bug (The)						Baguley	D	U
Dismantled. Also known as 'Clockwork Orange'.								
—		Railbus			1980	BRE	D	Op
Undergoing overhaul.								
—								
Built at Derby.								

EXMOOR STEAM RAILWAY

Barnstaple, DEVON

Name	Current No.	Type/Class	Origin	Wh.Arr.	Built	Builder		
Denzil				0-4-2T	1995	Exmoor Steam Railway	S	Op
Charlie	87			2-4-2	1998	Exmoor Steam Railway	S	Op
—	0			2-6-2 + 2-6-2	1937	Cockerill	S	St
Former South African Railways.								
—	109			2-6-2 + 2-6-2	1939	Beyer, Peacock	S	
Former South African Railways.								
—	115			2-6-2 + 2-6-2	1937	Beyer, Peacock	S	
Former South African Railways.								
—	130			2-6-2 + 2-6-2	1951	Beyer, Peacock	S	
Former South African Railways.								
—	135			2-8-2	1952	S F Belge	S	St O
Former South African Railways.								

Key: Wh.Arr. = Wheel Arrangement S = Steam D = Diesel E = Electric P = Petrol W = Wagon C = Coach R = Rolling Stock Op = Operational St = Static U = Under Restoration O = On Display G = Pre Group N = Pre Nationalisation

Exmoor Steam Railway — Foxfield Steam Railway

		DM			4wDM	1943	Motor Rail Ltd	D	St O

FAIRBOURNE & BARMOUTH

Name	Current No.	Type/Class	Origin	Wh.Arr.	Built	Builder	D	St O
Yeo				2-6-2	1978	D Curwen	S	O
Designed by D Curwen. Owned by Fairbourne Railway. Located at Fairbourne Railway.								
Russell				2-6-4	1979	John Milner, Neil Simkins	S	Op
Designed by John Milner. Owned by A Atkinson. Located at Fairbourne Railway. Rebuilt at Fairbourne workshops to resemble Welsh Highland Railway Prototype.								
Beddgelert				0-6-4	1979	D Curwen	S	Op
Designed by D Curwen. Owned by Fairbourne Railway. Located at Fairbourne Railway.								
Sherpa				0-4-0	1978	John Milner, Neil Simkins	S	Op
Designed by John Milner. Owned by Fairbourne Railway. Located at Fairbourne Railway.								

FFESTINIOG RAILWAY
Porthmadog, GWYNEDD

Name	Current No.	Type/Class	Origin	Wh.Arr.	Built	Builder	D	St O
Princess	1			0-4-0STT	1863	George England	S	
Prince	2			0-4-0STT	1863	George England	S	Op
Palmerston	4			0-4-0STT	1863	George England	S	Op
Welsh Pony	5			0-4-0STT	1867	George England	S	O
Moelwyn		DM		2-4-0DM	1918	Baldwin Locomotive Works	D	
Blanche				2-4-0STT	1893	Hunslet Engine Co Ltd	S	Op
Linda				2-4-0STT	1893	Hunslet Engine Co Ltd	S	Op
Mountaineer				2-6-2T	1917	Alco		Op
Harlech Castle		DH		0-6-0DH	1983	Baguley, Drewry	D	Op
Ashover		DM		4wDM	1948	F C Hibberd & Co Ltd	D	U
Conway Castle		DM		4wDM	1958	F C Hibberd & Co Ltd	D	Op
Moel Hebog		DM		0-4-0DM	1955	Hunslet Engine Co Ltd	D	Op
Mary Ann		DM		4wDM	1917	Motor Rail Ltd	D	Op
Vale of Ffestiniog				0-4-4T	1999	Funkey	S	Op

FOXFIELD STEAM RAILWAY
Stoke-on-Trent, STAFFORDSHIRE

Name	Current No.	Type/Class	Origin	Wh.Arr.	Built	Builder	D	St O
Whiston				0-6-0	1950	Hunslet Engine Co Ltd	S	Op
Wimblebury				0-6-0	1956	Hunslet Engine Co Ltd	S	U
Meaford No 2	2			0-6-0	1951	W G Bagnall	S	Op
Florence No 2	2			0-4-0	1951	Robert Stephenson, Hawthorn	S	St O U
Roker				0-4-0	1940	Peckett & Sons	S	St O U
Boots No 1	11			0-4-0	1930	Andrew Barclay & Sons	S	St U O
Owned by Foxfield Light Railway Society								
Ironbridge No 1	1			0-4-0	1933	Peckett & Sons	S	St O N

(continued — Foxfield Steam Railway)

Name	Current No.	Type/Class	Wh.Arr.	Built	Builder	Status
Hawarden			0-4-0	1940	W G Bagnall	S, Op, N
Henry Cort			0-4-0	1903	Peckett & Sons	S, St O, G N
Designed by Peckett & Sons. Owned by Foxfield Light Railway Society.						
Millom			0-4-0	1906	Avonside Engineering Co	S, U G N
Former Millom Ironworks Loco.						
Moss Bay			0-4-0	1920	Kerr, Stuart & Co Ltd	S, St O, G N
Owned by Staffordshire County Council.						
Lewisham			0-6-0	1927	W G Bagnall	S, Op, N
Owned by Foxfield Light Railway Society.						
Sentinel			4w	1956	Sentinel	S
Meaford No 4			0-6-0	1964	Andrew Barclay & Sons	D, St
Owned by Foxfield Light Railway Society.						
Helen			4w	1923	Simplex	D
Owned by Foxfield Light Railway Society.						
Megan		DM	0-4-0DM	1957	Thomas Hill	D, St
Owned by Foxfield Light Railway Society.						
Hercules	820		0-4-0	1946	Ruston & Hornsby Ltd	D, Op
Rachel			0-4-0	1941	Baguley	D, St O, U
Tonka					Ruston & Hornsby Ltd	D
Ludstone			0-6-0		Yorkshire Engine Co	D, Op
Owned by Foxfield Light Railway Society.						
Marston, Thompson & Evershed Limited No 3	3		0-4-0		Hawthorn Leslie & Co	S, Op, N
Rom River			u	1929	Kerr, Stuart & Co Ltd	D, St O, N
Owned by Foxfield Light Railway Society.						
Wolstanton No 3	3	DH	0-6-0	1959	W G Bagnall	D, Op
—		DM	4wDH	1961	W G Bagnall	D, St
Gas Oil			4wDM	1957	Ruston & Hornsby Ltd	D, Op, O
Robert Heath No 6	6		0-4-0	1886	Robert Heath	S, Op, G N
Designed by Falcon Design. Sole surviving Heath built loco.						
—	1827		0-4-0	1879	Beyer, Peacock	S, Op, G N
Designed by Beyer, Peacock. Former Beyer Peacock Gorton Works shunter.						
Bellerophon			0-6-0	1874	Haydock Foundry	S, Op, G N
Designed by Richard Evans. Owned by Vintage Carriages Trust.						
Dubsy			0-4-0	1901	Dubs	S, U, G N
Designed by Dubs. Former Shelton Steel Works Loco.						
Cranford			0-6-0	1924	Avonside Engineering Co	S, Op, N
Spondon No 2			4w	1939	English Electric	S, St O, N

FOYLE VALLEY RAILWAY CENTRE

						Londonderry, COUNTY LONDONDERRY
Name	**Current No.**	**Type/Class**	**Wh.Arr.**	**Built**	**Builder**	**Origin**
Columbkille	6		2-6-4T	1904		S
Meenglas	4		2-6-4T	1904		S

Key: Wh.Arr. = Wheel Arrangement   S = Steam   D = Diesel   E = Electric   P = Petrol   R = Rolling Stock   W = Wagon   C = Coach   Op = Operational   St = Static   O = On Display   U = Under Restoration   G = Pre Group   N = Pre Nationalisation

Steam Railway Directory   www.steamrailway.com

Foxfield Steam Railway — Foyle Valley Railway Centre

GARTELL LIGHT RAILWAY

Name	Current No.	Type/Class							
Mr G	6								

Templecombe, SOMERSET

Name	Current No.	Type/Class	Origin	Wh. Arr.	Built	Builder			
				0-4-2T	1998	North Dorset Loco Works	S	Op	

GIANTS CAUSEWAY & BUSHMILLS

Bushmills, COUNTY ANTRIM

Name	Current No.	Type/Class	Origin	Wh. Arr.	Built	Builder			
Tyrone	1		BAC Railway (Larne)	0-4-0	1904	Peckett & Sons	S	Op	
12ft in length. Originally owned by British Aluminium Co.									
Rory	2		Bluecircle Railway	0-4-0	1976	Simplex	D	Op	
11ft in length. Designed by Deutz. Originally owned by Bluecircle Cement.									
Shane	3		BNM Railway (Portarlington)	0-4-0WT	1949	Andrew Barclay & Sons	S	Op	
20ft in length. Originally owned by Bord Na Mona.									

GLOUCESTERSHIRE WARWICKSHIRE

Cheltenham, GLOUCESTERSHIRE

Name	Current No.	Type/Class	Origin	Wh. Arr.	Built	Builder			
Raveningham Hall	6960		GWR	4-6-0	1944	GWR	S	Op	N
BR No. 6960. 63ft in length. Designed by C B Collett, Hawksworth. Built at Swindon.									
	1450			0-4-2T			S		
Designed by C B Collett.									
Black Prince	92203		BR	2-10-0		BR	S		U
BR No. 92203. 66ft in length. Designed by David Shepherd.									
	47105			0-6-0ST		Brush Electrical Engineering	D		
						Hunslet Engine Co Ltd			
King George	2409			2-8-0	1905	GWR	S	Op	
Owned by Glos Works Railway.									
	2807		GWR	2-8-0		GWR	S		U G
BR No. 2807. Designed by Churchward. Owned by Cotswold Steam Preservation. The oldest surviving GWR engine.									
Peninsular & Oriental S N Co	35006		SR	4-6-2	1941	SR	S	Op	U
BR No. 35006. Designed by O V Bulleid. Owned by P & O Society.									
	8274		LMS & Turkish State Railways	2-8-0	1935	LMS	S		U
64ft in length. Designed by W A Stanier. Owned by Churchill 8F Locomotive Co Ltd. Rescued from Turkey.									
	7069		LMS	0-6-0		LMS			
Owned by Churchill 8F Locomotive Co Ltd. Historic diesel shunter, once captured by the Germans in World War 2.									
Clydebridge	37215		BR	Co-Co	1964	English Electric	D	Op	
BR No. 37215. Two owned by railway. Owned by Growler Group.									
	47105		BR	Co-Co			D	Op	
BR No. 47105.									
	76077		BR	2-6-0	1956	BR	S	Op	
BR No. 76077. 56ft in length. Designed by BR. Owned by Chris Hinton. Currently dismantled.									
	D8137		BR	Bo-Bo		English Electric	D		
BR No. 20137. 46.75ft in length. Designed by English Electric. Owned by Steve Madge.									
	D9539		BR	0-6-0	1965	BR	D	Op	U

| | 24081 | | BR | Bo-Bo | | | D | Op |

GREAT CENTRAL RAILWAY

Loughborough, LEICESTERSHIRE

Name	Current No.	Type/Class	Origin	Wh. Arr.	Built	Builder		
	1264			4-6-0	1947	North British Locomotive Co	s	Op
Designed by Edward Thompson.								
	45231			4-6-0	1936	Armstrong, Whitworth	s	U
Designed by W A Stanier. Awaiting overhaul.								
	5305			4-6-0	1937	Armstrong, Whitworth	s	U
Designed by W A Stanier.								
Witherslack Hall	6990			4-6-0	1948		s	Op
Sir Lamiel	30777			4-6-0	1925	North British Locomotive Co	s	U
Designed by W A Stanier.								
Boscastle	34039			4-6-2	1946	SR	s	Op
Designed by Maunsell.								
Brocklebank Line	35025			4-6-2	1948	BR	s	U
Designed by O V Bulleid.								
Designed by O V Bulleid.								
	47406	F/3		0-6-0T	1926	Vulcan Foundry	s	
Designed by Fowler.								
	48305			2-8-0	1943		s	Op
Designed by W A Stanier.								
	63601			2-8-0	1911	GCR	s	Op
Designed by J G Robinson.								
	69523			0-6-2T	1921	North British Locomotive Co	s	
Designed by Gresley.								
	78019			2-6-0	1954	BR	s	U
Designed by R A Riddles. Built at Darlington.								
Bardon	QWAG	DM /Industrial		4wDM	1954	Ruston & Hornsby Ltd	D	St O
	28	DM /Industrial		0-4-0DM	1956	Andrew Barclay & Sons	D	Op
	D123			1Co-Co1	1961		D	Op
	D1705			Co-Co	1965	Brush Electrical Engineering	D	Op
	D3101			0-6-0DE	1955	BR	D	St O
	D4067			0-6-0DE	1961	BR	D	Op
Built at Darlington.								
	D5830			A1A-A1A	1962	Brush Electrical Engineering	D	Op
	D7629			Bo-Bo	1961		D	Op
	D8098			Bo-Bo	1961		D	Op
	37075		BR	Co-Co	1961		D	Op
	25265		BR	Bo-Bo	1963		D	Op
Harlech Castle	DS830			A1A-A1A	1959		D	Op

Key: Wh. Arr. = Wheel Arrangement   S = Steam   D = Diesel   E = Electric   P = Petrol   R = Rolling Stock   W = Wagon   C = Coach   Op = Operational   St = Static   O = On Display   U = Under Restoration   G = Pre Group   N = Pre Nationalisation

A-Z SHOWING ROLLING STOCK

Gloucestershire Warwickshire — Great Central Railway

Great Central Railway — Gwili Railway

Name	Current No.	Type/Class	Origin	Wh. Arr.	Built	Builder		
—	51622		BR		1959			D
—	59276		BR		1958			D
Arthur Wright	D4279			0-4-0DE	1952	Fowler		D

GREAT WESTERN RAILWAY MUSEUM   Coleford, GLOUCESTERSHIRE

Name	Current No.	Type/Class	Origin	Wh. Arr.	Built	Builder		
—	45110			0-4-0	1936	Peckett & Sons	s	St
—			GWR	4-6-0			s	St
—			LSWR	0-4-2			s	St
—				0-4-0			s	St
Victor	2091	Saddle Tank		0-4-0	1952	W G Bagnall	s	St

GREAT WHIPSNADE RAILWAY   Dunstable, BEDFORDSHIRE

Name	Current No.	Type/Class	Origin	Wh. Arr.	Built	Builder		
Superior	4034			0-6-2	1920	Kerr, Stuart & Co Ltd	s	Op
Owned by Zoological Society of London.								
Excelsior	1049			0-4-2	1908	Kerr, Stuart & Co Ltd	s	Op
Owned by Zoological Society of London.								
Chevallier	1877			0-6-2	1915	Manning, Wardle & Co	s	St
Owned by Sir William McAlpine.								
Hercules	24376			0-6-0	1981		D	Op
Owned by Zoological Society of London.								
Hector	4160004			0-6-0	1951	John Fowler & Co	D	Op
Owned by Zoological Society of London.								
Victor	4160005			0-6-0	1951	John Fowler & Co	D	Op
Owned by Zoological Society of London.								
Mr Bill	10			0-4-0	1944	Ruston & Hornsby Ltd	D	Op
Owned by Zoological Society of London.								

GROUDLE GLEN RAILWAY   Douglas, ISLE OF MAN

Name	Current No.	Type/Class	Origin	Wh. Arr.	Built	Builder		
Sea Lion				2-4-0T	1896	W G Bagnall	s	Op
Annie				0-4-2T	1998	Richard Booth	s	Op
Owned by Richard Booth.								
Dolphin				0-4-0	1952	Hudson, Hunslet	D	
Walrus				0-4-0	1952	Hudson, Hunslet	D	St

GWILI RAILWAY   Carmarthen, CARMARTHENSHIRE

Name	Current No.	Type/Class	Origin	Wh. Arr.	Built	Builder

Gwili Railway

Name	Number	Description	Region	Builder	Date	Wh.Arr.	Type	Status
Welsh Guardsman	71516			Robert Stephenson, Hawthorn	1944	0-6-0ST	S	Op · U
Returned to service in December 2001 following a ten year overhaul.								
Olwen	7058			Robert Stephenson, Hawthorn	1942	0-4-0ST	S	Op
Withdrawn for repairs.								
Victory	2201			Andrew Barclay & Sons	1945	0-4-0ST	S	Op
Swansea Vale	9622			Sentinel	1958		S	Op · St
Owned by Caerphilly Railway Society.								
Built at Shrewsbury.								
Haulwen	5272			Hunslet Engine Co Ltd	1945	0-6-0ST	S	
Sir John	1914			Avonside Engineering Co	1914	0-6-0ST	S	St
Nellie	02101			Yorkshire Engine Co	1960	0-4-0DE	D	U
	D2178	DM /03		BR	1961		D	Op
Treatty	421702			Ruston & Hornsby Ltd	1959	0-6-0DM	D	Op
Built at Lincoln. Currently in store.								
Dylan Thomas	27654			North British Locomotive Co	1956		D	Op
	27878			North British Locomotive Co	1962		D	Op
	207103			Ruston & Hornsby Ltd	1941		D	
Idris	393302			Ruston & Hornsby Ltd	1955		D	Op · U
Swansea Jack	35012	Brake Second Corridor	BR		1957		C	
	3060	Semi Open Brake	BR		1955		C	
	24825	Second Corridor	BR		1956		C	
	24823	Second Corridor	BR		1956		C	
	24843	Tourist Second Open	BR		1956		C	
	4906	Kitchen Buffet Unclassified	BR		1961		C	
	21187	Brake Composite Corridor	BR		1958		C	
	15829	Composite Corridor	BR		1956		C	
	1106	Booth Car	BR		1962		C	
	10517	Sleeping Car	BR		1982		C	
	220	Brake Third	BR		1891		C	
	81547	Crane	BR		1958		R	
	19305	Crane			1958		R	
	4606	Scenery Van			1949		W	
	405	Scenery Van			1937		W	
	436	BY					W	
	DS8 PMV	Fruit Van	GWR				W	
	3403	Fruit Van	GWR				W	
	96302	Mink A Van	GWR		1920		W	
	28918	Pallet Van	GWR				W	
	47923	Pallet Van	BR				W	
	47107	Box Van	BR				W	
	2745	Bloater Van	GWR				W	
	79008	Mineral Open					W	
	80746		BR				W	

Key: **Wh.Arr.** = Wheel Arrangement   **S** = Steam   **D** = Diesel   **E** = Electric   **P** = Petrol   **R** = Rolling Stock   **W** = Wagon   **C** = Coach   **Op** = Operational   **St** = Static   **O** = On Display   **U** = Under Restoration   **G** = Pre Group   **N** = Pre Nationalisation

Steam Railway Directory www.steamrailway.com

	B943064	Bogie Bolster	BR		W
	42155		GWR		W
	41946		GWR		W
	DB993126	Dogfish	BR		W
	DB983914	Dogfish	BR		W
	2002	Tar Tank Wagon			W
	2009	Tar Tank Wagon			W
	48304	Tar Tank Wagon			W
	48325	Tanker			W
	35380	Brake Van	BR		W
	35798	Brake Van	GWR		W
	B95007	Brake Van	LMS		W

HEATHERSLAW LIGHT RAILWAY

Cornhill-on-Tweed, NORTHUMBERLAND

Name	Current No.	Type/Class	Origin	Wh. Arr.	Built	Builder			
Lady Augusta (The)	1		Heatherslaw Light Railway	0-4-2	1989	Ravenglass & Eskdale Railway	S		Op
12ft in length. Designed by HLR, Ravensglass. Owned by Hoots. Rebuilt in 1990.									
Clive	2	DH	Heatherslaw Light Railway	Bo-Bo	1988	Heatherslaw Light Railway		D	Op
14ft in length. Designed by N C Smith. Rebuilt in 1999 from D-6-0 to Bo-Bo.									
		Fully Open	Heatherslaw Light Railway		1989	Heatherslaw Light Railway			R
Four owned by railway. 16ft in length. Designed by N C Smith.									
		Semi Open	Heatherslaw Light Railway	Bogie	1989	Heatherslaw Light Railway			R
Two owned by railway. 16ft in length. Designed by N C Smith.									
		Fully Closed	Heatherslaw Light Railway	Bogie	1989	Heatherslaw Light Railway			R
Four owned by railway. 18ft in length. Designed by N C Smith.									
			Heatherslaw Light Railway	Bogie	1989	Heatherslaw Light Railway		W	Op
16ft in length. Designed by N C Smith.									
			Heatherslaw Light Railway	Bogie	1991	Heatherslaw Light Railway		W	Op
16ft in length. Designed by N C Smith.									
		Ballast Wagon	Heatherslaw Light Railway		1991	Heatherslaw Light Railway		W	
Three owned by railway. Designed by N C Smith.									
		Crane			2001	Heatherslaw Light Railway			Op
45ft in length. Designed by N C Smith. Self Balancing.									
			Heatherslaw Light Railway		1999	Heatherslaw Light Railway			Op
Designed by N C Smith.									

HOLLYBUSH GARDEN CENTRE

Wolverhampton, MIDLANDS (WEST)

Name	Current No.	Type/Class	Origin	Wh. Arr.	Built	Builder		
Malandra			Leisurerail Ltd	0-4-2	1987	T M A Engineering	S	Op
Owned by Leisurerail Ltd.								
Samuel Whitbread			Leisurerail Ltd	0-4-2	1987	John Foreshaw	S	Op

Owned by Leisurerail Ltd.

Name	Current No.	Type/Class	Origin	Wh. Arr.	Built	Builder	Type	Status	Era
Kestrel	384		Leisurerail Ltd	Bo-Bo	1991	Eric Smith	D	Op	G

Designed by Eric Smith. Owned by Leisurerail Ltd.

American GP40	645		Leisurerail Ltd	Bo-Bo	1998	R Greatrex	D	C	

Designed by R Greatrex. Owned by Leisurerail Ltd.

HOLLYCOMBE STEAM COLLECTION — Liphook, HAMPSHIRE

Name	Current No.	Type/Class	Origin	Wh. Arr.	Built	Builder	Type	Status	Era
Commander B	50			0-4-0ST	1899	Hawthorn Leslie & Co	S	Op	G
Caledonia	70			0-4-0WT	1931	Andrew Barclay & Sons	S	Op	N
—	16	DM		4wDM	1941	Ruston & Hornsby Ltd	D		N

Owned by Hollycombe Working Steam Museum. (Commander B)
Owned by Hollycombe Working Steam Museum. (Caledonia)
Owned by Hollycombe Working Steam Museum. (16)

INDUSTRIAL RAILWAY MUSEUM — Bangor, GWYNEDD

Name	Current No.	Type/Class	Origin	Wh. Arr.	Built	Builder	Type	Status
Charles	283			0-4-0	1882	Hunslet Engine Co Ltd	S	O
—				0-4-0	1904	Hunslet Engine Co Ltd	S	O
—	859			0-4-0	1885	Black, Hawthorn	S	St O
—	1361			0-4-0	1870	Neilson & Co	S	St O
Hawarden	526			0-4-0	1899	Hudswell, Clarke & Co	S	St O
Vesta	1223				1916	Hudswell, Clarke & Co	S	St O
Fire Queen			Padarn Railway	0-4-0	1848	A Horlock	S	St O
Haydock			National Coal Board	0-6-0	1879	Robert Stephenson	S	O
Acorn	327904			0-4-0	1948	Ruston & Hornsby Ltd	D	Op O
—				0-4-0	1880			R C O

Designed by Hunslet Engine Co Ltd. Owned by National Trust. (Charles)
Designed by Hunslet Engine Co Ltd. Owned by National Trust. Spent entire working life at Penrhyn Quarries.
Designed by Black, Hawthorn. Owned by National Trust.
Designed by Neilson. Owned by North Thames Gas Board.
Owned by National Trust. (Hawarden)
Owned by National Trust. (Vesta)
Designed by A Horlock. On loan by Sir John Smith to The National Trust.
Owned by National Trust. (Haydock)
Owned by National Trust. (Acorn)
Owned by National Trust.

IRCHESTER NARROW GAUGE MUSEUM — Wellingborough, HAMPSHIRE

Name	Current No.	Type/Class	Origin	Wh. Arr.	Built	Builder

Key: Wh. Arr. = Wheel Arrangement   S = Steam   D = Diesel   E = Electric   P = Petrol   R = Rolling Stock   W = Wagon   C = Coach   Op = Operational   St = Static   O = On Display   U = Under Restoration   G = Pre Group   N = Pre Nationalisation

Steam Railway Directory   www.steamrailway.com   Hollybush Garden Centre — Irchester Narrow Gauge Museum

Steam Railway Directory   www.steamrailway.com

Irchester Narrow Gauge Museum — Isle of Wight Steam Railway

				Builder				
Built at Bristol.	85		Saddle Tank	1934	Peckett & Sons		S	Op
Built at Bristol.	86		Saddle Tank	1934	Peckett & Sons		S	Op
Built at Bristol.	87		Saddle Tank	1942	Peckett & Sons		S	St O
Built at Bristol. Rock (The)			DM	1941	Hunslet Engine Co Ltd	D		
Owned by R L Kingston.	ED10		DM /48	1958	Ruston & Hornsby Ltd	D		Op
Owned by E Hampton.			DM	1941	Ruston & Hornsby Ltd	D		Op
Owned by Northamptonshire Locomotive Group.			4wPM	1918	Motor Rail Ltd, Tramcar Co	D		
Cambrai			0-6-0T	1888	Corpet	S		St O

IRISH STEAM PRESERVATION SOC

Stradbally, COUNTY LOAIS

Name	Current No.	Type/Class	Wh.Arr.	Built	Origin	Builder		
—	2	Well Tank	0-4-0	1949		Andrew Barclay & Sons	S	Op
Nippy		DM	4w	1936		Planet	D	Op
—	4	DM	4w	1952		Ruston	D	Op

ISLE OF MAN RAILWAY

Douglas, ISLE OF MAN

Name	Current No.	Type/Class	Wh.Arr.	Built	Origin	Builder	
Loch	4		2-4-0	1874	Isle of Man Railway	Beyer, Peacock	
Owned by Isle of Man Transport.							
G H Wood	10		2-4-0		Isle of Man Railway	Beyer, Peacock	S
Owned by Isle of Man Transport.							
Maitland	11		2-4-0		Isle of Man Railway	Beyer, Peacock	S
Owned by Isle of Man Transport.							
Hutchinson	12		2-4-0		Isle of Man Railway	Beyer, Peacock	S
Owned by Isle of Man Transport.							
Caledonia	15		0-6-0		Isle of Man Railway	Dubs	S
Owned by Isle of Man Transport.							

ISLE OF WIGHT STEAM RAILWAY

Ryde, ISLE OF WIGHT

Name	Current No.	Type/Class	Wh.Arr.	Built	Origin	Builder		
Calbourne	W24		0-4-4T	1891		Beyer, Peacock	S	Op G N
BR No. W24. Designed by Adams. Owned by Isle of Wight Railway Co Ltd.								
Freshwater	W8		0-6-0T	1876			S	Op G N
BR No. 32646. Designed by W Stroudley. Owned by Isle of Wight Railway Co Ltd.								
Newport	W11		0-6-0T	1878			S	Op G N

174   Section 1b.

© HCC Publishing Ltd

BR No. 32640. Designed by Adams. Owned by Isle of Wight Railway Co Ltd

Name	Current No.	Type/Class	Origin	Wh.Arr.	Built	Builder	Type	Status
Invincible *Owned by Isle of Wight Railway Co Ltd*	37			0-4-0T	1915	Hawthorn Leslie & Co	S	U
—	D2554	DM /05	BR	0-6-0DM	1956		D	Op
—	D2059	DM /03	BR	0-6-0DM	1959		D	Op
Ajax	38			0-6-0T	1918	Andrew Barclay & Sons	S	U

KEIGHLEY & WORTH VALLEY

Keighley, YORKSHIRE (WEST)

Name	Current No.	Type/Class	Origin	Wh.Arr.	Built	Builder	Type	Status
—	78022		BR	2-6-0	1954		S	U
Awaiting repairs.								
—	48431			2-8-0	1899		S	U
—	85			0-6-2			S	Op
—	47279			0-6-0T	1924		S	Op
—	80002						S	U
Boiler repairs in progress.								
—	90773						S	U
Undergoing full overhaul.								
—	75078						S	U
Full overhaul recently commenced.								
City of Wells	34092						S	U
—	41241		LMS	2-6-2T	1949		S	U
—	43924		MR	0-6-0	1920		S	U
Bahamas	45596		LMS	4-6-0	1935		S	U
In store.								
—	1054		LNWR	0-6-2T	1888		S	U
In store.								
—	30072		SR	0-6-0T	1943		S	U
In store.								
—	5775		GWR	0-6-0PT	1929		S	U
In store.								
—	52044			0-6-0	1887		S	U
—	51218			0-4-0ST	1901		S	U
—	752			0-6-0ST	1881		S	U
—	5820			2-8-0	1945		S	U
—	68077		LNER	0-6-0ST	1947		S	U
In store.								
—	D226		BR	0-6-0DE	1956		D	Op
—	D2511	DM	BR	0-6-0DM	1961		D	Op
—	D3336		BR	0-6-0DE	1954		D	Op
—	D5209		BR	Bo-Bo	1963		D	Op
—	D8031		BR	Bo-Bo	1960		D	Op

Key: Wh.Arr. = Wheel Arrangement S = Steam D = Diesel E = Electric P = Petrol R = Rolling Stock W = Wagon C = Coach Op = Operational St = Static O = On Display U = Under Restoration G = Pre Group N = Pre Nationalisation

A-Z SHOWING ROLLING STOCK

Isle of Wight Steam Railway — Keighley & Worth Valley

Steam Railway Directory www.steamrailway.com

Name	Current No.	Type/Class	Origin	Builder	Built	Wh.Arr.	Status	
—	50928		BR		1959		D	Op
—	51565		BR		1959		D	Op
—	79962	Railbus			1958		D	Op
—	79964	Railbus			1958		D	Op
—	31							U
Hamburg				Hudswell, Clarke & Co	1903	0-6-0T	S	
In store.								
Nunlow				Hudswell, Clarke & Co	1938	0-6-0T	S	
In store.								
Brussels				Hudswell, Clarke & Co	1945	0-6-0ST	S	
In store.								
Tiny				Andrew Barclay & Sons	1949	0-4-0ST	S	
Merlin	231	DM		Hudswell, Clarke & Co	1951	0-6-0DM	D	Op
Austins No 1	MDHB 32	DM		Peckett & Sons	1961	0-6-0DM	D	Op
—		DM		Hunslet Engine Co Ltd	1944	0-6-0DM	D	Op

KEITH & DUFFTOWN RAILWAY

Keith, MORAY

Name	Current No.	Type/Class	Origin	Builder	Built	Wh.Arr.	Status	
Spirit of Speyside	53628		BR		1958		D	Op
Owned by Diesel Unit Preservation Associates Ltd.								
Spirit of Banffshire	51568		BR					
Spirit O' Fife		DM		English Electric	1967	0-6-0	D	Op
Wee Mac (The)		DM			1979	0-4-0	D	Op
					1981			
Prototype.								
—	81295	Kitchen Car	BR		1957			C
—	AD975758	Cafeteria Car	BR		1957			C
—	13437	First Corridor	BR		1967			C
Awaiting restoration.								
—	B953691	Brake Van	BR					W
—	B954819	Brake Van	BR					W
—	B905112	Lowmac	BR					W
Built at Swindon.								
—	DB996996	Bogie Rail Wagon	BR		1958			W

KENT & EAST SUSSEX RAILWAY

Tenterden, KENT

Name	Current No.	Type/Class	Origin	Builder	Built	Wh.Arr.	Status		
Gazelle	1			Dodman & Co	1893	0-4-2WT	S	St O	G
Owned by National Railway Museum. Rebuilt in 1911 by WG Bagnall as a 0-4-2WT (used to be 2-2-2WT).									
Bodiam	3					0-6-0T	S		U
BR No. 32670. Designed by W Stroudley.									
Knowle	2678				1880	0-6-0T	S		Op
BR No. 32678. Designed by W Stroudley.									

Kent & East Sussex Railway — Kent & East Sussex Railway

Name / Notes	No.	Type	Wh. Arr.	Rly	Builder	Date	Class	Status	U
Sutton — BR No. 32650. Designed by W Stroudley.	32650		0-6-0T				s	St O	
Pride of Sussex — BR No. 31556. Prev. No. 753.	1556					1908	s	Op	
Marcia	12		0-4-0T		Peckett & Sons	1923	s	Op	U
Charwelton — Originally owned by Hardman & Holden.	14		0-6-0ST		Manning, Wardle & Co	1917	s	Op	U
Norwegian — Awaiting restoration.	376		2-6-0			1919	s	Op	
Wainwright	DS238					1941	s	Op	
Maunsell — BR No. 30070. Designed by Colonel Howard G Hill.	65					1941	s	Op	
Holman F Stephens — BR No. 30065. Designed by Colonel Howard G Hill.	23	Saddle Tank	0-6-0		Hunslet Engine Co Ltd	1952	s	Op	
Rolvenden	24	Saddle Tank	0-6-0		Hunslet Engine Co Ltd	1953	s	Op	
Northiam — Formerly William H Austen.	25	Saddle Tank	0-6-0		Hunslet Engine Co Ltd	1953	s	Op	
Designed by F W Hawkesworth. Built at Swindon.	1638		0-6-0PT		BR	1953	s	Op	U
Built at Swindon.	20	Railcar		GWR		1940	D	Op	U
Built at Dagenham.	40		Bo-Bo			1932	D E	Op	
Built at Lincoln.	41		0-4-0		Ruston & Hornsby Ltd	1958	D	Op	
Titan	43		0-4-0			1951	D	Op	
Dover Castle — Prev. No. 13174.	D3174		0-6-0	BR		1955	D	Op	
	D2023		0-6-0			1958	D	Op	
	D2024		0-6-0			1958	D	St	
Built at Swindon. On loan to Channel Tunnel.	48		0-6-0			1964	D	Op	
Ashford	D6570	DMU/108	Bo-Bo				D	Op	
Theodora	51					1926	D	Op	
Barbara — Awaiting overhaul.	52						D	Op	
BR No. 1869. Built at Wolverton.	59	Restaurant Miniature Buffet				1961		C	
BR No. 25446. Built at Wolverton.	63	Second Corridor				1957		C	
BR No. 3753. Built at Doncaster.		Tourist Second Open				1953		C	
BR No. 4355.	68	Tourist Second Open			BRCW	1956		C	

Key: Wh.Arr. = Wheel Arrangement   S = Steam   D = Diesel   E = Electric   P = Petrol   R = Rolling Stock   W = Wagon   C = Coach   Op = Operational   St = Static   O = On Display   U = Under Restoration   G = Pre Group   N = Pre Nationalisation

Steam Railway Directory www.steamrailway.com

Kent & East Sussex Railway — Kent & East Sussex Railway

Note	Number	Description	Builder	Year	Preserved
17.5ft in length.	1010	Brake Van			W
	56495	Brake Van	SR	1941	W
Built at Lancing.	104	Brake Van	LNWR	1923	W
Awaiting overhaul.	103686	Ventilated Van	GWR		W
Built at Swindon.	107	Banana Van	LMS		W
	109	Diesel Crane	Smith, Rodley	1935	W
	111	Drop Side Wagon			W
	114	Plank Wagon			W
2 plank wagon (formerly 3 plank).					
Built at Motherwell.	7522	Tank Wagon	Hurst, Nelson & Co Ltd	1943	W
	1151	Covered Goods Van	S J Claye Ltd	1913	W
	121		LNWR	1911	W
Built at Lancing Works.	M51548, FN128	Ventilated Van	SR	1940	W
	2338	Tank Wagon	R Y Pickering & Co Ltd	1941	W
	DS451	Steam Crane	Taylor & Hubbard Ltd	1949	W
	DS70003	Match Wagon			W
	135	Box Van	Midland Railway	1886	W
Prev. No. 589. Built at Newtonheath.	136	Box Van		1922	W
Prev. No. 606. 27ft in length.	137	Double Bolster Wagon			W
Built at Wolverton.	501348	Van		1934	W
Built at Ashford.	63101	Plank Dropside		1937	W
	DB993605	Ballast Hopper			W
	DS1770	Steam Crane			W
	146	Bogie Bolster Flat Wagon			W
	S11530	Plank Open Wagon			W
Built at Ipswich.	151	Steam Crane	Ransomes, Rapier	1926	W
	AD3088	Bogie Match Wagon		1949	W
	B483720	Plank Open Wagon		1959	W
Built at Shildon.	DB993620				W
	S5916, FN155	Open Wagon			W
	B460168	Steel Bodied Open		1952	W
	B460575	Steel Bodied Wagon		1952	W

	Type/Class	Origin	Built	Builder	Status
DS3141	Crane Match Wagon		1900	Metropolitan Carriage & Wagon Co	W
163	Bogie Bolster				W
DS62862	Weltrol Bogie Trolley		1957	Head Wrightson	Op
DB994441	Brake Van		1949		W
DB994457			1959		W
KDB733694			1959		W
169	Tube Wagon		1954	Faverdale Carriage & Wagon Co	W
KDB932502	Plate Wagon		1954	BR	W

Built at Shildon.

	Type/Class	Origin	Built	Builder	Status
KDB741895	Pipe Wagon		1961		W

Built at Wolverton.

	Type/Class	Origin	Built	Builder	Status
DB989104			1959	Metropolitan Cammell	W
ADB975472	Staff & Tool Van	BR	1972		c
69	Restaurant Unclassified	BR	1960		c

BR No. 1955. Built at Ashford/Swindon.

	Type/Class	Origin	Built	Builder	Status
72	Brake Second Open	BR			c

BR No. 9377. Built at Wolverton.

	Type/Class	Origin	Built	Builder	Status
73	Brake Second Open	BR	1956		c

BR No. 9269. Built at Doncaster.

	Type/Class	Origin	Built	Builder	Status
75		BR	1956		c

BR No. 9254.

	Type/Class	Origin	Built	Builder	Status
85	Tourist Second Open		1957		c

BR No. 4640.

	Type/Class	Origin	Built	Builder	Status
86	Composite Corridor	BR	1956		c

BR No. 7927. Built at Wolverton.

	Type/Class	Origin	Built	Builder	Status
	Brake Composite Corridor	BR	1961		c

BR No. 21238. Built at Swindon.

KERR MINIATURE RAILWAY

Arbroath, ANGUS

Name	Current No.	Type/Class	Origin	Wh.Arr.	Built	Builder	Status
Ivor				0-6-0	1972	Coleby, Simkins	S
Powered by a single cylinder.							
King George	2005				1935	HCS Bullock	Op
Auld Reekie	9872				1936	Jennings	Op
Known as 'the grand old lady' of the line.							
				Bo-Bo			Op
Part of 'The Twins'.							

Key: Wh.Arr. = Wheel Arrangement S = Steam D = Diesel E = Electric P = Petrol R = Rolling Stock W = Wagon C = Coach Op = Operational St = Static O = On Display U = Under Restoration G = Pre Group N = Pre Nationalisation

© HCC Publishing Ltd

KEW BRIDGE STEAM MUSEUM — Brentford, LONDON (GREATER)

Name	Current No.	Type/Class	Origin	Wh. Arr.	Built	Builder	Status
Cloister			Dinorwic Quarry	0-4-0ST	1891	Hunslet Engine Co Ltd	S Op N
Designed by Hunslet Engine Co Ltd. Owned by Hampshire Narrow Gauge Railway Society.							
Wendy	2091			0-4-0	1919	W G Bagnall	S Op N
Designed by W G Bagnall. Owned by Hampshire Narrow Gauge Railway Society.							
Alister	44052		Beesten UDC	0-4-0	1958	R A Lister & Co Ltd	D Op
Designed by R B & Lister & Co Ltd.							

KIRKLEES LIGHT RAILWAY — Huddersfield, YORKSHIRE (WEST)

Name	Current No.	Type/Class	Origin	Wh. Arr.	Built	Builder	Status
Fox		Saddle Tank		2-6-2T	1989	Brian Taylor	S Op
Badger				0-6-4T	1991	Brian Taylor	S Op
Designed by Brian Taylor.							
Hawk		DH		0-4-0	1998	Brian Taylor	S Op
Jay				0-4-0	1992	Brian Taylor	D
Only used as secondary.							
Owl				4w-4wT	2000	Brian Taylor	S C Op
Five owned by railway. 20ft in length. Designed by Kirklees Light Railway. Steam Heated. 20 seats in 5 x 4 compartments.							
—	Brake		Kirklees Light Railway				C Op
Two owned by railway. 20ft in length. Designed by Kirklees Light Railway. Steam heated. 16 seats in 4 x 4 compartments.							
—	Open		Kirklees Light Railway				Op
Three owned by railway. 20ft in length. 20 seats in 5 x 4 compartments.							
—	Semi Open		Kirklees Light Railway				
20ft in length. 20 seats in 5 x 4 compartments.							
Tram Engine	7			0-4-0	1995	Brian Taylor	Op

LAKESIDE & HAVERTHWAITE RLWY — Ulverston, CUMBRIA

Name	Current No.	Type/Class	Origin	Wh. Arr.	Built	Builder	Status
—	42073			2-6-4T	1950		S
—	42085			2-6-4T	1951		S
—	5643			0-6-2T	1924		U
Cumbria	3794			0-6-0ST	1953	Hunslet Engine Co Ltd	S U
David	2333			0-4-0ST	1953	Andrew Barclay & Sons	S
—	20			0-4-0	1863		S O
The oldest working standard gauge steam loco in Britain.							
—	D2072	DM/03	BR	0-6-0DM	1959		D O
—	20214		BR	Bo-Bo	1967		D O
—	D5301		BR	Bo-Bo	1958		D O

Name	Current No.	Type/Class	Builder	Wh. Arr.	Built			
Rachel	52077	DM	BRCW	4wDM	1961		D	P Op
Repulse	9		Motor Rail Ltd	0-6-0ST	1924		s	Op
Princess	11		Hunslet Engine Co Ltd	0-6-0ST	1950		s	Op
Askham Hall	14		W G Bagnall	0-4-0ST	1942		s	O
Alexandra	15			0-4-0ST	1935		s	O
Fluff	929	DM	Andrew Barclay & Sons	0-6-0DM	1902		D	O
Sir James	16	F	Hunslet Engine Co Ltd, Fowler	0-6-0DM	1937		D	
	21		Andrew Barclay & Sons	0-6-0F	1917		s	

LAPPA VALLEY STEAM RAILWAY — Newquay, CORNWALL

Name	Current No.	Type/Class	Builder	Wh. Arr.	Built	Origin		
Zebedee	1	Pannier Tank	Severn Lamb	0-6-4	1974		s	Op
Built at Stratford.								
Muffin	2		Berwin Engineering	0-6-0	1967		s	Op
Built at Chippenham.								
Gladiator	3		Mini Rail Ltd	4w + 4w Bogie	1960		D	Op
Pooh	4		R A Lister & Co Ltd	4w	1952		D	Op
Built at Dursley.								

LAUNCESTON STEAM RAILWAY — Launceston, CORNWALL

Name	Current No.	Type/Class	Builder	Wh. Arr.	Built	Origin		
Lilian			Hunslet Engine Co Ltd	0-4-0ST	1883		s	Op
Velinheli			Hunslet Engine Co Ltd	0-4-0ST	1886		s	Op
Covertcoat			Hunslet Engine Co Ltd	0-4-0ST	1898		s	Op
Sybil			W G Bagnall	0-4-0ST	1906		s	Op
Dorothea			Hunslet Engine Co Ltd	0-4-0ST	1901		s	Op
		DM	Motor Rail Ltd	4wDM	1933		D	O
		DM	Motor Rail Ltd	4wDM	1917		D	O

LAVENDER LINE — Uckfield, SUSSEX (EAST)

Name	Current No.	Type/Class	Builder	Wh. Arr.	Built	Origin		
Annie	945		Andrew Barclay & Sons	0-4-0ST	1904		s	
Blackie	68012		Hunslet Engine Co Ltd	0-6-0ST	1944		s	U
Rebuilt in 1964.								
Sir Herbert Walker	E6003		BR	Bo-Bo	1962		D	Op
Built at Eastleigh.								
	73004		BR	Bo-Bo			D	
Built at Eastleigh.								
	AB354	DM	Andrew Barclay & Sons	0-4-0DM	1941		D	U

Key: Wh. Arr. = Wheel Arrangement   S = Steam   D = Diesel   E = Electric   P = Petrol   R = Rolling Stock   W = Wagon   C = Coach   Op = Operational   St = Static   O = On Display   U = Under Restoration   G = Pre Group   N = Pre Nationalisation

Steam Railway Directory   www.steamrailway.com   Lakeside & Haverthwaite Rlwy — Lavender Line

© HCC Publishing Ltd   Section 1b.   181

Lavender Line — Leighton Buzzard Railway

Current No.	Type/Class	Origin	Builder	Built	Wh. Arr.		
	DM		Drewry Car Co, Vulcan	1945	0-4-0DM	D	U
	DM		F C Hibberd & Co Ltd	1957	0-4-0DM	D	Op U
	DM		F C Hibberd & Co Ltd	1960	0-4-0DM	D	U
4830	Tourist Second Open		BR	1959			C
	Built at Wolverton.						
21249	Brake Composite Corridor		BR	1962		D	C
	Built at Swindon.						
59511	TCL		Pressed Steel Co Ltd	1959		D	C

LEADHILLS & WANLOCKHEAD

Name	Current No.	Type/Class	Builder	Wh. Arr.	Built		
Elvan			Motor Rail Ltd			D	Op
Little Clyde			Ruston & Hornsby Ltd			D	Op
7.5ft in length.							
Luce			Ruston & Hornsby Ltd			D	Op
Nith			Hudswell, Clarke & Co			D	Op
16ft in length.							
Clyde	HE6347		Hunslet Engine Co Ltd	0-4-0WT	1975	S	D
Charlotte	6335		Orenstein, Koppel		1913	S	U

Biggar, LANARKSHIRE

LEIGHTON BUZZARD RAILWAY

Leighton Buzzard, BEDFORDSHIRE

Name	Current No.	Type/Class	Origin	Wh. Arr.	Builder	Built			
Chaloner	1		Pen-Yr-Orsedd Quarry	0-4-0VBRT	De Winton	1877	S	Op O	
Rishra	3		Calcutta Corporation	0-4-0T	Baguley	1921	S	Op O	U
Sezela No 4	5		Sezela Sugar Estate	0-4-0T	Avonside Engineering Co	1915	S	O	U
Elf			Cameroon Development Corp	0-6-0WT	Orenstein, Koppel	1936	S	Op O	
Alice			Dinorwic Quarry	0-4-0ST	Hunslet Engine Co Ltd	1902	S	Op O	
PC Allen	11		Solvay	0-4-0WT	Orenstein, Koppel	1913	S	Op O	
			Amalgamated Roadstone Corp	0-4-0WT	Freudenstein	1901	S	St	
Pixie	114		Devon County Council	0-4-0ST	Kerr, Stuart & Co Ltd	1922	S	Op O	
Peter Pan	4		Devon County Council	0-4-0ST	Kerr, Stuart & Co Ltd	1922	S	Op O	
Doll	740		Stewarts & Lloyds	0-6-0T	Andrew Barclay & Sons	1919	S	O	U
	778		Central Railway, India	0-6-0T	Orenstein, Koppel	1907	S	O	U
			War Department Light Railways	4-6-0T	Baldwin Locomotive Works	1917	S	O	U
Built for use on World War 1 battlefield supply lines.									
Festoon	21		George Garside (Sand) Ltd	4WPM		1929	P		
The oldest locomotive to have run on the Leighton Buzzard Railway system.									
Damredub	12	DM	Standard Bottle Co	4WPM	Motor Rail Ltd	1930	D	Op O	
	17	DM	George Garside (sand) Ltd	4WDM	Motor Rail Ltd	1936	D	Op O	
Formerly used in Leighton Buzzard Sand Quarries.									
Red Rum	34	DM	George Garside (Sand) Ltd	4WDM	Motor Rail Ltd	1936	D	Op O	
Formerly used in Leighton Buzzard Sand Quarries.									
Arkle	13	DM	George Garside (Sand) Ltd	4WDM	Motor Rail Ltd	1937	D	Op O	

Table — Leighton Buzzard Railway rolling stock directory (continued)

Name	No.	Type	Owner	Year	Wh.Arr.	Builder	Status
Formerly used in Leighton Buzzard Sand Quarries.							
Caravan	36	DM	Redland Flettons Ltd	1938	4WDM	Motor Rail Ltd	D
—	25	DM	Joseph Arnold & Sons Ltd	1938	4WDM	Motor Rail Ltd	D
Formerly used in Leighton Buzzard Sand Quarries.							
—	44	DM	Leighton Buzzard Railway	1941	4WDM	Motor Rail Ltd	D St O
—	30	DM	Joseph Arnold & Sons Ltd	1941	4WDM	Motor Rail Ltd	D
Formerly used in Leighton Buzzard Sand Quarries.							
Haydn Taylor	10	DM	British Industrial Sand Ltd	1945	4WDM	Motor Rail Ltd	D Op O
—	43	DM	Leighton Buzzard Railway	1954	4WDM	Motor Rail Ltd	D Op O
Formerly used on Leighton Buzzard Light Railway mainline.							
Feanor	18	DM	British Industrial Sand Ltd	1956	4WDM	Motor Rail Ltd	D Op O
—	24	DM	British Industrial Sand Ltd	1965	4WDM	Motor Rail Ltd	D
—	23	DM	British Industrial Sand Ltd	1965	4WDM	Motor Rail Ltd	D U
—	25	DM	British Industrial Sand Ltd	1966	4WDM	Motor Rail Ltd	D U
Beaudesert	80	DH	Leighton Buzzard Railway	1999	4WDH	Alan Keel Ltd	D Op O
A one off design to Leighton Buzzard Railway specification using parts from an earlier Simplex T series locomotive.							
—	28	DM	West Kent Main Sewerage Board	1932	4WDM	Ruston & Hornsby Ltd	D O
—	32	DM	Associated Portland Cement MFRS	1934	4WDM	Ruston & Hornsby Ltd	D
RAF Stanbridge	37	DM	Broomfield Brickworks	1934	4WDM	Ruston & Hornsby Ltd	D
Yimkin	28	DM	Ministry of Defence	1940	4WDM	Ruston & Hornsby Ltd	D
—	26	DM	Ministry of Defence	1941	4WDM	Ruston & Hornsby Ltd	D
—	46	DM		1942	4WDM	Ruston & Hornsby Ltd	D O
—	8	DM /13DL	Fetherleys Brickworks	1943	4WDM	Ruston & Hornsby Ltd	D
Sarah	42	DM /20DL	Far Ings Tileries	1944	4WDM	Ruston & Hornsby Ltd	D Op O
Trent	40	DM /30DL	Severn Trent Water Authority	1949	4WDM	Ruston & Hornsby Ltd	D
T W Lewis	LM39	DM /40DL	Amalgamated Roadstone Corp	1954	4WDM	Ruston & Hornsby Ltd	D
—	27	DM	Springfield Tileries	1957	4WDM	Ruston & Hornsby Ltd	D
—	41	DM	Richardsons Moss Litter Co Ltd	1941	4WDM	Hunslet Engine Co Ltd	D
—	14	DM	Arnold Nathan Ltd	1946	4WDM	Hunslet Engine Co Ltd	D
Macnamara	48	DM	Ministry of Defence	1952	4WDM	Hunslet Engine Co Ltd	D Op O
Creepy	29	DM	Ministry of Defence	1963	4WDM	Hunslet Engine Co Ltd	D Op O
Binky	35	DM	National Coal Board	1966	0-4-0DM	Hunslet Engine Co Ltd	D U
Underground mine locomotive.							
—	50	DM	Associated Portland Cement MFRS	1927	4WPM	F C Hibberd & Co Ltd	D Op O
This is the oldest surviving locomotive by this manufacturer.							
Bluebell	1	DM	Hall & Co	1938	4wDM	F C Hibberd & Co Ltd	D
—	15	DM	Butterley Brick Co	1941	4WDM	F C Hibberd & Co Ltd	D
—	49	DM	Hammill Brick Co	1941	4WDM	F C Hibberd & Co Ltd	D
—	33	DM	Commonwealth Smelting	1954	4WDM	F C Hibberd & Co Ltd	D
Madge	9	DM	Oxted Greystone Lime Co	1935	4WDM	Orenstein, Koppel	D
Falcon	7	DM	Woodham Brick Co Ltd		4WPM	Orenstein, Koppel	D U
—	31	DM	Prenton Brick & Tile Co Ltd	1931	4WDM	R A Lister & Co Ltd	D St O
Harry Barnett	16	DM	Guard Bridge Paper Co	1939	4WDM	R A Lister & Co Ltd	D Op O
—	38	DM	Eclipse Peat Co Ltd	1951	4WDM	R A Lister & Co Ltd	D Op O

Key: Wh.Arr. = Wheel Arrangement   S = Steam   D = Diesel   E = Electric   P = Petrol   R = Rolling Stock   W = Wagon   C = Coach   Op = Operational   St = Static   O = On Display   U = Under Restoration   G = Pre Group   N = Pre Nationalisation

Steam Railway Directory www.steamrailway.com

Leighton Buzzard Railway — Leighton Buzzard Railway

Steam Railway Directory — www.steamrailway.com

Leighton Buzzard Railway — Leighton Buzzard Railway

Notes	No./Type	Type	Year	Builder	Owner	Status
Under construction using Ruston & Hornsby parts.	47	DM		Hudson	Staveley Iron & Steel Ltd	D
	22	DM	1929	Hudson	Leighton Buzzard Railway	D U
Locomotive chassis rebuilt as brake van by Leighton Buzzard Railway.	5	4WDM	1931	Motor Rail Ltd	St Albans Sand & Gravel Co	R C Op O
Locomotive chassis rebuilt as tool van by Leighton Buzzard Railway.	3	4WDM	1935	Motor Rail Ltd	St Albans Sand & Gravel Co	R W Op O
Ex WDLR Bogie wagon rebuilt as PW mess van by Leighton Buzzard Railway.				Hudson	Leighton Buzzard Railway	R W Op O
Two owned by railway. Ex bogie wagon rebuilt as passenegr coach by Leighton Buzzard Railway.	7			Hudson	Leighton Buzzard Railway	R C Op O
Bogie tipping wagon rebuilt as passenger coach by Leighton Buzzard Railway.	8			Hudson	W R Cunis	R C Op O
Standard gauge railcar rebuilt as passenger coach.	9		1959	Baguley	Ministry of Defence	R C Op O
	11		1940	Hudson	Ministry of Defence	R C Op O
Bogie wagon rebuilt as passenger coach by Leighton Buzzard Railway.	12		1940	Hudson	Ministry of Defence	W St
Three owned by railway. Underground mine coaches.	20			Leighton Buzzard Railway	R C Op O
Restoration to original design from bare chassis. Heritage Railway Association Award Winner.	F38			Tredomen Engineering	BR	R C St O
Contains historical display on military narrow gauge railways.	D39		1940	Hudson	Ministry of Defence	R W
	NGB4404		1940	Hudson	Ministry of Defence	R W
	Flat Wagon		1992	John Thompson	Royal Ordnance	R W Op O
Nine owned by railway.	Covered Goods Van				Ministry of Defence	R W Op O
Five owned by railway.	Drop Side Wagon				Ministry of Defence	R W Op O
Seven owned by railway.	Bogie Dropside Wagon				Ministry of Defence	R W Op O
Two owned by railway.				Hudson	British Industrial Sand Ltd	R W Op O
Seven owned by railway. Used for track ballast.					Polish Railways	
Two owned by railway.	Underground Coal Wagon	4w			British Coal	R W St O
Five owned by railway.	Slate Wagon				Dinorwic Quarry	R W St O
Reconstructed using original parts.	Peat Wagon	4w			Hollands Moss Peat Co Ltd	R W Op O
Five owned by railway.		4w			Parkhill Mine	R W U

Eight owned by railway.

	Current No.						R	W	Op	St
	162	Leighton Buzzard Railway								0
		Oakley Slate Quarry					R	W		
Three owned by railway. Slate rubbish wagons.		Oakley Slate Quarry					R	W		
Three owned by railway. Slate slab wagons.							R	W		St 0

LINCOLNSHIRE WOLDS RAILWAY

Grimsby, LINCOLNSHIRE (NORTH EAST)

Name	Current No.	Type/Class	Origin	Wh. Arr.	Built	Builder	
Fulstow No 2	D3167			0-4-0ST	1928	Peckett & Sons	Op
Lion				0-4-0ST	1914	Peckett & Sons	Op

LLANBERIS LAKE RAILWAY

Caernarfon, GWYNEDD

Name	Current No.	Type/Class	Origin	Wh. Arr.	Built	Builder		
Elidir				0-4-0	1889	Hunslet Engine Co Ltd	S	Op
Dolbadarn				0-4-0	1922	Hunslet Engine Co Ltd	S	Op
Thomas Bach				0-4-0	1904	Hunslet Engine Co Ltd	S	Op
Coed Gorau	441427				1961		D	
Twll Coed	268878				1956		D	
Braich	203031				1942		D	
Llanelli	451901				1961		D	

LLANGOLLEN RAILWAY

Llangollen, DENBIGHSHIRE

Name	Current No.	Type/Class	Origin	Wh. Arr.	Built	Builder		
Foxcote Manor	7822		GWR	4-6-0	1950	BR	S	Op
BR No. 7822. Designed by C B Collett. Owned by Foxcote Manor Society.								
Black 5 Magpie	44806		LMS	4-6-0	1944		S	Op
BR No. 44806. Designed by W A Stanier. Owned by K Aldcroft. Built at Derby.								
	4141		GWR	2-6-2	1938	GWR	S	Op
BR No. 4141. Designed by C B Collett. Owned by Prof J Kennedy.								
	7754		GWR	0-6-0	1930	North British Locomotive Co	S	Op
BR No. 7754. Designed by C B Collett. Owned by Llangollen Railway Trust.								
	47298		LMS	0-6-0	1924	LMS	S	Op
BR No. 47298. Designed by Fowler. Owned by Major H Parker.								
	47449		BR		1963	BR	D	Op
Owned by Llangollen Diesel Group.								
	25313						D	Op

Leighton Buzzard Railway — Llangollen Railway

Key: Wh. Arr. = Wheel Arrangement **S** = Steam **D** = Diesel **E** = Electric **P** = Petrol **R** = Rolling Stock **W** = Wagon **C** = Coach **Op** = Operational **St** = Static **U** = Under Restoration **O** = On Display **G** = Pre Group **N** = Pre Nationalisation

Steam Railway Directory www.steamrailway.com

Steam Railway Directory   www.steamrailway.com

Llangollen Railway — Mangapps Railway Museum

46010	Owned by Martin Bell.	
7663	Owned by Llangollen Diesel Group.	

LONDON TRANSPORT MUSEUM

London, LONDON (GREATER)

Name	Current No.	Type/Class	Origin	Wh. Arr.	Built	Builder				
	23			4-4-0T	1866	Beyer, Peacock		D	Op	
Built at Manchester.										
John Hampden	5			Bo-Bo	1922	BR		E	D	Op
Built at Manchester.										

MANGAPPS RAILWAY MUSEUM

Burnham-on-Crouch, ESSEX

Name	Current No.	Type/Class	Origin	Wh. Arr.	Built	Builder	S	E/D	Op/St/C	O/U
Brookfield	2613			0-6-0	1940	W G Bagnall	S		Op	O
Owned by R Moore. Designed as a metre gauge loco for export to Turkey but diverted to Royal Navy due to World War 2. Worked at Brookfield Foundry which was worked by Navy.										
Empress	3061		NCB	0-6-0	1954	W G Bagnall				O U
Owned by R Moore. Ex Cadley Hall Colliery.										
Minnie	358		Skinningrove Steel Works	0-6-0	1878	Fox, Walker & Co	S		St	O
Owned by J A Jolly. One of only 3 Fox Walker loco's in Britain.										
Toto				0-4-0	1919	Andrew Barclay & Sons				O U
Owned by R Moore.										
			NCB	0-4-0	1943	Andrew Barclay & Sons	S			O U
Owned by Richard & Tony Goulding. Ex Kinneil Colliery.										
Elland			CEGB	0-4-0	1954	Hudswell, Clarke & Co		D	Op	O
Ex Elland Power Station.										
	D2089		BR	0-6-0	1960	Drewry Car Co		D	Op	O
BR No. 03089.										
	03399		BR	0-6-0	1961	Drewry Car Co		D	Op	O
BR No. D2399. Ex Colchester & Ipswich.										
	2325		RSH	0-6-0	1961	Drewry Car Co		D	Op	O
Ex NCB.										
	11104		Adams	0-6-0	1948	Drewry Car Co, Vulcan		D	Op	O
Adapted to resemble a BR Wisbech & Upwell. The No 11104 was not used in the BR Drewry No series.										
	7502	London Underground Tube Car	RFS Industries		1965	Strachan, Henshaw		D	Op St	O
	1030				1959	Metropolitan Cammell		E	Op St	O
	2044		BR		1959	Metropolitan Cammell		E	Op St	O
	54287		BR		1961	Pressed Steel Co Ltd			C	O
BR No. 54287.										
			BR		1960				C	O
BR No. 59664.										
	22624		LT		1938				C	O

Notes	Number	Description	Company	Year	Manufacturer	Status
Body & undertrame only.	347			1864	Metropolitan Carriage & Wagon Co	C
	63875			1888		C
Built at Stratford. Body & underframe only	472E			1890		C
Body & undertrame only.	S31875			1921		C
Built at Eastleigh. Former brake down van.						
	DE320779			1926		Op O
	DE320803			1927	Cravens	Op O
Prev Nos. 61684, E82347E.	S2735		NER	1952		N
	S2195		BR	1939		St
Body and underframe only.	M94109	Covered Carriage Truck		1959		C St
	E9066E	Restaurant Pantry Car	LNER	1928		C St
Prev Nos. 42972, DE320927.	DE320651			1910		C
	957			1906		C
	43264			1956		C
Built at Swindon.	E9115E		GNR	1936		C
Built at York.	13324			1961		C
Ex Old Oak Common.	60101			1921		C
Originally built as two 4 wheel coaches.	33	Cattle Van	GER	1891		St
Body & underframe only.	W2009W			1927		R C
	E70692E		LNER	1950		C O
Underframe only.	DS70165			1922		St
Body & underframe only.	381			1864	Metropolitan Carriage & Wagon Co	C
	ADM47			1942		R
	ADB965204			1965	BR	R
Built at Swindon. Independent snow plough from LNER class V2 tender.						R

Key: Wh. Arr. = Wheel Arrangement   S = Steam   D = Diesel   E = Electric   P = Petrol   R = Rolling Stock   W = Wagon   C = Coach   Op = Operational   St = Static   O = On Display   U = Under Restoration   G = Pre Group   N = Pre Nationalisation

Steam Railway Directory   www.steamrailway.com

©HCC Publishing Ltd

MARKEATON PARK LIGHT RAILWAY

Derby, DERBYSHIRE

Name	Current No.	Type/Class	Wh. Arr.	Origin	Built	Builder		
Markeaton Lady			0-4-2T		1996	Exmoor Steam Railway	s	Op
Owned by Markeaton Park.								
Cromwell			0-4-0		1970	Alan Keef Ltd	D	Op
Owned by J Shackle.								
Baby Deltic	D5905		Bo-Bo		1995	Joe Brown	D	U
Owned by Markeaton.								
—			4w		1996	Exmoor Steam Railway	C	Op
Three owned by railway: Owned by Markeaton.								

MIDDLETON RAILWAY

Leeds, YORKSHIRE (WEST)

Name	Current No.	Type/Class	Wh. Arr.	Origin	Built	Builder		
Windle	68153		4w VBGT		1933	Sentinel	s	
	53		0-4-0WT		1909	Borrows	s	
	1310		0-4-0T		1891		s	Op
Owned by Steam Power Trust.								
Matthew Murray	2702		0-4-0ST		1943	W G Bagnall	s	
Henry De Lacy II	1309		0-4-0ST		1917	Hudswell, Clarke & Co	s	
	6		0-4-0ST		1935		s	
Owned by Steam Power Trust.								
John Blenkinsop	385		0-4-0WT		1895	Hartmann	s	
Mirvale	2003		0-4-0ST		1941	Peckett & Sons	s	
	1882		0-4-0ST		1955	Hudswell, Clarke & Co	s	
Sir Berkeley	1625		0-4-0VBT		1890	Cockerill	s	st
	1210		0-6-0ST		1891	Manning, Wardle & Co	s	
Owned by Vintage Carriages Trust.								
Brookes No 1	2387		0-6-0ST		1941	Hunslet Engine Co Ltd	s	Op
Owned by Brookes No 1 Society.								
—	1329		0-6-0T		1921		s	
	2103		0-4-0ST		1948	Peckett & Sons	s	Op
	1697		0-6-0ST		1903	Manning, Wardle & Co	s	Op
Matthew Murray	3900002	DM	0-6-0DM		1932		D	Op
John Alcock	1786	DM	0-4-0DM		1945	Fowler	D	Op
Courage	631	DM	0-4-0DM		1935	Hunslet Engine Co Ltd	D	Op
Carroll	577	DM	0-4-0DM		1946	Hudswell, Clarke & Co	D	Op
Mary	138C	DH	0-4-0DM		1932	Hudswell, Clarke & Co	D	Op
			0-4-0DH			Thomas Hill		
Rebuilt in 1965.								
—	91		0-4-0DE		1958	Brush Electrical Engineering, Beyer, Peacock	D	Op
Olive	RDB998901	DM	0-4-0DM		1950	Ruston & Hornsby Ltd	D	Op

MIDLAND RAILWAY CENTRE

Ripley, DERBYSHIRE

Name / Notes	Current No.	Type/Class	Origin	Wh. Arr.	Built	Builder	Power	Status	Era
Princess Margaret Rose *BR No. 46203. Designed by W A Stanier. Built at Crewe.*	46203			4-6-2	1935		S	St O	N
Duchess of Sutherland *BR No. 46233. Designed by W A Stanier. Built at Crewe.*	6233			4-6-2	1938		S	Op	N
BR No. 44027. Designed by Fowler. Built at Derby.	44027			0-6-0	1924		S	U	N
BR No. 44932. Designed by W A Stanier. Built at Horwich.	44932			4-6-0	1945		S	U	N
BR No. 45491. Designed by W A Stanier. Built at Derby.	45491			4-6-0	1943		S	U	N
BR No. 47564. Designed by Fowler.	47564	F/3		0-6-0T	1928		S	St	N
BR No. 47327. Designed by Fowler.	16410	F/3		0-6-0T	1926	North British Locomotive Co	S	U	N
BR No. 47357. Designed by Fowler.	47357	F/3		0-6-0T	1926	North British Locomotive Co	S	Op	N
BR No. 47445. Designed by Fowler.	47445	F/3		0-6-0T	1927	Hunslet Engine Co Ltd	S	St	N
BR No. 2002. Designed by Matthew Kirtley. Built at Derby.	158A			2-4-0	1866		S	St O	G
BR No. 53809. Prev. Nos. 89, 9689, 13809. Designed by Fowler.	53809			2-8-0	1925	Robert Stephenson	S	U	N
Designed by R A Riddles. Built at Derby.	73129			4-6-0	1956		S	U	
Designed by R A Riddles. Built at Brighton.	80080		BR	2-6-4T	1954		S	O	
Designed by R A Riddles. Built at Brighton.	80098		BR	2-6-4T	1955		S	Op	
Designed by R A Riddles. Built at Swindon.	92214			2-10-0	1959		S	St O	
Designed by R A Riddles. Built at Swindon.	92219		BR	2-10-0	1959		S	U	
Built at Swindon.	D2138	DM /03		0-6-0DM	1960		D	Op	
Built at Crewe.	08590		BR	0-6-0DE	1959		D	Op	
Built at Derby.	12077		BR	0-6-0DE	1950		D	Op	
—	D8001		BR	Bo-Bo	1957	English Electric	D	Op	
—	20205		BR	Bo-Bo	1967	English Electric	D	U	

Steam Railway Directory www.steamrailway.com

Midland Railway Centre — Midland Railway Centre

Key: Wh.Arr. = Wheel Arrangement   **S** = Steam   **D** = Diesel   **E** = Electric   **P** = Petrol   **R** = Rolling Stock   **W** = Wagon   **C** = Coach   **Op** = Operational   **St** = Static   **O** = On Display   **U** = Under Restoration   **G** = Pre Group   **N** = Pre Nationalisation

A-Z SHOWING ROLLING STOCK

A-Z SHOWING ROLLING STOCK

Midland Railway Centre — Midland Railway Centre

Steam Railway Directory   www.steamrailway.com

Name	Number	Notes	Owner	Wheel	Year	Builder		
Traction	20227		BR	Bo-Bo	1967	English Electric	D	Op
	D7671		BR	Bo-Bo	1967		D	Op
Built at Derby.								
	31108	*Prev. No. D5526.*	BR	A1A-A1A	1959	Brush Electrical Engineering	D	Op
	5580		BR	A1A-A1A	1960	Brush Electrical Engineering	D	St O U
	31271		BR	A1A-A1A	1961	Brush Electrical Engineering	D	Op
	33201		BR	Bo-Bo	1962	Robert Stephenson, Hawthorn	D	Op
Aureol	37190		BR	Co-Co	1964	English Electric	D	Op
	40012	*Prev. No. D212.*	BR	Co-Co	1959	English Electric	D	U
Andania	40013	*Prev. No. D213.*	BR		1959	English Electric	D	Op
Great Gable	D4	*Built at Derby.*	BR		1959		D	U
Royal Tank Regiment	45041	*Built at Derby.*	BR		1962		D	Op
	45133	*Prev. No. D40. Built at Derby.*	BR		1961		D	Op
	46045	*Prev. No. D182. Built at Derby.*	BR		1963		D	Op
	47401	*Prev. No. D1500.*	BR	Co-Co	1963	Brush Electrical Engineering	D	St O
	D1516		BR	Co-Co	1963	Brush Electrical Engineering	D	Op
Sir Edward Elgar	50007	*Prev. No. D407.*	BR	Co-Co	1967	English Electric	D	U
Tulyar	55015	*Prev. No. D9015.*	BR	Co-Co	1961	English Electric	D	U
Western Lady	D1048		BR	C-C	1962		D	Op
	50019	*Built at Derby.*	BR	C-C	1956		D	Op
	55966	*Built at Derby.*	BR		1959		D	Op
	55976	*Built at Derby.*	BR		1956		D	Op
	56006	*Built at Derby.*	BR		1956		D	Op
	59609	*Built at Derby.*	BR		1959		D	Op
	79018		BR		1977		D	U
	79612		BR		1977		D	U
	56171				1957		D	U
	50416	*Driving Motor Brake Second*			1957		D	Op
Gladys	24			0-4-0ST	1894	Andrew Barclay & Sons	S	St O
Stanton				0-4-0CT	1925	Peckett & Sons	S	St O
Whitehead		*Awaiting restoration.*		0-4-0ST	1908		S	Op

© HCC Publishing Ltd

Name	Current No.	Type/Class	Origin	Wh.Arr.	Built	Builder	Status
Lytham St Annes				0-4-0ST	1949	Peckett & Sons	S St O
Brown Bailey				0-4-0ST	1894	Nasmyth, Wilson	S St O
Castle Donnington No 1				0-4-0ST	1954	Robert Stephenson, Hawthorn	S U
Neepsend				4wVBT	1947	Sentinel	
Andy	RS9	DM		0-4-0DM	1923	Fowler	D St O
—	RS12	DM		0-4-0DM	1921	Motor Rail Ltd	D O U
Boots No 2				0-4-0DM	1912	Motor Rail Ltd	S D St O
Castle Donnington No 2		DM		0-4-0F	1935	Andrew Barclay & Sons	D St O
Boots				0-4-0DM	1957	Andrew Barclay & Sons	Op D
Electra			BR	0-4-0DE	1955	Ruston & Hornsby Ltd	Op D
—	27000	TC		Co-Co	1953		R D U
—	29663	TC			1931		U
—	29666	TC			1931		U
—	29670	TC			1931		U

MID-NORFOLK RAILWAY

Dereham, NORFOLK

Name	Current No.	Type/Class	Origin	Wh.Arr.	Built	Builder	Status
Ramillies	50019			Co-Co	1968	English Electric	Op D E U

BR No. 50019. Owned by Class 50 Loco Association.

—	D8069				1961	English Electric	Op D E

BR No. 20069. Owned by Type One Fund.

—	31235			A1A-A1A	1960	Brush Electrical Engineering	Op D E

BR No. 31235. Owned by Colne Valley Diesels Ltd.

—	55006				1958		Op D

Two owned by railway. Owned by Railcar Enterprises.

—	51572				1958	BR	Op D

Owned by Railcar Enterprises.

Name	Current No.	Type/Class	Origin	Wh.Arr.	Built	Builder	Status
—	141108	Driving Motor Brake Second /119					
—	51073	Driving Motor Brake Second /117					
—	51360						U
—	55006						D
—	59575	Trailer Buffet /111					C
—	56301	Tourist Second Open					
—	5536	First Corridor					
—	13446	Brake Second Open					
—	68003	Luggage Van /419					R
—	D8994107	Tench Wagon					R W
—	B950567	Brake Van					R
—	B73006	Tube Wagon					R
—	B741748	Pipe Wagon					R W

Key: Wh.Arr. = Wheel Arrangement   **S** = Steam   **D** = Diesel   **E** = Electric   **C** = Coach   **W** = Wagon   **P** = Petrol   **R** = Rolling Stock   **St** = Static   **O** = On Display   **Op** = Operational   **U** = Under Restoration   **G** = Pre Group   **N** = Pre Nationalisation

Steam Railway Directory   www.steamrailway.com   Midland Railway Centre — Mid-Norfolk Railway

A-Z SHOWING ROLLING STOCK

Steam Railway Directory   www.steamrailway.com

Capacity 12 tonnes.

B927541	Bogie Bolster		R
HW402	Ballast Hopper		R
MNR291	Box Wagon	LNWR	R W
M93226	General Utility Van		R
E94597	Covered Carriage Truck		R
80214			R
ADB977383	QRA Re Railing Van		R
497753	Wickham Trolley		R
2408	Tank Wagon		R W
269	Flat Wagon		R
	Dogfish Ballast Hopper		R

Two owned by railway.

1380	Great Eastern Coach Body		Op
56224		BR	1959

MID-SUFFOLK LIGHT RAILWAY   Stowmarket, SUFFOLK

Name	Current No.	Type/Class	Ordain	Wh. Arr.	Built	Builder		
Alston	1604			0-6-0ST	1928	Hudswell, Clarke & Co	S	St
—	304470	DM		0-4-0DM	1951	Ruston & Hornsby Ltd	D	Op

Owned by Mid Suffolk Light Railway.

MOORS VALLEY RAILWAY   Ringwood, HAMPSHIRE

Name	Current No.	Type/Class	Ordain	Wh. Arr.	Built	Builder		
Horace		DH		0-4-2DH	1999	Rowan Oak Engineering	D	Op
Built at Bratton Flemming.								
Talos	3			0-4-2T	1978	Roger Marsh & Co	S	Op
Designed by Roger Marsh. Owned by J Haylock.								
Tinkerbell	4			0-4-2T	1968	Roger Marsh & Co	S	Op
Designed by Roger Marsh. Owned by J Haylock. Built at Coventry.								
Sapper	5			4-6-0	1982	Roger Marsh & Co	S	Op
Designed by J Haylock, Roger Marsh. Owned by J Haylock.								
Medea	6			2-6-2T	1981	J Haylock	S	Op
Designed by J Haylock, M Sharp. Owned by J Haylock.								
Aelfred	7			2-6-4T	1985	M Haylock, J Haylock & G Brown	S	Op
Designed by M Haylock. Owned by M Haylock.								
Jason	9			2-4-4T	1989	J Haylock	S	Op
Designed by J Haylock. Owned by J Haylock.								
Offa	10			2-6-2	1991	J Haylock	S	Op
Designed by J Haylock. Owned by J Haylock.								
Zeus	11			2-6-2	1991	J Haylock & A Culver	S	Op
Designed by J Haylock, A Culver. Owned by A Culver.								

Name	Current No.	Type/Class	Wh. Arr.	Built	Builder		
Pioneer	12		4-6-2	1992	J Haylock	S	Op
Tiny Tim	13		0-4-0TT	1993	J Haylock		Op
Horton	14		2-4-0	1991	J Haylock		Op
William Rufus	15		2-4-0 + 0-4-2T	1997	J Haylock	S	Op
Robert Snooks	16		0-4-0T	1999	A Manktelow, M Colbourne	S	Op
Hartfield	17		2-4-4T	1999	M Colbourne	S	Op

Pioneer — Designed by J Haylock. Owned by J Haylock.
Tiny Tim — Designed by J Haylock.
Horton — Designed by J Haylock. Owned by J Haylock.
William Rufus — Designed by J Haylock. Owned by J Haylock.
Robert Snooks — Designed by J Haylock, A Manktelow. Owned by A Manktelow.
Hartfield — Designed by J Haylock, M Colbourne. Owned by M Colbourne.

MULL RAILWAY

Isle of Mull, ARGYLL AND BUTE

Name	Current No.	Type/Class	Origin	Wh. Arr.	Built	Builder		
Lady of the Isles				2-6-4T	1982	Roger Marsh & Co	S	Op
Victoria				2-6-2T	1993	Mouse Boiler Works	S	Op
Waverley				4-4-2	1952	D Curwen	S	Op
Frances				Bo-Bo	1999	Mouse Boiler Works	D	
Glen Auldyn				Bo-Bo	1986	Bob Davies, D Vere	D	Op
—				Bo-Bo	1973	Tony Alcock	D	Op

Lady of the Isles — 8.25ft in length. Designed by Roger Marsh.
Victoria — 11.75ft in length. Designed by David Vere.
Waverley — 12.25ft in length. Designed by D Curwen. Owned by Waverley Group.
Frances — 13.5ft in length. Designed by D Curwen. Diesel Hydraulic Perkins 100 series.
Glen Auldyn — 12ft in length. Designed by Bob Davies. Diesel Hydraulic Engine Perkins 4108.
— 6.5ft in length. Designed by Tony Alcock. Based on BR CL 26.

MUSEUM OF ARMY TRANSPORT

Beverley, YORKSHIRE (EAST)

Name	Current No.	Type/Class	Origin	Wh. Arr.	Built	Builder		
Waggoner	92	Saddle Tank		0-6-0ST	1953	Hunslet Engine Co Ltd	S	St O
Woolmer				0-6-0ST	1910		S	St O
Rorke's Drift		DM		0-4-0DM	1934	Drewry Car Co	D	Op St O

Woolmer — The first standard gauge loco to be operated on the Woolmer Instructional Military Railway.

MUSEUM OF SCIENCE & INDUSTRY

Manchester, MANCHESTER (GREATER)

Name	Current No.	Type/Class	Origin	Wh. Arr.	Built	Builder			
—	1378		GWR	2-4-0T	1873	English Electric	S	E	Op O
Pender							S		St O

Key: Wh.Arr. = Wheel Arrangement S = Steam D = Diesel E = Electric P = Petrol R = Rolling Stock W = Wagon C = Coach Op = Operational St = Static O = On Display U = Under Restoration G = Pre Group N = Pre Nationalisation

Steam Railway Directory www.steamrailway.com

Museum of Science & Industry — National Railway Museum

	Current No.	Type/Class				4-8-2 + 2-8-4	Beyer, Garrett s		o
	2352								
Lord Ashfield	5	F					$		0
Ariadne	1505						E		0
	3157			LMS		Vulcan Foundry	$		0
		Medical Examination Carriage							0 U

NARROW GAUGE RAILWAY MUSEUM — Tywyn, GWYNEDD

Name	Current No.	Type/Class	Origin	Wh. Arr.	Built	Builder			
George Henry				0-6-0	1877	Winton	$		0
Jubilee				0-4-0	1879	Manning, Wardle & Co	$		0
Dot				0-4-0		Beyer, Peacock	$	St	0
Guiness Brewery Loco No 13				0-4-0	1895		$		0
Designed by Samuel Geoghegan.									
Dundee Gas Works Loco	2			0-4-0	1902	Kerr, Stuart & Co Ltd	$		0
Rough Pup				0-4-0	1892	Hunslet Engine Co Ltd	$	P	0
Baguley					1919		$		0

NATIONAL RAILWAY MUSEUM — York, YORKSHIRE (NORTH)

Name	Current No.	Type/Class	Origin	Wh. Arr.	Built	Builder			
Puffing Billy			Wylam Colliery	0-4-0	1813		$	St	0
Located at Science Museum.									
				0-4-0	1822		$		
Located at Beamish. Built at Hetton Colliery.									
Locomotion	1			0-4-0	1825	Robert Stephenson	$	St	0
Designed by G Stephenson. Located at Darlington Railway & Museum.									
Agenoria				0-4-0	1829		$		
Designed by Foster, Rastrick.									
Rocket				0-2-2	1829		$	St	0
Designed by Robert Stephenson. Located at Science Museum.									
Sans Pareil				0-4-0	1829		$		
				0-2-2	1829		$		
Located at Museum of Science & Industry.									
					1840		$		
Located at Timothy Hackworth. Tender only.									
Derwent	25			0-6-0	1845		$		
Located at Darlington Railway & Museum.									
Columbine	1868			2-2-2	1845		$		
Located at Science Museum.									
Coppernob	3			0-4-0	1846		$		
Designed by Edward Bury.									
Pet	1439			0-4-0ST	1865		$		
				0-4-0ST	1865		$		
Located at Eastleigh Lakeside Railway. Ramsbottom Tank.									

Name	Number	Wh.Arr.	Year	S	St	O	G	Op
Located at Midland Railway Centre.								
	158A	2-4-0	1866	S				
Aerolite	66	2-2-4T	1869	S	St	O	G	
Bauxite	298	2-4-0WT	1874	S	St	O	G	
Built at Hepburn Works.	2	0-4-0ST	1874					
	1275	0-6-0	1874	S				
	910	2-4-0	1875	S				
Located at Darlington Railway & Museum.								
Boxhill	82	0-6-0T	1880	S	St	O	G	
Gladstone	214	0-4-2	1882	S	St	O	G	
	1463	2-4-0	1885	S	St	O	G	
Located at Darlington Railway & Museum.								
Wren	1008	0-4-0ST	1887	S	St	O	G	
Hardwicke	790	2-4-2T	1889	S	St	O	G	
	563	4-4-0	1892	S	St	O	G	
	1621	4-4-0	1893	S	St	O	G	
	490	2-4-0	1894	S	St	O	G	
Located at Bressingham Steam.								
	245	0-4-4T	1897	S				
	2516	0-6-0	1897	S				
Located at Steam Museum.								
	28	0-6-2T	1897					
Located at Dean Forest Railway.								
Henry Oakley	990	4-4-2	1898	S	St	O	G	
Located at Bressingham Steam.								
	673	4-2-2	1899	S				
	1247	0-6-0ST	1899	S				
	120	4-4-0	1899					
Located at Bluebell Railway.								
	737	4-4-0	1901	S				
	1000	4-4-0	1902	S				
	251	4-4-2	1902	S				
City of Truro	3717	4-4-0	1903	S	St	O	G	
	87	0-6-0T	1904	S				
	1217	0-6-0	1905	S				
	2818	2-8-0	1905	S				
Lode Star	4003	4-6-0	1907	S	St	O	G	
Thundersley	80	4-4-2T	1909	S	St	O	G	
Located at Bressingham Steam.								
	102	2-8-0	1911	S				Op
Located at Great Central Railway.								

Key: Wh.Arr. = Wheel Arrangement   S = Steam   D = Diesel   E = Electric   P = Petrol   R = Rolling Stock   W = Wagon   C = Coach   Op = Operational   St = Static   O = On Display   U = Under Restoration   G = Pre Group   N = Pre Nationalisation

National Railway Museum — National Railway Museum

National Railway Museum — National Railway Museum

Steam Railway Directory www.steamrailway.com

Name / Number		Wheel	Year		Status
901		0-8-0	1919		St O G
Located at North Yorkshire Moors Railway					
506		4-4-0	1920		St O G
485		0-8-0	1921		Op St G
		0-6-2T	1922		St U G
Located at Churnet Valley Railway.					Op St G
Caerphilly Castle 4073	GWR	4-6-0	1923	GWR	St O G
60ft in length. Designed by C B Collett. Located at Steam Museum. Built at Swindon.					
4027		0-6-0	1924		St O M
Located at Midland Railway Centre.					
		2-2-2	1925		St O M
Sir Lamiel 777		4-6-0	1925		
Located at Steam Museum.					
Located at Humberside Locomotive Preservation Group.					
2700		2-6-0	1926		
Located at Barrow Hill Roundhouse.					
Lord Nelson 850		4-6-0	1926		
Located at Eastleigh Lakeside Railway.					
2700		2-6-0	1926		
Located at Eastleigh Lakeside Railway.					
925		4-4-0	1934		
2500		2-6-4T	1934		
4089			1935		
Sectionalised reproduction.					
Green Arrow 607		4-8-4	1935		
Designed by Cantile.					
5000		4-6-0	1935		
Mallard 4771		2-6-2	1936		
4468		4-6-2	1938		
Designed by Gresley.					
Duchess of Hamilton 33001		0-6-0	1942		
Designed by W A Stanier.					
Eustace Forth 34051		0-4-0ST	1942		
Located at Bluebell Railway.		4-6-2	1945		St O
Winston Churchill 9400		0-6-0PT	1947		St O
Located at Steam Museum.					
Ellerman Lines 35029		4-6-2	1949		St O
Designed by O V Bulleid. Sectioned exhibit.					
Oliver Cromwell 70013		4-6-2	1951	BR	St O
Located at Bressingham Steam.		0-4-0F	1956		St O
			1957		St O
Evening Star 92220	BR	2-10-0	1960	BR	St O
Designed by R A Riddles. Built at Swindon. The last steam loco to be built by BR.					
Rocket 5		0-2-2	1979		Op O

Located at Barrow Hill Roundhouse.

Located at Stephenson Railway Museum.

Located at St Leonards Railway Engineering Centre.

Located at St Leonards Railway Engineering Centre.

In store.

In store.

Magnetic – Levitational experimental prototype passenger car.

Located at Steam Museum.

Located at Embsay & Bolton Abbey Rlwy.

Located at Darlington Railway & Museum.

Located at Timothy Hackworth.

Located at Darlington Railway & Museum. Coach Body Only.

Number	Description	Year	Status
45049		1985	S
3267		1959	D
		1949	D / St O
S8143S		1904	R
S11179S		1915	R
12123		1925	R
		1937	R
		1937	R
28361		1937	R
29896		1941	R
		1941	R
49006		1975	R
4		1983	R
		1934	R
112		1850	R
1002		1890	C
WR537		1899	C
		1911	C
197266	Ballast Plough Brake	1932	W
80659		1936	C
DB74007		1949	C
2		1834	R
59		1834	R
31	First & Second Composite	1834	R
		1842	R
		1845	R
		1846	R
179	Third	1850	R
	Third	1850	R

Key: Wh.Arr. = Wheel Arrangement **S** = Steam **D** = Diesel **E** = Electric **P** = Petrol **R** = Rolling Stock **W** = Wagon **C** = Coach **Op** = Operational **St** = Static **O** = On Display **U** = Under Restoration **G** = Pre Group **N** = Pre Nationalisation

Steam Railway Directory   www.steamrailway.com

National Railway Museum — National Railway Museum

A-Z SHOWING ROLLING STOCK

National Railway Museum — National Railway Museum

		1	1850
			1851
			1861
			1869
		1032	1872
		186	1885
		901	1885
		948	1887
		820	1897
		12	1898
		57A	1899
		76	1900
		800	1902
		801	1902
		3598	1903
Stored off site.			1905
Stored off site.		395	1908
		396	1908
Located at Bressingham Steam.		109	1908
Stored off site.		DE320709	1910
		3463	1913
		2911	1914
Stored off site.			1920
Located at Severn Valley Railway.	Dining Car	9653	1925
Located at Severn Valley Railway.	Dining Car	9654	1925
Located at Severn Valley Railway.		7828	1925
		14241	1928
			1930
Reproduction.		9631	1930
Reproduction.			1930
Reproduction.		13254	1934
	Third Open		1936

Located at North Yorkshire Moors Railway.

Note	Current No.	Type/Class	Built	
	3792		1936	R
	9135		1937	R
	5987		1937	R
			1938	R
Reproduction on wagon frame.	4920	TPO	1939	R
Located at Nene Valley Railway.	798		1941	R
Located at Glasgow Museum of Transport.	799		1941	R
	9006		1945	R
Stored off site. Queen Elizabeth the Queen Mothers Saloon.	9007		1945	R
Queen Elizabeth the Queen Mothers Saloon.				
	27093	Third Brake	1950	R
Located at Midland Railway Centre.	E43046		1955	R
	Sc1100		1960	R
Stored off site.	311	Kitchen Car	1960	R
Located at North Yorkshire Moors Railway.	326		1960	R
	W13252		1962	R
Stored off site.	35468		1962	R
	21274		1964	R
Stored off site.	5455		1969	R
			1985	R
Reproduction broad gauge.				
Reproduction broad gauge.				

NATIONAL TRAMWAY MUSEUM

Matlock, DERBYSHIRE

Name	Current No.	Type/Class	Origin	Wh.Arr.	Built	Builder	S	E	St O
		Tram Engine		0-4-0VB	1885	Beyer, Peacock			St O
		DM		4w	1927	English Electric		E	Op O
Rupert *Not on display.*		DM		4w	1944	Ruston & Hornsby Ltd	D		Op
GMJ		DM		4w	1952	Ruston & Hornsby Ltd	D		Op

Key: **Wh.Arr.** = Wheel Arrangement **S** = Steam **D** = Diesel **E** = Electric **P** = Petrol **R** = Rolling Stock **C** = Coach **W** = Wagon **Op** = Operational **St** = Static **O** = On Display **U** = Under Restoration **G** = Pre Group **N** = Pre Nationalisation

Steam Railway Directory www.steamrailway.com

National Railway Museum — National Tramway Museum

A-Z SHOWING ROLLING STOCK

National Tramway Museum — NIRT

Steam Railway Directory www.steamrailway.com

Not on display.

Not on display, stored off site.

Name	Current No.	Type/Class	Origin	Wh. Arr.	Built	Builder				Status
—	2126	DM		4w	1954	Ruston & Hornsby Ltd				U

NATIONAL WATERWAYS MUSEUM — Gloucester, GLOUCESTERSHIRE

Name	Current No.	Type/Class	Origin	Wh. Arr.	Built	Builder				Status
—				0-4-0F	1942	Andrew Barclay & Sons				St O

NENE VALLEY RAILWAY — Peterborough, CAMBRIDGESHIRE

Name	Current No.	Type/Class	Origin	Wh. Arr.	Built	Builder	S	D	E	Status	N
City of Peterborough	73050		BR	4-6-0	1954	BR	S			U	
BR No. 73050. Two owned by railway. Designed by R A Riddles. Owned by City of Peterborough.											
92 Squadron	34081		BR	4-6-2	1948		S			Op	
BR No. 34081. Three owned by railway. Designed by O V Bulleid. Owned by Battle of Britain Locomotive Society.											
Thomas	1800			0-6-0T	1947	Hudswell, Clarke & Co	S			Op	N
Three owned by railway. Designed by Hudswell, Clarke & Co.											
	101A			4-6-0	1944	Nydquist, Holm	S			Op	N
Three owned by railway. Designed by Nydquist, Holm. Owned by 1697 Syndicate.											
Mayflower	1306		LNER	4-6-0	1948		S			U	
	D9516	DH/14	BR	0-6-0DH	1964			D		Op	
	D9523	DH/14	BR	0-6-0DH	1964			D		Op	
Atlantic Conveyor	D306		BR	1Co-Co1	1960			D		Op	
	7173		DB	2-6-2T	1936		S			St O	
	656		DB	2-10-0	1943		S			St O	
	1178		DSB	0-6-0T	1949		S			St O	
Toby				2-6-2T	1914	Cockerill	S			U	
Muriel				0-4-0VBT	1890	English Electric		D		Op	
Rhos		DH		0-6-0DH	1966	Hudswell, Clarke & Co	S			St O	
Derek Crouch				0-6-0ST	1918	Hudswell, Clarke & Co	S			St O	
Jacks Green				0-6-0ST	1924	Hunslet Engine Co Ltd	S			St O	
	75006			0-6-0ST	1939	Hunslet Engine Co Ltd	S			St O	
Doncaster				0-4-0DE	1943	Yorkshire Engine Co		D	E	Op	
Janus				0-6-0DE	1957	Yorkshire Engine Co		D	E	Op	
					1958						

NIRT — Northampton, NORTHAMPTONSHIRE

Name	Current No.	Type/Class	Origin	Wh. Arr.	Built	Builder	S			Status
Belvedere	9365			0-4-0TG	1946	Sentinel	S			St O
Owned by Northamptonshire Ironstone Railway Trust. Located at Northamptonshire Ironstone Railway Trust.										
Musketeer	9369			0-4-0TG	1946	Sentinel	S			O

Name	Current No.	Wh.Arr.	Built	Builder	Fuel	Status	Era
Hytton	3967 DH	0-4-0DH	1961	Planet	D	Op	N
Vigilant	287	0-4-0	1883	Hunslet Engine Co Ltd	S		U
—	D697 DM	0-4-0	1950	Hudswell, Clarke & Co	D	Op	N
—	2087 DM	0-4-0DM	1940	Hunslet Engine Co Ltd	D	Op	G
Sir Alfred Wood	319294	0-6-0	1953	Eddie Tratser	D	Op	N
Shire Lodge	327974	0-4-0	1954	Ruston & Hornsby Ltd	D	Op	G
Ivor	395305	0-4-0	1956	Ruston & Hornsby Ltd	D		U
—	4220001	0-4-0	1959	Fowler	D	Op	N
Lois	4220033	0-4-0	1965	Fowler	D		U

Owner/location notes:
- *Owned by Northamptonshire Ironstone Railway Trust. Located at Northamptonshire Ironstone Railway Trust.* — **Hytton**
- *Owned by Northamptonshire Ironstone Railway Trust. Located at Northamptonshire Ironstone Railway Trust.* — **Vigilant**
- *Located at Northamptonshire Ironstone Railway Trust.*
- *Owned by Northamptonshire Ironstone Railway Trust. Located at Northamptonshire Ironstone Railway Trust.*
- *Owned by I Cave. Located at Northamptonshire Ironstone Railway Trust.* — **Sir Alfred Wood**
- *Designed by Ruston, Hornsby. Owned by Eddie Trasler. Located at Northamptonshire Ironstone Railway Trust.* — **Shire Lodge**
- *Owned by 2E Loco Group. Located at Northamptonshire Ironstone Railway Trust.* — **Ivor**
- *Owned by 2E Loco Group. Located at Northamptonshire Ironstone Railway Trust. Formerly named Amoco.*
- *Owned by AEM Ltd. Located at Northamptonshire Ironstone Railway Trust.* — **Lois**
- *Owned by 2E Loco Group. Located at Northamptonshire Ironstone Railway Trust.*

NORTH GLOUCESTERSHIRE RAILWAY

Cheltenham, GLOUCESTERSHIRE

Name	Current No.	Type/Class	Origin	Wh.Arr.	Built	Builder	Fuel	Era
Isiburtu	5			4-4-0T	1946	W G Bagnall	S	N
George B				0-4-0ST	1898	Hunslet Engine Co Ltd	S	G
Chaka				0-4-2T	1940	Hunslet Engine Co Ltd	S	N
Justine				0-4-0WT	1906	Arn Jung	S	G
Brigadelok				0-8-0T	1918	Henschel	S	G
—	2	DM		4wDM	1949	R A Lister & Co Ltd	P	
Spitfire	3	PM		4wPM	1928	Motor Rail Ltd	P	
—	1			4wPM	1937	Motor Rail Ltd	D	
—	L5	DM		4wDM	1932	Ruston & Hornsby Ltd	D	
—		DM		4wDM	1936	Ruston & Hornsby Ltd	D	
—		DM		4wDM	1953	Ruston & Hornsby Ltd	D	

NORTH NORFOLK RAILWAY

Sheringham, NORFOLK

Name	Current No.	Type/Class	Origin	Wh.Arr.	Built	Builder	Fuel	Status	Era
—	61572	B12	LNER	4-6-0	1928	LNER	S	Op	N

BR No. 61572. Prev. No. 8572.

Key: Wh.Arr. = Wheel Arrangement S = Steam D = Diesel E = Electric P = Petrol R = Rolling Stock W = Wagon C = Coach Op = Operational St = Static O = On Display U = Under Restoration G = Pre Group N = Pre Nationalisation

Steam Railway Directory www.steamrailway.com NIRT — North Norfolk Railway

North Norfolk Railway — North Norfolk Railway

Steam Railway Directory www.steamrailway.com

1572. Designed by Holden. Owned by Midland & Great Northern Joint Railway Society.

BR No. 65462. Prev. No. 7564

564. Designed by Worsdell. Owned by Midland & Great Northern Joint Railway Society.

BR No. 69621. Prev. No. 999E

999. Designed by Hill. Owned by East Anglian Museum. Built at Stratford. Last steam loco built at Stratford works. Name is carried on special occasions.

BR No. 37032. Prev. No. D6732. Designed by English Electric. Built at Vulcan Foundry. The first class 37 to run in preservation.

BR No. 27103. Prev. No. 27212

27066. Designed by BRCW. Built at Birmingham.

BR No. 25057. Designed by BR. Built at Derby.

Prev. No. 1. Owned by Midland & Great Northern Joint Railway Society. Built at RSH.

BR No. D5207. Designed by BR.

BR No. E79960.

Owned by Midland & Great Northern Joint Railway Society.

Name	No.	Class	Operator	Wheel	Year	Builder			
—	65462		GER	0-6-0	1912	GER	S		U G
A J Hill	7999	N7	GER	0-6-2T	1924	GER	S		U N
7999									
9621									
Ring Haw		Saddle Tank		0-6-0ST	1940	Hunslet Engine Co Ltd	S	Op	
—	3809			0-6-0	1954	Hunslet Engine Co Ltd	S	Op	
Wissington				0-6-0ST	1938	Hudswell, Clarke & Co	S	St 0	
Mirage	D6732	DE /37	BR	Co-Co	1961	English Electric	D	Op	
—	D5386	DE /27	BR	Bo-Bo	1962	BRCW	D	Op	
—	D5207	DE /25	BR	Bo-Bo	1963	BR	D	Op	
—	D2267	Shunter /04	Ford Motor Co	0-6-0DM	1958	Drewry Car Co	D	St 0	
—	D5207		BR	Bo-Bo	1963	BR	D	Op	
—	E79960			4w	1958		D	R	
—	2370	F		0-6-0F	1929	W G Bagnall	S		
—	68009			0-6-0ST	1953	Hunslet Engine Co Ltd	S		

No.	Class / Type	Wh. Arr.	Builder	Year	Type	Stock / Status
12131	DE/11	0-6-0DE	BR	1952	D	
D3935	DE/08	0-6-0DE	BR	1961	D	
D2051	DM/03	0-6-0DM	BR	1959	D	
D2063	DM/03	0-6-0DM	BR	1959	D	
D2280	DM/04	0-6-0DM	Drewry Car Co	1960	D	
	DMU		Pressed Steel Co Ltd	1958		R C Op N
51769	RB		LNER	1937		R C Op
129	DMU / RB		LNER			
6843	TZ	4w	MCW	1887		C U G
6843	BY / GNR	4w	LNER	1929		C U N
DRB4w	DMU		MCW	1958		R
51346	DMU/117		Pressed Steel Co Ltd	1959		R
51388	DMU/117		Pressed Steel Co Ltd	1959		R
59516	DMU/117		Pressed Steel Co Ltd	1960		R
88DS			Ruston & Hornsby Ltd	1957		R
129			MCW	1887		R
295	Brake Third Corridor		GER	1907		R
5318	Directors Saloon		LNWR	1913		R
6843	BY		LNER	1924		R
6843	BY		LNER	1929		R
3395	Third Corridor		Metropolitan Cammell	1931		R

Tippockety — TZ

Notes:

- Prev. No. 3825. Designed by Hunslet Engine Co Ltd.
- BR No. 12131. Built at Darlington.
- BR No. 08767. Built at Horwich.
- Ford Motor Co.
- BR No. D2051. Prev. No. 4. Built at Doncaster.
- BR No. 03063. Designed by BR. Built at Doncaster.
- Ford Motor Co.
- BR No. D2280. Prev. No. 2. Built at RSH.
- BR No. E9128E. Owned by Midland & Great Northern Joint Railway Society.
- Owned by Midland & Great Northern Joint Railway Society.
- BR No. E70246E. Owned by Midland & Great Northern Joint Railway Society.
- Two owned by railway. These were a BR experiment to reprieve branch lines.
- Owned by Midland & Great Northern Joint Railway Society.
- Owned by Midland & Great Northern Joint Railway Society. Built at Stratford.
- Owned by Midland & Great Northern Joint Railway Society.
- Owned by C & W Trust. Built at Doncaster.
- Owned by Midland & Great Northern Joint Railway Society. Built at Doncaster.
- Owned by Midland & Great Northern Joint Railway Society.

Key: Wh. Arr. = Wheel Arrangement   S = Steam   D = Diesel   E = Electric   P = Petrol   R = Rolling Stock   W = Wagon   C = Coach   Op = Operational   St = Static   O = On Display   U = Under Restoration   G = Pre Group   N = Pre Nationalisation

Number	Description		Year	Builder	R
87			1932	Metropolitan Cammell	R
91			1932	Metropolitan Cammell	R
52256	Tourist Third Open		1935	LNER	R

Owned by Midland & Great Northern Joint Railway Society. Built at York.

| 51769 | Restaurant Buffet | | 1937 | LNER | R |

Owned by Midland & Great Northern Joint Railway Society

| 70621 | Brake Gangwayed | | 1945 | LNER | R |

Owned by Midland & Great Northern Joint Railway Society

| E3868 | Tourist Second Open | BR | 1953 | BR | R |
| E43034 | Composite Lavatory | BR | 1954 | BR | R |

Built at Doncaster.

| E43041 | Composite Lavatory | BR | 1954 | BR | R |

Built at Doncaster.

E46147	Gangwayed Brake Second	BR	1954	BR	R
E43357		BR	1955	BR	R
E43359	Brake Second	BR	1955	BR	R

Built at York.

| E21103 | Brake Composite Corridor | BR | 1956 | Metropolitan Cammell | R |
| E4521 | Tourist Second Open | BR | 1956 | BR | R |

Built at York.

M81033	Brake Gangwayed	BR	1956	Cravens	R
M81269	Brake Gangwayed	BR	1957	Pressed Steel Co Ltd	R
E4651	Tourist Second Open	BR	1957	BR	R

Built at York.

| 15997 | Composite Corridor | BR | 1957 | BR | R |

Built at Wolverton.

| W35148 | Brake Second Corridor | BR | 1958 | Charles Roberts & Co Ltd | R |

Modified to take wheelchairs.

| 514765 | PMV | | 1958 | BR | R |

Owned by Midland & Great Northern Joint Railway Society. Built at Swindon.

| M4843 | Tourist Second Open | BR | 1959 | BR | R |

Built at Wolverton.

| E94464 | Covered Carriage Truck | | 1960 | BR | R |
| M26012 | Second Corridor | | 1962 | BR | R |

Built at Earlstown.

Built at Derby.

| E10525 | | | 1982 | BR | R |

Built at Derby.

| 16 | FZ | | 1878 | GER | R |

Owned by Midland & Great Northern Joint Railway Society. Built at Stratford.

| 1361 | SZ | | 1892 | GER | R |

Owned by Midland & Great Northern Joint Railway Society. Built at Stratford.

| 252 | SZ | | 1902 | GER | R |

Owned by Midland & Great Northern Joint Railway Society. Built at Stratford.

| 1600 | TZ | | 1896 | GER | R |

Owned by Midland & Great Northern Joint Railway Society. Built at Stratford.

Number	Description		Year	Builder/Owner	
523			1899	GER	R

Built at Stratford.

| 969 | TZ | | | GER | R |

Owned by Midland & Great Northern Joint Railway Society. Built at Stratford.

| 769 | TZ | | | GER | R |

Owned by Midland & Great Northern Joint Railway Society. Built at Stratford.

| 34495 | Brake Second Corridor | | 1954 | GCW | R |
| D570283 | PMV | | 1939 | SR | R |

Owned by Midland & Great Northern Joint Railway Society. Built at Ashford.

| 1137 | PMV | | 1936 | SR | R |

Owned by Midland & Great Northern Joint Railway Society. Built at Ashford.

| | Brake Gangwayed (Z) | | | GNR | |

Owned by Midland & Great Northern Joint Railway Society.

| 4807 | Flat Wagon | | 1890 | | W |

Owned by Midland & Great Northern Joint Railway Society.

| | Van | | 1908 | Harrison, Camm | W |

Owned by Midland & Great Northern Joint Railway Society.

| 421220 | 5 Plank Wagon | | 1936 | LMS | W |
| 129148 | 5 Plank Wagon | | 1936 | GWR | W |

Built at Swindon.

| 163058 | Tanker | | 1942 | Hurst, Nelson & Co Ltd | R |

Owned by Midland & Great Northern Joint Railway Society.

| 164686 | Tanker | | 1944 | Hurst, Nelson & Co Ltd | R |

Owned by Midland & Great Northern Joint Railway Society.

| 51167 | Brake Van | | 1944 | SR | R |

Built at Ashford.

| B940007 | Bogie Bolster | | 1949 | BR | R |

Built at Swindon.

| 756939 | | | 1949 | BR | R |

Built at Wolverton.

| 755094 | Fruit Van | | 1950 | BR | R |

Built at Darlington.

| 904093 | | | 1953 | BR | W |

Owned by Midland & Great Northern Joint Railway Society. Built at Swindon.

| M726631 | Plate Wagon | | 1947 | LMS | R |

Built at Wolverton.

| HW426 | Ballast Hopper | | 1955 | GRCW | R |

Built at Gloucester.

| HW429 | Ballast Hopper | | 1955 | GRCW | R |

Built at Gloucester.

| DB950133 | Brake Van | | 1945 | BR | R |

Owned by Midland & Great Northern Joint Railway Society. Built at Wolverton.

Key: Wh.Arr. = Wheel Arrangement | S = Steam | D = Diesel | E = Electric | P = Petrol | R = Rolling Stock | W = Wagon | C = Coach | Op = Operational | St = Static | O = On Display | U = Under Restoration | G = Pre Group | N = Pre Nationalisation

Steam Railway Directory www.steamrailway.com   North Norfolk Railway — North Norfolk Railway

Steam Railway Directory   www.steamrailway.com

Current No.	Type	Built	Builder		
1476	PMV	1951	BR		R
Owned by Midland & Great Northern Joint Railway Society. Built at Wolverton.					
ADB904148	Lowmac	1960	BR		R
Built at Shildon.					
ADB904149	Lowmac	1960	BR		R
Built at Shildon.					
KDB740487	Pipe Wagon	1949	BR	W	
Built at Darlington.					
KDB740918	Pipe Wagon	1954	BR	W	
Built at Wolverton.					
B783071		1962	BR		R
Owned by Midland & Great Northern Joint Railway Society. Built at Wolverton.					
53083	Tanker	1965	BR	W	
Built at Shildon.					
514207		1940	LMS	W	
Built at Wolverton.					
DS1749	Hand Crane	1943	Booths		R
DS1749	Match Wagon	1943	Booths		R
2536	Steam Crane	1941	Grafton Crane Co		R
ADE320883	Crane Runner	1922	GNR		R
Built at Doncaster.					
1510		1913	GER		R
Owned by Midland & Great Northern Joint Railway Society. Built at Stratford.					
			LNER		R
Owned by Midland & Great Northern Joint Railway Society. Built at Stratford. Former use a s a snowplough.					

NORTH YORKSHIRE MOORS RAILWAY

Pickering, YORKSHIRE (NORTH)

Name	Current No.	Type/Class	Origin	Wh. Arr.	Built	Builder		
	5			0-6-2T	1909	Robert Stephenson, Hawthorn	s	G
Owned by Mr & Mrs R N Jones. Built at Darlington.								
	29			0-6-2T	1904	Kitson & Co	s	G
Owned by Lambton No 29 Syndicate. Built at Leeds.								
	825			4-6-0	1927	SR	s	M
Prev. No. 30825. Owned by Essex Loco Society. Built at Eastleigh.								
	901			0-8-0	1919	NER	s	G
Owned by National Railway Museum. Built at Darlington.								
	2238			0-8-0	1918	NER	s	G
Owned by NELPG. Built at Darlington.								
	2253			2-8-0	1943	Baldwin Locomotive Works	s	M
Owned by Peter Best.								
	2392			0-6-0	1923	LNER	s	M
Owned by NELPG. Built at Darlington.								
Antwerp	3180			0-6-0ST	1944	Hunslet Engine Co Ltd	s	M
Owned by National Coal Mining Museum.								

North Yorkshire Moors Railway roster:

Name / Notes	Number	Wh.Arr.	Builder	Year	Type	
Dame Vera Lynn	3672	2-10-0	North British Locomotive Co	1944	S	■■
	3814	2-8-0	GWR	1940	S	■
Owned by Peter Robinson. Built at Swindon.						
	6619	0-6-2T	GWR	1928	S	■
Owned by Peter Proud & Kevin Gould. Built at Swindon.						
Repton	30926	4-4-0	SR	1934	S	■
Built at Eastleigh.						
Hartland	34101	4-6-2	BR	1950	S	
Owned by Richard Shaw. Built at Eastleigh.						
George Stephenson	44767	4-6-0	LMS	1947	S	
Owned by Ian Storey. Built at Crewe.						
Eric Treacy	45428	4-6-0	A Whitworth	1937	S	■
Blue Peter	60532	4-6-2	BR	1948	S	■
Owned by Drury Family. Built at Doncaster.						
	62005	2-6-0	North British Locomotive Co	1949	S	
	69023	0-6-0T	BR	1951	S	
Owned by NELPG. Built at Glasgow.						
Braveheart	75014	4-6-0	BR	1951	S	
Owned by NELPG. Built at Darlington.						
Owned by 75014 Steam Loco Operators Group. Built at Swindon.						
	80135	2-6-4T	BR	1956	S	
Owned by Jos de Crau. Built at Brighton.						
	90775	2-10-0	North British Locomotive Co	1943	S	■
Owned by Essex Loco Society. Built at Glasgow.						
Ron Rothwell	DSRM1	DH	Thomas Hill	1963	D	
Built at Rotherham.						
	DSRM2	DH	Thomas Hill	1963	D	
Built at Rotherham.						
	2	DM	Ruston & Hornsby Ltd	1958	D	
	3	DM	Ruston & Hornsby Ltd	1960	D	
	ED16	DM	Drewry Car Co	1941	D	
Located at Middleton Railway.						
	D2207	DM/04	Drewry Car Co	1953	D	■
Owned by North Yorkshire Moors Railway York Group. Built at Burton on Trent.						
	08556	0-6-0DE	BR	1959	D	
Prev. No. 11108. Built at Burton on Trent.						
	08850	0-6-0DE	BR	1961	D	
Built at Darlington.						
Neil D Barker	12139	0-6-0DE	English Electric	1948	D	
Helen Turner	D5032	Bo-BoDE	BR	1959	D	
Built at Horwich.						
Owned by TJ Thomson & Co. Built at Crewe.						
	D5061	Bo-BoDE	BR	1960	D	
Diana (The)	D7541	Bo-BoDE	BR	1965	D	
Owned by Class 24 Society. Built at Crewe.						

Key: Wh.Arr. = Wheel Arrangement   **S** = Steam   **D** = Diesel   **E** = Electric   **P** = Petrol   **R** = Rolling Stock   **C** = Coach   **W** = Wagon   **Op** = Operational   **St** = Static   **O** = On Display   **U** = Under Restoration   **G** = Pre Group   **N** = Pre Nationalisation

Steam Railway Directory www.steamrailway.com

No.	Name / Notes	Type	Arr.	Builder	Year	Code
D7628	**Sybilla** — *Prev. No. 25191. Built at Derby.*		Bo-BoDE	Beyer, Peacock	1965	D
D9009	**Alycidon** — *Prev. No. 25278. Owned by Jos de Crau. Built at Manchester.*		Co-CoDE	English Electric	1961	D
50027	**Lion** — *Prev. No. 55009. Owned by Deltic Preservation Society. Built at Newton le Willows.*		Co-CoDE	English Electric	1968	D
E34557	*Owned by Class 50 Support Group.*	Support Coach		BR	1955	c
80217	*Owned by NELPG. Built at Wolverton.*	Support Coach		BR	1963	c
ADB975455	*Owned by 75014 Owners Group. Built at Wolverton.*	Riding Van		RCW	1957	R
173	*Owned by Drury Family. Built at Gloucester.*			BR	1961	R
174	*Built at Derby.*			Metropolitan Cammell	1956	R
E13043				BR	1954	R
E110E	*Built at Swindon.*	Full Brake (BG)		BR	1948	c
E70687	*Owned by Martyn Rush. Built at York.*	6w Van (BZ)		BR	1950	R
E80796	*Built at Stratford.*	Full Brake (BG)		RCW	1956	c
E86639	*Built at Birmingham.*	General Utility Van		BR	1959	R
93545	*Built at York.*	General Utility Van		BR	1959	R
93813	*Built at York.*	General Utility Van		Pressed Steel Co Ltd	1959	R
2		Tool Van		Metropolitan Carriage & Wagon Co	1885	R
98799	*Owned by Hull & Barnsley RSF.*	Box Van		NER	1908	R
DE632802	*Capacity 8 tonnes.*	Box Van		LNER	1923	R
M288824	*Capacity 10 tonnes. Owned by North Yorkshire Moors Railway Teeside Group.*			LMS	1933	R
W112835	*Capacity 7 tonnes. Owned by NRM. Built at Derby.*				1931	R
85630	*Owned by NELPG. Built at Swindon.*	Van		Charles Roberts & Co Ltd	1940	R
E1308	*Capacity 10 tonnes.*	Covered Carriage Truck		BR	1950	R
577	*Owned by LNERCA. Built at York.*	5 Plank Wagon			1885	w
3697	*Owned by Hull & Barnsley RSF.*	5 Plank Wagon		Charles Roberts & Co Ltd	1905	w

Owned by Hull & Barnsley RSF.

No.	Type	Year	Maker	
107	5 Plank Wagon			W

Owned by R Smith.

| M479157 | 3 Plank Wagon | 1948 | BR | W |

Capacity 8 tonnes. Owned by Farwath RS Group. Built at Derby.

| S14036 | Shoc Wagon | 1948 | BR | W |

Owned by NRM. Built at Ashford.

| B234830 | Mineral Wagon | 1955 | Cravens | W |

Capacity 16 tonnes.

| E269379 | Open Goods Wagon | 1948 | BR | W |

Capacity 13 tonnes.

| B741620 | Pipefit | 1956 | BR | W |

Capacity 12 tonnes. Owned by Pickering Station Group. Built at Wolverton.

United Molasses

| 6 | Tank Wagon | 1925 | Charles Roberts & Co Ltd | W |

St Ivel

| W44019 | Tank Wagon | 1938 | LMS | W |

Owned by Peter Robinson. Built at Derby.

Shell Mex

| 7285 | Tank Wagon | 1943 | Charles Roberts & Co Ltd | W |

Esso

| 2716 | Tank Wagon | 1950 | Charles Roberts & Co Ltd | W |

Owned by North Yorkshire Moors Railway Northallerton Group.

Express Dairy

| B3192 | Tank Wagon | 1952 | BR | W |

Owned by Peter Best. Built at Derby.

| LP202 | Tank Wagon | 1963 | Charles Roberts & Co Ltd | W |

Owned by North Yorkshire Moors Railway Members.

| 131 | Ballast Hopper | 1893 | GWR | W |

Owned by North Yorkshire Moors Railway York Group.

| 4503 | Coal Hopper Wagon | 1920 | NER | W |

Capacity 20 tonnes.

| 4561 | Coal Hopper Wagon | 1920 | NER | W |

Capacity 20 tonnes.

| DS62058 | Ballast Hopper | 1947 | SR | W |

Capacity 40 tonnes. Built at Ashford.

| DS62064 | Ballast Hopper | 1947 | SR | W |

Capacity 40 tonnes. Owned by North Yorkshire Moors Railway York Group. Built at Ashford.

| E274006 | Coal Hopper Wagon | | LNER | W |

Owned by North Yorkshire Moors Railway York Group.

| E307005 | Coal Hopper Wagon | 1949 | | W |

Capacity 21 tonnes. Owned by North Yorkshire Moors Railway York Group.

| B415776 | Coal Hopper Wagon | 1954 | BR | W |

Capacity 21 tonnes. Owned by North Yorkshire Moors Railway York Group. Built at Shildon.

| B418444 | Coal Hopper Wagon | 1955 | BR | W |

Capacity 21 tonnes. Owned by North Yorkshire Moors Railway York Group. Built at Shildon.

| B419025 | Coal Hopper Wagon | 1956 | BR | W |

Capacity 21 tonnes. Owned by North Yorkshire Moors Railway York Group. Built at Shildon.

| B428991 | Coal Hopper Wagon | 1957 | Standard Railway Wagon Co Ltd | W |

Key: Wh.Arr. = Wheel Arrangement S = Steam D = Diesel E = Electric P = Petrol R = Rolling Stock W = Wagon C = Coach Op = Operational St = Static O = On Display U = Under Restoration G = Pre Group N = Pre Nationalisation

North Yorkshire Moors Railway — North Yorkshire Moors Railway

A-Z SHOWING ROLLING STOCK

Steam Railway Directory www.steamrailway.com

North Yorkshire Moors Railway — North Yorkshire Moors Railway

Notes	Number	Type	Year	Manufacturer	
Capacity 21 tonnes. Owned by North Yorkshire Moors Railway York Group.	B431861	Coal Hopper Wagon	1958	Pressed Steel Co Ltd	w
Capacity 21 tonnes. Owned by North Yorkshire Moors Railway York Group.	B445025	Ironstone Hopper	1949	BR	w
Capacity 25 tonnes. Built at Shildon.	M300045	Flat Truck	1910	Caledonian Railway	R
Capacity 40 tonnes.	ADS61024	Lowmac	1921	LSWR	w
Owned by NRM. Built at Eastleigh.	E217315	Lowmac	1939	LNER	w
Capacity 21 tonnes.	E269004	Lowmac	1945	LNER	w
Capacity 21 tonnes. Owned by North Yorkshire Moors Railway York Group.	B904551	Lowmac	1951	BR	w
Capacity 25 tonnes. Owned by North Yorkshire Moors Railway York Group. Built at Swindon.	B905100	Lowmac	1958	BR	w
Capacity 15 tonnes. Built at Swindon.	B904152	Lowmac	1960	BR	w
Capacity 21 tonnes. Built at Shildon.	E230908	Lowmac	1939	LNER	w
Owned by North Yorkshire Moors Railway York Group.	B900935		1960	BR	w
Capacity 25 tonnes. Built at Swindon.	DW103310	Bogie Bolster /B		GWR	w
Capacity 30 tonnes. Owned by North Yorkshire Moors Railway York Group. Built at Swindon.	B940081	Bogie Bolster /C	1951	Metropolitan Cammell	w
Owned by Peter Best.	DS64752		1948	BR	w
Capacity 40 tonnes. Owned by North Yorkshire Moors Railway York Group. Built at Ashford.	DB946060		1962	Standard Railway Wagon Co Ltd	w
Capacity 50 tonnes.	DB994275		1956	Head Wrightson	w
Capacity 50 tonnes.	B451885		1952	BR	w
Capacity 13 tonnes. Owned by Peter Best. Built at Shildon.	B452670		1955	BR	w
Capacity 13 tonnes. Owned by Peter Best. Built at Shildon.	B932267	Plate Wagon	1954	BR	w
Owned by North Yorkshire Moors Railway York Group. Built at Shildon.	B933122	Plate Wagon	1958	BR	w
Built at Shildon.	B934279	Plate Wagon	1959	BR	w
Built at Shildon.	B934280	Plate Wagon	1959	BR	w
Built at Shildon.	B934281	Plate Wagon	1959	BR	w

Notes	Number	Type	Year	Builder	Status
Built at Shildon.	B934386	Plate Wagon	1960	BR	W
Built at Shildon.	23791	Brake Van	1914	GNR	R
Capacity 20 tonnes. Owned by North Yorkshire Moors Railway Members. Built at Doncaster.	DE301559	Brake Van		LNER	R
Capacity 20 tonnes. Owned by Peter Robinson.	E187774	Brake Van	1936	LNER	R
Capacity 20 tonnes. Owned by NRM. Built at Darlington.	E246710	Brake Van	1941	LNER	R
Capacity 20 tonnes. Owned by NRM. Built at Darlington.	M732170	Brake Van	1946	LMS	R
Capacity 20 tonnes.		Brake Van		LMS	R
Owned by North Yorkshire Moors Railway Members.	68494	Brake Van	1925	GWR	R
Capacity 20 tonnes. Owned by Peter Robinson. Built at Swindon.	B954854	Brake Van	1959	BR	R
Capacity 20 tonnes. Owned by Peter Best. Built at Faverdale.	B955225	Brake Van	1962	BR	R
Capacity 20 tonnes. Built at Ashford.	1111	Luggage Composite	1890	NER	C
Owned by NER Coach Group. Built at York.	3453	Auto Coach	1904	NER	C
Owned by NER Coach Group. Built at York.	40	Brake Third	1907	R Y Pickering & Co Ltd	G
Owned by H & B R Stock Fund. Built at Wishaw.	58	Brake Third Lavatory	1908	BRCW	G
Owned by H & B R Stock Fund. Built at Birmingham.	945	Third Open	1924	LNER	N
Owned by NER Coach Group. Built at York.	1077	Brake Third Composite	1924	LNER	N
Owned by North Yorkshire Moors Railway York Group. Built at York.	E1299	Sleeper /Third Class	1930	LNER	N
Owned by R Houlton. Built at York.	3291	Third Corridor	1930	Metropolitan Cammell	N
Owned by Gresley Owners Group.	1782	Second Corridor	1934	LMS	N
Built at Wolverton.	43567	Brake Third Open	1935	LNER	N
Owned by LNERCA. Built at York.	23890	Tourist Third Open	1935	BRCW	N
Owned by LNERCA Members. Built at Birmingham. RF - Formerly TK.	24109	Tourist Third Open	1936	BRCW	N

North Yorkshire Moors Railway — North Yorkshire Moors Railway

Key: Wh.Arr. = Wheel Arrangement S = Steam D = Diesel E = Electric P = Petrol R = Rolling Stock W = Wagon C = Coach Op = Operational St = Static O = On Display U = Under Restoration G = Pre Group N = Pre Nationalisation

Steam Railway Directory www.steamrailway.com

Steam Railway Directory www.steamrailway.com

Note	No.	Description	Year	Builder	c	*
Owned by Colin Sykes. Built at Birmingham.	23956	Tourist Third Open	1936	Metropolitan Cammell		*
Owned by NRM. Built at Birmingham.	641	Buffet Car	1937	LNER	c	*
Owned by LNERCA Members. Built at York.	649	Buffet Car	1937	LNER		*
Owned by Brian Crouch. Built at York.	56856	Tourist Third Open	1938	Metropolitan Cammell		*
Owned by Gresley Owners Group. Built at Birmingham.	S4035S	Brake Third Corridor	1949	BR		*
Owned by Richard Shaw. Built at Eastleigh.	E1623	Third Corridor	1950	BR		*
Owned by LNERCA Members. Built at York.	E18477E	Composite Corridor	1950	BR	c	*

Garnet

Note	No.	Description	Year	Builder	c
	79	Brake Third Pullman	1928	Metropolitan Carriage & Wagon Co	c
Owned by Jos de Crau.	E327	Pullman First Parlour	1960	Metropolitan Cammell	c
Owned by Jos de Crau.	E328	Pullman First Parlour	1960	Metropolitan Cammell	c
	1666	Restaurant Buffet Refurbished	1960	Pressed Steel Co Ltd	c
	E318	Pullman First Kitchen	1961	Metropolitan Cammell	c

Robin

Note	No.	Description	Year	Builder	c
Owned by Jos de Crau.	M324	Restaurant First	1961	BR	c
Owned by Jos de Crau. Built at Swindon.	W80974	Inspection Saloon	1948	BR	c
Built at Swindon.	172		1951	BR	c
Built at Swindon. Formerly BG W334.	SC3798	Tourist Second Open	1953	BR	c
Owned by Peter Best. Built at York.	SC3801	Tourist Second Open	1953	BR	c
Owned by Jos de Crau. Built at York.	M3805	Tourist Second Open	1953	BR	c
Owned by Jos de Crau. Built at York.	E3860	Tourist Second Open	1953	BR	c
Built at York.	E3872	Tourist Second Open	1954	BR	c
Built at York.	E3948	Tourist Second Open	1954	BR	c
Built at Eastleigh.	E24808	Second Corridor	1954	RCW	c
Owned by Jos de Crau. Built at Birmingham.	E9235	Brake Second Open	1955	BR	c
Built at Doncaster.	W4198	Tourist Second Open	1956	BR	c

Owned by P N Wilson. Built at York.

Built at Doncaster.

Owned by Jos de Crau. Built at Doncaster.

Built at Birmingham.

Owned by P J Hunt. Built at Birmingham.

Built at Birmingham.

Current No.	Type/Class	Built	Builder		Status
SC4207	Tourist Second Open	1956	BR		C
SC4252	Tourist Second Open	1956	BR		C
E4286	Tourist Second Open	1956	BRCW		C
E4290	Tourist Second Open	1956	BRCW		C
M4425	Tourist Second Open	1956	BRCW		C

NORTHAMPTON & LAMPORT RAILWAY

Northampton, NORTHAMPTONSHIRE

Name	Current No.	Type/Class	Origin	Wh.Arr.	Built	Builder	Type	Status
Colwyn	45	Saddle Tank		0-6-0ST	1933	Kitson & Co	s	C
Westminster	2104	Saddle Tank		0-4-0ST	1948	Peckett & Sons	s	Op St O
Vanguard	1378	Saddle Tank		0-6-0ST	1914	Peckett & Sons	s	U
Northampton	5374			0-6-0T	1959		s	U
Castell Dinas Bran	7646			0-6-0T	1959		s	U
	25035			Bo-Bo	1963		D	U
	26010			Bo-Bo	1959		D	U
Stored.	D5401			Bo-Bo	1962		D	U
Stored.	D7629			Bo-Bo	1965	Beyer, Peacock	D	U
Stored. Royal Artilleryman (The)	45118			1Co-Co1	1962		D	Op
Merry Tom	764	DM /88		4wDM	1949	Ruston & Hornsby Ltd	D	U
Sir Gyles	146C	DS /165		0-4-0	1953	Ruston & Hornsby Ltd	D	U
Bunty	PWM651	DH		0-4-0DH	1964	Ruston & Hornsby Ltd	D	
	21	DH		0-6-0	1958	Fowler	D	
Built at Leeds.	52361	Driving Motor Brake Second /117			1959	Pressed Steel Co Ltd	D	Op
Stored.	51402	DMS /117			1960	Pressed Steel Co Ltd	D	Op
	W55001				1958			U
Stored.	W55003				1958		D	C
	W297W				1949			U
Located at Mid-Hants Railway. Built at Swindon.	1647	Restaurant Buffet Refurbished	BR		1960	Pressed Steel Co Ltd		C

Key: Wh.Arr. = Wheel Arrangement **S** = Steam **D** = Diesel **E** = Electric **P** = Petrol **W** = Wagon **C** = Coach **R** = Rolling Stock **Op** = Operational **St** = Static **O** = On Display **U** = Under Restoration **G** = Pre Group **N** = Pre Nationalisation

Steam Railway Directory   www.steamrailway.com

North Yorkshire Moors Railway — Northampton & Lamport Railway

Steam Railway Directory   www.steamrailway.com

Northampton & Lamport Railway — Nottingham Transport Ctre

Name	Current No.	Type/Class	Origin	Wh. Arr.	Built	Builder	Status
—	M3919	Tourist Second Open	BR		1958		c
—	5001	Tourist Second Open	BR		1962		c u
Built at Wolverton.							
—	16012	Composite Corridor	BR		1957		c
—	34712	Brake Second Corridor	BR		1955		c
Awaiting overhaul.							
—	M24576	Second Corridor			1953		c
—	M13092				1954		c
—	M84031	Gangwayed Brake			1956		c
—	M9225	Brake Second Open	BR		1955		c Op
—	5229	Tourist Second Open	BR		1996		c Op
—	9102	Brake Second Open			1996		c
—	W9485	Tube Wagon					w
—	W1009				1951		w
—	W48339	Tar Tank Wagon			1940		w
—	W17293				1943		w
Built at Swindon.							
—	44551	Ventilated Box Van			1931		w
—	S2439S	PMV			1931		w
—	S1834	PMV			1943		w
—	61	Open Wagon			1892		w
—	B021172	Covered Goods Van					w
—	M35062	Covered Carriage Truck			1926		Op
Built at Wolverton.							
—	M37326	Covered Carriage Truck			1952		w
—	M476325	3 Plank Goods Wagon			1938		w
—	M499227	Tube Wagon			1936		w
Built at Wolverton.							
—	M730003	Brake Van			1935		w
Built at Derby.							
—	B951805	Brake Van	BR		1952		w Op
—	B935493	Drop Side Plate Wagon	BR		1960		w
Built at Shildon.							
—	94062	Tank Wagon	BR		1959	Pressed Steel Co Ltd	w
—	94071	Ballast Hopper Wagon	BR		1958		w
—	ADB999074	Dogfish Ballast Hopper			1959		w

NOTTINGHAM TRANSPORT CTRE

Ruddington, NOTTINGHAMSHIRE

Name	Current No.	Type/Class	Origin	Wh. Arr.	Built	Builder

© *HCC* Publishing Ltd

A-Z SHOWING ROLLING STOCK

No./Name	Notes	Company	Description	Wh. Arr.	Date	Builder	Flags
13180				0-4-0	1920	Motor Rail Ltd	D, Op, U
08885				0-4-0DE	1961	Ruston & Hornsby Ltd	D, Op, U
D9520	DH/14			0-6-0	1955	BR	D, Op
56				0-6-0	1962	BR	D, Op
63				0-6-0DH	1964	BR	D, Op
68088				0-6-0ST	1950	Robert Stephenson, Hawthorn	S
Sad Sam				0-6-0ST	1954	Robert Stephenson, Hawthorn	S
45379	Designed by W A Stanier. Owned by P Wainwright.			0-4-0T	1923	Worsdell	S
				0-4-0T	1931	Hunslet Engine Co Ltd	S
				4-6-0	1937	Armstrong, Whitworth	S
Julia				0-6-0ST	1937	Hudswell, Clarke & Co	S
					1952		
S272		BR	Brake First Corridor				R
17055	Owned by Tony Sparks.	BR	Brake First Corridor				R
E9389	Owned by Dave Allen.	BR	Brake Second Open				R
E3095	Owned by Dave Allen.	BR	First Open		1959		R, W
5209	Used for transporting fuel oil.		Tank Wagon				W
DB993039	Capacity 24 tonnes.		Dogfish Ballast Wagon		1957		W
DB993597	Capacity 24 tonnes.		Dogfish Ballast Wagon		1959		W
DB983586	Capacity 24 tonnes.		Dogfish Ballast Wagon		1959		W
M16168		BR	Composite Corridor		1961		R
S1874S		SR	PMV		1942		R
M691576			Hopper Wagon				W
23053	Currently used for coaling locomotives.		Rectank Bogie Wagon		1924		W
			Flat Wagon				W
357488		LMS	Brake Van				R
357771		LMS	Brake Van				R
DB784455					1962		R
287664	Body is being completely rebuilt.	LNER	Brake Van		1947		R
B954353		BR	Brake Van		1959		R, Op
DB994271		BR	Brake Van		1956		R
B779761	Owned by Mark Hellebaut.	BR	Palvan		1958		R

Steam Railway Directory www.steamrailway.com

Current No.	Type/Class	Origin	Built	Builder	Status
B782111	Palvan	BR	1960		R
B778771	Palvan	BR			R
	Cinema Coach				W
M401732	5 Plank Wagon	LMS			R
M500348	Van	LMS			R
16190	Composite Corridor	BR	1961		W
DS62014	Bogie Ballast Wagon	SR	1928		R
DB993874	Shark Plough Brake	BR			R
952282	Brake Van	BR			R
E86129	General Utility Van	BR	1958	Pressed Steel Co Ltd	R
E1693	Restaurant Buffet Refurbished	BR	1961	BRCW	R
M691793	Ironstone Hopper	LMS	1938		R
M33655	Tube Wagon	LMS	1925	Wolverton Works	W
M492136	Tube Wagon	LMS	1938	Wolverton Works	W
228	Open Tourist Saloon	GCR	1910		R
695	Open Saloon Brake	GCR	1910		R
799	Clerestory Roofed Carriage		1905		R
			1903		R
411453	5 Plank Open	LMS	1937		R
68500	PMV	GWR	1947		R
S1563			1950		R
977019	Covered Carriage Truck		1960		R Op

Owned by Dave Morris.

Owned by Arthur Barber.

This is one of only two such vehicles, modified by BR from second class open coaches, for showing films.

Owned by Richard Meakin.

Owned by Richard Meakin.

Awaiting restoration.

Owned by Richard Meakin.

Owned by Richard Meakin.

Owned by Richard Meakin.

The last surviving Barnum brake carriage in existence.

Body only still exists. Will be rebuilt when a suitable chassis can be found.

Built at Derby.

Prev. No. S94393. Built at Earlstown.

OLD KILN LIGHT RAILWAY

Farnham, SURREY

Name	Current No.	Type/Class	Origin	Wh. Arr.	Built	Builder	Status	
Elouise	9998		Portuguese Forestry Commission	0-6-0WT	1922	Orenstein, Koppel	s	Op
Pamela	920		Penrhyn Slate Quarry	0-4-0ST	1906	Hunslet Engine Co Ltd	s	U
							C	Op

Designed by Orenstein, Koppel.

Designed by Hunslet Engine Co Ltd. Built at Leeds.

Only known replica example.

Formerly based at Dean Hill. Re gauged from 2'6'' to 2'.

Brake Van   Ministry of Defence   W   Op   U

PAIGNTON & DARTMOUTH RAILWAY   Paignton, DEVON

Name	Current No.	Type/Class	Origin	Wh.Arr.	Built	Builder			
Lydham Manor	7827		BRW	4-6-0	1950		S	Op	
Goliath	5139		GWR	2-8-0	1924		S	Op	N
Warrior	4555		GWR	2-6-2	1924		S	Op	N
Trojan	4588		GWR	2-6-2	1927		S	U	N
Ajax	6435		GWR	0-6-0	1932		S	Op	N
Hercules	D7535			Bo-Bo		BR	D	Op	
Sampson	D3014			0-6-0			D	Op	
Titan	D2192			0-6-0			D	Op	

BR No. 7827. Designed by C B Collett. Owned by Dart Valley Railway PLC. Built at Swindon.
BR No. 5239. Designed by Churchward. Owned by Dart Valley Railway PLC. Built at Swindon.
BR No. 4555. Designed by Churchward. Owned by Dart Valley Railway PLC. Built at Swindon.
BR No. 4588. Designed by Churchward. Owned by Dart Valley Railway PLC.
BR No. 6435. Owned by Dart Valley Railway PLC.
BR No. 7535. Owned by Dart Valley Railway PLC.
BR No. 25185. Owned by Dart Valley Railway PLC.
Owned by Dart Valley Railway PLC.
Owned by Dart Valley Railway PLC.

PALLOT STEAM MUSEUM   Jersey, CHANNEL ISLANDS

Name	Current No.	Type/Class	Origin	Wh.Arr.	Built	Builder			
J T Daly	2450			0-4-0	1931	W G Bagnall	S	St	O
La Meuse				0-6-0	1931		S	St	O
Foleshill	2085			0-4-0	1948		S	St	O
Kestrel	2129			0-4-0	1952		S	Op	

Owned by L C Pallot Trust.
Owned by L C Pallot Trust.
Owned by L C Pallot Trust.
Owned by L C Pallot Trust.

PEAK RAIL   Matlock, DERBYSHIRE

Name	Current No.	Type/Class	Origin	Wh.Arr.	Built	Builder		
Duke (The)	68012			0-6-0ST	1944	W G Bagnall	S	
Warrington	68006			0-6-0ST	1944		S	
Vulcan	828		Vulcan Foundry	0-4-0ST	1902		S	

BR No. 2746. Owned by Peak Rail & T Oaks.

Key: Wh.Arr. = Wheel Arrangement   S = Steam   D = Diesel   E = Electric   P = Petrol   C = Coach   W = Wagon   R = Rolling Stock   Op = Operational   St = Static   O = On Display   U = Under Restoration   G = Pre Group   N = Pre Nationalisation

Steam Railway Directory   www.steamrailway.com

A-Z SHOWING ROLLING STOCK

Steam Railway Directory www.steamrailway.com

Name / Notes	No.	Type	Origin	Wheel	Built	Builder	Status
Owned by Vulcan Group.							
– BR No. 48624. Owned by BF Group.	8624		LMS		1943	SR	s
Zebedee	7597		RSH	0-6-0T	1949	Robert Stephenson, Hawthorn	s
Owned by Peak Rail & Peak Railway Heritage Trust.							
Penybont	D8						
Owned by North Notts Loco Group. Built at Derby.	03158		BR		1959	Derby Works	D
BR No. 03158.							
Margaret Anne	03027		BR		1960	Swindon Works	D
BR No. 03027. Built at Swindon.							
	03084		BR		1958		D
BR No. 03084. Built at Doncaster.							
Cynthia	DS88	Shunter		0-4-0DM	1957	Ruston & Hornsby Ltd	D
Castlefield		DH		0-6-0DH	1960	Thomas Hill	D
		Yard Shunter		0-6-0DM	1959	Hudswell, Clarke & Co	D
Bullion Van	99204						R C
	1835	Miniature Buffet	BR		1955		C Op
	2080	Sleeping Car	BR		1960		C
	3825	Tourist Second Open	BR		1959		C U
Originally used on the Keighley and Worth Valley Railway.	4623	Tourist Second Open	BR		1953		C
Awaiting restoration.	4974	Tourist Second Open	BR		1957		C
	7663	Composite Corridor	BR		1962		C Op
Two owned by railway.	26025	Second Corridor	BR		1956		C
	26043	Second Corridor	BR		1960		C Op
	26049	Second Corridor	BR		1960		C Op
	26014	Second Corridor	BR		1960		C U
Awaiting restoration.	35193	Brake Second Corridor	BR		1958		C
	92158	Brake Gangwayed	BR		1958		C
	84554	Brake Gangwayed	BR		1958		C
	93183	General Utility Van	BR		1958		Op
	5235	Second Open	BR		1966		C
Built at Derby. Currently in use as a dining car.	5166	Tourist Second Open	BR		1966		R
Built at Derby.	9394	Brake Second Open	BR		1966	Derby Works	R C
	9105	Brake Second Open	BR		1966	Derby Works	R C
Built at Derby.	14060	Brake Composite Corridor	BR		1967		R
Awaiting restoration.	M6815M	Brake Composite Corridor	BR		1935		R U

Notes	No.	Type	Co.	Builder / Owner	Year	Status
Saw departmental service as an office.	M27109M	Third Open	BR		1945	R
	M9205M	Third Open	BR		1936	R
Provides invaluable accommodation, transport and mobile workshop for on track working parties.	53933	Driving Motor Brake Second				R
Part of the three car set.	51566	DMC				R
Part of the three car set.	59387	Trailer Second Lavatory	BR			R
	51937	Driving Motor Brake Second	BR			W, Op
	DRS81139	Diesel Crane	BR	Smith, Rodley	1957	W, Op
	ADRC95223	Steam Crane	BR	Cowan, Sheldon	1936	
Built at Carlisle.	DX68051	Wickham Trolley		D Wickham & Co Ltd	1954	W
	ADE941753	Covered Goods Van		Charles Roberts & Co Ltd		R
Wooden underframe, sliding door.	B950003	Crane Runner				R
Has GER axleboxes.	D950173	Brake Van		Derby Works	1950	W
Standard 20t brake van restored by the Sheffield group.	D950885	Brake Van	BR			R
Built at Derby. Restored by Amber Valley.	DB993768	Standard Brake Van	LMS			R
	DB994256	Shark Brake Van	BR	Head Wrightson	1956	W
Equipped with ballast levelling ploughs.	DB996406	Dogfish Ballast Hopper	BR		1956	W
	B983904	Dogfish Ballast Hopper	BR	Shildon Wagon Works	1961	Op
Built at Shildon.	B993076	Fish Van	BR	Charles Roberts & Co Ltd	1956	W
	ADM40252	Fish Van	LMS		1949	R
Built at Wolverton. Built 'double skinned'.	ADM40294	Fish Van	LMS			R
Built 'double skinned'.	KDS13	Austrian Ferry Wagons			1958	W
Two owned by railway. Built for ferry traffic between Austria and the UK.	SUKO67024	Parcels Van			1936	R
Designed by SECR.	2210	Tank Wagon		R Y Pickering & Co Ltd	1967	W
Converted into a mobile steam locomotive watering facility.	KDB768358	Tank Wagon	BR			W
Mobile watering facility (400 gallon).		Box Van				R

Key: Wh.Arr. = Wheel Arrangement   S = Steam   D = Diesel   E = Electric   P = Petrol   R = Rolling Stock   W = Wagon   C = Coach   Op = Operational   St = Static   O = On Display   U = Under Restoration   G = Pre Group   N = Pre Nationalisation

Steam Railway Directory   www.steamrailway.com

Name	Current No.	Type/Class	Origin	Built			
—	KDB771392	Box Van	BR				R
—	KDB784652	Box Van	BR				R
—	772584	Box Van					R

Built at Wigan. Wooden Undertrame, mounted with a BR standard 12t van body.

	WGB4015	Pallet Van	BR				W
—	KDB740699	Plank Pipe Wagon		1950			W
—		Plank Wooden Mineral Wagon	LMS				W

Wooden undertrame.

| | D8986179 | Ballast Wagon | BR | | | | W |

PERRYGROVE RAILWAY

Coleford, GLOUCESTERSHIRE

Name	Current No.	Type/Class	Origin	Wh. Arr.	Built	Builder		
Spirit of Adventure	PG1			0-6-0T	1993	Exmoor Steam Railway	s	Op

11ft in length. Designed by Exmoor Steam Railway. Owned by Mr & Mrs Crofts.

| **Ursula** | | | Eaton Hall | 0-6-0T | 1999 | J Waterfield | s | Op |

11ft in length. Designed by A P Heywood.

| **Workhorse** | 2 | DM | Motor Rail | 0-4-0DM | 1963 | Motor Rail Ltd, Perrygrove Railway | D | Op |

5ft in length.

PLYM VALLEY RAILWAY

Plymouth, DEVON

Name	Current No.	Type/Class	Origin	Wh. Arr.	Built	Builder		
—	3	Van Guard Shunter		0-4-0ST	1926	Hawthorn Leslie & Co	s	Op
—	13002	Shunter /08		0-4-0	1963	Thomas Hill	D	Op
Built at Derby.					1952	BR	D	Op
William Cookworthy	37207				1963		D	Op / U
	DMS51407				1960	Pressed Steel Co Ltd	D	Op
—	DMBS51365				1960	Pressed Steel Co Ltd	D	Op / U
City of Plymouth	75079			4-6-0	1956		D	U

Owned by Plym Valley Railway Association. Built at Swindon.

| — | W18591 | Second Corridor | | | 1957 | | | c |

Prev. No. 25591.

| — | S16204 | Composite Corridor | | | 1961 | | | c / u |

Restoration almost complete.

| — | W34945 | Brake Second Corridor | | | 1956 | | | c / u |

Restoration almost complete.

| | | | | | 1885 | | | st 0 |

Built at Lancing. Victorian coach, former LBSCR. Was used as a home for over 60 years.

—	M93927	General Utility Van						w
—	S56541	Brake Van						R
—	49004	Brake Van						R

© HCC Publishing Ltd

Designed by SR.

Name	Current No.	Type/Class	Origin	Builder	Built	Wh.Arr.		
—		3 Plank Open Wagon					W	
—		4 Plank Open Wagon					W	
—		7 Plank Open Wagon					W	
—	334	Bogie Tube Wagon		Devonport Dockyard			W	

Used to carry Naval guns throughout the Yard.

| — | 103584 | Fish Van | | | 1920 | | W | St O |
| — | | Ventilated Van | | | 1943 | | W | St O |

Built at Darlington.

| — | 5193 | Shunting Crane | | T Smith & Sons | 1956 | 0-4-0 | | Op |

PONTYPOOL & BLAENAVON RAILWAY

Blaenavon, TORFAEN

Name	Current No.	Type/Class	Origin	Builder	Built	Wh.Arr.		
Bickmarsh Hall	5967		GWR		1937	4-6-0	S	St
Awaiting restoration.								
Renown	50029		BR		1968	Co-Co	D	
Awaiting restoration.								
Repulse	50030		BR		1968	Co-Co	D	
Awaiting restoration.								
Eagle	50043		BR		1968	Co-Co	D	
Awaiting restoration.								
Nora	5			Andrew Barclay & Sons	1920	0-4-0ST	S	St
Harry				Andrew Barclay & Sons	1926	0-4-0ST	S	St U
Llanwern	8				1944	0-6-0ST	S	U
—	104	DH		English Electric	1968	0-6-0DH	D	Op
—	106	DH		English Electric	1971	0-6-0DH	D	

Awaiting restoration.

RAILWAY AGE

Crewe, CHESHIRE

Name	Current No.	Type/Class	Origin	Builder	Built	Wh.Arr.		
Cornwall	3020			Crewe Works	1847	2-2-2	S	Op

Designed by Francis Trevithick. Owned by National Railway Museum. Built at Crewe.

RAILWORLD

Peterborough, CAMBRIDGESHIRE

Name	Current No.	Type/Class	Origin	Builder	Built	Wh.Arr.		
Vauclain Danish Compound Pacific	DSB996		Danish State Railway	Frichs of Aarhus	1950	4-6-2	S	St O

Awaiting restoration.

Key: Wh.Arr. = Wheel Arrangement   S = Steam   D = Diesel   E = Electric   P = Petrol   W = Wagon   R = Rolling Stock   C = Coach   Op = Operational   St = Static   O = On Display   U = Under Restoration   G = Pre Group   N = Pre Nationalisation

Plym Valley Railway — Railworld

Steam Railway Directory   www.steamrailway.com

© HCC Publishing Ltd

Steam Railway Directory www.steamrailway.com

	Current No.	Origin	Wh. Arr.	Built	Builder			
70.5ft in length. Designed by Nydquist, Holm.								
Alco 660HP American Switcher	804	British Steel	Bo-Bo	1949	Alco	D		st O
45ft in length.								
Britains Experimental Hover Train		Tracked Hover Craft Ltd		1970	Tracked Hover Craft Ltd		W	st O
72.5ft in length. Designed by Tracked Hover Craft Ltd.								

RAVENGLASS & ESKDALE
Ravenglass, CUMBRIA

Name	Current No.	Type/Class	Origin	Wh. Arr.	Built	Builder		
River Irt				0-8-2	1894	Heywood	s	Op
River Esk				2-8-2	1923	Davey Paxman	s	Op
River Mite				2-8-2	1966	Clarkson	s	Op
Northern Rock				2-6-2	1976	Ravenglass & Eskdale Railway	s	Op
Bonnie Dundee				0-4-2	1901	Kerr, Stuart & Co Ltd		Op
Shelagh of Eskdale				4-6-4D	1969	Ravenglass & Eskdale Railway	D	Op

RHYL MINIATURE RAILWAY
Rhyl, DENBIGHSHIRE

Name	Current No.	Type/Class	Origin	Wh. Arr.	Built	Builder		
Joan	101			4-4-2	1920	Albert Barnes & Co	s	Op
Designed by Henry Greenly.								
Clara		DM		0-4-2DM	1961	Guest & Saunders Light Engineering	s	Op
Built at Stourbridge.								
u	KD1			4-4w-4-4w-4DER	1983	Rapido Rail	D	E
—		DM		4wDM	1938	R A Lister & Co Ltd	D	Op
Built at Dursley.								

ROMNEY HYTHE & DYMCHURCH
New Romney, KENT

Name	Current No.	Type/Class	Origin	Wh. Arr.	Built	Builder		
Northern Chief				4-6-2	1925	Davey Paxman	s	Op
27.5ft in length. Designed by Henry Greenly.								
Green Goddess				4-6-2	1925	Davey Paxman	s	Op
27.5ft in length. Designed by Henry Greenly.								
Southern Maid				4-6-2	1926	Davey Paxman	s	Op
27.5ft in length. Designed by Henry Greenly.								
Hurricane				4-6-2	1927	Davey Paxman	s	Op
27.5ft in length. Designed by Henry Greenly.								
Typhoon				4-6-2	1927	Davey Paxman	s	U
27.5ft in length. Designed by Henry Greenly.								
Hercules				4-8-2	1927	Davey Paxman	s	Op
25ft in length. Designed by Henry Greenly.								
Samson				4-8-2	1927	Davey Paxman	s	Op
25ft in length. Designed by Henry Greenly.								

Name	Wh.Arr.	Built	Builder		
Winston Churchill *28ft in length. Designed by Henry Greenly.*	4-6-2	1931	Yorkshire Engine Co	S	Op
Dr Syn *28ft in length. Designed by Henry Greenly, ALS Richardson.*	4-6-2	1931	Yorkshire Engine Co	S	Op
Bug (The) *16.75ft in length. Designed by Roland Martens.*	0-4-0	1926	Krauss	S	Op
John Southland *20ft in length. Designed by Romney, Hythe & Dymchurch Railway.*	Bo-Bo	1983	T M A Engineering	D	
Captain Howey *20ft in length. Designed by Romney, Hythe & Dymchurch Railway.*	Bo-Bo	1989	T M A Engineering	D	Op
Gladys Bar Car *32ft in length.*					C

ROYAL VICTORIA RAILWAY

Southampton, HAMPSHIRE

Name	Current No.	Type/Class	Origin	Wh.Arr.	Built	Builder		
Isambard Kingdom Brunel *16ft in length. Designed by D Curwen. Owned by P Bowers.*	4			2-6-0T	1977	D Curwen	S	Op
Ivor *11ft in length. Designed by Hunslet Engine Co Ltd. Owned by Brian Gent.*	2			0-4-0T	1993	Jones, Mills	S	
Sir Walter Gower *9ft in length. Designed by Ivatt. Owned by Helen Allenby*				4-4-2T	1970	Gower, Boughton	S	O
Maurice the Major *10ft in length. Designed by P Bowers. Owned by P Bowers.*	3	DH		Bo-Bo	1995	P Bowers	D	
Artic Prince *11ft in length. Designed by Western Region BR Scalev. Owned by Brian Gent.*	DT062		Weston Region Style	Bo-Bo	1982	Mardyke	D	
Claude the Colonel *9ft in length. Designed by P Bowers. Owned by P Bowers.*	5			4w-4w	2000	P Bowers	D	Op
Four owned by railway. 12ft in length. Designed by P Bowers. Owned by P Bowers.		3 Compartment Open		Articulated	1998	P Bowers	C	Op
Four owned by railway. 12ft in length. Designed by P Bowers.				Articulated	1998	P Bowers	C	Op
Two owned by railway. 12ft in length. Designed by Mardyke. Owned by B Gent.		5 Plank Wagon		4w Bogie	1982	Mardyke	C	Op
6ft in length. Designed by P Bowers. Owned by P Bowers.		Flat Wagon		4w	1999	P Bowers	W	Op O
14ft in length. Designed by D Curwen, J Crosskey. Owned by J Crosskey. On loan from J Crosskey.		Flat Bogie		4w	1976	D Curwen	W	Op O
14ft in length. Designed by Mardyke. Owned by J Crosskey. On loan from J Crosskey				4w	1982	Mardyke	W	Op O

RPSI

Whitehead, COUNTY ANTRIM

Name	Current No.	Type/Class	Origin	Wh.Arr.	Built	Builder

Key: Wh.Arr. = Wheel Arrangement   **S** = Steam   **D** = Diesel   **E** = Electric   **P** = Petrol   **R** = Rolling Stock   **W** = Wagon   **C** = Coach   **Op** = Operational   **St** = Static   **O** = On Display   **U** = Under Restoration   **G** = Pre Group   **N** = Pre Nationalisation

A-Z SHOWING ROLLING STOCK

Steam Railway Directory www.steamrailway.com

RPSI — Ruislip Lido Railway

			Built	Builder		
Slieve Gullion	171	4-4-0	1913	Beyer, Peacock	s	Op
Located at Railway Preservation Society of Ireland.						
Lough Erne	27	0-6-4T	1949	Beyer, Peacock	s	
Located at Railway Preservation Society of Ireland.						
R H Smith	3	0-6-0ST	1928	Avonside Engineering Co	s	Op
Located at Railway Preservation Society of Ireland.						
Guinness	3BG	0-4-0ST	1919	Hudswell, Clarke & Co	s	
Located at Railway Preservation Society of Ireland.						
	4	2-6-4T	1947		s	Op
Located at Railway Preservation Society of Ireland. In traffic.						
Merlin	85	4-4-0	1932	Beyer, Peacock	s	Op
Owned by Ulster Folk & Transport Msuseum. Located at Railway Preservation Society of Ireland.						
	184	0-6-0	1880		s	
Located at Railway Preservation Society of Ireland. In store.						
	186	0-6-0	1879	Sharp, Stewart & Co	s	u
Located at Railway Preservation Society of Ireland.						
	461	2-6-0	1922		s	
Located at Railway Preservation Society of Ireland. In store.						

RUDYARD LAKE RAILWAY — Leek, STAFFORDSHIRE

Name	Current No.	Type/Class	Wh. Arr.	Built	Origin		
River Churnet	6		2-4-2T	1993	Exmoor Steam Railway	s	Op
Designed by T Stirland.							
Merlin	7		2-4-2T	1998	Exmoor Steam Railway	s	Op
Designed by T Stirland.							
Rudyard Lady	5		Bo-Bo		L A Smith	D	Op
Designed by P Hanton.							
Mildred	2		4WD		T Stanhope	D	Op
Designed by T Stanhope.							
			8w Bogie				C Op
Seven owned by railway. 14ft in length.							
			8w Bogie				W Op
Four owned by railway. 12ft in length.							
	8		4w				W Op

RUISLIP LIDO RAILWAY — Ruislip, LONDON (GREATER)

Name	Current No.	Type/Class	Wh. Arr.	Built	Builder		
Robert		DH	4w-4w	1985	Severn Lamb	D	Op
Lady of the Lakes		DM	4w-4w	1990	Ravenglass & Eskdale Railway	D	Op
Graham Alexander		DH	4w-4w	1998	Severn Lamb	D	Op
Mad Bess		Saddle Tank	2-4-0			s	Op

SCOTTISH RAILWAY CENTRE

Ayr, AYRSHIRE

Name	Current No.	Type/Class	Origin	Builder	Built	Wh.Arr.			
Harlaxton		DM		Andrew Barclay & Sons	1941	0-6-0ST	s	Op	N
Lily of the Valley		DH		Fowler	1943	0-4-0DM	D	St	
Tees Storage		DM		North British Locomotive Co	1959	0-4-0DH	D	Op	N
Blinkin Bess		DM		Ruston & Hornsby Ltd	1950	4wDM	D	St	
Johnnie Walker		DM		Ruston & Hornsby Ltd	1959	4wDM	D	St	

SEVERN VALLEY RAILWAY

Bewdley, WORCESTERSHIRE

Name	Current No.	Type/Class	Origin	Builder	Built	Wh.Arr.			
—	5164		GWR	GWR	1930	2-6-2T	s	Op	N
BR No. 5164. 41ft in length. Designed by Churchward. Owned by 51XX Fund. Built at Swindon.									
—	4566		GWR	GWR	1924	2-6-2T	s		U
BR No. 4566. 36ft in length. Designed by Churchward. Owned by 4566 Fund. Built at Swindon.									
Hagley Hall	4930		GWR	GWR	1929	4-6-0	s	St	O
BR No. 4930. 63ft in length. Designed by C B Collett. Built at Swindon.									
—	5764		GWR	GWR	1929	0-6-0PT	s	Op	N
BR No. 5764. 31ft in length. Designed by C B Collett. Owned by Pannier Tank Fund. Built at Swindon.									
—	7714		GWR	Kerr, Stuart & Co Ltd	1930	0-6-0PT	s	Op	N
BR No. 7714. 31ft in length. Designed by C B Collett. Owned by Pannier Tank Fund.									
—	7325		GWR	GWR	1932	2-6-0	s		O
BR No. 7325. 59ft in length. Designed by Churchward. Owned by Great Western Association.									
Bradley Manor	7802		GWR	GWR	1938	4-6-0	s	Op	N
BR No. 7802. 62ft in length. Designed by C B Collett. Owned by Erlestoke Manor Fund. Built at Swindon.									
Erlestoke Manor	7812		GWR	GWR	1939	4-6-0	s		U
BR No. 7812. 62ft in length. Designed by C B Collett. Owned by Erlestoke Manor Fund.									
Hinton Manor	7819		GWR	GWR	1939	4-6-0	s	St	
BR No. 7819. 62ft in length. Designed by C B Collett. Owned by Hinton Manor Fund.									
—	2968		LMS	LMS	1934	2-6-0	s	Op	U
BR No. 42968. 60ft in length. Designed by W A Stanier. Owned by Stanier Mogul Fund.									
—	43106		LMS	BR	1951	2-6-0	s		U
BR No. 43106. 56ft in length. Designed by Ivatt 4 Fund. Built at Darlington.									
—	45110 Black Five		LMS	Vulcan Foundry	1935	4-6-0	s	Op	N
BR No. 45110. 64ft in length. Designed by W A Stanier.									
—	46443		LMS	BR	1950	2-6-0	s	Op	
BR No. 46443. 53ft in length. Designed by Ivatt. Owned by SVR 46443 Fund.									
—	46521		LMS	BR	1953	2-6-0	s	St	
BR No. 46521. 53ft in length. Designed by Ivatt. Built at Swindon.									
—	47383		LMS	Vulcan Foundry	1926	0-6-0T	s	Op	N
BR No. 47383. 31ft in length. Designed by Fowler. Owned by Manchester Rail Travel Society.									

| Key: | Wh.Arr. = Wheel Arrangement | **S** = Steam | **D** = Diesel | **P** = Petrol | **E** = Electric | **C** = Coach | **W** = Wagon | **R** = Rolling Stock | **Op** = Operational | **St** = Static | **O** = On Display | **U** = Under Restoration | **G** = Pre Group | **N** = Pre Nationalisation |

Scottish Railway Centre — Severn Valley Railway

A-Z SHOWING ROLLING STOCK

Steam Railway Directory   www.steamrailway.com

Name	No.	Operator	Builder	Year	Wheels	Type	Status	Code
—	48773	LMS	North British Locomotive Co	1940	2-8-0	S	Op	N
Union of South Africa	60009	LNER	LNER	1937	4-6-2	S	Op	N
Great Marquess (The)	3442	LNER	LNER	1938	2-6-0	S		U N
—	75069	BR	BR	1955	4-6-0	S		U
—	80079	BR	BR	1954	2-6-4T	S		
Gordon	600	Army	North British Locomotive Co	1943	2-10-0	S		U
Lady Armaghdale (The)	686	Manchester Ship Canal	Hunslet Engine Co Ltd	1898	0-6-0T	S		U G
Warwickshire	2047	Rugby Portland Cement	Manning, Wardle & Co	1926	0-6-0ST	S	St O	N
Cornwall	D821	BR	BR	1960	B-B	D	Op	
Western Ranger	D1013	BR	BR	1962	C – C	D	Op	
Western Champion	D1015	BR	BR	1963	C – C	D	Op	
Western Courier	D1062	BR	BR	1963	C – C	D	Op	
—	D7029	BR	Beyer, Peacock	1962	B-B	D	Op	U
Hood	D431	BR	Vulcan Foundry	1968	Co-Co	D	Op	
Ark Royal	D435	BR	Vulcan Foundry	1968	Co-Co	D	Op	
Exeter	D444	BR	Vulcan Foundry	1968	Co-Co	D	Op	
—	D5410	BR	Birmingham Carriage & Wagon Co Ltd	1962	Bo-Bo	D	Op	
—	D7633	BR	Beyer, Peacock	1965	Bo-Bo	D	Op	
—	12099	LMS	BR	1952	0-6-0	D	Op	
—	D3022	BR		1953	0-6-0	D	Op	
—	D3586	BR	BR	1958	0-6-0	D	Op	
Alan	11509	Patent Shaft Steelworks	Ruston & Hornsby Ltd	1957	0-4-0	D	Op	
Silver Spoon	11510	British Sugar Corporation	Ruston & Hornsby Ltd	1950	0-4-0	D	St	
—	D2957	Mersey Ironworks	Ruston & Hornsby Ltd	1953	0-4-0	D	Op	

BR No. 48773. 63ft in length. Designed by W A Stanier. Owned by Stanier 8F Loco Society.
BR No. 60009. 70ft in length. Designed by Gresley.
BR No. 61994. 58ft in length. Designed by Gresley. Built at Darlington.
BR No. 75069. 62ft in length. Designed by R A Riddles. Owned by 75069 Fund. Built at Swindon.
BR No. 80079. 45ft in length. Designed by R A Riddles. Owned by Passenger Tank Fund.
59ft in length. Designed by R A Riddles. Owned by Royal Corps of Transport Museum Trustees.
24ft in length. Owned by Warwickshire Industrial Loco Trust.
25ft in length. Owned by Warwickshire Industrial Locomotive Trust.
BR No. D821. 60ft in length. Owned by Diesel Traction Group.
BR No. D1013. 68ft in length. Built at Swindon.
BR No. D1015. 68ft in length. Built at Swindon.
BR No. D1062. 68ft in length. Owned by Western Loco Association.
BR No. D7029. 52ft in length. Owned by Diesel Traction Group.
BR No. D431. 67ft in length. Owned by 50 Fund.
BR No. D435. 67ft in length. Owned by 50 Fund.
BR No. D444. 67ft in length. Owned by 50 Fund.
BR No. D5410. 51ft in length. Owned by Sandwell Met Council.
BR No. D7633. 51ft in length. Owned by Severn Valley Railway & PW Fund.
BR No. 12099. 29ft in length. Built at Derby.
BR No. 13022. 29ft in length. Owned by Class 08 Society.
BR No. D3586. 29ft in length. Built at Crewe.
22ft in length.
22ft in length.
22ft in length.

Name	Current No.	Type/Class	Origin	Wh.Arr.	Built	Builder		
— 22ft in length.								
—	D2961			0-4-0	1957	Ruston & Hornsby Ltd	D	Op
Taw Valley	34027		SR	4-6-2	1946	BR	s	Op
BR No. 34027. Designed by O V Bulleid. Built at Eastleigh.								

SITTINGBOURNE & KEMSLEY   Sittingbourne, KENT

Name	Current No.	Type/Class	Origin	Wh.Arr.	Built	Builder		
Premier	886			0-4-2ST	1905	Kerr, Stuart & Co Ltd	s	St O
Leader	926			0-4-2ST	1905	Kerr, Stuart & Co Ltd	s	Op
Currently stripped down for major overhaul.								
Melior	4219			0-4-2ST	1924	Kerr, Stuart & Co Ltd	s	Op
Unique	2216			2-4-0F	1924	W G Bagnall	s	St O
Alpha	2472			0-6-2T	1932	W G Bagnall	s	St O U
Triumph	2511			0-6-2T	1934	W G Bagnall	s	Op
Superb	2624			0-6-2T	1940	W G Bagnall	s	Op
Victor	4182	DM		0-4-0DM	1953	Hudson, Hunslet	D	Op
Edward Lloyd	435403	DM		0-4-0DM	1961	Ruston & Hornsby Ltd	D	Op
Bear	614			0-4-0ST	1896	Peckett & Sons	s	St O
No 1	1876			0-4-0F	1925	Andrew Barclay & Sons		St O
	3719			0-4-0ST	1928	Hawthorn Leslie & Co		St O
Chattenden	196				1941	Cravens		R
Upnor	199	Closed			1941	Cravens		R
Lodge Hill	200	Closed			1941	Cravens		R
Four Elms	204	Closed			1941	Cravens		R
—	626				1972	Sittingbourne & Kemsley Light Railway		R
—	633	Closed			1972	Sittingbourne & Kemsley Light Railway		R
—	641	Closed			1957	Bowaters		C
—	647	Semi Open			1974	Sittingbourne & Kemsley Light Railway		R
—	655	Open			1971	Sittingbourne & Kemsley Light Railway		R
—	657	Closed			1975	Bowaters		R
—	658	Open			1957	Sittingbourne & Kemsley Light Railway		R
—	659	Closed			1957	Bowaters		R
—	660	Closed			1957	Bowaters		R

SNOWDON MOUNTAIN RAILWAY   Caernarfon, GWYNEDD

Name	Current No.	Type/Class	Origin	Wh.Arr.	Built	Builder		
Enid	2			0-4-2T	1895	Swiss Locomotive Works	s	Op
Wyddfa	3			0-4-2T	1895	Swiss Locomotive Works	s	Op
Snowdon	4			0-4-2T	1896	Swiss Locomotive Works	s	Op
Moel Siabod	5			0-4-2T	1896	Swiss Locomotive Works	s	Op
Padarn	6			0-4-2T	1922	Swiss Locomotive Works	s	U

Key: Wh.Arr. = Wheel Arrangement   S = Steam   D = Diesel   E = Electric   P = Petrol   R = Rolling Stock   W = Wagon   C = Coach   Op = Operational   St = Static   O = On Display   U = Under Restoration   G = Pre Group   N = Pre Nationalisation

A-Z SHOWING ROLLING STOCK

Name	Current No.	Type/Class	Wh.Arr.	Built	Builder				
Ralph	7		0-4-2T	1923	Swiss Locomotive Works	s		s	U
Eryri	8		0-4-2T	1923	Swiss Locomotive Works	s		Op	
Ninian	9	DH	0-4-0DH	1986	Hunslet Engine Co Ltd	D		Op	U
Yeti	10	DH	0-4-0DH	1986	Hunslet Engine Co Ltd	D		Op	U
Peris	11	DH	0-4-0DH	1991	Hunslet Engine Co Ltd	D		Op	
George	12	DH	0-4-0DH	1992	Hunslet Engine Co Ltd	D		Op	

SOMERSET & DORSET RAILWAY

Watchet, SOMERSET

Name	Current No.	Type/Class	Wh.Arr.	Built	Builder	Origin			
—	53808	Saddle Tank	0-4-0		Peckett & Sons		s		
—			2-8-0				s		U

SOUTH DEVON RAILWAY

Buckfastleigh, DEVON

Name	Current No.	Type/Class	Wh.Arr.	Built	Builder	Origin			
Dumbleton Hall	4920		4-6-0	1929	GWR				
—	3803		2-8-0				s		
—	5526		2-6-2T				s		
—	5786		0-6-0T				s		
—	3205		0-6-0	1946			s		
Designed by C B Collett. Built at Swindon.									
—	1369		0-6-0T	1934			s		
—	1420		0-4-2T	1933			s		
Errol Lonsdale	30587		2-4-0T		LSWR		s		
Sapper	68011		0-6-0T	1953			s		U
Glendower	WD132		0-6-0T	1942			s	Op	U
Ashley	1738		0-4-0T	1940	Peckett & Sons		s	Op	U
Lady Angela	5474		0-4-0T	1926			s	Op	U
Percy			0-6-0	1926	Kitson & Co		s	Op	
Tiny	151		0-4-0T	1868	SDR		s	St O	
Owned by NRM.								St O	
—	63078	5 Plank Open				GWR			W
—	108207	5 Plank Open				GWR			W
—	95979	Box Van				GWR			W
—	96835	Box Van				GWR			W
—	104700					GWR			W
—	125814					GWR			W
—	59119	Iron Mink				GWR			W
Numbered 47528 at present.									
—	2016	Milk Tank				GWR			W

No.	Description	Company	Type
3037	Milk Tank	GWR	W
7303	Tar Tank Wagon	GWR	W
42223		GWR	W
68777		GWR	W
35420		GWR	W
92035		GWR	W
92092		GWR	W
41873	Shunter	GWR	W
100715	Sleeper Wagon	GWR	W
506327	Box Van	LMS	W
513212	Box Van	LMS	W
4492		LMS	W
263278	Lowmac	LNER	W
766158	Box Van	BR	W
778436	Box Van	BR	W
786393	Box Van	BR	W
MOD4122	Shoc Van	BR	W
070863	Bogie Bolster	BR	W
993247	Dogfish	BR	W
993471	Dogfish	BR	W
984176	Dogfish	BR	W
984872		BR	W
743010		BR	W
743031		BR	W
741574	Tube Wagon	BR	W
950344	Brake Van	BR	W
953640	Brake Van	BR	W
993710	Shark Brake Van	BR	W
550179	Mineral Wagon	BR	W
550472	Mineral Wagon	BR	W
587511	Mineral Wagon	BR	W
592433	Mineral Wagon	BR	W
59408	5 Plank Open	BR	W
9111	Super Saloon		C
276	Parcels Train Brake Van		C
1285	Tourist Second Open		C
6515	Brake Composite Corridor		C
7377	Brake Composite Corridor		C
2180	Brake Third Corridor		C
W225	Auto Trailer		C

A-Z SHOWING ROLLING STOCK

South Devon Railway — South Devon Railway

Key: Wh.Arr. = Wheel Arrangement   S = Steam   D = Diesel   E = Electric   P = Petrol   R = Rolling Stock   W = Wagon   C = Coach   Op = Operational   St = Static   O = On Display   U = Under Restoration   G = Pre Group   N = Pre Nationalisation

Steam Railway Directory www.steamrailway.com

Name	Current No.	Type/Class						
—	W240	Auto Trailer						C
—	8249	Saloon						C
—	7	Dynamometer Carriage						C
Now used as a saloon carriage.								
—	7090	Slip Coach						C
—	594							C
Large van designed for moving stage scenery.								

SOUTH DOWNS LIGHT RAILWAY

Pulborough, SUSSEX (WEST)

Name	Current No.	Type/Class	Origin	Wh. Arr.	Built	Builder			
Ayrshire Yeomanry	5156		LMS	4-6-2	1952	Trevor Guest	S	Op	N
BR No. 45156. 12ft in length. Owned by Chris English.									
Sir Nigel Gresley	4498		LNER	4-6-2	1967	Bill Kirkland	S	Op	N
12ft in length. Owned by John Young & Chris English. 10.25" gauge.									
Sir Sagramore	771		SR	4-6-0	1994	Peter Howard	S	Op	N
12ft in length. Owned by Chris English.									
City of Westminster	46258		LMS	4-6-2	1995	Dave Wiseman	S	Op	N
BR No. 46258. 14ft in length. Owned by Dave Wiseman.									
	75080		BR	4-6-0		Dave Wiseman	S	Op	
BR No. 75080. 11ft in length. Owned by Dave Wiseman.									
Arthur	13245		LMS	2-6-0		Peter Howard	S	Op	N
11ft in length. Owned by Peter Taylor.									
Alice			NCB	0-6-0	1982	Jack Hudell	S	Op	
6ft in length. Owned by Julian Chivers.									
Royal Scot				0-4-2	2001	Giles Favell	S	Op	
10ft in length. Owned by Giles Favell.									
			LMS	4-6-0	2001	Barry Metcalfe	S	Op	
12ft in length. Owned by Barry Metcalfe.									
			BR	0-4-0 - 0-4-0	1999	Aiden Favell	D	Op	
12ft in length. Owned by Aiden Favell.									
			BR	0-4-0 - 0-4-0		Dave Wiseman	D	Op	
14ft in length. Owned by Dave Wiseman.									
Tweedledum				0-4-0	1950		D		U
4ft in length. Owned by Colin Pidgley.									
Flying Scotsman			LNER	4-6-2	1934		S		U
13ft in length. Owned by Colin Pidgley.									

SOUTH TYNEDALE RAILWAY

Alston, CUMBRIA

Name	Current No.	Type/Class	Origin	Wh. Arr.	Built	Builder			
Sao Domingos	3	Well Tank		0-6-0	1928	Orenstein, Koppel	S		U
Currently dismantled, awaiting rebuild.									
Thomas Edmondson	6			0-4-0T	1918	Henschel	S	O	U
20ft in length. Owned by South Tynedale Railway Preservation Society. In almost original condition.									

South Tynedale Railway — South Tynedale Railway

A-Z SHOWING ROLLING STOCK

Name	No.	Notes / Type	Wh.Arr.	Year	Builder	Type	Status
Nakio	10	18ft in length. Owned by South Tynedale Railway Preservation Society. Nearing completion of major rebuild.	0-6-0	1957	Hunslet Engine Co Ltd	S	U
Chaka's Kraal No 6	12		0-4-2	1940	Henschel	S	
Helen Kathryn	14	Formerly worked clearing bomb damage in various Eastern German cities.	0-4-0	1948		S	Op
	16	18.5ft in length. Designed by Avonside Engineering Co. Owned by South Tynedale Railway Preservation Society.		1937	Hunslet Engine Co Ltd	S	O U
Phoenix	4	Flame Proof Diesel NCB	0-6-0	1941	F C Hibberd & Co Ltd	D	Op
Naworth		Rebuilt at Alston for passenger service with large cab, airbrakes and electric start.		1952	Hudswell, Clarke & Co	D	Op
	9	Flame Proof Diesel NCB	0-4-0	1952	Hunslet Engine Co Ltd	D	Op
Cumbria	11	16ft in length. Owned by South Tynedale Railway Preservation Society. Rebuilt at Alston for passenger service. DM	4w	1967	Hunslet Engine Co Ltd	D	Op
Tiny Tim	13	Owned by Durham Narrow Gauge Group.	0-4-0	1958	Hunslet Engine Co Ltd	D	St O
	15	Owned by Ayle Colliery Company.	0-6-0	1965	Hunslet Engine Co Ltd	D	
			0-6-0	1960	Hudswell, Clarke & Co	D	
	17	11.5ft in length. BE	4w	1973	Baguley, Drewry	E	
		BE	4wBE	1958	English Electric, Baguley	E	Op
DB965082		Owned by DNGG. Permanent Way Trolley BR	4w	1957	D Wickham & Co Ltd	D W	Op
1		22ft in length. Wooden bodied. Compartment Coach		1955		C	
2		Rebuilt in 1992. Compartment Coach		1952		C	Op
3		27ft in length. Gangwayed Saloon Coach				C	
5					Hudson	C	Op
6					Hudson	C	Op
7		Three owned by railway, 32ft in length. Designed by South Tynedale Railway Preservation Society. Owned by South Tynedale Railway Preservation Society.			Hudson	R	
19		Brake Van	4w	1995	South Tynedale Railway Preservation Society	W	
22		Designed by South Tynedale Railway Preservation Society. Owned by South Tynedale Railway Preservation Society. Built at Alston. Built on a Roberts Chassis. All Steel Bogie Wagon		1955	Hudson	R W	Op
24		Three owned by railway, 22ft in length. Owned by South Tynedale Railway Preservation Society. Bogie Well Wagon	4w		Hudson	R W	Op
31		Seven owned by railway, 11ft in length. Owned by South Tynedale Railway Preservation Society. Bogie Well Wagon	4w			W	
33		26ft in length. Owned by South Tynedale Railway Preservation Society. 4w Skip			Hudson	R W	Op
37		Four owned by railway, 6.5ft in length. Owned by South Tynedale Railway Preservation Society. 4w Chassis	4w		Karl H Mul Hauser	R W	Op

Key: Wh.Arr. = Wheel Arrangement S = Steam D = Diesel E = Electric P = Petrol W = Wagon R = Rolling Stock C = Coach Op = Operational St = Static O = On Display U = Under Restoration G = Pre Group N = Pre Nationalisation

South Tynedale Railway — South Yorkshire Railway

Steam Railway Directory www.steamrailway.com

Owned by South Tynedale Railway Preservation Society.

No.	Type	Wh.Arr.	Builder	Built		
39	Compressor Wagon	2w	Vincenzo Valente		R W	Op

Owned by South Tynedale Railway Preservation Society. Converted from tipping wagon.

| 40 | Hopper Tipping Wagon | 4w | Vincenzo Valente | | R W | Op |

Six owned by railway. Owned by South Tynedale Railway Preservation Society. Two are fitted with hydraulic rams for tipping.

| 46 | Bogie Flat Wagon | | Hudson | | R W | Op |

Five owned by railway. 15.5ft in length. Owned by South Tynedale Railway Preservation Society.

| 51 | Weed Killer Wagon | 4w | South Tynedale Railway Preservation Society | 1990 | R W | Op |

7.25ft in length. Owned by South Tynedale Railway Preservation Society.

| 52 | 4w Hopper Wagon | 4w | Hall, Blenkinsop | 1990 | R W | Op |

14ft in length. Owned by South Tynedale Railway Preservation Society.

| 53 | 4w Wagon | 4w | | | R W | Op |

Five owned by railway. 9.25ft in length. Owned by South Tynedale Railway Preservation Society.

SOUTH YORKSHIRE RAILWAY

Sheffield, YORKSHIRE (SOUTH)

Name	Current No.	Type/Class	Origin	Wh.Arr.	Built	Builder	
Dorothy	D2337	DM/04	BR	0-6-0DM	1961	Drewry Car Co	D
—	D3000	DE/08	BR	0-6-0DE	1952	BR	D

BR No. D3000. Prev. No. 13000. Designed by BR. Built at Derby.

| Gwyneth | D3019 | DE/08 | BR | 0-6-0DE | 1953 | BR | |

BR No. D3019. Prev. No. 13019. Designed by BR. Built at Derby.

| — | D3023 | DE/08 | BR | 0-6-0DE | 1953 | BR | D |

BR No. 08016. Prev. No. D3023
13023. Designed by BR. Built at Derby.

| — | 08216 | DE/08 | BR | 0-6-0DE | 1956 | BR | D |

BR No. 08216. Prev. No. D3286
13286. Designed by BR. Built at Derby.

| — | 08390 | DE/08 | BR | 0-6-0DE | 1958 | BR | D |

BR No. 08390. Prev. No. D3513. Designed by BR.

| — | 08707 | DE/08 | BR | 0-6-0DE | 1960 | BR | D |

Prev. No. D3874.

| Christine | D4092 | DE/10 | BR | 0-6-0DE | 1962 | BR | D |
| | 12074 | DE/11 | BR | 0-6-0DE | 1950 | BR | D D |

BR No. 12074. Built at Derby.

| — | 12083 | DE/11 | BR | 0-6-0DE | 1950 | BR | D |

BR No. 12083. Built at Derby.

| — | D9502 | DH/14 | BR | 0-6-0DH | 1964 | BR | D |

BR No. D9502. Built at Swindon.

SPA VALLEY RAILWAY

Tunbridge Wells, KENT

Name	Current No.	Type/Class	Origin	Wh. Arr.	Built	Builder	Status
	26038	DE/26	BR	Bo-Bo	1959	BRCW	D … N

BR No. 26038. Prev. No. D5338. Built at Birmingham.

	53556	DMU/104	BR		1958		R
	47493	F/3	LMS & BR	0-6-0T	1927		S — U N

BR No. 47493. Built at Newton Le Willows.

| Lady Ingrid | 2315 | | | 0-4-0T | 1951 | Andrew Barclay & Sons | S — Op U |

Expected to be in service - Winter 2001/2.

| Fonmon | 1636 | | | 0-6-0ST | 1924 | Peckett & Sons | S — Op U |

Expected to be in service - Autumn 2001.

| Hotspur | 2944 | | Polish Railways | 0-6-0T | 1952 | | S — Op U |

Built at Poland.

| Spartan | 3135 | | Polish Railways | 0-6-0T | 1954 | | S — Op |

Built at Poland.

| Colonel Tomline | D3489 | | BR | 0-6-0 | 1958 | | D — Op |

BR No. D3489. Built at Darlington.

| | 15224 | | BR | 0-6-0 | 1949 | BR | D — Op |

BR No. 15224. Built at Ashford.

| Southerham | 2591 | DM | Metropolitan Railway/London Transport | 0-4-0DM | 1959 | Drewry Car Co, Vulcan | D |
| | 2749 | | | | 1932 | | C |

Two owned by railway. One coach - operational, one coach - under restoration. — W Op

Two owned by railway. — W Op

Cranes
Four owned by railway, 3 cranes - operational, 1 crane under restoration.

STEAM

Swindon, WILTSHIRE

Name	Current No.	Type/Class	Origin	Wh. Arr.	Built	Builder	Status
King George V	6000	GWR	GWR	4-6-0	1927	GWR	S — St O N

60ft in length. Designed by C B Collett. Owned by National Railway Museum. Located at Steam Museum. Built at Swindon.

| Dean Goods | 2516 | GWR | GWR | 0-6-0 | 1897 | GWR | S — St O N |

40ft in length. Designed by William Dean. Owned by National Collection. Located at Steam Museum. Built at Swindon.

| North Star | | GWR | GWR | 2-2-2 | 1925 | GWR | S — St O G N |

25ft in length. Designed by Robert Stephenson. Owned by National Collection. Built at Steam Museum. Broad gauge replica of locomotive built in 1837.

| | 9400 | GWR | GWR | 0-6-0 | 1947 | GWR | S — St O N |

30ft in length. Designed by Hawksworth. Owned by National Collection. Located at Steam Museum.

| | 4248 | GWR | GWR | 2-8-0 | 1916 | GWR | S — St O N |

45ft in length. Designed by Churchward. Located at Steam Museum. Displayed in stripped down condition.

| | 4 | | GWR | | 1934 | GWR | S D — St O N |

South Yorkshire Railway — STEAM

A-Z SHOWING ROLLING STOCK

Key: Wh.Arr. = Wheel Arrangement **S** = Steam **D** = Diesel **E** = Electric **P** = Petrol **W** = Wagon **R** = Rolling Stock **C** = Coach **Op** = Operational **St** = Static **O** = On Display **U** = Under Restoration **G** = Pre Group **N** = Pre Nationalisation

Steam Railway Directory www.steamrailway.com

Steam Railway Directory   www.steamrailway.com

Owned by National Collection. Located at Steam Museum.

	Current No.	Origin	Built	Builder					
Royal Saloon	9003	GWR	1897	GWR					N

60ft in length. Located at Steam Museum. Part of Royal Train built for Queen Victoria in 1897.

STRATHSPEY RAILWAY

Aviemore, HIGHLANDS

Name / Current No. / Type/Class	Origin	Built	Builder	Wh. Arr.	C	St	O	N
5025	LMS	1934	Vulcan Foundry	4-6-0	s		U	N
BR No. 45025. Designed by W A Stanier. Owned by Watkinson Trust. Only on view at special events.								
E V Cooper, Engineer								
46512	LMS	1952	BR	2-6-0	s	Op	U	N
BR No. 46512. Designed by Ivatt. Owned by Highland Locomotive Co Ltd.								
9	NCB	1943	Robert Stephenson, Hawthorn	0-6-0ST	s	Op		N
Designed by Ministry of Supply.								
828	Caledonian Railway	1899	Caledonian Railway	0-6-0	s		U	G
BR No. 57566. Designed by J F Macintosh. Owned by Scottish Locomotive Preservation Trust. Not on view.								
17	Weymss Private Railway	1935	Andrew Barclay & Sons	0-6-0T	s		U	
Designed by Andrew Barclay & Sons. Owned by Highland Locomotive Co Ltd. Not on view.								
D3594	BR	1963	Birmingham Carriage & Wagon Co Ltd	Bo-Bo	D	Op	U	
BR No. D3594. Not on view.								
D5325	BR	1958	Birmingham Carriage & Wagon Co Ltd	Bo-Bo	D	Op		
BR No. D5325. Owned by Highland Railway Diesel Loco Co. Located at Boat of Garten.								
D3605	BR	1959	BR	0-6-0DE	D	Op		
BR No. D3605. Owned by Highland Railway Diesel Loco Co.								
201	Caledonian Railway	1905	Cowan, Sheldon	4w	R	C	St	G
151	Highland Railway	1870	Metropolitan Carriage & Wagon Co	4w	R	C	St	G
Owned by Watkinson Trust. On view at special events.								
1211 Sleeping Car	LNER	1935	LNER		R	C	St	N
BR No. E1211E. Designed by Gresley. Located at Boat of Garten.								
33003	LMS	1939	LMS	6w	R	C	Op	
BR No. M33003M. Designed by LMS. Owned by Watkinson Trust. Built at Wolverton.								
45021 Sleeping Car	LMS	1944	LMS	12w	R	C	St	
BR No. M4J021M. Designed by LMS. Owned by Watkinson Trust. Built at Wolverton. Only on view at special events.								
394	LMS	1951	BR		R	C	St	N
BR No. M394M. Designed by LMS. Located at Boat of Garten.								
621 Sleeping Car	LMS	1951	BR		R	C	St	
BR No. M621M. Designed by LMS. Located at Boat of Garten. Built at Derby.								
2723	LMS	1945	LMS		R	C	U	N
BR No. M2723M. Designed by LMS. Owned by Watkinson Trust. Built at Wolverton.								
27043 Brake Third	LMS	1950	BR		R	C	Op	
BR No. M27043M. Designed by LMS. Owned by Watkinson Trust. Located at Boat of Garten. Built at Derby.								
104 Brake Third	BR	1955	BR		R	C	U	N
BR No. E43349. Designed by BR. Located at Boat of Garten.								
109 Restaurant Car	BR	1959	Birmingham Carriage & Wagon Co Ltd		R	C	Op	
BR No. E1928. Two owned by railway. Designed by BR. Located at Boat of Garten. Were part of a 'Flying Scotsman' Set.								

SWANAGE RAILWAY

Swanage, DORSET

Name	Current No.	Type/Class	Origin	Wh.Arr.	Built	Builder		
Harry A Frith	E828		SR	4-6-0	1923		s	U
Eddystone	34028		SR	4-6-2	1946		s	Op
257 Squadron	34072		SR	4-6-2	1948		s	Op
Port Line	35027		SR	4-6-2	1948		s	Op
Stan Symes	D6515	DM	BR	Bo-Bo	1957		D	Op
May	2			0-4-0DM	1960	Fowler	D	
Beryl				4wPM	1937	Planet	D	
Awaiting restoration.								
Progress				0-4-0ST	1923	Peckett & Sons	s	U

SWANSEA VALE RAILWAY

Swansea, SWANSEA

Name	Current No.	Type/Class	Origin	Wh.Arr.	Built	Builder		
	4270			2-8-0T	1919		s	
Located at Swansea Valley Railway.								
	51135	Driving Motor Brake Second /116			1958		D	Op
Located at Swansea Valley Railway.								
	51148	DMS /116			1958		D	Op
Owned by Llanelli & District Railway Society. Located at Swansea Valley Railway.								
	55026	DMU /121			1960		D	U
Located at Swansea Valley Railway.								
Llantarnam Abbey				0-6-0ST	1939	Andrew Barclay & Sons	s	U
BR No. 2074. Owned by Llantarnam Abbey Locomotive Association. Located at Swansea Valley Railway.								
				0-6-0ST	1955	Hunslet Engine Co Ltd	s	U
BR No. 3829. Located at Swansea Valley Railway.								
'Nickel Mond No 1'				0-4-0ST	1914	Peckett & Sons	s	Op
BR No. 1345. Located at Swansea Valley Railway.								
	12514	DM		0-6-0DM	1953	Hudswell, Clarke & Co	D	
Located at Swansea Valley Railway.								
	27914	DH		0-4-0DH	1961	North British Locomotive Co	D	
Located at Swansea Valley Railway.								
	312433	DM		4wDM	1951	Ruston & Hornsby Ltd	D	Op
Located at Swansea Valley Railway.								
		DH Crane						St O
BR No. ADW225. Located at Swansea Valley Railway.								
		Crane						St O
BR No. 060977. Located at Swansea Valley Railway. Coupled with 13T single bolster wagon.								
	W46137	Second Corridor	BR		1954			c
Located at Swansea Valley Railway.								

Key: Wh.Arr. = Wheel Arrangement   S = Steam   D = Diesel   E = Electric   P = Petrol   R = Rolling Stock   W = Wagon   C = Coach   Op = Operational   St = Static   O = On Display   U = Under Restoration   G = Pre Group   N = Pre Nationalisation

Steam Railway Directory   www.steamrailway.com

A-Z SHOWING ROLLING STOCK

Steam Railway Directory   www.steamrailway.com

Swansea Vale Railway — Swindon & Cricklade Railway

Description	Current No.	Type/Class	Origin	Wh. Arr.	Built	Builder	Status
	DMU /116						
Owned by Llanelli & District Railway Society. Located at Swansea Valley Railway.	M9396	Brake Second	BR				
Located at Swansea Valley Railway.	114762	Brake Van	GWR		1966		c
Located at Swansea Valley Railway.	DMT32331	Brake Van	BR		1946		R
Designed by LMS. Located at Swansea Valley Railway.	DW150351	Pooley Van	BR		1948		R
Located at Swansea Valley Railway.	40232	Tar Tank Wagon	NCB	4w			R
Located at Swansea Valley Railway.	40353	Tar Tank Wagon	NCB	4w			R
Located at Swansea Valley Railway.	48306	Tar Tank Wagon	NCB	4w			R
Located at Swansea Valley Railway.	NCO102		LMS				R
Capacity 12 tonnes. Located at Swansea Valley Railway.	163748		LMS				R
Two owned by railway. Capacity 12 tonnes. Located at Swansea Valley Railway.	DB996761	Bogie Bolster	BR		1951		R
Capacity 40 tonnes. Located at Swansea Valley Railway.	95156		GWR				R
Capacity 10 tonnes. Located at Swansea Valley Railway.	85121	Van	GWR		1940		R
Capacity 10 tonnes. Located at Swansea Valley Railway.	85189	Van	GWR		1940		R
Capacity 10 tonnes. Located at Swansea Valley Railway.	85192	Van	GWR		1940		R
BR No. DW30773. Capacity 14 tonnes. Located at Swansea Valley Railway.			GWR				R
BR No. DW80880. Capacity 20 tonnes. Located at Swansea Valley Railway.			GWR				

SWINDON & CRICKLADE RAILWAY

Swindon, WILTSHIRE

Name	Current No.	Type/Class	Origin	Wh. Arr.	Built	Builder		
Richard Trevithick	2354			0-4-0ST	1954	Andrew Barclay & Sons	s	Op
Converted from oil to coal firing.								
Slough Estates No 3	5637			0-6-0ST	1924	Hudswell, Clarke & Co	s	Op
				0-6-2T	1925		s	Op
Foremarke Hall	7903			4-6-0	1949	BR	D	Op
Built at Swindon.								
	03022	DM /03		0-6-0DM	1958		D	U

Built at Swindon.

Name	Current No.	Type/Class	Builder	Built	Wh.Arr.		
Woodbine	21442	DM				D	
Under going overhaul.							
Swordfish	2138	Saddle Tank	Fowler	1958	0-4-0DM	D	S · U
Salmon	2139	Saddle Tank	Fowler	1933	0-4-0DM	D	S · U
—	1857	Side Tank	Andrew Barclay & Sons	1941	0-6-0ST	S	S
—	3845		Andrew Barclay & Sons	1942	0-6-0ST	S	S
—			Hudswell, Clarke & Co	1952	0-6-0		
—				1942	2-8-0		

TALYLLYN RAILWAY

Tywyn, GWYNEDD

Name	Current No.	Type/Class	Origin	Builder	Built	Wh.Arr.	Type	Status
Talyllyn	1			Fletcher Jennings	1864	0-4-2ST	S	Op
18ft in length. Designed by Fletcher Jennings.								
Dolgoch	2			Fletcher Jennings	1866	0-4-0WT	S	Op
17.5ft in length. Designed by Fletcher Jennings.								
Sir Haydn	3		Corris Railway	Hughes Loco & Tramway Eng Works Ltd	1878	0-4-2ST	S	Op · G
16.5ft in length. Designed by Hughes Loco & Tramway Eng Works Ltd. Bought by Talyllyn Railway in 1951.								
Edward Thomas	4		Corris Railway	Kerr, Stuart & Co Ltd	1921	0-4-2ST	S	Op
16.5ft in length. Designed by Kerr, Stuart & Co Ltd. Bought by Talyllyn Railway in 1951.								
Douglas	6		Royal Air Force	Andrew Barclay & Sons	1918	0-4-0WT	S	Op · U · G
12.5ft in length. Designed by Andrew Barclay & Sons. Donated to Talyllyn Railway in 1953.								
Tom Rolt	7		Talyllyn Railway	Talyllyn Railway	1991	0-4-2T	S	Op
18.75ft in length. Designed by J L H Bate. Incorporates parts of Barclay 0-4-0T of 1948.								
Midlander	5			Ruston & Hornsby Ltd	1940	4w	D	Op
Merseysider	8			Ruston & Hornsby Ltd	1964	4w	D	Op
Alf	9			Hunslet Engine Co Ltd	1950	0-4-0	D	Op
Bryn Eglwys	10			Simplex	1985	4w	D	Op
—	1	3 Comp Closed		Brown, Marshalls		4w		C
—	2	3 Comp Closed		Brown, Marshalls		4w		C
—	3	3 Comp Closed		Brown, Marshalls		4w		C
—		3 Comp Closed				4w		C
—	5	Guards Van		Brown, Marshalls		4w		C
—	6	Guards Van		Falcon Works		4w		C
—	7			TR		4w		C
—	8	3 Comp Open Side		TR		4w		C
—	9	5 Comp Closed		TR		8w		C
—	10	3 Comp & Guard		W G Allen, Tisdales		8w		C
—	11	3 Comp Open Side		W G Allen, Tisdales		4w		C
—	12	3 Comp Open Side		TR		4w		C
—	13	3 Comp Open Side		TR		4w		C
—	14	2 Comp First Class		TR		4w		C
—	15	2 Comp First Class		TR		4w		C

Key: Wh.Arr. = Wheel Arrangement S = Steam D = Diesel E = Electric P = Petrol R = Rolling Stock W = Wagon C = Coach Op = Operational St = Static O = On Display U = Under Restoration G = Pre Group N = Pre Nationalisation

Steam Railway Directory   www.steamrailway.com

	Current No.	Type/Class		Wh. Arr.	Builder		
—	16	3 Comp & Guard		8w	Kerr, Stuart & Co Ltd		C
—	17	2 Saloons		8w	Metropolitan Carriage & Wagon Co		C
—	18	6 Comp Closed		8w	TR		C
—	19	6 Comp Closed Comp		8w	TR, Tisdale		C
—	20	3 Comp & Wheelchair		8w	TR, Tisdale		C
—	21	3 Comp & Wheelchair		8w	TR, Tisdale		C
—	22	4 Comp & Guard		8w	TR, Tisdale		C
—	23	6 Comp Closed		8w	TR, Tisdale		C

TANFIELD RAILWAY

Gateshead, COUNTY DURHAM

Name	Current No.	Type/Class	Origin	Wh. Arr.	Built	Builder		
Wellington				0-4-0ST	1873		s	C
Built at Tyneside. Stopped 10 year overhaul on loan to British Museum.								
Escucha				0-4-0ST	1883		s	C
Built at Tyneside. Formerly used in MFU, Spain.								
Enterprise				0-4-0ST	1884		s	C
Built at Tyneside.								
Cyclops				0-4-0ST	1907		s	C
Built at Tyneside.								
	2			0-4-0ST	1911		s	C
Built at Tyneside. Stopped 10 year overhaul.								
Stagshaw				0-6-0ST	1923		s	Op
Built at Tyneside.								
	3			0-6-0ST	1923		s	
Built at Tyneside.								
	13			0-4-0ST	1928		s	
Built at Tyneside. Overhaul started.								
	2			0-4-0DE	1933		D	Op
Built at Tyneside.								
	M2			4-6-2	1951		s	
Built at Tyneside.								
Huncoat				0-6-0F	1929			U
Built at Tyneside.								
Hendon				0-4-0CT	1940			U
Built at Tyneside. Cosmetically Restored.								
	62			0-6-0ST	1940			Op
Built at Tyneside. Undergoing Overhaul.								
	49			0-6-0ST	1943			Op
Built at Tyneside. Stopped 10 year overhaul boiler away for repairs.								
Sir Cecil A Cochrane				0-4-0ST	1948			Op
Built at Tyneside.								
	38			0-6-0ST	1954			U
Owned by Stopped - 10 year overhaul. Built at Tyneside.								
	1	DM		0-4-0DM	1958			Op

Built at Tyneside.

TEIFI VALLEY RAILWAY

Newcastle Emlyn, CARMARTHENSHIRE

Name	Current No.	Type/Class	Origin	Wh. Arr.	Built	Builder	Status
Alan George	606			0-4-0	1894	Hunslet Engine Co Ltd	S Op
Sgt Murphy				0-6-2T	1918	Kerr, Stuart & Co Ltd	S Op
Was originally a 0-6-0T.							
Sammy					1959	Simplex	D Op
Shelto					1941	Hudswell, Clarke & Co	D U
—					1934	Baguley	R C
—					1934	Baguley	R C
				0-4-0WT	1898	Borrows	Op U
				0-4-0DE	1953	Ruston & Hornsby Ltd	

TELFORD STEAM RAILWAY

Telford, SHROPSHIRE

Name	Current No.	Type/Class	Origin	Wh. Arr.	Built	Builder	Status
	5619		GWR	0-6-2	1924	GWR	S O U N
BR No. 5619. Designed by C B Collett.							
	3			0-4-0ST	1940	Peckett & Sons	S St
Designed by Peckett & Sons. Ex Ironbridge Power Station.							
	2142			0-4-0ST	1953	Peckett & Sons	S Op
Designed by Peckett & Sons. Owned by Darlington Railway Pres Soc.							
Thomas				0-4-0	1977	Alan Keef Ltd	S Op
Designed by Alan Keef. Built for Telford town park tramway.							
	38		GWR		1908	GWR	C St U
	14901		BR			BR	C Op
BR No. 14901. Converted by British Rail to include 2 lounge compartments.							

TIMOTHY HACKWORTH

Shildon, COUNTY DURHAM

Name	Current No.	Type/Class	Origin	Wh. Arr.	Built	Builder	Status
Merlin				0-4-0ST	1939	Peckett & Sons	S Op
Owned by Merlin Loco Group.							
Sanspariel			Liverpool & Manchester Railway	0-4-0	1980	BR	S Op
Designed by Hackworth. Owned by Sedgefield Borough Council. Replica of Sans Pariel.							
Braddyll			South Hetton Colliery	0-6-0	1837	Hackworth	S St O
Designed by Hackworth.							

Key: Wh. Arr. = Wheel Arrangement S = Steam D = Diesel E = Electric P = Petrol C = Coach W = Wagon R = Rolling Stock St = Static Op = Operational O = On Display U = Under Restoration G = Pre Group N = Pre Nationalisation

TRALEE & DINGLE RAILWAY

Tralee, COUNTY KERRY

Name	Current No.	Type/Class	Origin	Wh. Arr.	Built	Builder		Op	
—	5			2-6-2	1891	Hunslet Engine Co Ltd	s		St 0

Designed by Edgar C Bredin.

ULSTER FOLK & TRANSPORT

Holywood, COUNTY DOWN

Name	Current No.	Type/Class	Origin	Wh. Arr.	Built	Builder			
Maedh	800		GSR	4-6-0	1939	GSR Inchicore	s		St 0

Designed by Robert Stephenson.

| | 1 | | Londonderry Port & Harbour Commissioners | 0-6-0ST | 1891 | Robert Stephenson | s | | St 0 |
| Sutton | | | Great Northern Railway, Ireland | 2-4-2T | 1895 | GNRI | s | | St 0 |

Designed by Charles Clifford.

| Blanche | 2 | | Co Donegal Railway Joint Committee | 2-6-4T | 1912 | Nasmyth, Wilson | s | | St 0 |

Designed by Nasmyth Wilson.

| | 2 | | British Aluminium Co | 0-4-0T | 1904 | Peckett & Sons | s | | St 0 |

Designed by Peckett & Sons.

| | 246 | | War Department Light Railways | 0-4-0 | 1916 | Motor Rail Ltd. Tramcar Co | | P | St 0 |

Designed by Motor Rail Ltd

| Phoenix | | | Co Donegal Railway Joint Committee | 0-4-0T | 1928 | Atkinson, Walker | | D | St 0 |

Designed by Atkinson, Walker, GNRI. Originally built as a steam, rebuilt as a diesel.

| Kathleen | 1 | | Co Donegal Railway Joint Committee | 0-4-0 | 1906 | Robert Stephenson | | D | St 0 |
| | | | Cowan, Leitrim & Ruscommon Rly | 4-4-0 | 1887 | | s | | St 0 |

Designed by Robert Stephenson.

| | 2 | | Port Stewart Tramway | 0-4-0T | 1883 | Kitson & Co | s | | St 0 |

Designed by Kitson & Co.

| Dunluce Castle | 74 | | LMS & NCC | 4-4-0 | 1924 | North British Locomotive Co | s | | St 0 |

Designed by Fowler.

| | 30 | | Belfast & Co Down Railway | 4-4-2T | 1901 | Beyer, Peacock | s | | St 0 |

Designed by Beyer, Peacock.

| | 20 | | Guinness Railway | 0-4-0T | 1905 | Cork St Foundry | s | | St 0 |

Designed by Samuel Geoghegan.

| | | | Great Northern Railway, Ireland | 4w | 1928 | GNRI | s | | St 0 |

Designed by Howden, Meredith.

VALE OF GLAMORGAN RAILWAY

Barry, GLAMORGAN (VALE OF)

Name	Current No.	Type/Class	Origin	Wh. Arr.	Built	Builder		Op	
Pamela	3840		National Coal Board	0-6-0ST	1956	Hunslet Engine Co Ltd	s		Op 0
	5538			2-6-2T	1936	GWR	s		0

BR No. 5538. Built at Swindon.

| | 7705 | | Ely Paper Mills – Cardiff | 0-4-0ST | 1952 | Robert Stephenson, Hawthorn | s | | u |

Name	Current No.	Type/Class	Origin	Builder	Wh. Arr.	Built	Status
Bill Caddick			Manchester Ship Canal	Hudswell, Clarke & Co	0-6-0	1959	D R Op
BR No. 54279.							
	D8526		BR	BR		1960	Op
BR No. D6000.							
	54279	DMU/108				1982	Op
Built at Leeds.							
Steam Crane				Smith, Rodley		1925	Op

VALE OF RHEIDOL RAILWAY
Aberystwyth, CEREDIGION

Name	Current No.	Type/Class	Origin	Builder	Wh. Arr.	Built	Status
Owain Glyndwr	7			GWR	2-6-2T	1923	s Op
Llywelyn	8			GWR	2-6-2T	1923	s Op
Prince of Wales	9			GWR	2-6-2T	1923	s Op U
—	10			Brecon Mountain Railway	0-6-0	1987	D Op

VINTAGE CARRIAGES TRUST
Keighley, YORKSHIRE (WEST)

Name	Current No.	Type/Class	Origin	Builder	Wh. Arr.	Built	Status
Lord Mayor	176		Edmund Nuttall Contractors	Hudswell, Clarke & Co	0-4-0ST	1893	s C Op O G
MS & L Tricomposite			MS & L		4w	1876	
32.25ft in length.							
				Midland Railway	6w	1886	C Op U G
BR No. DM289677. 34ft in length.							
			East Coast Joint Stock	GNR	6w	1888	C Op U G
BR No. DE940281E. 35ft in length. Built at Doncaster. Restored externally.							
	2856			GNR	4w	1898	C Op O U G
Built at Doncaster.							
	427		Metropolitan	Metropolitan Carriage & Wagon Co	4w	1910	C Op G
54.25ft in length. Built at Birmingham.							
	465		Metropolitan	Metropolitan Carriage & Wagon Co	4w	1919	G
54.25ft in length. Built at Birmingham.							
	509		Metropolitan	Metropolitan Carriage & Wagon Co	4w	1923	C Op G
54.25ft in length. Built at Birmingham.							
	3554		SR	Metropolitan Carriage & Wagon Co	4w	1924	C Op O
BR No. 3554. 65.25ft in length. Designed by SECR, Maunsell. Built at Birmingham.							
			BR	BR	4w	1950	C O U
BR No. 1469. 67ft in length. Designed by O V Bulleid.							

Vale of Glamorgan Railway — Vintage Carriages Trust

A-Z SHOWING ROLLING STOCK

Steam Railway Directory   www.steamrailway.com

Key: Wh. Arr. = Wheel Arrangement $ = Steam   D = Diesel   E = Electric   P = Petrol   R = Rolling Stock   W = Wagon   C = Coach   Op = Operational   St = Static   O = On Display   U = Under Restoration   G = Pre Group   N = Pre Nationalisation

© HCC Publishing Ltd

Section 1b.   241

WATERCRESS LINE

Alresford, HAMPSHIRE

Name	Current No.	Type/Class	Origin	Wh. Arr.	Built	Builder			
Thomas	1			0-6-0	1954	Hunslet Engine Co Ltd	s	Op	
Douglas	10			0-6-0	1943	Hunslet Engine Co Ltd	s	Op	
	30499	LSWR		4-6-0	1920	LSWR	s	St	O G
	506	LSWR		4-6-0	1920	LSWR	s	Op	U G
James	5		SR	2-6-0	1928	SR	s	Op	N
	31806		SR	2-6-0	1928	SR	s	St	N
	31874	SECR		2-6-0	1925	SR	s		
Bodmin	34016		SR	4-6-2	1945	SR	s	Op	U
Canadian Pacific	35005		SR	4-6-2	1941	SR	s	Op	U
	41312		BR	2-6-2T	1952	BR	s		
	73096		BR	4-6-0	1955	BR	s	St	U
	76017		BR	2-6-0	1953	BR	s	St	U
Bittern	60019		LNER	4-6-2	1937	LNER	s	St	U
249 Squadron	34073		BR	4-6-2	1948	BR	s	St	U
Swanage	34105		BR	4-6-2	1950	BR	s	St	U
Shaw Savill	35009		SR	4-6-2	1942	SR	s	St U	N
British India Line	35018	MN		4-6-2	1945	SR	s	St	U
Franklin D Roosevelt	701	USATC		2-8-0	1944	American Locomotive Co	s	Op	
	D3358	BR	DE /08	0-6-0DE	1957	BR	D	Op	
	12049	BR	DE /11	0-6-0DE	1948	BR	D	Op	
	20188	BR	DE /20	Bo-Bo	1966	English Electric	D	Op	
	D5353	BR	DE /27	Bo-Bo	1961	BRCW	D	U	

Thomas – Prev. No. 3781. Located at Mid Hants Railway. Built at Leeds. Converted in 1990's by 2MT Mid-Hants Railway from 06-0ST.

Douglas – Prev. No. 2890. Owned by C Fuller. Located at Mid Hants Railway. Built at Leeds. Rebuilt in 2000.

30499 – BR No. 30499. Prev. No. 499. Owned by Urie Locomotive Society. Located at Mid Hants Railway. Built at Eastleigh.

506 – BR No. 30506. Designed by Urie. Owned by Urie Locomotive Society. Located at Mid Hants Railway. Built at Eastleigh.

James – BR No. 31625. Prev. Nos. A625, 1625. Designed by Maunsell. Located at Mid Hants Railway. Built at Ashford. Running as 'Thomas', character 'No5 James' is in red livery.

31806 – BR No. 31806. Prev. Nos. A806, 1806. Designed by Maunsell. Located at Mid Hants Railway. Built at Brighton. Previously class K (River Class) 2-6-4T.

31874 – BR No. 31874. Prev. No. A874, 1874, 1874. Designed by Maunsell. Built at Woolwich, Arsenal. Runs in red as 'No5 James' on the Mid-Hants Railway in 1990s.

Bodmin – BR No. 34016. Prev. No. 22C116. Designed by O V Bulleid. Located at Mid Hants Railway. Built at Brighton. Rebuilt in 1958 by Jarvis at Eastleigh to conventional form.

Canadian Pacific – BR No. 35005. Prev. No. 21C5. Designed by O V Bulleid. Owned by Marcus Robertson and Steam Dreams. Located at Mid Hants Railway. Built at Eastleigh. Rebuilt by Jarvis in 1959 at Eastleigh to conventional form.

41312 – BR No. 41312. Designed by Ivatt. Located at Mid Hants Railway. Built at Crewe.

73096 – BR No. 73096. Designed by R A Riddles. Located at Mid Hants Railway. Built at Derby.

76017 – BR No. 76017. Designed by R A Riddles. Owned by Standard 4 Locomotive Group. Located at Mid Hants Railway. Built at Horwich.

Bittern – BR No. 60019. Prev. Nos. LNER 4464, LNER 19. Designed by Gresley. Located at Mid Hants Railway. Built at Doncaster.

249 Squadron – BR No. 34073. Designed by O V Bulleid. Located at Mid Hants Railway. Built at Brighton.

Swanage – BR No. 34105. Designed by O V Bulleid. Owned by Light Pacific Group. Located at Mid Hants Railway. Built at Brighton.

Shaw Savill – BR No. 35009. Prev. No. SR21C9. Designed by O V Bulleid. Located at Mid Hants Railway. Built at Eastleigh. Frames and boiler at the designer outlet village, Swindon. Rebuilt from 'air-smoothed' to conventional form by Jarvis at Eastleigh in 1957.

British India Line – BR No. 35018. Prev. No. 21C18. Designed by O V Bulleid. Located at Mid Hants Railway. Built at Eastleigh. Rebuilt at Eastleigh in 1959 by Jarvis to conventional form.

Franklin D Roosevelt – Prev. No. 3278. Located at Mid Hants Railway. Built at USA. Built for D-Day, used in Italy, received from Greece as number 736-073.

D3358 – BR No. 08288. Prev. No. D3358. Located at Mid Hants Railway. Built at Derby.

12049 – BR No. 12049. Designed by English Electric, LMS. Located at Mid Hants Railway. Built at Derby.

20188 – BR No. 20188. Prev. No. D8188. Designed by English Electric. Owned by 72C Traction Group. Located at Mid Hants Railway. Built at Vulcan Foundry, Newton le Willows.

D5353 – BR No. 27007. Prev. No. D5353. Designed by BRCW. Located at Mid Hants Railway. Built at Birmingham.

Name	Current No.	Type/Class		Origin	Wh.Arr.	Built	Builder		
Captain Bill Smith RNR	D6525	DE /33		BR	Bo-Bo	1960	BRCW		D	Op

BR No. 33109. Prev. No. D6525. Designed by BRCW. Located at Mid Hants Railway. Built at Birmingham. 71A Locomotive Group.

| | D6593 | DE /33 | | BR | Bo-Bo | 1962 | BRW | D | Op |

BR No. 33208. Prev. No. 33208. Designed by BRW. Owned by 71A Locomotive Group. Located at Mid Hants Railway. Built at Birmingham.

| | 45132 | DE /45 | | BR | 1Co-Co1 | 1961 | BR | D | O |

BR No. 45132. Prev. No. DZZ. Designed by BR, Sulzer. Located at Mid Hants Railway. Built at Darby.

WELLINGTON COUNTRY PARK — Reading, BERKSHIRE

Name	Current No.	Type/Class	Origin	Wh.Arr.	Built	Builder		
Charlotte				Bo-Bo	1980	Crowhurst Engineering	D	Op

Modelled on a mining engine.

WELLS & WALSINGHAM — Wells-next-the-Sea, NORFOLK

Name	Current No.	Type/Class	Origin	Wh.Arr.	Built	Builder	
Norfolk Hero	3			2-6-0 + 0-6-2	1986	Neil Simkins	s

Designed by Neil Simkins. Owned by Wells & Walsingham Light Railway.

| **Weasel** | 2 | | | 0-6-0 | 1984 | Alan Keef Ltd | D |

Designed by T Martin. Owned by Wells & Walsingham Light Railway.

WELSH HIGHLAND RAILWAY — Porthmadog, GWYNEDD

Name	Current No.	Type/Class	Origin	Wh.Arr.	Built	Builder		
Russell				2-6-2	1906	Hunslet Engine Co Ltd	s	Op
Karen				0-4-2	1942		s	

Owned by Members Consortium.

| **Gelert** | 3050 | | | 0-4-2 | 1953 | W G Bagnall | s | Op |

Owned by Members Consortium.

| **Bagnall** | | | | 0-4-2 | 1951 | W G Bagnall | s | U |

Owned by Members Consortium.

| | 2667 | | | 2-8-2 | 1949 | Societe Franco Belge | s | U |
| **Pedemoura** | | | | 0-6-0 | 1924 | Orenstein, Koppel | s | U |

Owned by Consortium of Members.

Glaslyn	292030				1952	Ruston & Hornsby Ltd	D	Op
Kinnerley	354068				1953	Ruston & Hornsby Ltd	D	Op
	23387				1977		D	Op

Owned by Consortium of Members.

| **Eryri** | 23389 | | | | 1977 | | D | Op |

Owned by Members Consortium.

| | | | | 4 wheel | 1902 | | C | Op |

Key: Wh.Arr. = Wheel Arrangement **S** = Steam **D** = Diesel **E** = Electric **P** = Petrol **R** = Rolling Stock **W** = Wagon **C** = Coach **Op** = Operational **St** = Static **O** = On Display **U** = Under Restoration **G** = Pre Group **N** = Pre Nationalisation

Steam Railway Directory www.steamrailway.com

Watercress Line — Welsh Highland Railway

A-Z SHOWING ROLLING STOCK

© HCC Publishing Ltd

Section 1b.   243

Steam Railway Directory   www.steamrailway.com

Welsh Highland Railway — West Lancashire Light Rlwy

Notes		Built	Builder			
16ft in length.	Bogie	1980	Welsh Highland Railway Ltd		c Op	
12ft in length. Under construction.	4w		Welsh Highland Railway Ltd		c	
16ft in length.	Bogie	1981	Welsh Highland Railway Ltd		c Op	
26ft in length.	Bogie	1987	Welsh Highland Railway Ltd		c Op	U
26ft in length.	Bogie	1894	Metropolitan Carriage & Wagon Co		c Op	U
26ft in length.	Bogie	1893			c	
42	Bogie	1923	Hudson		c	

WELSHPOOL & LLANFAIR

Welshpool, POWYS

Name	Current No.	Type/Class	Origin	Wh. Arr.	Built	Builder		
Earl (The)	1			0-6-0T	1902	Beyer, Peacock	S	Op
BR No. 822. Rebuilt by the Great Western Railway in 1929.								
Countess	2			0-6-0T	1902	Beyer, Peacock	S	Op
BR No. 823.								
Chattenden	7	DM		0-6-0DM	1949	Drewry Car Co		
Dougal	8			0-4-0	1946	Andrew Barclay & Sons	D	
Sir Drefaldwyn	10		German Military	0-8-0T	1944	Societe Franco Beige	S	
Ferret	11			0-4-0	1941	Hunslet Engine Co Ltd	D	St
Joan	12		Sugar Cane, Antigua	0-6-2	1927	Kerr, Stuart & Co Ltd	S	St
	14			2-6-2	1954	Hunslet Engine Co Ltd	S	St O
Orion	5			2-6-2T	1948	Tubize	S	Op
Scooby	16	DM		0-4-0DM	1941	Hunslet Engine Co Ltd	D	Op

WEST LANCASHIRE LIGHT RLWY

Preston, LANCASHIRE

Name	Current No.	Type/Class	Origin	Wh. Arr.	Built	Builder	
Clwyd					1951	Ruston & Hornsby Ltd	D
Tawd					1943	Ruston & Hornsby Ltd	D
Irish Mail				0-4-0ST	1903	Hunslet Engine Co Ltd	S
Bradfield					1931	F C Hibberd & Co Ltd	P
Ex Liverpool Corporation Water Works.					1940	Ruston & Hornsby Ltd	D
Pathfinder					1946	Motor Rail Ltd	D
Joffre		RT		0-6-0T	1953	Hudson, Hunslet	
					1915	Kerr, Stuart & Co Ltd	S
					1946	F C Hibberd & Co Ltd	D
					1941	Ruston & Hornsby Ltd	D
					1939	R A Lister & Co Ltd	P

Name	Current No.	Type/Class	Origin	Wh.Arr.	Built	Builder			
—					1937	Baguley	P		
Mill Reef					1939	Hunslet Engine Co Ltd	D		
—					1950	Ruston & Hornsby Ltd	D		
—					1939	Motor Rail Ltd	D		
—					1964	Motor Rail Ltd	D		
—					1963		D		
Montalban				0-4-0T	1913	Orenstein, Koppel	s		
Utrillas				0-4-0T	1907	Orenstein, Koppel	s		
Jonathan				0-4-0ST	1898	Hunslet Engine Co Ltd	s		

Formerly called Bernstein.

Name	Current No.	Type/Class	Origin	Wh.Arr.	Built	Builder			
—					1949	Hudswell, Clarke & Co	D		
Dame Vera Duckworth					1959	F C Hibberd & Co Ltd	D		
—					1949	Ruston & Hornsby Ltd	D		
Stanhope				0-6-0T	1917	Chrzanow	s		
—				0-4-2T	1917	Kerr, Stuart & Co Ltd	s		

Ex Penrhyn Quarries.

Name	Current No.	Type/Class	Origin	Wh.Arr.	Built	Builder			
—				0-8-0T	1917	Henschel	s		

Ex Sena Sugar Estates, Mozambique.

WEST SOMERSET RAILWAY

Minehead, SOMERSET

Name	Current No.	Type/Class	Origin	Wh.Arr.	Built	Builder			
	53808			2-8-0	1925		s		
	3850			2-8-0	1942		s	Op	
	4160			2-6-2T	1948		s	Op	
	4561			2-6-2T	1924		s	Op	O
	5542			2-6-2T	1928		s	Op	
	6412			0-6-0PT	1934		s	Op	
Dinmore Manor	7820			4-6-0	1950		s	Op	
Odney Manor	7828			4-6-0	1950		s	Op	
Braughton	34046			4-6-2	1946		s	Op	U
	D2119	DM/03	BR	0-6-0DM	1959		D	Op	
	D2133	DM/03	BR	0-6-0DM	1959		D	Op	
	D2271	DM/04	BR	0-6-0DM	1952		D	Op	
	D3462		BR	0-6-0DE	1957		D	Op	
	D9526	DH/14	BR	0-6-0DH	1964		D	Op	U
	33048		BR	Bo-Bo	1961		D	Op	
	D7017		BR	B-B	1962		D	Op	U
	D7018		BR	B-B	1964		D	Op	
	D7523		BR	Bo-Bo	1963		D	Op	U

Key: Wh.Arr. = Wheel Arrangement **S** = Steam **D** = Diesel **E** = Electric **P** = Petrol **R** = Rolling Stock **C** = Coach **W** = Wagon **Op** = Operational **St** = Static **O** = On Display **U** = Under Restoration **G** = Pre Group **M** = Pre Nationalisation

West Somerset Railway — Windmill Farm Railway

Steam Railway Directory www.steamrailway.com

Western Campaigner

No.	Origin	Wh. Arr.	Built	Builder			
D1010	BR	C - C	1962			Op	
50413			1957				U
51352			1959		D	Op	
51376	BR		1959		D	Op	
51663	BR		1960		D	Op	
51852	BR		1960		D	Op	
51887	BR		1960		D		
59505			1959				
59678	BR		1960				

Name		Wh. Arr.	Built	Builder			
Isabel		0-6-0ST	1919	Peckett & Sons	s		
Kilmersdon		0-4-0ST	1929		s		
24	DM	4wDM	1941	Ruston	D	Op	U
16		4wDM	1937	Ruston	D	Op	U
501	DM	0-6-0DM	1964	Sentinel	D	Op	U
512	DM	0-4-0DE	1954	Brush Electrical Engineering, Bagnall	D		O
5193		0-4-0DE	1954	Brush Electrical Engineering, Bagnall	D		O
56097		2-6-2T	1934				U
56169			1957				U

WESTON PARK RAILWAY

Telford, SHROPSHIRE

Name	Current No.	Type/Class	Origin	Wh. Arr.	Built	Builder			
—		DH		4-8-2 + 2-8-4	2000	B & J Whalley (Engineering)	D	Op	
13.5ft in length.									
—				4-8-2 + 2-8-4	1975		s	Op	
19.5ft in length.				Op					
—					1975	Neil Simkins, Milner Engineering	s		

19.5ft in length. Owned by National Railway Museum.

WINDMILL FARM RAILWAY

Ormskirk, LANCASHIRE

Name	Current No.	Type/Class	Origin	Wh. Arr.	Built	Builder			
Cagney	44			4-4-0	1902		s		
Owned by S Townsend.									
Blue Pacific	4			4-6-2	1935	N Guinness	s		
In store.									
Whippet Quick		DM		4w-4DM	1935	R A Lister & Co Ltd	D	Op	
Owned by A Moss.									
Silver Jubilee	2	DM		4-6-4DM	1935	Smith, Rodley	D	Op	
Owned by C Gluyas.									
Gwril				4wPM	1943	R A Lister & Co Ltd	D	Op	
Owned by A Moss.									

Name		Current No.	Type/Class	Wh.Arr.	Built	Builder		
Prince William		5751		4-6-2	1946	Guest	S	Op
Owned by P Kelly.								
Princess Anne				4-6-2DE	1948	H Barlow	D	Op
Owned by S Bell.								
Duke of Edinburgh				4-6-2DE	1950	H Barlow	D	Op
Owned by A Moss.								
Katie				2-4-2	1954	Guest	S	U
Owned by A Moss.								
Battison	DH			2-6-4DH	1958	S Battison	D	
Owned by A Moss.								
Flying Scotsman	DH	4472		4-6-2DH	1972	Artisair	D	U
Owned by A Moss. In store.								
—		14		2w-2PM	1985	G Walker	P	
Owned by S Bell. In store.								
City of London	DH	2870		4-6-0DH	1987	Jubilee, Volante	D	Op
Owned by Q Jones.								
Joe Brown	DH	D6353		4w-4wDH	1998	J Brown	D	Op
Owned by A Moss.								
Bar Stool (The)				2w-2PM	1989	A Moss	P	Op
Owned by A Moss. In store.								

YEOVIL RAILWAY CENTRE

Yeovil, SOMERSET

Name	Current No.	Type/Class	Origin	Wh.Arr.	Built	Builder		
River Yeo	20188		BR	Bo-Bo	1967	English Electric	D	Op
Currently at Mid Hants Railway for main line certification.								
Pectin	1			0-4-0ST	1921	Peckett & Sons	S	Op

Windmill Farm Railway — Yeovil Railway Centre

A-Z SHOWING ROLLING STOCK

By County

SECTION 2

*This section helps to locate
a Steam Railway or Museum
by a county of your choice.
This is the conventional
way most directories display
their information.
The counties are also
categorised by Country.*

e.g. England, Staffordshire

Once you have located a
railway/museum using this
section you can then refer
to the railway or museum's
detailed profile in section 1.

ENGLAND

BEDFORDSHIRE

GREAT WHIPSNADE RAILWAY
Dunstable

LEIGHTON BUZZARD RAILWAY
Leighton Buzzard

BERKSHIRE

WELLINGTON COUNTRY PARK
Reading

BRISTOL

AVON VALLEY RAILWAY
Bristol

BRISTOL HARBOUR RAILWAY
Bristol

BUCKINGHAMSHIRE

BUCKINGHAMSHIRE RLWY CTRE
Aylesbury

CAMBRIDGESHIRE

NENE VALLEY RAILWAY
Peterborough

RAILWORLD
Peterborough

CHANNEL ISLANDS

ALDERNEY RAILWAY
St. Anne

PALLOT STEAM MUSEUM
Jersey

CHESHIRE

BROOKSIDE MINIATURE
Poynton

MOSELEY RAILWAY TRUST
Stockport

RAILWAY AGE
Crewe

CLEVELAND

TEESIDE SMALL GAUGE RAILWAY
Stockton-on-Tees

CORNWALL

BODMIN & WENFORD RAILWAY
Bodmin

LAPPA VALLEY STEAM RAILWAY
Newquay

LAUNCESTON STEAM RAILWAY
Launceston

COUNTY DURHAM

BEAMISH
Stanley

DARLINGTON RAILWAY CENTRE
Darlington

TANFIELD RAILWAY
Gateshead

TIMOTHY HACKWORTH
Shildon

CUMBRIA

LAKESIDE & HAVERTHWAITE RLWY
Ulverston

RAVENGLASS & ESKDALE
Ravenglass

SOUTH TYNEDALE RAILWAY
Alston

DERBYSHIRE

BARROW HILL ROUNDHOUSE
Chesterfield

DERBY INDUSTRIAL MUSEUM
Derby

MARKEATON PARK LIGHT RAILWAY
Derby

MIDLAND RAILWAY CENTRE
Ripley

NATIONAL TRAMWAY MUSEUM
Matlock

PEAK RAIL
Matlock

DEVON

BEER HEIGHTS
Seaton

BICTON WOODLAND RAILWAY
Budleigh Salterton

BIDEFORD RAILWAY MUSEUM
Bideford

DARTMOOR RAILWAY
Okehampton

DEVON RAILWAY CENTRE
Tiverton

DINGLES STEAM VILLAGE
Lifton

EXMOOR STEAM RAILWAY
Barnstaple

GORSE BLOSSOM MINIATURE
Newton Abbot

LYNTON & BARNSTAPLE RAILWAY
Barnstaple

PAIGNTON & DARTMOUTH RAILWAY
Paignton

PLYM VALLEY RAILWAY
Plymouth

SOUTH DEVON RAILWAY
Buckfastleigh

DORSET

SWANAGE RAILWAY
Swanage

ESSEX

AUDLEY END MINIATURE RAILWAY
Saffron Walden

BARLEYLANDS MINIATURE RAILWAY
Billericay

COLNE VALLEY RAILWAY
Halstead

EAST ANGLIAN RAILWAY MUSEUM
Colchester

MANGAPPS RAILWAY MUSEUM
Burnham-on-Crouch

MARDYKE MINIATURE RAILWAY
Rainham

GLOUCESTERSHIRE

DEAN FOREST RAILWAY
Lydney

GLOUCESTERSHIRE WARWICKSHIRE
Cheltenham

GREAT WESTERN RAILWAY MUSEUM
Coleford

NATIONAL WATERWAYS MUSEUM
Gloucester

NORTH GLOUCESTERSHIRE RAILWAY
Cheltenham

PERRYGROVE RAILWAY
Coleford

WINCHCOMBE RAILWAY
Cheltenham

HAMPSHIRE

EASTLEIGH LAKESIDE RAILWAY
Eastleigh

HOLLYCOMBE STEAM COLLECTION
Liphook

IRCHESTER NARROW GAUGE MUSEUM
Wellingborough

MOORS VALLEY RAILWAY
Ringwood

ROYAL VICTORIA RAILWAY
Southampton

WATERCRESS LINE
Alresford

ISLE OF MAN

GROUDLE GLEN RAILWAY
Douglas

ISLE OF MAN RAILWAY
Douglas

SNAEFELL MOUNTAIN RAILWAY
Douglas

ISLE OF WIGHT

ISLE OF WIGHT STEAM RAILWAY
Ryde

KENT

BREDGAR & WORMSHILL
Sittingbourne

EAST KENT LIGHT RAILWAY
Dover

KENT & EAST SUSSEX RAILWAY
Tenterden

ROMNEY HYTHE & DYMCHURCH
New Romney

SITTINGBOURNE & KEMSLEY
Sittingbourne

SPA VALLEY RAILWAY
Tunbridge Wells

LANCASHIRE

EAST LANCASHIRE RAILWAY
Bury

ST ANNES MINI RAILWAY
Lytham St. Annes

WEST LANCASHIRE LIGHT RLWY
Preston

WINDMILL FARM RAILWAY
Ormskirk

LEICESTERSHIRE

ABBEY PUMPING STATION
Leicester

CADEBY LIGHT RAILWAY
Hinckley

GREAT CENTRAL RAILWAY
Loughborough

SNIBSTON DISCOVERY PARK
Coalville

LINCOLNSHIRE (NORTH EAST)

CLEETHORPES LIGHT RAILWAY
Cleethorpes

LINCOLNSHIRE WOLDS RAILWAY
Grimsby

LINCOLNSHIRE (NORTH)

APPLEBY-FRODINGHAM RAILWAY
Brigg

LONDON (GREATER)

GREAT COCKCROW RAILWAY
Chertsey

KEW BRIDGE STEAM MUSEUM
Brentford

LONDON TRANSPORT MUSEUM
London

OLD STATION MUSEUM
London

RUISLIP LIDO RAILWAY
Ruislip

SCIENCE MUSEUM
Kensington

MANCHESTER (GREATER)

MUSEUM OF SCIENCE & INDUSTRY
Manchester

MIDLANDS (WEST)

CHASEWATER RAILWAY
Walsall

HOLLYBUSH GARDEN CENTRE
Wolverhampton

TYSELEY LOCOMOTIVE WORKS
Birmingham

VINTAGE TRAINS
Birmingham

NORFOLK

BRESSINGHAM STEAM
Diss

BURE VALLEY RAILWAY
Norwich

FORNCETT INDUSTRIAL MUSEUM
Norwich

MID-NORFOLK RAILWAY
Dereham

NORTH NORFOLK RAILWAY
Sheringham

WELLS & WALSINGHAM
Wells-next-the-Sea

NORTHAMPTONSHIRE

NIRT
Northampton

NORTHAMPTON & LAMPORT RAILWAY
Northampton

RUSHDEN HISTORICAL TNSPRT SOC
Rushden

NORTHUMBERLAND

HEATHERSLAW LIGHT RAILWAY
Cornhill-on-Tweed

NOTTINGHAMSHIRE

NOTTINGHAM TRANSPORT CTRE
Ruddington

OXFORDSHIRE

CHINNOR & PRINCES RISBOROUGH
Princes Risborough

CHOLSEY & WALLINGFORD RAILWAY
Wallingford

DIDCOT RAILWAY CENTRE
Didcot

RUTLAND

RUTLAND RAILWAY MUSEUM
Oakham

SHROPSHIRE

BLISTSHILL VICTORIAN TOWN
Telford

CAMBRIAN RAILWAY SOCIETY
Oswestry

TELFORD STEAM RAILWAY
Telford

WESTON PARK RAILWAY
Telford

SOMERSET

EAST SOMERSET RAILWAY
Shepton Mallet

GARTELL LIGHT RAILWAY
Templecombe

SOMERSET & DORSET RAILWAY
Watchet

WEST SOMERSET RAILWAY
Minehead

YEOVIL RAILWAY CENTRE
Yeovil

STAFFORDSHIRE

AMERTON RAILWAY
Stafford

CHURNET VALLEY RAILWAY
Cheddleton

FOXFIELD STEAM RAILWAY
Stoke-on-Trent

HILCOTE VALLEY RAILWAY
Stafford

RUDYARD LAKE RAILWAY
Leek

SUFFOLK

EAST ANGLIA TRANSPORT MUSEUM
Lowestoft

MID-SUFFOLK LIGHT RAILWAY
Stowmarket

SURREY

OLD KILN LIGHT RAILWAY
Farnham

SUSSEX (EAST)

BLUEBELL RAILWAY
Uckfield

LAVENDER LINE
Uckfield

ROTHER VALLEY RAILWAY
Robertsbridge

SUSSEX (WEST)

AMBERLEY WORKING MUSEUM
Arundel

LITTLEHAMPTON MINIATURE RLWY
Littlehampton

SOUTH DOWNS LIGHT RAILWAY
Pulborough

TYNE AND WEAR

BOWES RAILWAY
Gateshead

MONKWEARMOUTH STATION MUSEUM
Sunderland

NORTH TYNESIDE STEAM RAILWAY
North Shields

WARWICKSHIRE

BATTLEFIELD LINE
Nuneaton

WILTSHIRE

STEAM
Swindon

SWINDON & CRICKLADE RAILWAY
Swindon

WORCESTERSHIRE

KIDDERMINSTER RAILWAY MUSEUM
Kidderminster

SEVERN VALLEY RAILWAY
Bewdley

YORKSHIRE (EAST)

MUSEUM OF ARMY TRANSPORT
Beverley

YORKSHIRE (NORTH)

DERWENT VALLEY
York

EMBSAY & BOLTON ABBEY RLWY
Skipton

NATIONAL RAILWAY MUSEUM
York

NORTH YORKSHIRE MOORS RAILWAY
Pickering

YORKSHIRE (SOUTH)

ELSECAR HERITAGE CENTRE
Barnsley

SOUTH YORKSHIRE RAILWAY
Sheffield

YORKSHIRE (WEST)

ABBEY LIGHT RAILWAY
Leeds

ARMLEY MILLS
Leeds

KEIGHLEY & WORTH VALLEY
Keighley

KIRKLEES LIGHT RAILWAY
Huddersfield

MIDDLETON RAILWAY
Leeds

VINTAGE CARRIAGES TRUST
Keighley

IRELAND

COUNTY DONEGAL

DONEGAL RAILWAY HERITAGE CTRE
Donegal

FINTOWN & GLENTIES RAILWAY
Glenties

COUNTY KERRY

TRALEE & DINGLE RAILWAY
Tralee

COUNTY LEITRIM

CAVAN & LEITRIM RAILWAY
Dromod

COUNTY LOAIS

IRISH STEAM PRESERVATION SOC
Stradbally

COUNTY TIPPERARY

IRISH TRACTION GROUP
Carrick-on-Suir

NORTHERN IRELAND

COUNTY ANTRIM

GIANTS CAUSEWAY & BUSHMILLS
Bushmills

RPSI
Whitehead

COUNTY DOWN

DOWNPATRICK & ARDGLASS
Downpatrick

ULSTER FOLK & TRANSPORT
Holywood

COUNTY LONDONDERRY

FOYLE VALLEY RAILWAY CENTRE
Londonderry

SCOTLAND

ABERDEENSHIRE

ALFORD VALLEY RAILWAY
Alford

ANGUS

CALEDONIAN RAILWAY
Brechin

KERR MINIATURE RAILWAY
Arbroath

ARGYLL AND BUTE

MULL RAILWAY
Isle of Mull

AYRSHIRE

SCOTTISH RAILWAY CENTRE
Ayr

FIFE

ST ANDREWS
St. Andrews

GLASGOW (CITY OF)

GLASGOW MUSEUM OF TRANSPORT
Glasgow

HIGHLANDS

GLENFINNAN STATION MUSEUM
Glenfinnan

STRATHSPEY RAILWAY
Aviemore

LANARKSHIRE

LEADHILLS & WANLOCKHEAD
Biggar

LANARKSHIRE (NORTH)

SUMMERLEE HERITAGE PK
Coatbridge

LOTHIAN (EAST)

PRESTONGRANGE INDUSTRIAL
Prestonpans

LOTHIAN (WEST)

ALMOND VALLEY HERITAGE TRUST
Livingston

BO'NESS & KINNEIL RAILWAY
Bo'ness

MORAY

KEITH & DUFFTOWN RAILWAY
Keith

WALES

CARMARTHENSHIRE

GWILI RAILWAY
Carmarthen

TEIFI VALLEY RAILWAY
Newcastle Emlyn

CEREDIGION

VALE OF RHEIDOL RAILWAY
Aberystwyth

CONWY

CONWY VALLEY
Betws-y-Coed

DENBIGHSHIRE

GOLDEN VALLEY LIGHT RAILWAY
Ripley

LLANGOLLEN RAILWAY
Llangollen

RHYL MINIATURE RAILWAY
Rhyl

GLAMORGAN (VALE OF)

VALE OF GLAMORGAN RAILWAY
Barry

GWYNEDD

BALA LAKE RAILWAY
Bala

FAIRBOURNE & BARMOUTH
Fairbourne

FFESTINIOG RAILWAY
Porthmadog

INDUSTRIAL RAILWAY MUSEUM
Bangor

LLANBERIS LAKE RAILWAY
Caernarfon

NARROW GAUGE RAILWAY MUSEUM
Tywyn

SNOWDON MOUNTAIN RAILWAY
Caernarfon

TALYLLYN RAILWAY
Tywyn

WELSH HIGHLAND RAILWAY
Caernarfon

WELSH HIGHLAND RAILWAY
Porthmadog

WELSH SLATE MUSEUM
Caernarfon

MERTHYR TYDFIL

BRECON MOUNTAIN RAILWAY
Merthyr Tydfil

POWYS

CORRIS RAILWAY MUSEUM
Machynlleth

WELSHPOOL & LLANFAIR
Welshpool

SWANSEA

SWANSEA INDUSTRIAL MUSEUM
Swansea

SWANSEA VALE RAILWAY
Swansea

TORFAEN

GRIFFITHSTOWN RAILWAY MUSEUM
Pontypool

PONTYPOOL & BLAENAVON RAILWAY
Blaenavon

By COUNTY by COUNTRY

Ceredigion — Torfaen

A-Z of Stations

SECTION 3

*With details showing their
location.*

**e.g. Cheddleton, Churnet Valley
          Railway, Staffordshire, England**

Once you have located a
railway/museum using this
section you can then refer
to the railway or museum's
detailed profile in section 1.

ABERGYNOLWYN, TALYLLYN RAILWAY, **Gwynedd,** Wales.

ABERYSTWYTH, VALE OF RHEIDOL RAILWAY, **Ceredigion,** Wales.

ALFORD, ALFORD VALLEY RAILWAY, **Aberdeenshire,** Scotland.

ALRESFORD, WATERCRESS LINE, **Hampshire,** England.

ALSTON, SOUTH TYNEDALE RAILWAY, **Cumbria,** England.

ALTON, WATERCRESS LINE, **Hampshire,** England.

AMERTON STATION, AMERTON RAILWAY, **Staffordshire,** England.

ANDREWS HOUSE, TANFIELD RAILWAY, **County Durham,** England.

ARLEY, SEVERN VALLEY RAILWAY, **Worcestershire,** England.

ASHEY, ISLE OF WIGHT STEAM RAILWAY, **Isle of Wight,** England.

AVIEMORE, STRATHSPEY RAILWAY, **Highlands,** Scotland.

AVIEMORE (SPEYSIDE) - CLOSED, STRATHSPEY RAILWAY, **Highlands,** Scotland.

AYLSHAM, BURE VALLEY RAILWAY, **Norfolk,** England.

BALA, BALA LAKE RAILWAY, **Gwynedd,** Wales.

BALLASALLA, ISLE OF MAN RAILWAY, **Isle of Man,** England.

BALLYARD, TRALEE & DINGLE RAILWAY, **County Kerry,** Ireland.

BARRY ISLAND, VALE OF GLAMORGAN RAILWAY, **Glamorgan (Vale of),** Wales.

BEACH HALT, FAIRBOURNE & BARMOUTH, **Gwynedd,** Wales.

BECCONSALL, WEST LANCASHIRE LIGHT RLWY, **Lancashire,** England.

BENNY HALT, LAPPA VALLEY STEAM RAILWAY, **Cornwall,** England.

BERWYN, LLANGOLLEN RAILWAY, **Denbighshire,** Wales.

BEWDLEY, SEVERN VALLEY RAILWAY, **Worcestershire,** England.

BIRKHILL, BO'NESS & KINNEIL RAILWAY, **Lothian (West),** Scotland.

BISHOPS LYDEARD, WEST SOMERSET RAILWAY, **Somerset,** England.

BITTON, AVON VALLEY RAILWAY, **Bristol,** England.

BLAENAUFFEST, FFESTINIOG RAILWAY, **Gwynedd,** Wales.

BLEDLOW BRIDGE HALT, CHINNOR & PRINCES RISBOROUGH, **Oxfordshire,** England.

BLENNERVILLE, TRALEE & DINGLE RAILWAY, **County Kerry,** Ireland.

BLUE ANCHOR, WEST SOMERSET RAILWAY, **Somerset,** England.

BLUNSDON, SWINDON & CRICKLADE RAILWAY, **Wiltshire,** England.

BOAT OF GARTEN, STRATHSPEY RAILWAY, **Highlands,** Scotland.

BODIAM, KENT & EAST SUSSEX RAILWAY, **Kent,** England.

BODMIN GENERAL, BODMIN & WENFORD RAILWAY, **Cornwall,** England.

BODMIN PARKWAY STATION, BODMIN & WENFORD RAILWAY, **Cornwall,** England.

BOLTON ABBEY, EMBSAY & BOLTON ABBEY RLWY, **Yorkshire (North),** England.

BO'NESS, BO'NESS & KINNEIL RAILWAY, **Lothian (West),** Scotland.

BONTNEWYDD, WELSH HIGHLAND RAILWAY, **Gwynedd,** Wales.

BOOT FAIR, BARLEYLANDS MINIATURE RAILWAY, **Essex,** England.

BOSCARNE JUNCTION, BODMIN & WENFORD RAILWAY, **Cornwall,** England.

BOSTON LODGE HALT, FFESTINIOG RAILWAY, **Gwynedd,** Wales.

BRAMPTON, BURE VALLEY RAILWAY, **Norfolk,** England.

BRANDS SIDINGS, GOLDEN VALLEY LIGHT RAILWAY, **Denbighshire,** Wales.

BRAYE ROAD, ALDERNEY RAILWAY, **Channel Islands,** England.

BRECHIN, CALEDONIAN RAILWAY, **Angus,** Scotland.

BRIDGE OF DUN, CALEDONIAN RAILWAY, **Angus,** Scotland.

BRIDGE ROAD, ABBEY LIGHT RAILWAY, **Yorkshire (West),** England.

BRIDGNORTH, SEVERN VALLEY RAILWAY, **Worcestershire,** England.

BRISTOL INDUSTRIAL MUSEUM, BRISTOL HARBOUR RAILWAY, **Bristol,** England.

BRONWYDD ARMS, GWILI RAILWAY, **Carmarthenshire,** Wales.

BROOKSIDE CENTRAL, BROOKSIDE MINIATURE, **Cheshire,** England.

BROOMHILL, STRATHSPEY RAILWAY, **Highlands,** Scotland.

BROWNHILLS WEST, CHASEWATER RAILWAY, **Midlands (West),** England.

BRYNGLAS, TALYLLYN RAILWAY, **Gwynedd,** Wales.

BUCKFASTLEIGH, SOUTH DEVON RAILWAY, **Devon,** England.

BUNGALOW, SNAEFELL MOUNTAIN RAILWAY, **Isle of Man,** England.

BURLESCOMBE, DIDCOT RAILWAY CENTRE, **Oxfordshire,** England.

BURLEY CROSSING, SITTINGBOURNE & KEMSLEY, **Kent,** England.

BURY, EAST LANCASHIRE RAILWAY, **Lancashire,** England.

BUSHMILLS, GIANTS CAUSEWAY & BUSHMILLS, **County Antrim,** Northern Ireland.

BUTTERLEY, MIDLAND RAILWAY CENTRE, **Derbyshire,** England.

BUTTERLEY PARK, GOLDEN VALLEY LIGHT RAILWAY, **Denbighshire,** Wales.

BUXTON, BURE VALLEY RAILWAY, **Norfolk,** England.

CAERNARFON, WELSH HIGHLAND RAILWAY, **Gwynedd,** Wales.

CALAFERNIA CROSSING, NORTH GLOUCESTERSHIRE RAILWAY, **Gloucestershire,** England.

CAMPBELLS PLATFORM, FFESTINIOG RAILWAY, **Gwynedd,** Wales.

CARROG, LLANGOLLEN RAILWAY, **Denbighshire,** Wales.

CASTLE CAEREINION, WELSHPOOL & LLANFAIR, **Powys,** Wales.

CASTLE HEDINGHAM, COLNE VALLEY RAILWAY, **Essex,** England.

CASTLETOWN, ISLE OF MAN RAILWAY, **Isle of Man,** England.

CAUSEY ARCH, TANFIELD RAILWAY, **County Durham,** England.

CAVERSWALL RD STATION, FOXFIELD STEAM RAILWAY, **Staffordshire,** England.

CEI LLYDAN, LLANBERIS LAKE RAILWAY, **Gwynedd,** Wales.

CHAPEL ROAD, ROYAL VICTORIA RAILWAY, **Hampshire,** England.

CHARTLEY RD, AMERTON RAILWAY, **Staffordshire,** England.

CHASETOWN, CHASEWATER RAILWAY, **Midlands (West),** England.

CHASEWATER HEATHS, CHASEWATER RAILWAY, **Midlands (West),** England.

CHEDDLETON, CHURNET VALLEY RAILWAY, **Staffordshire,** England.

CHINNOR STATION, CHINNOR & PRINCES RISBOROUGH, **Oxfordshire,** England.

CHOLSEY, CHOLSEY & WALLINGFORD RAILWAY, **Oxfordshire,** England.

CHURSTON, PAIGNTON & DARTMOUTH RAILWAY, **Devon,** England.

CLAYTON WEST, KIRKLEES LIGHT RAILWAY, **Yorkshire (West),** England.

CLOGWYN, SNOWDON MOUNTAIN RAILWAY, **Gwynedd,** Wales.

COCKCROW HILL, GREAT COCKCROW RAILWAY, **London (Greater),** England.

COLBY, ISLE OF MAN RAILWAY, **Isle of Man,** England.

COLESLOGGETT, BODMIN & WENFORD RAILWAY, **Cornwall,** England.

COLTISHALL, BURE VALLEY RAILWAY, **Norfolk,** England.

CONSALL, CHURNET VALLEY RAILWAY, **Staffordshire,** England.

CORFE CASTLE, SWANAGE RAILWAY, **Dorset,** England.

CORRIS, CORRIS RAILWAY MUSEUM, **Powys,** Wales.

CRAIGNURE, MULL RAILWAY, **Argyll and Bute,** Scotland.

CRANMORE, EAST SOMERSET RAILWAY, **Somerset,** England.

CRANMORE WEST, EAST SOMERSET RAILWAY, **Somerset,** England.

CREATE CENTRE, BRISTOL HARBOUR RAILWAY, **Bristol,** England.

CROWCOMBE HEATHFIELD, WEST SOMERSET RAILWAY, **Somerset,** England.

CUCKOOS NEST, KIRKLEES LIGHT RAILWAY, **Yorkshire (West),** England.

CYFRONYDD, WELSHPOOL & LLANFAIR, **Powys,** Wales.

DAMENS, KEIGHLEY & WORTH VALLEY, **Yorkshire (West),** England.

DANYCOED HALT, GWILI RAILWAY, **Carmarthenshire,** Wales.

DARLEY DALE, PEAK RAIL, **Derbyshire,** England.

DDUALLT, FFESTINIOG RAILWAY, **Gwynedd,** Wales.

DEESIDE HALT, LLANGOLLEN RAILWAY, **Denbighshire,** Wales.

DELPH, WEST LANCASHIRE LIGHT RLWY, **Lancashire,** England.

A-Z of STATIONS

Castletown — Delph

DEREHAM, MID-NORFOLK RAILWAY, **Norfolk,** England.

DEVILS BRIDGE, VALE OF RHEIDOL RAILWAY, **Ceredigion,** Wales.

DIDCOT HALT, DIDCOT RAILWAY CENTRE, **Oxfordshire,** England.

DILHORNE PARK STATION, FOXFIELD STEAM RAILWAY, **Staffordshire,** England.

DINAS, WELSH HIGHLAND RAILWAY, **Gwynedd,** Wales.

DOLGOCH, TALYLLYN RAILWAY, **Gwynedd,** Wales.

DONIFORD HALT, WEST SOMERSET RAILWAY, **Somerset,** England.

DOUGLAS, ISLE OF MAN RAILWAY, **Isle of Man,** England.

DOWNPATRICK, DOWNPATRICK & ARDGLASS, **County Down,** Northern Ireland.

DROMOD, CAVAN & LEITRIM RAILWAY, **County Leitrim,** Ireland.

DRUMMUIR, KEITH & DUFFTOWN RAILWAY, **Moray,** Scotland.

DUFFTOWN, KEITH & DUFFTOWN RAILWAY, **Moray,** Scotland.

DUNGENESS, ROMNEY HYTHE & DYMCHURCH, **Kent,** England.

DUNSTER, WEST SOMERSET RAILWAY, **Somerset,** England.

DYMCHURCH, ROMNEY HYTHE & DYMCHURCH, **Kent,** England.

EAST TANFIELD, TANFIELD RAILWAY, **County Durham,** England.

EAST WHEAL ROSE, LAPPA VALLEY STEAM RAILWAY, **Cornwall,** England.

EASTLEIGH PARKWAY, EASTLEIGH LAKESIDE RAILWAY, **Hampshire,** England.

EMBSAY, EMBSAY & BOLTON ABBEY RLWY, **Yorkshire (North),** England.

ESKDALE (DALEGARTH), RAVENGLASS & ESKDALE, **Cumbria,** England.

ETAL CASTLE, HEATHERSLAW LIGHT RAILWAY, **Northumberland,** England.

EVERGLADES JUNCTION, GREAT COCKCROW RAILWAY, **London (Greater),** England.

EYTHORNE, EAST KENT LIGHT RAILWAY, **Kent,** England.

FAIRBOURNE, FAIRBOURNE & BARMOUTH, **Gwynedd,** Wales.

FARM MUSEUM, BARLEYLANDS MINIATURE RAILWAY, **Essex,** England.

FERRY MEADOWS, NENE VALLEY RAILWAY, **Cambridgeshire,** England.

FORT WILLIAM, GLENFINNAN STATION MUSEUM, **Highlands,** Scotland.

FURNACE SIDINGS PLATFORM, PONTYPOOL & BLAENAVON RAILWAY, **Torfaen,** Wales.

GALFA, WELSHPOOL & LLANFAIR, **Powys,** Wales.

GELERTS FARM HALT, WELSH HIGHLAND RAILWAY, **Gwynedd,** Wales.

GIANTS CAUSEWAY, GIANTS CAUSEWAY & BUSHMILLS, **County Antrim,** Northern Ireland.

GILFACH DDU, LLANBERIS LAKE RAILWAY, **Gwynedd,** Wales.

GLENFINNAN, GLENFINNAN STATION MUSEUM, **Highlands,** Scotland.

GLENGONNAR HALT, LEADHILLS & WANLOCKHEAD, **Lanarkshire,** Scotland.

GLYNDYFRDWY, LLANGOLLEN RAILWAY, **Denbighshire,** Wales.

GOATHLAND, NORTH YORKSHIRE MOORS RAILWAY, **Yorkshire (North),** England.

GOLF HALT, FAIRBOURNE & BARMOUTH, **Gwynedd,** Wales.

GOODRINGTON, PAIGNTON & DARTMOUTH RAILWAY, **Devon,** England.

GOTHERINGTON, GLOUCESTERSHIRE WARWICKSHIRE, **Gloucestershire,** England.

GREEN LANE, GREAT COCKCROW RAILWAY, **London (Greater),** England.

GROOMBRIDGE, SPA VALLEY RAILWAY, **Kent,** England.

GROSMONT, NORTH YORKSHIRE MOORS RAILWAY, **Yorkshire (North),** England.

GROUDLE LHEN COAN, GROUDLE GLEN RAILWAY, **Isle of Man,** England.

HALFWAY HALT, CLEETHORPES LIGHT RAILWAY, **Lincolnshire (North East),** England.

HAMMERSMITH, MIDLAND RAILWAY CENTRE, **Derbyshire,** England.

HAMPTON LOADE, SEVERN VALLEY RAILWAY, **Worcestershire,** England.

HARDWICK CENTRAL, GREAT COCKCROW RAILWAY, **London (Greater),** England.

HARMANS CROSS, SWANAGE RAILWAY, **Dorset,** England.

HAUGHTON, ALFORD VALLEY RAILWAY, **Aberdeenshire,** Scotland.

HAUGHTON PARK, ALFORD VALLEY RAILWAY, **Aberdeenshire,** Scotland.

HAVENSTREET, ISLE OF WIGHT STEAM RAILWAY, **Isle of Wight,** England.

HAVERTHWAITE, LAKESIDE & HAVERTHWAITE RLWY, **Cumbria,** England.

HAWORTH, KEIGHLEY & WORTH VALLEY, **Yorkshire (West),** England.

HAYES KNOLL, SWINDON & CRICKLADE RAILWAY, **Wiltshire,** England.

HEATHERSLAW, HEATHERSLAW LIGHT RAILWAY, **Northumberland,** England.

HEMINGFIELD BASIN, ELSECAR HERITAGE CENTRE, **Yorkshire (South),** England.

HENIARTH, WELSHPOOL & LLANFAIR, **Powys,** Wales.

HENLLAN, TEIFI VALLEY RAILWAY, **Carmarthenshire,** Wales.

HERMITAGE RAILWAY, BICTON WOODLAND RAILWAY, **Devon,** England.

HEYWOOD, PERRYGROVE RAILWAY, **Gloucestershire,** England.

HIGH ROCKS, SPA VALLEY RAILWAY, **Kent,** England.

HIGHLEY, SEVERN VALLEY RAILWAY, **Worcestershire,** England.

HOLLYBUSH CENTRAL, HOLLYBUSH GARDEN CENTRE, **Midlands (West),** England.

HOLLYCOMBE, HOLLYCOMBE STEAM COLLECTION, **Hampshire,** England.

HOLT, NORTH NORFOLK RAILWAY, **Norfolk,** England.

HOOD ROAD, VALE OF GLAMORGAN RAILWAY, **Glamorgan (Vale of),** Wales.

HORSEHAY & DAWLEY, TELFORD STEAM RAILWAY, **Shropshire,** England.

HOSPITAL FIELD HALT, KERR MINIATURE RAILWAY, **Angus,** Scotland.

A-Z of STATIONS

Glyndyfrdwy — Hospital Field Halt

HOSTED KEYNES, BLUEBELL RAILWAY, **Sussex (East),** England.

HUNTHOUSE WOOD, RUDYARD LAKE RAILWAY, **Staffordshire,** England.

HYTHE, ROMNEY HYTHE & DYMCHURCH, **Kent,** England.

INGROW (WEST), KEIGHLEY & WORTH VALLEY, **Yorkshire (West),** England.

IRTON ROAD, RAVENGLASS & ESKDALE, **Cumbria,** England.

IRWELL VALE, EAST LANCASHIRE RAILWAY, **Lancashire,** England.

ISFIELD, LAVENDER LINE, **Sussex (East),** England.

KEIGHLEY, KEIGHLEY & WORTH VALLEY, **Yorkshire (West),** England.

KEITH TOWN, KEITH & DUFFTOWN RAILWAY, **Moray,** Scotland.

KELLING HEATH PARK HALT, NORTH NORFOLK RAILWAY, **Norfolk,** England.

KEMSLEY DOWN, SITTINGBOURNE & KEMSLEY, **Kent,** England.

KIDDERMINSTER, SEVERN VALLEY RAILWAY, **Worcestershire,** England.

KINGSCOTE, BLUEBELL RAILWAY, **Sussex (East),** England.

KINGSLEY & FROGHALL, CHURNET VALLEY RAILWAY, **Staffordshire,** England.

KINGSMERE, MOORS VALLEY RAILWAY, **Hampshire,** England.

KINGSWAY, CLEETHORPES LIGHT RAILWAY, **Lincolnshire (North East),** England.

KINGSWEAR, PAIGNTON & DARTMOUTH RAILWAY, **Devon,** England.

KINNEIL, BO'NESS & KINNEIL RAILWAY, **Lothian (West),** Scotland.

KIRKHAUGH, SOUTH TYNEDALE RAILWAY, **Cumbria,** England.

KIRKSTALL ABBEY, ABBEY LIGHT RAILWAY, **Yorkshire (West),** England.

KIRS MAGNAS HALT, DOWNPATRICK & ARDGLASS, **County Down,** Northern Ireland.

LAKESIDE, CLEETHORPES LIGHT RAILWAY, **Lincolnshire (North East),** England.

LAKESIDE, LAKESIDE & HAVERTHWAITE RLWY, **Cumbria,** England.

LAKESIDE, MOORS VALLEY RAILWAY, **Hampshire,** England.

LAKESIDE, RUDYARD LAKE RAILWAY, **Staffordshire,** England.

LAKESIDE, WESTON PARK RAILWAY, **Shropshire,** England.

LAUNCESTON, LAUNCESTON STEAM RAILWAY, **Cornwall,** England.

LAXEY STATION, SNAEFELL MOUNTAIN RAILWAY, **Isle of Man,** England.

LEADHILLS, LEADHILLS & WANLOCKHEAD, **Lanarkshire,** Scotland.

LEEKBROOK JUNCTION, CHURNET VALLEY RAILWAY, **Staffordshire,** England.

LEICESTER NORTH, GREAT CENTRAL RAILWAY, **Leicestershire,** England.

LEVISHAM, NORTH YORKSHIRE MOORS RAILWAY, **Yorkshire (North),** England.

LIME KILN HALT, GROUDLE GLEN RAILWAY, **Isle of Man,** England.

LLANBERIS, SNOWDON MOUNTAIN RAILWAY, **Gwynedd,** Wales.

LLANDYFRIOG, TEIFI VALLEY RAILWAY, **Carmarthenshire,** Wales.

LLANFAIR CAEREINION, WELSHPOOL & LLANFAIR, **Powys,** Wales.

LLANGOLLEN, LLANGOLLEN RAILWAY, **Denbighshire,** Wales.

LLANGOWER, BALA LAKE RAILWAY, **Gwynedd,** Wales.

LLANUWCHLLYN, BALA LAKE RAILWAY, **Gwynedd,** Wales.

LLWYFAN CERRIG, GWILI RAILWAY, **Carmarthenshire,** Wales.

LOOP LINE PLATFORM, DOWNPATRICK & ARDGLASS, **County Down,** Northern Ireland.

LOUGHBOROUGH CENTRAL, GREAT CENTRAL RAILWAY, **Leicestershire,** England.

LUDBOROUGH, LINCOLNSHIRE WOLDS RAILWAY, **Lincolnshire (North East),** England.

LYDNEY JUNCTION, DEAN FOREST RAILWAY, **Gloucestershire,** England.

LYDNEY TOWN, DEAN FOREST RAILWAY, **Gloucestershire,** England.

MAESPAETH, CORRIS RAILWAY MUSEUM, **Powys,** Wales.

MAIN STATION, BICTON WOODLAND RAILWAY, **Devon,** England.

MALLAIG, GLENFINNAN STATION MUSEUM, **Highlands,** Scotland.

MANNEZ QUARRY, ALDERNEY RAILWAY, **Channel Islands,** England.

MARKEATON ST, MARKEATON PARK LIGHT RAILWAY, **Derbyshire,** England.

MARSH MILLS, PLYM VALLEY RAILWAY, **Devon,** England.

MATLOCK RIVERSIDE, PEAK RAIL, **Derbyshire,** England.

MEDSTEAD & FOUR MARKS, WATERCRESS LINE, **Hampshire,** England.

MELDON, DARTMOOR RAILWAY, **Devon,** England.

MENDIP VALE, EAST SOMERSET RAILWAY, **Somerset,** England.

MERRYFIELD LANE, EAST SOMERSET RAILWAY, **Somerset,** England.

MEWSBROOK PARK, LITTLEHAMPTON MINIATURE RLWY, **Sussex (West),** England.

MIDDLETON, MIDDLETON RAILWAY, **Yorkshire (West),** England.

MILTON REGIS, SITTINGBOURNE & KEMSLEY, **Kent,** England.

MINEHEAD, WEST SOMERSET RAILWAY, **Somerset,** England.

MINFFORD, FFESTINIOG RAILWAY, **Gwynedd,** Wales.

MINNIVEY, SCOTTISH RAILWAY CENTRE, **Ayrshire,** Scotland.

MONKS BROOK HALT, EASTLEIGH LAKESIDE RAILWAY, **Hampshire,** England.

MUCH NATTER, BEER HEIGHTS, **Devon,** England.

MUNCASTER MILL, RAVENGLASS & ESKDALE, **Cumbria,** England.

MUNDY HALT, MARKEATON PARK LIGHT RAILWAY, **Derbyshire,** England.

MURRAY PARK, ALFORD VALLEY RAILWAY, **Aberdeenshire,** Scotland.

MURTON PARK, DERWENT VALLEY, **Yorkshire (North),** England.

A-Z of STATIONS

Museum — Pickering

MUSEUM, NIRT, **Northamptonshire,** England.

MUSEUM STATION, NORTH TYNESIDE STEAM RAILWAY, **Tyne and Wear,** England.

NANT GWERNOL, TALYLLYN RAILWAY, **Gwynedd,** Wales.

NEW ROMNEY, ROMNEY HYTHE & DYMCHURCH, **Kent,** England.

NEWBY BRIDGE, LAKESIDE & HAVERTHWAITE RLWY, **Cumbria,** England.

NEWLANDS END, GOLDEN VALLEY LIGHT RAILWAY, **Denbighshire,** Wales.

NEWMILLS, LAUNCESTON STEAM RAILWAY, **Cornwall,** England.

NEWTON DALE, NORTH YORKSHIRE MOORS RAILWAY, **Yorkshire (North),** England.

NORCHARD, DEAN FOREST RAILWAY, **Gloucestershire,** England.

NORDEN, SWANAGE RAILWAY, **Dorset,** England.

NORFOLK GARDENS, LITTLEHAMPTON MINIATURE RLWY, **Sussex (West),** England.

NORTHIAM, KENT & EAST SUSSEX RAILWAY, **Kent,** England.

NORTON LAKESIDE, CHASEWATER RAILWAY, **Midlands (West),** England.

OAKIRON, PERRYGROVE RAILWAY, **Gloucestershire,** England.

OAKWORTH, KEIGHLEY & WORTH VALLEY, **Yorkshire (West),** England.

OKEHAMPTON, DARTMOOR RAILWAY, **Devon,** England.

OLD KILN HALT, OLD KILN LIGHT RAILWAY, **Surrey,** England.

ORTON MERE, NENE VALLEY RAILWAY, **Cambridgeshire,** England.

OXENHOPE, KEIGHLEY & WORTH VALLEY, **Yorkshire (West),** England.

PAGE'S PARK, LEIGHTON BUZZARD RAILWAY, **Bedfordshire,** England.

PAIGNTON, PAIGNTON & DARTMOUTH RAILWAY, **Devon,** England.

PANT, BRECON MOUNTAIN RAILWAY, **Merthyr Tydfil,** Wales.

PARKEND, DEAN FOREST RAILWAY, **Gloucestershire,** England.

PELAW MAIN JUNCTION, BOWES RAILWAY, **Tyne and Wear,** England.

PEN Y MOUNT, WELSH HIGHLAND RAILWAY, **Gwynedd,** Wales.

PENDRE, TALYLLYN RAILWAY, **Gwynedd,** Wales.

PENLLYN, LLANBERIS LAKE RAILWAY, **Gwynedd,** Wales.

PENRHYN, FFESTINIOG RAILWAY, **Gwynedd,** Wales.

PENRITYN POINT, FAIRBOURNE & BARMOUTH, **Gwynedd,** Wales.

PERCY MAIN, NORTH TYNESIDE STEAM RAILWAY, **Tyne and Wear,** England.

PERRYGROVE, PERRYGROVE RAILWAY, **Gloucestershire,** England.

PETERBOROUGH, NENE VALLEY RAILWAY, **Cambridgeshire,** England.

PICCADILLY, ROYAL VICTORIA RAILWAY, **Hampshire,** England.

PICKERING, NORTH YORKSHIRE MOORS RAILWAY, **Yorkshire (North),** England.

𝅘𝅥 **PITSFORD & BRAMPTON,** NORTHAMPTON & LAMPORT RAILWAY, **Northamptonshire,** England.

𝅘𝅥 **PLAS HALT,** FFESTINIOG RAILWAY, **Gwynedd,** Wales.

𝅘𝅥 **PLYMOUTH ROAD,** VALE OF GLAMORGAN RAILWAY, **Glamorgan (Vale of),** Wales.

𝅘𝅥 **PONTPRENSHITY,** TEIFI VALLEY RAILWAY, **Carmarthenshire,** Wales.

𝅘𝅥 **PONTSTICILL,** BRECON MOUNTAIN RAILWAY, **Merthyr Tydfil,** Wales.

𝅘𝅥 **PORT ERIN,** ISLE OF MAN RAILWAY, **Isle of Man,** England.

𝅘𝅥 **PORT ST MARY,** ISLE OF MAN RAILWAY, **Isle of Man,** England.

𝅘𝅥 **PORTHMADOG,** FFESTINIOG RAILWAY, **Gwynedd,** Wales.

𝅘𝅥 **PORTHMADOG,** WELSH HIGHLAND RAILWAY, **Gwynedd,** Wales.

𝅘𝅥 **QUAINTON ROAD,** BUCKINGHAMSHIRE RLWY CTRE, **Buckinghamshire,** England.

𝅘𝅥 **QUORN AND WOODHOUSE,** GREAT CENTRAL RAILWAY, **Leicestershire,** England.

𝅘𝅥 **RAMSBOTTOM,** EAST LANCASHIRE RAILWAY, **Lancashire,** England.

𝅘𝅥 **RAVENGLASS,** RAVENGLASS & ESKDALE, **Cumbria,** England.

𝅘𝅥 **RAWTENSTALL,** EAST LANCASHIRE RAILWAY, **Lancashire,** England.

𝅘𝅥 **RHYDYRONEN,** TALYLLYN RAILWAY, **Gwynedd,** Wales.

𝅘𝅥 **ROCKINGHAM ST,** ELSECAR HERITAGE CENTRE, **Yorkshire (South),** England.

𝅘𝅥 **ROLVENDEN,** KENT & EAST SUSSEX RAILWAY, **Kent,** England.

𝅘𝅥 **ROMNEY SANDS,** ROMNEY HYTHE & DYMCHURCH, **Kent,** England.

𝅘𝅥 **ROOKWOOD,** PERRYGROVE RAILWAY, **Gloucestershire,** England.

𝅘𝅥 **ROPLEY,** WATERCRESS LINE, **Hampshire,** England.

𝅘𝅥 **ROTHLEY,** GREAT CENTRAL RAILWAY, **Leicestershire,** England.

𝅘𝅥 **ROWLEY ROAD,** BUCKINGHAMSHIRE RLWY CTRE, **Buckinghamshire,** England.

𝅘𝅥 **ROWSLEY SOUTH,** PEAK RAIL, **Derbyshire,** England.

𝅘𝅥 **RUDYARD,** RUDYARD LAKE RAILWAY, **Staffordshire,** England.

𝅘𝅥 **RUISLIP LIDO,** RUISLIP LIDO RAILWAY, **London (Greater),** England.

𝅘𝅥 **SAMPFORD COURTENAY,** DARTMOOR RAILWAY, **Devon,** England.

𝅘𝅥 **SANTON,** ISLE OF MAN RAILWAY, **Isle of Man,** England.

𝅘𝅥 **SEA LION ROCKS,** GROUDLE GLEN RAILWAY, **Isle of Man,** England.

𝅘𝅥 **SHACKERSTONE,** BATTLEFIELD LINE, **Warwickshire,** England.

𝅘𝅥 **SHEFFIELD PARK,** BLUEBELL RAILWAY, **Sussex (East),** England.

𝅘𝅥 **SHELLEY,** KIRKLEES LIGHT RAILWAY, **Yorkshire (West),** England.

𝅘𝅥 **SHENTON,** BATTLEFIELD LINE, **Warwickshire,** England.

𝅘𝅥 **SHEPHERDSWELL,** EAST KENT LIGHT RAILWAY, **Kent,** England.

𝅘𝅥 **SHERINGHAM,** NORTH NORFOLK RAILWAY, **Norfolk,** England.

SITTINGBOURNE VIADUCT, SITTINGBOURNE & KEMSLEY, **Kent,** England.

SIX PIT, SWANSEA VALE RAILWAY, **Swansea,** Wales.

SKELMANTHORPE, KIRKLEES LIGHT RAILWAY, **Yorkshire (West),** England.

SMALLBROOK, ISLE OF WIGHT STEAM RAILWAY, **Isle of Wight,** England.

SPRING VILLAGE, TELFORD STEAM RAILWAY, **Shropshire,** England.

SPRINGWELL, BOWES RAILWAY, **Tyne and Wear,** England.

SS GREAT BRITAIN, BRISTOL HARBOUR RAILWAY, **Bristol,** England.

ST MARYS BAY, ROMNEY HYTHE & DYMCHURCH, **Kent,** England.

ST MARYS HALT, DEAN FOREST RAILWAY, **Gloucestershire,** England.

STAVERTON, SOUTH DEVON RAILWAY, **Devon,** England.

STOGUMBER, WEST SOMERSET RAILWAY, **Somerset,** England.

STONEHENGE WORKS, LEIGHTON BUZZARD RAILWAY, **Bedfordshire,** England.

STONY SHAW, BREDGAR & WORMSHILL, **Kent,** England.

STOPHAM ROAD, SOUTH DOWNS LIGHT RAILWAY, **Sussex (West),** England.

STRADBALLY, IRISH STEAM PRESERVATION SOC, **County Loais,** Ireland.

SUMMER SEAT, EAST LANCASHIRE RAILWAY, **Lancashire,** England.

SUMMIT, SNAEFELL MOUNTAIN RAILWAY, **Isle of Man,** England.

SUMMIT, SNOWDON MOUNTAIN RAILWAY, **Gwynedd,** Wales.

SUNNISIDE, TANFIELD RAILWAY, **County Durham,** England.

SWANAGE, SWANAGE RAILWAY, **Dorset,** England.

SWANWICK JUNCTION, MIDLAND RAILWAY CENTRE, **Derbyshire,** England.

SYLFAEN, WELSHPOOL & LLANFAIR, **Powys,** Wales.

TAN-Y-BWELCH, FFESTINIOG RAILWAY, **Gwynedd,** Wales.

TANYGRISAU, FFESTINIOG RAILWAY, **Gwynedd,** Wales.

TENTERDEN, KENT & EAST SUSSEX RAILWAY, **Kent,** England.

THE DAM, RUDYARD LAKE RAILWAY, **Staffordshire,** England.

THE GREEN, RAVENGLASS & ESKDALE, **Cumbria,** England.

THUXTON, MID-NORFOLK RAILWAY, **Norfolk,** England.

TODDINGTON, GLOUCESTERSHIRE WARWICKSHIRE, **Gloucestershire,** England.

TODDINGTON HALT, NORTH GLOUCESTERSHIRE RAILWAY, **Gloucestershire,** England.

TOROSAY, MULL RAILWAY, **Argyll and Bute,** Scotland.

TOTNES, SOUTH DEVON RAILWAY, **Devon,** England.

TRAME JUNCTION, CHINNOR & PRINCES RISBOROUGH, **Oxfordshire,** England.

TUNBRIDGE WELLS WEST, SPA VALLEY RAILWAY, **Kent,** England.

A-Z of STATIONS

Tunnel — Yaxham

TUNNEL, NIRT, **Northamptonshire,** England.

TYWYN WHARF, TALYLLYN RAILWAY, **Gwynedd,** Wales.

WAINHILL HALT, CHINNOR & PRINCES RISBOROUGH, **Oxfordshire,** England.

WALLINGFORD, CHOLSEY & WALLINGFORD RAILWAY, **Oxfordshire,** England.

WALSINGHAM, WELLS & WALSINGHAM, **Norfolk,** England.

WANSFORD, NENE VALLEY RAILWAY, **Cambridgeshire,** England.

WARHAM HALT, WELLS & WALSINGHAM, **Norfolk,** England.

WARREN WOOD, BREDGAR & WORMSHILL, **Kent,** England.

WASHFORD, WEST SOMERSET RAILWAY, **Somerset,** England.

WATCHET, WEST SOMERSET RAILWAY, **Somerset,** England.

WAUNFAWR, WELSH HIGHLAND RAILWAY, **Gwynedd,** Wales.

WAVENEY, BRESSINGHAM STEAM, **Norfolk,** England.

WELLS-NEXT-THE-SEA, WELLS & WALSINGHAM, **Norfolk,** England.

WELSHPOOL, WELSHPOOL & LLANFAIR, **Powys,** Wales.

WESTLINKS, KERR MINIATURE RAILWAY, **Angus,** Scotland.

WESTON CENTRAL, WESTON PARK RAILWAY, **Shropshire,** England.

WEYBOURNE, NORTH NORFOLK RAILWAY, **Norfolk,** England.

WHISTLE INN HALT, PONTYPOOL & BLAENAVON RAILWAY, **Torfaen,** Wales.

WHITECROFT, DEAN FOREST RAILWAY, **Gloucestershire,** England.

WIGHTON HALT, WELLS & WALSINGHAM, **Norfolk,** England.

WILLITON, WEST SOMERSET RAILWAY, **Somerset,** England.

WINCHCOMBE, GLOUCESTERSHIRE WARWICKSHIRE, **Gloucestershire,** England.

WITTERSHAM, KENT & EAST SUSSEX RAILWAY, **Kent,** England.

WOODY BAY, LYNTON & BARNSTAPLE RAILWAY, **Devon,** England.

WOODY BAY, RUISLIP LIDO RAILWAY, **London (Greater),** England.

WOOTTON, ISLE OF WIGHT STEAM RAILWAY, **Isle of Wight,** England.

WROXHAM, BURE VALLEY RAILWAY, **Norfolk,** England.

WYMONDHAM ABBEY, MID-NORFOLK RAILWAY, **Norfolk,** England.

YAXHAM, MID-NORFOLK RAILWAY, **Norfolk,** England.

SECTION 4

The Section lists stations in the order they would be visited on a journey at each railway within county within country

**e.g. England, Cornwall,
       Lappa Valley Steam Railway,
       (1)Benny Halt
       (2)East Wheal Rose**

Once you have located a railway/museum using this section you can then refer to the railway or museum's detailed profile in section 1.

STEAM
RAILWAY

ENGLAND

BEDFORDSHIRE

LEIGHTON BUZZARD RAILWAY
(1) PAGE'S PARK

(2) STONEHENGE WORKS

BRISTOL

AVON VALLEY RAILWAY
(1) BITTON

BRISTOL HARBOUR RAILWAY
(1) BRISTOL INDUSTRIAL MUSEUM

(2) CREATE CENTRE

(3) SS GREAT BRITAIN

BUCKINGHAMSHIRE

BUCKINGHAMSHIRE RLWY CTRE
(1) QUAINTON ROAD

(2) ROWLEY ROAD

CAMBRIDGESHIRE

NENE VALLEY RAILWAY
(1) WANSFORD

(2) FERRY MEADOWS

(3) ORTON MERE

(4) PETERBOROUGH

CHANNEL ISLANDS

ALDERNEY RAILWAY
(1) BRAYE ROAD

(2) MANNEZ QUARRY

CHESHIRE

BROOKSIDE MINIATURE
(1) BROOKSIDE CENTRAL

CORNWALL

BODMIN & WENFORD RAILWAY
(1) BODMIN GENERAL

(2) BODMIN PARKWAY STATION

(3) BOSCARNE JUNCTION

(4) COLESLOGGETT

LAPPA VALLEY STEAM RAILWAY
(1) BENNY HALT

(2) EAST WHEAL ROSE

LAUNCESTON STEAM RAILWAY
(1) LAUNCESTON

(2) NEWMILLS

COUNTY DURHAM

TANFIELD RAILWAY
(1) SUNNISIDE

(2) ANDREWS HOUSE

(3) CAUSEY ARCH

(4) EAST TANFIELD

CUMBRIA

LAKESIDE & HAVERTHWAITE RLWY
(1) HAVERTHWAITE

(2) NEWBY BRIDGE

(3) LAKESIDE

RAVENGLASS & ESKDALE
(1) RAVENGLASS

(2) MUNCASTER MILL

(3) IRTON ROAD

(4) THE GREEN

(5) ESKDALE (DALEGARTH)

SOUTH TYNEDALE RAILWAY
(1) ALSTON

(2) KIRKHAUGH

DERBYSHIRE

MARKEATON PARK LIGHT RAILWAY
(1) MARKEATON ST

(2) MUNDY HALT

MIDLAND RAILWAY CENTRE
(1) BUTTERLEY

(2) SWANWICK JUNCTION

(3) HAMMERSMITH

PEAK RAIL
(1) ROWSLEY SOUTH

(2) DARLEY DALE

(3) MATLOCK RIVERSIDE

DEVON

BEER HEIGHTS
(1) MUCH NATTER

STATIONS by Journey Order

Bedfordshire — Devon

BICTON WOODLAND RAILWAY
(1) MAIN STATION

(2) HERMITAGE RAILWAY

DARTMOOR RAILWAY
(1) OKEHAMPTON

(2) MELDON

(3) SAMPFORD COURTENAY

LYNTON & BARNSTAPLE RAILWAY
(1) WOODY BAY

PAIGNTON & DARTMOUTH RAILWAY
(1) PAIGNTON

(2) GOODRINGTON

(3) CHURSTON

(4) KINGSWEAR

PLYM VALLEY RAILWAY
(1) MARSH MILLS

SOUTH DEVON RAILWAY
(1) BUCKFASTLEIGH

(2) STAVERTON

(3) TOTNES

DORSET

SWANAGE RAILWAY
(1) SWANAGE

(2) HARMANS CROSS

(3) CORFE CASTLE

(4) NORDEN

ESSEX

BARLEYLANDS MINIATURE RAILWAY
(1) FARM MUSEUM

(2) BOOT FAIR

COLNE VALLEY RAILWAY
(1) CASTLE HEDINGHAM

GLOUCESTERSHIRE

DEAN FOREST RAILWAY
(1) NORCHARD

(2) LYDNEY TOWN

(3) ST MARYS HALT

(4) LYDNEY JUNCTION

(5) WHITECROFT

(6) PARKEND

GLOUCESTERSHIRE WARWICKSHIRE
(1) TODDINGTON

(2) WINCHCOMBE

(3) GOTHERINGTON

NORTH GLOUCESTERSHIRE RAILWAY
(1) TODDINGTON HALT

(2) CALAFERNIA CROSSING

PERRYGROVE RAILWAY
(1) PERRYGROVE

(2) ROOKWOOD

(3) HEYWOOD

(4) OAKIRON

HAMPSHIRE

EASTLEIGH LAKESIDE RAILWAY
(1) EASTLEIGH PARKWAY

(2) MONKS BROOK HALT

HOLLYCOMBE STEAM COLLECTION
(1) HOLLYCOMBE

MOORS VALLEY RAILWAY
(1) KINGSMERE

(2) LAKESIDE

ROYAL VICTORIA RAILWAY
(1) CHAPEL ROAD

(2) PICCADILLY

WATERCRESS LINE
(1) ALRESFORD

(2) ROPLEY

(3) MEDSTEAD & FOUR MARKS

(4) ALTON

ISLE OF MAN

GROUDLE GLEN RAILWAY
(1) GROUDLE LHEN COAN

(2) LIME KILN HALT

(3) SEA LION ROCKS

ISLE OF MAN RAILWAY
(1) DOUGLAS

(2) SANTON

Steam Railway

The "Olton Hall"
No. 5972,
Built 1937

This locomotive was
transformed into the
"Hogwart's Express"
for the 2001 movie
"Harry Potter and the
Philosopher's Stone."

This locomotive will
be traveling to
locations across the
UK during 2002 to
help promote the film.

The "Flying Scotsman" is kept at a private site in Southall, West London.
It is however viewable at special events at a number of locations across the country throughout the year.

East Somerset Railway

West Somerset Railway

Lincolnshire Wolds Railway

No. 1264
Wheel Arrangement 4-6-0
Built 1947.
Picture copyright
Great Central Railway PLC.

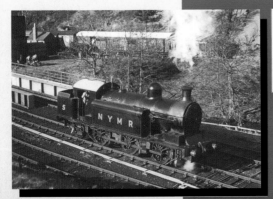

No. 5
Wheel Arrangement 0-6-2
Built 1909
North Yorkshire
Moors Railway

Museum of the Great Western Railway

Leighton Buzzard Railway

Keighley & Worth Valley Railway

No. 1638
16XX Class
Wheel Arrangement 0-6-0PT
Kent & East Sussex Railway

Black Prince
No. 92203
Wheel Arrangement 2-10-0
Gloucestershire Warwickshire
Steam Railway

Talyllyn
Wheel Arrangement 0-4-2ST
Built 1864
Talyllyn Railway

(3) BALLASALLA

(4) CASTLETOWN

(5) COLBY

(6) PORT ST MARY

(7) PORT ERIN

𝗛𝗖𝗖 SNAEFELL MOUNTAIN RAILWAY
(1) LAXEY STATION

(2) BUNGALOW

(3) SUMMIT

ISLE OF WIGHT

𝗛𝗖𝗖 ISLE OF WIGHT STEAM RAILWAY
(1) HAVENSTREET

(2) WOOTTON

(3) SMALLBROOK

(4) ASHEY

KENT

𝗛𝗖𝗖 BREDGAR & WORMSHILL
(1) WARREN WOOD

(2) STONY SHAW

𝗛𝗖𝗖 EAST KENT LIGHT RAILWAY
(1) SHEPHERDSWELL

(2) EYTHORNE

𝗛𝗖𝗖 KENT & EAST SUSSEX RAILWAY
(1) TENTERDEN

(2) ROLVENDEN

(3) WITTERSHAM

(4) NORTHIAM

(5) BODIAM

𝗛𝗖𝗖 ROMNEY HYTHE & DYMCHURCH
(1) HYTHE

(2) DYMCHURCH

(3) ST MARYS BAY

(4) NEW ROMNEY

(5) ROMNEY SANDS

(6) DUNGENESS

𝗛𝗖𝗖 SITTINGBOURNE & KEMSLEY
(1) SITTINGBOURNE VIADUCT

(2) MILTON REGIS

(3) BURLEY CROSSING

(4) KEMSLEY DOWN

𝗛𝗖𝗖 SPA VALLEY RAILWAY
(1) TUNBRIDGE WELLS WEST

(2) HIGH ROCKS

(3) GROOMBRIDGE

LANCASHIRE

𝗛𝗖𝗖 EAST LANCASHIRE RAILWAY
(1) BURY

(2) SUMMER SEAT

(3) RAMSBOTTOM

(4) IRWELL VALE

(5) RAWTENSTALL

𝗛𝗖𝗖 WEST LANCASHIRE LIGHT RLWY
(1) BECCONSALL

(2) DELPH

LEICESTERSHIRE

𝗛𝗖𝗖 GREAT CENTRAL RAILWAY
(1) LOUGHBOROUGH CENTRAL

(2) QUORN AND WOODHOUSE

(3) ROTHLEY

(4) LEICESTER NORTH

LINCOLNSHIRE (NORTH EAST)

𝗛𝗖𝗖 CLEETHORPES LIGHT RAILWAY
(1) LAKESIDE

(2) HALFWAY HALT

(3) KINGSWAY

𝗛𝗖𝗖 LINCOLNSHIRE WOLDS RAILWAY
(1) LUDBOROUGH

LONDON (GREATER)

𝗛𝗖𝗖 GREAT COCKCROW RAILWAY
(1) HARDWICK CENTRAL

(2) EVERGLADES JUNCTION

(3) COCKCROW HILL

(4) GREEN LANE

𝗛𝗖𝗖 RUISLIP LIDO RAILWAY
(1) RUISLIP LIDO

(2) WOODY BAY

MIDLANDS (WEST)

𝗛𝗖𝗖 CHASEWATER RAILWAY
(1) BROWNHILLS WEST

STATIONS by Journey Order

Isle of Man — Midlands (West)

(2) NORTON LAKESIDE

(3) CHASEWATER HEATHS

(4) CHASETOWN

HOLLYBUSH GARDEN CENTRE
(1) HOLLYBUSH CENTRAL

NORFOLK

BRESSINGHAM STEAM
(1) WAVENEY

BURE VALLEY RAILWAY
(1) AYLSHAM

(2) BRAMPTON

(3) BUXTON

(4) COLTISHALL

(5) WROXHAM

MID-NORFOLK RAILWAY
(1) DEREHAM

(2) YAXHAM

(3) THUXTON

(4) WYMONDHAM ABBEY

NORTH NORFOLK RAILWAY
(1) SHERINGHAM

(2) WEYBOURNE

(3) KELLING HEATH PARK HALT

(4) HOLT

WELLS & WALSINGHAM
(1) WELLS-NEXT-THE-SEA

(2) WARHAM HALT

(3) WIGHTON HALT

(4) WALSINGHAM

NORTHAMPTONSHIRE

NIRT
(1) MUSEUM

(2) TUNNEL

NORTHAMPTON & LAMPORT RAILWAY
(1) PITSFORD & BRAMPTON

NORTHUMBERLAND

HEATHERSLAW LIGHT RAILWAY
(1) HEATHERSLAW

(2) ETAL CASTLE

OXFORDSHIRE

CHINNOR & PRINCES RISBOROUGH
(1) CHINNOR STATION

(2) WAINHILL HALT

(3) BLEDLOW BRIDGE HALT

(4) TRAME JUNCTION

CHOLSEY & WALLINGFORD RAILWAY
(1) WALLINGFORD

(2) CHOLSEY

DIDCOT RAILWAY CENTRE
(1) DIDCOT HALT

(2) BURLESCOMBE

SHROPSHIRE

TELFORD STEAM RAILWAY
(1) SPRING VILLAGE

(2) HORSEHAY & DAWLEY

WESTON PARK RAILWAY
(1) WESTON CENTRAL

(2) LAKESIDE

SOMERSET

EAST SOMERSET RAILWAY
(1) CRANMORE

(2) CRANMORE WEST

(3) MERRYFIELD LANE

(4) MENDIP VALE

WEST SOMERSET RAILWAY
(1) MINEHEAD

(2) DUNSTER

(3) BLUE ANCHOR

(4) WASHFORD

(5) WATCHET

(6) DONIFORD HALT

(7) WILLITON

(8) STOGUMBER

(9) CROWCOMBE HEATHFIELD

(10) BISHOPS LYDEARD

STAFFORDSHIRE

AMERTON RAILWAY
(1) AMERTON STATION

(2) CHARTLEY RD

CHURNET VALLEY RAILWAY
(1) CHEDDLETON

(2) LEEKBROOK JUNCTION

(3) CONSALL

(4) KINGSLEY & FROGHALL

FOXFIELD STEAM RAILWAY
(1) CAVERSWALL RD STATION

(2) DILHORNE PARK STATION

RUDYARD LAKE RAILWAY
(1) RUDYARD

(2) THE DAM

(3) LAKESIDE

(4) HUNTHOUSE WOOD

SURREY

OLD KILN LIGHT RAILWAY
(1) OLD KILN HALT

SUSSEX (EAST)

BLUEBELL RAILWAY
(1) SHEFFIELD PARK

(2) KINGSCOTE

(3) HOSTED KEYNES

LAVENDER LINE
(1) ISFIELD

SUSSEX (WEST)

LITTLEHAMPTON MINIATURE RLWY
(1) MEWSBROOK PARK

(2) NORFOLK GARDENS

SOUTH DOWNS LIGHT RAILWAY
(1) STOPHAM ROAD

TYNE AND WEAR

BOWES RAILWAY
(1) SPRINGWELL

(2) PELAW MAIN JUNCTION

NORTH TYNESIDE STEAM RAILWAY
(1) MUSEUM STATION

(2) PERCY MAIN

WARWICKSHIRE

BATTLEFIELD LINE
(1) SHACKERSTONE

(2) SHENTON

WILTSHIRE

SWINDON & CRICKLADE RAILWAY
(1) BLUNSDON

(2) HAYES KNOLL

WORCESTERSHIRE

SEVERN VALLEY RAILWAY
(1) KIDDERMINSTER

(2) BEWDLEY

(3) ARLEY

(4) HIGHLEY

(5) HAMPTON LOADE

(6) BRIDGNORTH

YORKSHIRE (NORTH)

DERWENT VALLEY
(1) MURTON PARK

EMBSAY & BOLTON ABBEY RLWY
(1) EMBSAY

(2) BOLTON ABBEY

NORTH YORKSHIRE MOORS RAILWAY
(1) PICKERING

(2) LEVISHAM

(3) NEWTON DALE

(4) GOATHLAND

(5) GROSMONT

YORKSHIRE (SOUTH)

ELSECAR HERITAGE CENTRE
(1) ROCKINGHAM ST

(2) HEMINGFIELD BASIN

YORKSHIRE (WEST)

ABBEY LIGHT RAILWAY
(1) BRIDGE ROAD

(2) KIRKSTALL ABBEY

KEIGHLEY & WORTH VALLEY
(1) KEIGHLEY

(2) INGROW (WEST)

(3) DAMENS

STATIONS by Journey Order

Staffordshire — Yorkshire (West)

(4) OAKWORTH

(5) HAWORTH

(6) OXENHOPE

KIRKLEES LIGHT RAILWAY
(1) CLAYTON WEST

(2) SKELMANTHORPE

(3) CUCKOOS NEST

(4) SHELLEY

MIDDLETON RAILWAY
(1) MIDDLETON

IRELAND
COUNTY KERRY

TRALEE & DINGLE RAILWAY
(1) BALLYARD

(2) BLENNERVILLE

COUNTY LEITRIM

CAVAN & LEITRIM RAILWAY
(1) DROMOD

COUNTY LOAIS

IRISH STEAM PRESERVATION SOC
(1) STRADBALLY

NORTHERN IRELAND
COUNTY ANTRIM

GIANTS CAUSEWAY & BUSHMILLS
(1) GIANTS CAUSEWAY

(2) BUSHMILLS

COUNTY DOWN

DOWNPATRICK & ARDGLASS
(1) DOWNPATRICK

(2) LOOP LINE PLATFORM

(3) KIRS MAGNAS HALT

SCOTLAND
ABERDEENSHIRE

ALFORD VALLEY RAILWAY
(1) ALFORD

(2) HAUGHTON PARK

(3) HAUGHTON

(4) MURRAY PARK

ANGUS

CALEDONIAN RAILWAY
(1) BRECHIN

(2) BRIDGE OF DUN

KERR MINIATURE RAILWAY
(1) WESTLINKS

(2) HOSPITAL FIELD HALT

ARGYLL AND BUTE

MULL RAILWAY
(1) CRAIGNURE

(2) TOROSAY

AYRSHIRE

SCOTTISH RAILWAY CENTRE
(1) MINNIVEY

HIGHLANDS

GLENFINNAN STATION MUSEUM
(1) FORT WILLIAM

(2) GLENFINNAN

(3) MALLAIG

STRATHSPEY RAILWAY
(1) AVIEMORE

(2) AVIEMORE (SPEYSIDE) - CLOSED

(3) BOAT OF GARTEN

(4) BROOMHILL

LANARKSHIRE

LEADHILLS & WANLOCKHEAD
(1) LEADHILLS

(2) GLENGONNAR HALT

LOTHIAN (WEST)

BO'NESS & KINNEIL RAILWAY
(1) BO'NESS

(2) KINNEIL

(3) BIRKHILL

MORAY

KEITH & DUFFTOWN RAILWAY
(1) DUFFTOWN

(2) DRUMMUIR

(3) KEITH TOWN

WALES
CARMARTHENSHIRE

GWILI RAILWAY
(1) BRONWYDD ARMS

(2) LLWYFAN CERRIG

(3) DANYCOED HALT

TEIFI VALLEY RAILWAY
(1) HENLLAN

(2) PONTPRENSHITY

(3) LLANDYFRIOG

CEREDIGION

VALE OF RHEIDOL RAILWAY
(1) ABERYSTWYTH

(2) DEVILS BRIDGE

DENBIGHSHIRE

GOLDEN VALLEY LIGHT RAILWAY
(1) BUTTERLEY PARK

(2) BRANDS SIDINGS

(3) NEWLANDS END

LLANGOLLEN RAILWAY
(1) LLANGOLLEN

(2) BERWYN

(3) DEESIDE HALT

(4) GLYNDYFRDWY

(5) CARROG

GLAMORGAN (VALE OF)

VALE OF GLAMORGAN RAILWAY
(1) BARRY ISLAND

(2) HOOD ROAD

(3) PLYMOUTH ROAD

GWYNEDD

BALA LAKE RAILWAY
(1) LLANUWCHLLYN

(2) LLANGOWER

(3) BALA

FAIRBOURNE & BARMOUTH
(1) FAIRBOURNE

(2) BEACH HALT

(3) GOLF HALT

(4) PENRITYN POINT

FFESTINIOG RAILWAY
(1) PORTHMADOG

(2) BOSTON LODGE HALT

(3) MINFFORD

(4) PENRHYN

(5) PLAS HALT

(6) TAN-Y-BWELCH

(7) CAMPBELLS PLATFORM

(8) DDUALLT

(9) TANYGRISAU

(10) BLAENAUFFEST

LLANBERIS LAKE RAILWAY
(1) GILFACH DDU

(2) CEI LLYDAN

(3) PENLLYN

SNOWDON MOUNTAIN RAILWAY
(1) LLANBERIS

(2) CLOGWYN

(3) SUMMIT

TALYLLYN RAILWAY
(1) TYWYN WHARF

(2) PENDRE

(3) RHYDYRONEN

(4) BRYNGLAS

(5) DOLGOCH

(6) ABERGYNOLWYN

(7) NANT GWERNOL

WELSH HIGHLAND RAILWAY
(1) CAERNARFON

(1) PORTHMADOG

(2) BONTNEWYDD

(2) GELERTS FARM HALT

(3) DINAS

(3) PEN Y MOUNT

(4) WAUNFAWR

MERTHYR TYDFIL

BRECON MOUNTAIN RAILWAY
(1) PANT

(2) PONTSTICILL

POWYS

STATIONS by Journey Order

Carmarthenshire — Powys

CORRIS RAILWAY MUSEUM
(1) CORRIS

(2) MAESPAETH

WELSHPOOL & LLANFAIR
(1) WELSHPOOL

(2) GALFA

(3) SYLFAEN

(4) CASTLE CAEREINION

(5) CYFRONYDD

(6) HENIARTH

(7) LLANFAIR CAEREINION

SWANSEA

SWANSEA VALE RAILWAY
(1) SIX PIT

TORFAEN

PONTYPOOL & BLAENAVON RAILWAY
(1) FURNACE SIDINGS PLATFORM

(2) WHISTLE INN HALT

A-Z of Rolling Stock by Name

SECTION 5A

This section gives you details where the stock can be located, also showing it's current number and icons displaying what type of stock it is and it's status

Type Icons:
>   L - Loco
>   R - Rolling Stock
>   W - Wagon
>   C - Coach

Status Icons:
>   O - Operational
>   S - Static
>   D - On Display

e.g. Acorn, Industrial Railway Museum, 327904, LOD

Once you have located a railway/museum using this section you can then refer to the railway or museum's detailed profile in section 1.

249 SQUADRON *No. (34073)*
WATERCRESS LINE
L **S**

257 SQUADRON *No. (34072)*
SWANAGE RAILWAY
L **O**

2ND AIR DIVISION USAAF *No. (3)*
BURE VALLEY RAILWAY
L **O**

3RD CARABINIER *No. (D99)*
EAST LANCASHIRE RAILWAY

92 SQUADRON *No. (34081)*
NENE VALLEY RAILWAY
L **O**

A J HILL *No. (7999)*
NORTH NORFOLK RAILWAY
L

ACKTON HALL NO 3
LINCOLNSHIRE WOLDS RAILWAY

ACORN *No. (327904)*
INDUSTRIAL RAILWAY MUSEUM
L **O** **D**

ADAM
CAMBRIAN RAILWAY SOCIETY

AELFRED *No. (7)*
MOORS VALLEY RAILWAY
L **O**

AEROLITE *No. (66)*
NATIONAL RAILWAY MUSEUM
L

AGENORIA
NATIONAL RAILWAY MUSEUM
L

AIREDALE NO 3
EMBSAY & BOLTON ABBEY RLWY
L

AJAX *No. (38)*
ISLE OF WIGHT STEAM RAILWAY
L

AJAX *No. (6435)*
PAIGNTON & DARTMOUTH RAILWAY
L **O**

ALAN *No. (11509)*
SEVERN VALLEY RAILWAY
L **S**

ALAN BLOOM
BRESSINGHAM STEAM
L **O**

ALAN GEORGE *No. (606)*
TEIFI VALLEY RAILWAY
L **O**

ALAN MEADEN *No. (5)*
CORRIS RAILWAY MUSEUM

ALBERT
EAST KENT LIGHT RAILWAY
L **O**

ALCO 660HP AMERICAN SWITCHER *No. (804)*
RAILWORLD
L **S** **D**

ALEXANDER
EAST ANGLIAN RAILWAY MUSEUM
L

ALEXANDRA *No. (929)*
LAKESIDE & HAVERTHWAITE RLWY
L **O**

ALF *No. (9)*
TALYLLYN RAILWAY
L **O**

ROLLING STOCK by **NAME**

Alfie — Armistice

ALFIE *No. (D2272)*
SOUTH YORKSHIRE RAILWAY

ALFRED *No. (3058)*
BODMIN & WENFORD RAILWAY
L **O**

ALFRED PAGET *No. (11)*
CHASEWATER RAILWAY
L

ALICE
LEIGHTON BUZZARD RAILWAY
L **O** **D**

ALICE
SOUTH DOWNS LIGHT RAILWAY
L **O**

ALISON *No. (5)*
GARTELL LIGHT RAILWAY

ALISTER *No. (44052)*
KEW BRIDGE STEAM MUSEUM
L **O**

ALPHA *No. (2472)*
SITTINGBOURNE & KEMSLEY
L **S** **O**

ALSTON *No. (1604)*
MID-SUFFOLK LIGHT RAILWAY
L **S**

ALYCIDON *No. (D9009)*
NORTH YORKSHIRE MOORS RAILWAY
L

AMERICAN GP40 *No. (645)*
HOLLYBUSH GARDEN CENTRE
L **G**

ANDANIA *No. (40013)*
MIDLAND RAILWAY CENTRE
L

ANDREW *No. (2)*
GARTELL LIGHT RAILWAY

ANDY
MIDLAND RAILWAY CENTRE
L **D**

ANN
EMBSAY & BOLTON ABBEY RLWY
L **O**

ANNIE
EMBSAY & BOLTON ABBEY RLWY
L **O**

ANNIE
GROUDLE GLEN RAILWAY
L

ANNIE *No. (945)*
LAVENDER LINE
L

ANTWERP *No. (3180)*
NORTH YORKSHIRE MOORS RAILWAY
L

APPRENTICE (THE)
BURE VALLEY RAILWAY
L

ARIADNE *No. (1505)*
MUSEUM OF SCIENCE & INDUSTRY
L **D**

ARK ROYAL
SEVERN VALLEY RAILWAY
L **O**

ARKLE *No. (13)*
LEIGHTON BUZZARD RAILWAY
L **O** **D**

ARMISTICE *No. (4)*
BREDGAR & WORMSHILL
L **O**

ARNOLD J RIMMER *No. (2)*
CLEETHORPES LIGHT RAILWAY
L

ARTHUR
BUCKINGHAMSHIRE RLWY CTRE
L

ARTHUR
SOUTH DOWNS LIGHT RAILWAY
L O

ARTHUR WRIGHT *No. (D4279)*
GREAT CENTRAL RAILWAY
L

ARTIC PRINCE *No. (D7062)*
ROYAL VICTORIA RAILWAY
L O

ASBESTOS *No. (4)*
CHASEWATER RAILWAY
L

ASHFORD *No. (D6570)*
KENT & EAST SUSSEX RAILWAY
L O

ASHLEY
SOUTH DEVON RAILWAY
L

ASHOVER
FFESTINIOG RAILWAY
L

ASKHAM HALL *No. (15)*
LAKESIDE & HAVERTHWAITE RLWY
L D

ATLANTIC CONVEYOR *No. (D306)*
NENE VALLEY RAILWAY
L O

ATLAS *No. (2)*
ABBEY LIGHT RAILWAY
L O

AULD REEKIE *No. (9872)*
KERR MINIATURE RAILWAY
O

AUREOL *No. (40012)*
MIDLAND RAILWAY CENTRE
L O

AUSTINS NO 1
KEIGHLEY & WORTH VALLEY
L O

AYRSHIRE YEOMANRY *No. (5156)*
SOUTH DOWNS LIGHT RAILWAY
L O

BABY DELTIE *No. (D5905)*
MARKEATON PARK LIGHT RAILWAY
L

BABY RUSTON
EMBSAY & BOLTON ABBEY RLWY
L O

BADGER
KIRKLEES LIGHT RAILWAY
L O

BAGNALL
WELSH HIGHLAND RAILWAY
L

BAGULEY *No. (10)*
ABBEY LIGHT RAILWAY
L

BAGULEY *No. (11)*
ABBEY LIGHT RAILWAY
L

BAGULEY
NARROW GAUGE RAILWAY MUSEUM
L D

BAHAMAS *No. (45596)*
KEIGHLEY & WORTH VALLEY
L

ROLLING STOCK by NAME

Arnold J Rimmer — Bahamas

BAR STOOL (THE)
WINDMILL FARM RAILWAY
O

BARBARA *No. (52)*
KENT & EAST SUSSEX RAILWAY
C

BARBER *No. (441)*
ARMLEY MILLS
L S

BARBOUILLEUR *No. (1126)*
AMBERLEY WORKING MUSEUM
L

BARCLAY *No. (7)*
CALEDONIAN RAILWAY
L O

BARDON *No. (28)*
GREAT CENTRAL RAILWAY
L O

BARRINGTON
COLNE VALLEY RAILWAY
L

BASIL
AVON VALLEY RAILWAY
L

BATTISON
WINDMILL FARM RAILWAY
L

BAUXITE *No. (2)*
NATIONAL RAILWAY MUSEUM
L

BAXTER *No. (3)*
BLUEBELL RAILWAY
L

BEA NO 2
EMBSAY & BOLTON ABBEY RLWY
L

BEAR *No. (614)*
SITTINGBOURNE & KEMSLEY
L S D

BEATRICE *No. (2705)*
EMBSAY & BOLTON ABBEY RLWY
L

BEAUDESERT *No. (80)*
LEIGHTON BUZZARD RAILWAY
L O D

BECKTON NO 1
BRESSINGHAM STEAM
L S D

BECKTON NO 25
BRESSINGHAM STEAM
L S D

BEDDGELERT
FAIRBOURNE & BARMOUTH
L O

BELLEROPHON
FOXFIELD STEAM RAILWAY
L O

BELVEDERE *No. (9365)*
NIRT
L S D

BELVOIR
EAST ANGLIAN RAILWAY MUSEUM
L

BERRYLAND
DEVON RAILWAY CENTRE
L D

BERYL
SWANAGE RAILWAY
L

BICKMARSH HALL *No. (5967)*
PONTYPOOL & BLAENAVON RAILWAY
L S

ROLLING STOCK by NAME

Bicton — Bluebell

BICTON *No.(2)*
BICTON WOODLAND RAILWAY
L O

BIGGA
SOUTH YORKSHIRE RAILWAY

BILL CADDICK *No.(D8526)*
VALE OF GLAMORGAN RAILWAY
L O

BINKY *No.(35)*
LEIGHTON BUZZARD RAILWAY
L

BIRCH GROVE *No.(473)*
BLUEBELL RAILWAY
L O

BIRKENHEAD
EAST ANGLIAN RAILWAY MUSEUM
L

BITTERN *No.(60019)*
WATERCRESS LINE
L

BLACK 5 MAGPIE *No.(44806)*
LLANGOLLEN RAILWAY
L O

BLACK PRINCE *No.(92203)*
BARLEYLANDS MINIATURE RAILWAY
L O

BLACK PRINCE *No.(92203)*
GLOUCESTERSHIRE WARWICKSHIRE
L

BLACKIE *No.(68012)*
LAVENDER LINE
L O

BLACKMOOR VALE *No.(21C123)*
BLUEBELL RAILWAY
L O

BLANCHE
FFESTINIOG RAILWAY
L O

BLANCHE *No.(2)*
ULSTER FOLK & TRANSPORT
L S D

BLICKLING HALL *No.(6)*
BURE VALLEY RAILWAY
L O

BLINKIN BESS
SCOTTISH RAILWAY CENTRE
L S

BLUE CIRCLE *No.(9449)*
BLUEBELL RAILWAY

BLUE CIRCLE
BUCKINGHAMSHIRE RLWY CTRE
L

BLUE PACIFIC *No.(4)*
WINDMILL FARM RAILWAY
L

BLUE PETER *No.(60532)*
NORTH YORKSHIRE MOORS RAILWAY
L

BLUE STAR *No.(35010)*
COLNE VALLEY RAILWAY
L

BLUEBELL *No.(323)*
BLUEBELL RAILWAY
L S D

BLUEBELL *No.(1)*
LEIGHTON BUZZARD RAILWAY
L

BLUEBELL *No.(D2246)*
SOUTH YORKSHIRE RAILWAY

BOB DAVIES
BALA LAKE RAILWAY
L **O**

BODIAM *No. (3)*
KENT & EAST SUSSEX RAILWAY
L

BODMIN *No. (34016)*
WATERCRESS LINE
L **O**

BONNIE DUNDEE
RAVENGLASS & ESKDALE
L **O**

BONNIE PRINCE CHARLIE *No. (1)*
DIDCOT RAILWAY CENTRE
L

BOOTS
MIDLAND RAILWAY CENTRE
L **O**

BOOTS NO 1 *No. (1)*
FOXFIELD STEAM RAILWAY
L **S**

BOOTS NO 2
MIDLAND RAILWAY CENTRE
L **S** **O**

BORIS *No. (1)*
DEVON RAILWAY CENTRE
L **O**

BOROUGH OF DARLINGTON *No. (78018)*
DARLINGTON RAILWAY PRES SOC
L

BORROWSTOWNESS
BO'NESS & KINNEIL RAILWAY
L

BOSCASTLE *No. (34039)*
GREAT CENTRAL RAILWAY
L

BOXHILL *No. (82)*
NATIONAL RAILWAY MUSEUM
L

BRADDYLL
TIMOTHY HACKWORTH
L **S** **O**

BRADFIELD
WEST LANCASHIRE LIGHT RLWY
L

BRADLEY MANOR *No. (7802)*
SEVERN VALLEY RAILWAY
L **O**

BRAICH *No. (203031)*
LLANBERIS LAKE RAILWAY
L

BRAUGHTON *No. (34046)*
WEST SOMERSET RAILWAY
L

BRAVEHEART *No. (75014)*
NORTH YORKSHIRE MOORS RAILWAY
L

BRAWLASS
ALFORD VALLEY RAILWAY
L

BRECHIN CITY *No. (D3059)*
CALEDONIAN RAILWAY
L

BREDGAR *No. (5)*
BREDGAR & WORMSHILL

BRIGADELOK
NORTH GLOUCESTERSHIRE RAILWAY
L

BRITAINS EXPERIMENTAL HOVER TRAIN
RAILWORLD
W **S** **O**

BRITANNIA *No. (70000)*
BARLEYLANDS MINIATURE RAILWAY
L **O**

BRITISH INDIA LINE *No. (35018)*
WATERCRESS LINE
L **S**

BROCKLEBANK LINE *No. (35025)*
GREAT CENTRAL RAILWAY
L

BRONHILDE *No. (1)*
BREDGAR & WORMSHILL
L **O**

BRONLLWYD
BRESSINGHAM STEAM
L **O**

BROOKES NO 1 *No. (2387)*
MIDDLETON RAILWAY
L **O**

BROOKFIELD *No. (2613)*
MANGAPPS RAILWAY MUSEUM
L **O** **D**

BROOKSIDE
BROOKSIDE MINIATURE
L **O**

BROWN BAILEY
MIDLAND RAILWAY CENTRE
L **S** **D**

BRUSSELS *No. (118)*
KEIGHLEY & WORTH VALLEY
L

BRYN EGLWYS *No. (10)*
TALYLLYN RAILWAY
L **O**

BUFFS (THE) *No. (427)*
EAST KENT LIGHT RAILWAY
L **O**

BUG (THE)
EMBSAY & BOLTON ABBEY RLWY
L

BUG (THE)
ROMNEY HYTHE & DYMCHURCH
L **O**

BULLION VAN *No. (99204)*
PEAK RAIL
C

BUNTY *No. (146C)*
NORTHAMPTON & LAMPORT RAILWAY
L

BURGUNDY *No. (110)*
EAST SOMERSET RAILWAY
L

BURMA STAR *No. (33056)*
CHURNET VALLEY RAILWAY
L

BURT
AMBERLEY WORKING MUSEUM
L

BURTON AGNES HALL *No. (6998)*
DIDCOT RAILWAY CENTRE
L

CADBURY NO 1
TYSELEY LOCOMOTIVE WORKS

CAERPHILLY CASTLE *No. (4073)*
NATIONAL RAILWAY MUSEUM
L **S** **D**

CAGNEY *No. (44)*
WINDMILL FARM RAILWAY
L

CALBOURNE *No. (W24)*
ISLE OF WIGHT STEAM RAILWAY
L **O**

ROLLING STOCK by NAME

Britannia — Calbourne

CALEDONIA *No. (70)*
HOLLYCOMBE STEAM COLLECTION
L O

CALEDONIA *No. (15)*
ISLE OF MAN RAILWAY
L

CALIBAN *No. (1925)*
LAKESIDE & HAVERTHWAITE RLWY

CALVERTON
ARMLEY MILLS
L S

CAMBRAI
IRCHESTER NARROW GAUGE MUSEUM
L S D

CAMELOT *No. (73082)*
BLUEBELL RAILWAY
L O

CANADIAN PACIFIC *No. (35005)*
WATERCRESS LINE
L O

CAPPER
ARMLEY MILLS
L S D

CAPTAIN BILL SMITH RNR *No. (D6525)*
WATERCRESS LINE
L O

CAPTAIN HOWEY
ROMNEY HYTHE & DYMCHURCH
L O

CARAVAN *No. (36)*
LEIGHTON BUZZARD RAILWAY
L

CARPENTER *No. (3270)*
CHOLSEY & WALLINGFORD RAILWAY
L O

CARROLL *No. (631)*
MIDDLETON RAILWAY
L O

CASTELL DINAS BRAN *No. (25035)*
NORTHAMPTON & LAMPORT RAILWAY
L

CASTLE DONNINGTON NO 1
MIDLAND RAILWAY CENTRE
L

CASTLE DONNINGTON NO 2
MIDLAND RAILWAY CENTRE
L O

CASTLEFIELD
PEAK RAIL
L

CATHRYN
SOUTH YORKSHIRE RAILWAY

CCSW
AMBERLEY WORKING MUSEUM
L

CEMENT *No. (20685)*
ARMLEY MILLS
L S

CHAKA
NORTH GLOUCESTERSHIRE RAILWAY
L

CHAKA'S KRAAL NO 6 *No. (12)*
SOUTH TYNEDALE RAILWAY
L

CHALONER *No. (1)*
LEIGHTON BUZZARD RAILWAY
L O D

CHARLES *No. (283)*
INDUSTRIAL RAILWAY MUSEUM
L D

CHARLIE
EXMOOR STEAM RAILWAY
L **O**

CHARLOTTE *No. (6335)*
LEADHILLS & WANLOCKHEAD
L

CHARLOTTE
WELLINGTON COUNTRY PARK
L **O**

CHARWELTON *No. (14)*
KENT & EAST SUSSEX RAILWAY
L

CHATTENDEN *No. (196)*
SITTINGBOURNE & KEMSLEY
R

CHATTENDEN *No. (7)*
WELSHPOOL & LLANFAIR
L **O**

CHEETAL
ARMLEY MILLS
L **S** **D**

CHEVALLIER *No. (1877)*
GREAT WHIPSNADE RAILWAY
L **S**

CHILMARK *No. (12)*
BALA LAKE RAILWAY
L

CHRISTINE *No. (D4092)*
SOUTH YORKSHIRE RAILWAY
L

CHURCHILL
DERWENT VALLEY
L **O**

CITY OF ABERDEEN
BO'NESS & KINNEIL RAILWAY
L

CITY OF LONDON *No. (2870)*
WINDMILL FARM RAILWAY
L **O**

CITY OF PETERBOROUGH *No. (73050)*
NENE VALLEY RAILWAY
L

CITY OF PLYMOUTH *No. (75079)*
PLYM VALLEY RAILWAY
L

CITY OF TRURO *No. (3717)*
NATIONAL RAILWAY MUSEUM
L

CITY OF WELLS *No. (34092)*
KEIGHLEY & WORTH VALLEY
L

CITY OF WESTMINSTER *No. (46258)*
SOUTH DOWNS LIGHT RAILWAY
L **O**

CLARA
RHYL MINIATURE RAILWAY
L **O**

CLAUDE THE COLONEL *No. (5)*
ROYAL VICTORIA RAILWAY
L **O**

CLAYTON *No. (D8568)*
CHINNOR & PRINCES RISBOROUGH
L

CLINTON *No. (4)*
BICTON WOODLAND RAILWAY
L **O**

CLIVE *No. (2)*
HEATHERSLAW LIGHT RAILWAY
L **O**

CLOISTER
KEW BRIDGE STEAM MUSEUM
L **O**

ROLLING STOCK by NAME

Charlie — Cloister

₩₩ CLUN CASTLE *No. (7029)*
TYSELEY LOCOMOTIVE WORKS

₩₩ CLWYD
WEST LANCASHIRE LIGHT RLWY
🅛

₩₩ CLYDE *No. (HE6347)*
LEADHILLS & WANLOCKHEAD
🅛 🅞

₩₩ CLYDEBRIDGE *No. (37215)*
GLOUCESTERSHIRE WARWICKSHIRE
🅛 🅞

₩₩ CLYDESMILL
BO'NESS & KINNEIL RAILWAY
🅛

₩₩ COED GORAU *No. (441427)*
LLANBERIS LAKE RAILWAY
🅛

₩₩ COFFEE POT
BEAMISH
🅛 🅢 🅓

₩₩ COFFIN
ARMLEY MILLS
🅛 🅢

₩₩ COGAN HALL *No. (5952)*
CAMBRIAN RAILWAY SOCIETY

₩₩ COLIN MCANDREW *No. (3)*
CHASEWATER RAILWAY
🅛 🅢 🅓

₩₩ COLONEL TOMLINE *No. (D3489)*
SPA VALLEY RAILWAY
🅛 🅞

₩₩ COLUMBINE *No. (1868)*
NATIONAL RAILWAY MUSEUM
🅛

₩₩ COLUMBKILLE *No. (6)*
FOYLE VALLEY RAILWAY CENTRE
🅛

₩₩ COLWYN *No. (45)*
NORTHAMPTON & LAMPORT RAILWAY
🅛

₩₩ COMMANDER B *No. (50)*
HOLLYCOMBE STEAM COLLECTION
🅛 🅞

₩₩ CONWAY CASTLE
FFESTINIOG RAILWAY
🅛 🅞

₩₩ COOKHAM MANOR *No. (7808)*
DIDCOT RAILWAY CENTRE
🅛

₩₩ COPPERNOB *No. (3)*
NATIONAL RAILWAY MUSEUM
🅛

₩₩ CORAL A *No. (41723)*
DIDCOT RAILWAY CENTRE
🅦

₩₩ CORNWALL *No. (3020)*
RAILWAY AGE
🅛 🅞

₩₩ CORNWALL *No. (D821)*
SEVERN VALLEY RAILWAY
🅛 🅞

₩₩ COUNTESS *No. (2)*
WELSHPOOL & LLANFAIR
🅛

₩₩ COUNTESS FITZWILLIAM
ELSECAR HERITAGE CENTRE
🅛

₩₩ COURAGE *No. (1786)*
MIDDLETON RAILWAY
🅛 🅞

COVENTRY NO 1
BUCKINGHAMSHIRE RLWY CTRE
L

COVERTCOAT
LAUNCESTON STEAM RAILWAY
L O

CRANES
SPA VALLEY RAILWAY
W O

CRANFORD
FOXFIELD STEAM RAILWAY
D

CRANFORD NO 2
EMBSAY & BOLTON ABBEY RLWY
L O

CREEPY *No. (29)*
LEIGHTON BUZZARD RAILWAY
L O D

CROCODILE F *No. (41934)*
DIDCOT RAILWAY CENTRE
W

CROMWELL
MARKEATON PARK LIGHT RAILWAY
L O

CUB (THE)
CLEETHORPES LIGHT RAILWAY
L

CUMBRIA *No. (3794)*
LAKESIDE & HAVERTHWAITE RLWY
L O

CUMBRIA *No. (11)*
SOUTH TYNEDALE RAILWAY
L O

CUNARDER *No. (47160)*
SWANAGE RAILWAY

CYCLOPS
TANFIELD RAILWAY
L

CYNTHIA *No. (DS88)*
PEAK RAIL
L

DAME VERA DUCKWORTH
WEST LANCASHIRE LIGHT RLWY
L

DAME VERA LYNN *No. (3672)*
NORTH YORKSHIRE MOORS RAILWAY
L

DAMREDUB *No. (17)*
LEIGHTON BUZZARD RAILWAY
L O D

DAVID *No. (2333)*
LAKESIDE & HAVERTHWAITE RLWY
L O

DAVID PAYNE *No. (185)*
DARLINGTON RAILWAY PRES SOC
L S D

DEAN GOODS *No. (2516)*
STEAM
L S D

DEFIANT *No. (5080)*
TYSELEY LOCOMOTIVE WORKS

DELTA
CADEBY LIGHT RAILWAY
L

DENZIL
EXMOOR STEAM RAILWAY
L O

DEREK CROUCH
NENE VALLEY RAILWAY
L S D

DERWENT *No. (25)*
NATIONAL RAILWAY MUSEUM
L

DERWENT II
DARLINGTON RAILWAY PRES SOC
L O

DEWAR HIGHLANDER
CALEDONIAN RAILWAY
L O

DIANA (THE) *No. (D7541)*
NORTH YORKSHIRE MOORS RAILWAY
L

DICKIE *No. (3)*
BEER HEIGHTS
L O

DINMOR *No. (3900011)*
CAVAN & LEITRIM RAILWAY
L O

DINMORE MANOR *No. (7820)*
WEST SOMERSET RAILWAY
L O

DITCHEAT MANOR *No. (7821)*
CAMBRIAN RAILWAY SOCIETY

DOLBADARN
LLANBERIS LAKE RAILWAY
L O

DOLGOCH *No. (2)*
TALYLLYN RAILWAY
L O

DOLL *No. (4)*
LEIGHTON BUZZARD RAILWAY
L O

DOLPHIN
GROUDLE GLEN RAILWAY
L

DONCASTER
NENE VALLEY RAILWAY
L O

DOROTHEA
LAUNCESTON STEAM RAILWAY
L O

DOROTHY *No. (D2337)*
SOUTH YORKSHIRE RAILWAY
L

DOT
NARROW GAUGE RAILWAY MUSEUM
L O

DOUGAL *No. (8)*
WELSHPOOL & LLANFAIR
L O

DOUGLAS *No. (6)*
TALYLLYN RAILWAY
L O

DOUGLAS *No. (10)*
WATERCRESS LINE
L O

DOVER CASTLE *No. (D3174)*
KENT & EAST SUSSEX RAILWAY
L O

DR SYN
ROMNEY HYTHE & DYMCHURCH
L O

DREADNOUGHT
AMERTON RAILWAY
L O

DROMAD
CAVAN & LEITRIM RAILWAY
L O

DRUID *No. (6)*
ABBEY LIGHT RAILWAY
L O

DRUMBO
DONEGAL RAILWAY HERITAGE CTRE
L

DUBSY
FOXFIELD STEAM RAILWAY
L

DUCHESS OF HAMILTON
NATIONAL RAILWAY MUSEUM
L

DUCHESS OF SUTHERLAND *No. (6233)*
MIDLAND RAILWAY CENTRE
L O

DUKE (THE) *No. (68012)*
PEAK RAIL
L

DUKE OF EDINBURGH
WINDMILL FARM RAILWAY
L O

DUKE OF GLOUCESTER *No. (71000)*
EAST LANCASHIRE RAILWAY

DUMBLETON HALL *No. (4920)*
SOUTH DEVON RAILWAY
L

DUNDEE GAS WORKS LOCO *No. (2)*
NARROW GAUGE RAILWAY MUSEUM
L D

DUNLOP NO 7
BATTLEFIELD LINE
L

DUNLUCE CASTLE *No. (74)*
ULSTER FOLK & TRANSPORT
L S D

DYLAN THOMAS *No. (27654)*
GWILI RAILWAY
L

E B WILSON *No. (252)*
ARMLEY MILLS

E V COOPER, ENGINEER *No. (46512)*
STRATHSPEY RAILWAY
L O

EAGLE *No. (50043)*
PONTYPOOL & BLAENAVON RAILWAY
L

EARL (THE) *No. (1)*
WELSHPOOL & LLANFAIR
L O

EARL BATHURST *No. (5051)*
DIDCOT RAILWAY CENTRE
L O

EARL FITZWILLIAM
ELSECAR HERITAGE CENTRE
L

EARL MOUNTBATTEN OF BURMA *No. (33203)*
SOUTH YORKSHIRE RAILWAY

EARL OF BERKELEY *No. (3217)*
BLUEBELL RAILWAY
L

EARL OF MOUNT EDGCUMBE *No. (5043)*
TYSELEY LOCOMOTIVE WORKS

EASTLEIGH *No. (1994)*
EASTLEIGH LAKESIDE RAILWAY
L O

EASTLEIGH *No. (33026)*
TYSELEY LOCOMOTIVE WORKS

EDDYSTONE *No. (34028)*
SWANAGE RAILWAY
L

EDWARD LLOYD *No. (435403)*
SITTINGBOURNE & KEMSLEY
L O

ROLLING STOCK by NAME

Drumbo — Edward Lloyd

EDWARD THOMAS *No. (4)*
TALYLLYN RAILWAY
L **O**

EDWIN HULSE *No. (2)*
AVON VALLEY RAILWAY
L

EIGIAU *No. (6)*
BREDGAR & WORMSHILL
L **O**

ELECTRA *No. (27000)*
MIDLAND RAILWAY CENTRE
R **S** **D**

ELF *No. (5)*
LEIGHTON BUZZARD RAILWAY
L **O** **D**

ELIDIR
LLANBERIS LAKE RAILWAY
L **O**

ELIZABETH
ALDERNEY RAILWAY
L **O**

ELIZABETH *No. (1888)*
ARMLEY MILLS
L **S** **D**

ELLAND
MANGAPPS RAILWAY MUSEUM
L **O** **D**

ELLERMAN LINES *No. (35029)*
NATIONAL RAILWAY MUSEUM
L **S** **D**

ELOUISE *No. (9998)*
OLD KILN LIGHT RAILWAY
L **O**

ELVAN
LEADHILLS & WANLOCKHEAD
L **O**

EMPRESS *No. (3061)*
MANGAPPS RAILWAY MUSEUM
L **D**

ENGINEER NO 1
AVON VALLEY RAILWAY
L

ENID *No. (2)*
SNOWDON MOUNTAIN RAILWAY
L **O**

ENTERPRISE
TANFIELD RAILWAY
L

ERIC TREACY *No. (45428)*
NORTH YORKSHIRE MOORS RAILWAY
L

ERLESTOKE MANOR *No. (7812)*
SEVERN VALLEY RAILWAY
L

ERROL LONSDALE *No. (68011)*
SOUTH DEVON RAILWAY
L **O**

ERYRI *No. (8)*
SNOWDON MOUNTAIN RAILWAY
L **O**

ERYRI *No. (23389)*
WELSH HIGHLAND RAILWAY
L **O**

ESCUCHA
TANFIELD RAILWAY
L

ESSO *No. (2716)*
NORTH YORKSHIRE MOORS RAILWAY
W

EUSTACE FORTH
NATIONAL RAILWAY MUSEUM
L

EVENING STAR *No. (92220)*
NATIONAL RAILWAY MUSEUM
L **S** **D**

EXCELSIOR *No. (1049)*
GREAT WHIPSNADE RAILWAY
L **O**

EXETER
SEVERN VALLEY RAILWAY
L **O**

EXPRESS DAIRY *No. (B3192)*
NORTH YORKSHIRE MOORS RAILWAY
W

FALCON *No. (7)*
LEIGHTON BUZZARD RAILWAY
L **O** **D**

FEANOR *No. (18)*
LEIGHTON BUZZARD RAILWAY
L **O** **D**

FENCHURCH *No. (672)*
BLUEBELL RAILWAY
L **O**

FERRET *No. (11)*
WELSHPOOL & LLANFAIR
L **S**

FESTIVAL OF BRITAIN
ARMLEY MILLS
L **S**

FESTOON *No. (21)*
LEIGHTON BUZZARD RAILWAY
L

FICOL
ARMLEY MILLS
L **S**

FIRE QUEEN
INDUSTRIAL RAILWAY MUSEUM
L **S** **D**

FIREFLY
RUTLAND RAILWAY MUSEUM

FLEET *No. (7)*
CHASEWATER RAILWAY
L **O**

FLORENCE *No. (92)*
EASTLEIGH LAKESIDE RAILWAY
L **O**

FLORENCE NO 2 *No. (2)*
FOXFIELD STEAM RAILWAY
L

FLUFF *No. (16)*
LAKESIDE & HAVERTHWAITE RLWY
L **D**

FLYING SCOTSMAN *No. (4472)*
BRESSINGHAM STEAM
L

FLYING SCOTSMAN
SOUTH DOWNS LIGHT RAILWAY
L

FLYING SCOTSMAN *No. (4472)*
WINDMILL FARM RAILWAY
L

FOLESHILL *No. (2085)*
PALLOT STEAM MUSEUM
L **S** **D**

FONMON *No. (1636)*
SPA VALLEY RAILWAY
L **O**

FOREMARKE HALL *No. (7903)*
SWINDON & CRICKLADE RAILWAY
L

FORT WILLIAM
ARMLEY MILLS
L **S**

ROLLING STOCK by NAME

Evening Star — Fort William

⚒⚒ FOUR ELMS *No.(204)*
SITTINGBOURNE & KEMSLEY
R

⚒⚒ FOX
KIRKLEES LIGHT RAILWAY
L O

⚒⚒ FOXCOTE MANOR *No.(7822)*
LLANGOLLEN RAILWAY
L O

⚒⚒ FRANCES
MULL RAILWAY
L

⚒⚒ FRANCIS HENRY LLOYD *No.(3)*
EASTLEIGH LAKESIDE RAILWAY
L O

⚒⚒ FRANKLIN D ROOSEVELT *No.(701)*
WATERCRESS LINE
L

⚒⚒ FRESHWATER *No.(W8)*
ISLE OF WIGHT STEAM RAILWAY
L O

⚒⚒ FULSTOW NO 2
LINCOLNSHIRE WOLDS RAILWAY
O

⚒⚒ G H WOOD *No.(10)*
ISLE OF MAN RAILWAY
L

⚒⚒ GALATEA *No.(5699)*
TYSELEY LOCOMOTIVE WORKS

⚒⚒ GAMMA
TANFIELD RAILWAY

⚒⚒ GARNET *No.(E327)*
NORTH YORKSHIRE MOORS RAILWAY
C

⚒⚒ GAS OIL
FOXFIELD STEAM RAILWAY
L S

⚒⚒ GATESHEAD *No.(D1501)*
EAST LANCASHIRE RAILWAY

⚒⚒ GAZELLE *No.(1)*
KENT & EAST SUSSEX RAILWAY
L S D

⚒⚒ GELERT *No.(3050)*
WELSH HIGHLAND RAILWAY
L O

⚒⚒ GEM *No.(8)*
BEER HEIGHTS
L O

⚒⚒ GENERAL LORD ROBERTSON *No.(610)*
AVON VALLEY RAILWAY
L

⚒⚒ GEORGE *No.(12)*
SNOWDON MOUNTAIN RAILWAY
L O

⚒⚒ GEORGE
SOUTH YORKSHIRE RAILWAY

⚒⚒ GEORGE B
NORTH GLOUCESTERSHIRE RAILWAY
L

⚒⚒ GEORGE B/WELLINGTON
TEIFI VALLEY RAILWAY

⚒⚒ GEORGE EDWARDS *No.(33)*
PRESTONGRANGE INDUSTRIAL

⚒⚒ GEORGE HENRY
NARROW GAUGE RAILWAY MUSEUM
L D

⚒⚒ GEORGE MASON *No.(08123)*
CHOLSEY & WALLINGFORD RAILWAY
L D

ʌʌʎ GEORGE STEPHENSON *No.(44767)*
NORTH YORKSHIRE MOORS RAILWAY
L

ʌʌʎ GIBRALTAR
BUCKINGHAMSHIRE RLWY CTRE
L

ʌʌʎ GLADIATOR *No.(3)*
LAPPA VALLEY STEAM RAILWAY
L O

ʌʌʎ GLADSTONE *No.(214)*
NATIONAL RAILWAY MUSEUM
L S D

ʌʌʎ GLADYS
MIDLAND RAILWAY CENTRE
L S D

ʌʌʎ GLADYS
ROMNEY HYTHE & DYMCHURCH
C

ʌʌʎ GLASLYN *No.(292030)*
WELSH HIGHLAND RAILWAY
L O

ʌʌʎ GLEN AULDYN
MULL RAILWAY
L O

ʌʌʎ GLENDOWER
SOUTH DEVON RAILWAY
L

ʌʌʎ GMJ
NATIONAL TRAMWAY MUSEUM
L O

ʌʌʎ GOLIATH *No.(5139)*
PAIGNTON & DARTMOUTH RAILWAY
L O

ʌʌʎ GOLSPIE
AMERTON RAILWAY
L

ʌʌʎ GORDON
AMERTON RAILWAY
L

ʌʌʎ GORDON *No.(600)*
SEVERN VALLEY RAILWAY
L

ʌʌʎ GORDON HIGHLANDER
ALFORD VALLEY RAILWAY
L O

ʌʌʎ GOTHENBURG *No.(32)*
EAST LANCASHIRE RAILWAY

ʌʌʎ GOWRIE
BARLEYLANDS MINIATURE RAILWAY
L O

ʌʌʎ GRAF SCHWERIN-LOWITZ
BRECON MOUNTAIN RAILWAY
L

ʌʌʎ GRAHAM ALEXANDER
RUISLIP LIDO RAILWAY
L O

ʌʌʎ GRAIN *No.(42239)*
DIDCOT RAILWAY CENTRE
W

ʌʌʎ GRANVILLE *No.(102)*
BRESSINGHAM STEAM
L S D

ʌʌʎ GREAT GABLE *No.(D4)*
MIDLAND RAILWAY CENTRE
L O

ʌʌʎ GREAT MARQUESS (THE) *No.(3442)*
SEVERN VALLEY RAILWAY
L

ʌʌʎ GREEN ARROW *No.(4771)*
NATIONAL RAILWAY MUSEUM
L

ROLLING STOCK by NAME

George Stephenson — Green Arrow

ROLLING STOCK by **NAME**

Green Goddess — Hawarden

GREEN GODDESS
ROMNEY HYTHE & DYMCHURCH
L O

GREENBAT *No. (12)*
ABBEY LIGHT RAILWAY
L O

GRUMPY *No. (WD70031)*
AVON VALLEY RAILWAY
L

GUINESS BREWERY LOCO NO 13
NARROW GAUGE RAILWAY MUSEUM
L O

GUINNESS *No. (3BG)*
RPSI
L

GWRIL
WINDMILL FARM RAILWAY
L O

GWYNETH *No. (D3019)*
SOUTH YORKSHIRE RAILWAY
L

H W ROBINSON
EMBSAY & BOLTON ABBEY RLWY
L O

HAGLEY HALL *No. (4930)*
SEVERN VALLEY RAILWAY
L S D

HAMBURG *No. (31)*
KEIGHLEY & WORTH VALLEY
L

HARDWICKE *No. (790)*
NATIONAL RAILWAY MUSEUM
L S D

HARLAXTON
SCOTTISH RAILWAY CENTRE
L O

HARLECH CASTLE
FFESTINIOG RAILWAY
L O

HARLECH CASTLE *No. (25265)*
GREAT CENTRAL RAILWAY
L O

HARROGATE *No. (3)*
BREDGAR & WORMSHILL
L O

HARRY *No. (2589)*
BARROW HILL ROUNDHOUSE
L O

HARRY
PONTYPOOL & BLAENAVON RAILWAY
L

HARRY A FRITH *No. (E828)*
SWANAGE RAILWAY
L O

HARRY BARNETT *No. (38)*
LEIGHTON BUZZARD RAILWAY
L O D

HARTFIELD *No. (17)*
MOORS VALLEY RAILWAY
L O

HARTLAND *No. (34101)*
NORTH YORKSHIRE MOORS RAILWAY
L

HAULWEN *No. (5272)*
GWILI RAILWAY
L

HAWARDEN
FOXFIELD STEAM RAILWAY
L O

HAWARDEN *No. (526)*
INDUSTRIAL RAILWAY MUSEUM
L S D

ROLLING STOCK by NAME

Hawk — Hood

HAWK
KIRKLEES LIGHT RAILWAY
L **O**

HAYDN TAYLOR *No. (10)*
LEIGHTON BUZZARD RAILWAY
L **O** **D**

HAYDOCK
INDUSTRIAL RAILWAY MUSEUM
L **D**

HECTOR *No. (4160004)*
GREAT WHIPSNADE RAILWAY
L **O**

HELEN
FOXFIELD STEAM RAILWAY
L **S**

HELEN KATHRYN *No. (14)*
SOUTH TYNEDALE RAILWAY
L **O**

HELEN TURNER *No. (D5032)*
NORTH YORKSHIRE MOORS RAILWAY
L

HEM HEATH *No. (3D)*
CHASEWATER RAILWAY
L **O**

HENBURY *No. (1940)*
BRISTOL HARBOUR RAILWAY
L **O**

HENDON
TANFIELD RAILWAY

HENRY
TYSELEY LOCOMOTIVE WORKS

HENRY CORT
FOXFIELD STEAM RAILWAY
L **S** **D**

HENRY DE LACY II *No. (1309)*
MIDDLETON RAILWAY
L

HENRY OAKLEY *No. (990)*
NATIONAL RAILWAY MUSEUM
L **S** **D**

HERCULES
FOXFIELD STEAM RAILWAY
L **O**

HERCULES *No. (24376)*
GREAT WHIPSNADE RAILWAY
L **O**

HERCULES *No. (D7535)*
PAIGNTON & DARTMOUTH RAILWAY
L **O**

HERCULES
ROMNEY HYTHE & DYMCHURCH
L **O**

HINDERTON HALL *No. (5900)*
DIDCOT RAILWAY CENTRE
L **S**

HINTON MANOR *No. (7819)*
SEVERN VALLEY RAILWAY
L **S**

HODBARROW *No. (299)*
ARMLEY MILLS
L **S**

HOLMAN F STEPHENS *No. (23)*
KENT & EAST SUSSEX RAILWAY
L

HOLY WAR *No. (3)*
BALA LAKE RAILWAY
L **O**

HOOD
SEVERN VALLEY RAILWAY
L **O**

HORACE
MOORS VALLEY RAILWAY
L O

HORDEN
TANFIELD RAILWAY

HORTON *No.(14)*
MOORS VALLEY RAILWAY
L O

HOTSPUR *No.(2944)*
SPA VALLEY RAILWAY
L

HOTWHEELS
SOUTH YORKSHIRE RAILWAY

HOWE *No.(50023)*
BARROW HILL ROUNDHOUSE
L S

HUDSON FORDSON
ARMLEY MILLS
L O

HUDSON GOGO *No.(8)*
ABBEY LIGHT RAILWAY
L

HUDSON HUNSLET
ARMLEY MILLS
L O

HUNCOAT
TANFIELD RAILWAY

HUNSLET TAYLOR
ARMLEY MILLS
L S D

HURRICANE
ROMNEY HYTHE & DYMCHURCH
L O

HUTCHINSON *No.(12)*
ISLE OF MAN RAILWAY
L

HUTNIK *No.(3138)*
APPLEBY-FRODINGHAM RAILWAY
L O

HYDRA D *No.(42193)*
DIDCOT RAILWAY CENTRE
W

HYLTON *No.(3967)*
NIRT
L O

IBSTOCK
AMBERLEY WORKING MUSEUM
L

IDRIS *No.(207103)*
GWILI RAILWAY
L O

ILLINGWORTH
EMBSAY & BOLTON ABBEY RLWY
L

INDIAN RAILWAYS HILL ENGINE *No.(MLR740)*
RAILWORLD

INVINCIBLE *No.(37)*
ISLE OF WIGHT STEAM RAILWAY
L O

IRIS *No.(459515)*
CHINNOR & PRINCES RISBOROUGH
L

IRISH MAIL
WEST LANCASHIRE LIGHT RLWY
L

IRON MINK *No.(11152)*
DIDCOT RAILWAY CENTRE
W

IRONBRIDGE NO 1 *No. (1)*
FOXFIELD STEAM RAILWAY
L **S** **D**

IRWELL
TANFIELD RAILWAY

ISABEL
AMERTON RAILWAY
L **O**

ISABEL
WEST SOMERSET RAILWAY
L

ISAMBARD KINGDOM BRUNEL *No. (4)*
ROYAL VICTORIA RAILWAY
L **O**

ISIBUTU *No. (5)*
NORTH GLOUCESTERSHIRE RAILWAY
L

IVOR
DEVON RAILWAY CENTRE
L **O**

IVOR
KERR MINIATURE RAILWAY
L **O**

IVOR *No. (395305)*
NIRT
L

IVOR *No. (2)*
ROYAL VICTORIA RAILWAY
L

J T DALY *No. (2450)*
PALLOT STEAM MUSEUM
L **S** **D**

JACK *No. (684)*
ARMLEY MILLS
L **O**

JACK
HOLLYCOMBE STEAM COLLECTION

JACKS GREEN
NENE VALLEY RAILWAY
L **S** **D**

JACOB *No. (680)*
BEAMISH
L

JAMES *No. (5)*
WATERCRESS LINE
L **O**

JAMES GORDON
ALFORD VALLEY RAILWAY
L **O**

JANE
BROOKSIDE MINIATURE
L **O**

JANUS
APPLEBY-FRODINGHAM RAILWAY

JANUS
NENE VALLEY RAILWAY
L **O**

JASON *No. (9)*
MOORS VALLEY RAILWAY
L **O**

JAY
KIRKLEES LIGHT RAILWAY
L

JEAN
BROOKSIDE MINIATURE
L **O**

JEFFREY
EAST ANGLIAN RAILWAY MUSEUM
L

ROLLING STOCK by NAME

Jessie — Kathleen

JESSIE *No. (E1104)*
BATTLEFIELD LINE
C

JIM *No. (DS48)*
DERWENT VALLEY
L

JIMMY *No. (6)*
BEER HEIGHTS
L O

JOAN *No. (101)*
RHYL MINIATURE RAILWAY
L O

JOAN *No. (12)*
WELSHPOOL & LLANFAIR
L S D

JOE BROWN *No. (D6353)*
WINDMILL FARM RAILWAY
L O

JOFFRE
WEST LANCASHIRE LIGHT RLWY
L

JOHN ALCOCK *No. (1697)*
MIDDLETON RAILWAY
L O

JOHN BLENKINSOP *No. (2003)*
MIDDLETON RAILWAY
L

JOHN HAMPDEN *No. (5)*
LONDON TRANSPORT MUSEUM
L S D

JOHN SOUTHLAND
ROMNEY HYTHE & DYMCHURCH
L O

JOHNNIE WALKER
SCOTTISH RAILWAY CENTRE
L S

JONATHAN
WEST LANCASHIRE LIGHT RLWY
L

JOSIAH WEDGWOOD *No. (3777)*
CHURNET VALLEY RAILWAY
L

JUBILEE
EAST ANGLIAN RAILWAY MUSEUM
L

JUBILEE
NARROW GAUGE RAILWAY MUSEUM
L S D

JUDITH *No. (D2324)*
SOUTH YORKSHIRE RAILWAY

JULIA
NOTTINGHAM TRANSPORT CTRE
L

JUNIN
ARMLEY MILLS
L S

JUNO
BUCKINGHAMSHIRE RLWY CTRE
L

JUPITER
COLNE VALLEY RAILWAY
L

JUSTINE
NORTH GLOUCESTERSHIRE RAILWAY
L

KAREN
WELSH HIGHLAND RAILWAY
L D

KATHLEEN
ULSTER FOLK & TRANSPORT
L S D

KATIE *No.(2)*
BREDGAR & WORMSHILL
L O

KATIE
WINDMILL FARM RAILWAY
L

KELTON FELL
BO'NESS & KINNEIL RAILWAY
L

KEN *No.(67)*
SOUTH YORKSHIRE RAILWAY

KESTREL *No.(384)*
HOLLYBUSH GARDEN CENTRE
L O

KESTREL *No.(2129)*
PALLOT STEAM MUSEUM
L O

KILBAGGIE
BO'NESS & KINNEIL RAILWAY
L

KILMERSDON
WEST SOMERSET RAILWAY
L

KING EDWARD I *No.(6024)*
DIDCOT RAILWAY CENTRE
L O

KING EDWARD II *No.(6023)*
DIDCOT RAILWAY CENTRE
L

KING GEORGE *No.(2409)*
GLOUCESTERSHIRE WARWICKSHIRE
L O

KING GEORGE *No.(2005)*
KERR MINIATURE RAILWAY
O

KING GEORGE V *No.(6000)*
STEAM
L S D

KING HAAKON VII *No.(377)*
BRESSINGHAM STEAM
L S D

KINGSWOOD
AVON VALLEY RAILWAY
L

KINNERLEY *No.(354068)*
WELSH HIGHLAND RAILWAY
L O

KNOWLE *No.(2678)*
KENT & EAST SUSSEX RAILWAY
L O

KOLHAPUR *No.(5593)*
TYSELEY LOCOMOTIVE WORKS

KONIGSWINTER *No.(1)*
CLEETHORPES LIGHT RAILWAY
L

L2
TANFIELD RAILWAY

LA MEUSE
PALLOT STEAM MUSEUM
L S D

LADY ANGELA
SOUTH DEVON RAILWAY
L

LADY ARMAGHDALE (THE) *No.(686)*
SEVERN VALLEY RAILWAY
L

LADY AUGUSTA (THE) *No.(1)*
HEATHERSLAW LIGHT RAILWAY
L O

⚙ LADY INGRID *No. (2315)*
SPA VALLEY RAILWAY
L **O**

⚙ LADY JOAN *No. (1)*
BREDGAR & WORMSHILL
L **O**

⚙ LADY NAN *No. (1719)*
EAST SOMERSET RAILWAY
L **O**

⚙ LADY OF LEGEND *No. (2999)*
DIDCOT RAILWAY CENTRE
L

⚙ LADY OF THE ISLES *No. (2298)*
MULL RAILWAY
L **O**

⚙ LADY OF THE LAKES
RUISLIP LIDO RAILWAY
L **O**

⚙ LADY VICTORIA
BO'NESS & KINNEIL RAILWAY
L

⚙ LAMPORT NO 3 *No. (2670)*
BATTLEFIELD LINE
L **O**

⚙ LAYER
ARMLEY MILLS
L **S**

⚙ LEADER *No. (926)*
SITTINGBOURNE & KEMSLEY
L **O**

⚙ LEANDER *No. (5690)*
EAST LANCASHIRE RAILWAY

⚙ LEC *No. (3)*
BODMIN & WENFORD RAILWAY
L **O**

⚙ LEWIN *No. (18)*
BEAMISH
L **S** **O**

⚙ LEWISHAM
FOXFIELD STEAM RAILWAY
L **O**

⚙ LILIAN
LAUNCESTON STEAM RAILWAY
L **O**

⚙ LILY OF THE VALLEY
SCOTTISH RAILWAY CENTRE
L **S**

⚙ LINDA *No. (2648)*
BATTLEFIELD LINE
L

⚙ LINDA *No. (5)*
BEER HEIGHTS
L **O**

⚙ LINDA
FFESTINIOG RAILWAY
L **O**

⚙ LION *No. (08022)*
CHOLSEY & WALLINGFORD RAILWAY
L **O**

⚙ LION
LINCOLNSHIRE WOLDS RAILWAY
O

⚙ LION *No. (50027)*
NORTH YORKSHIRE MOORS RAILWAY
L

⚙ LISTER
DEVON RAILWAY CENTRE
L **O**

⚙ LITTLE CLYDE
LEADHILLS & WANLOCKHEAD
L **O**

LITTLE TITAN
BURE VALLEY RAILWAY
[O]

LITTLETON NO 5
AVON VALLEY RAILWAY

LLANELLI *No. (451901)*
LLANBERIS LAKE RAILWAY
[L]

LLANTARNAM ABBEY
SWANSEA VALE RAILWAY
[L]

LLANWERN *No. (104)*
PONTYPOOL & BLAENAVON RAILWAY
[L] [O]

LLWELYN *No. (8)*
VALE OF RHEIDOL RAILWAY
[L] [O]

LOCH *No. (4)*
ISLE OF MAN RAILWAY
[L]

LOCOMOTION *No. (1)*
BEAMISH
[L] [O] [D]

LOCOMOTION *No. (1)*
NATIONAL RAILWAY MUSEUM
[L] [S] [D]

LODE STAR *No. (4003)*
NATIONAL RAILWAY MUSEUM
[L] [S] [D]

LODGE HILL *No. (200)*
SITTINGBOURNE & KEMSLEY
[R]

LOFTI
ARMLEY MILLS
[L] [S]

LOIS *No. (4220033)*
NIRT
[L] [O]

LORD ASHFIELD *No. (5)*
MUSEUM OF SCIENCE & INDUSTRY
[L] [D]

LORD FISHER *No. (1398)*
EAST SOMERSET RAILWAY
[L] [O]

LORD GRANBY *No. (633)*
ARMLEY MILLS
[L] [S]

LORD KING
BO'NESS & KINNEIL RAILWAY
[L]

LORD MAYOR
VINTAGE CARRIAGES TRUST
[L] [S] [D]

LORD NELSON *No. (850)*
NATIONAL RAILWAY MUSEUM
[L]

LORD ROBERTS
BO'NESS & KINNEIL RAILWAY
[L]

LORIOT L *No. (42271)*
DIDCOT RAILWAY CENTRE
[W]

LOUGH ERNE *No. (27)*
RPSI
[L]

LOWECO *No. (1)*
ABBEY LIGHT RAILWAY
[L] [O]

LUCE
LEADHILLS & WANLOCKHEAD
[L] [O]

ROLLING STOCK by NAME

Ludstone — Mary Ann

Ludstone
FOXFIELD STEAM RAILWAY
L O

LUTON *No. (1210)*
ARMLEY MILLS
L S D

LYDHAM MANOR *No. (7827)*
PAIGNTON & DARTMOUTH RAILWAY
L

LYTHAM ST ANNES
MIDLAND RAILWAY CENTRE
L S D

MACAW B *No. (70335)*
DIDCOT RAILWAY CENTRE
W

MACNAMARA *No. (48)*
LEIGHTON BUZZARD RAILWAY
L O D

MAD BESS
RUISLIP LIDO RAILWAY
L O

MADGE *No. (9)*
LEIGHTON BUZZARD RAILWAY
L

MAEDB *No. (800)*
ULSTER FOLK & TRANSPORT
L S D

MAID MARIAN *No. (5)*
BALA LAKE RAILWAY
L O

MAID OF BENFLEET
BARLEYLANDS MINIATURE RAILWAY
L S D

MAITLAND *No. (11)*
ISLE OF MAN RAILWAY
L

MAJOR (THE)
AMBERLEY WORKING MUSEUM
L

MALANDRA
HOLLYBUSH GARDEN CENTRE
L O

MALLARD *No. (4468)*
NATIONAL RAILWAY MUSEUM
L

MANNERTREU
BRESSINGHAM STEAM
L O

MARCIA *No. (12)*
KENT & EAST SUSSEX RAILWAY
L O

MARGARET ANNE *No. (03158)*
PEAK RAIL
L

MARKEATON LADY
MARKEATON PARK LIGHT RAILWAY
L O

MARSTON, THOMPSON & EVERSHED LIMITED NO 3 *No. (3)*
FOXFIELD STEAM RAILWAY
L

MARTELLO *No. (662)*
BRESSINGHAM STEAM
L S D

MARY *No. (577)*
MIDDLETON RAILWAY
L O

MARY ANN
FFESTINIOG RAILWAY
L

⚙ MATTHEW MURRAY *No.(2702)*
MIDDLETON RAILWAY
L

⚙ MATTHEW MURRAY *No.(1601)*
MIDDLETON RAILWAY
L O

⚙ MAUDE *No.(673)*
BO'NESS & KINNEIL RAILWAY
L

⚙ MAUNSELL *No.(65)*
KENT & EAST SUSSEX RAILWAY
L O

⚙ MAURICE THE MAJOR *No.(3)*
ROYAL VICTORIA RAILWAY
L

⚙ MAY *No.(2)*
SWANAGE RAILWAY
L O

⚙ MAYFLOWER *No.(1306)*
NENE VALLEY RAILWAY
L

⚙ MEAFORD NO 1
EMBSAY & BOLTON ABBEY RLWY
L O

⚙ MEAFORD NO 2 *No.(2)*
FOXFIELD STEAM RAILWAY
L O

⚙ MEAFORD NO 4
FOXFIELD STEAM RAILWAY
L

⚙ MEDEA *No.(6)*
MOORS VALLEY RAILWAY
L O

⚙ MEENGLAS *No.(4)*
FOYLE VALLEY RAILWAY CENTRE
L

⚙ MEGAN
FOXFIELD STEAM RAILWAY
L S

⚙ MEIRIONNYDD *No.(11)*
BALA LAKE RAILWAY
L O

⚙ MELIOR *No.(4219)*
SITTINGBOURNE & KEMSLEY
L O

⚙ MENELAEUS *No.(1883)*
CALEDONIAN RAILWAY
L

⚙ MERLIN *No.(231)*
KEIGHLEY & WORTH VALLEY
L O

⚙ MERLIN *No.(85)*
RPSI
L O

⚙ MERLIN *No.(7)*
RUDYARD LAKE RAILWAY
L O

⚙ MERLIN
TIMOTHY HACKWORTH
L O

⚙ MERRY TOM
NORTHAMPTON & LAMPORT RAILWAY
L

⚙ MERSEYSIDER *No.(8)*
TALYLLYN RAILWAY
L

⚙ MET
DARLINGTON RAILWAY CENTRE
L S

⚙ METEOR
AVON VALLEY RAILWAY
L

ROLLING STOCK by NAME

Matthew Murray — Meteor

M·W·F MIDLANDER *No. (5)*
TALYLLYN RAILWAY
L O

M·W·F MIGHTY MAX
BROOKSIDE MINIATURE
L O

M·W·F MILDRED *No. (2)*
RUDYARD LAKE RAILWAY
L O

M·W·F MILL REEF
WEST LANCASHIRE LIGHT RLWY
L

M·W·F MILLOM
FOXFIELD STEAM RAILWAY
L

M·W·F MINNIE *No. (358)*
MANGAPPS RAILWAY MUSEUM
L S D

M·W·F MIRAGE *No. (D6732)*
NORTH NORFOLK RAILWAY
L O

M·W·F MIRVALE *No. (1882)*
MIDDLETON RAILWAY
L S

M·W·F MOEL HEBOG
FFESTINIOG RAILWAY
L O

M·W·F MOEL SIABOD *No. (5)*
SNOWDON MOUNTAIN RAILWAY
L O

M·W·F MOELWYN
FFESTINIOG RAILWAY
L O

M·W·F MONARCH
WELSHPOOL & LLANFAIR

M·W·F MONARCH (THE) *No. (1001)*
EASTLEIGH LAKESIDE RAILWAY
L O

M·W·F MONCKTON NO 1
EMBSAY & BOLTON ABBEY RLWY
L

M·W·F MONTALBAN
WEST LANCASHIRE LIGHT RLWY
L

M·W·F MONTY *No. (6)*
AMBERLEY WORKING MUSEUM
L

M·W·F MOORBARROW
LINCOLNSHIRE WOLDS RAILWAY

M·W·F MORAYSHIRE *No. (246)*
BO'NESS & KINNEIL RAILWAY
L

M·W·F MORNING STAR *No. (92207)*
EAST LANCASHIRE RAILWAY

M·W·F MOSELEY
DARLINGTON RAILWAY PRES SOC
L

M·W·F MOSS BAY
FOXFIELD STEAM RAILWAY
L S D

M·W·F MOUNTAINEER
FFESTINIOG RAILWAY
L O

M·W·F MR BILL *No. (10)*
GREAT WHIPSNADE RAILWAY
L O

M·W·F MR G *No. (6)*
GARTELL LIGHT RAILWAY
L

MR HUMPHRIES *No. (52012)*
CALEDONIAN RAILWAY
R

MR MERCURY *No. (1)*
EAST LANCASHIRE RAILWAY

MR P *No. (7)*
BEER HEIGHTS
L O

MRS SLOCOMBE *No. (51993)*
CALEDONIAN RAILWAY
L R

MS & L TRICOMPOSITE *No. (176)*
VINTAGE CARRIAGES TRUST
C O D

MUFFIN *No. (2)*
LAPPA VALLEY STEAM RAILWAY
L O

MUFFIN *No. (242688)*
NIRT

MUIR HILL *No. (9)*
ABBEY LIGHT RAILWAY
L

MURIEL
NENE VALLEY RAILWAY
L O

MUSKETEER *No. (9369)*
NIRT
L D

NACOB
ARMLEY MILLS
L S

NAKLO *No. (10)*
SOUTH TYNEDALE RAILWAY
L

NAWORTH *No. (4)*
SOUTH TYNEDALE RAILWAY
L O

NEEPSEND
MIDLAND RAILWAY CENTRE
L S D

NEIL D BARKER *No. (12 139)*
NORTH YORKSHIRE MOORS RAILWAY
L

NELLIE *No. (02101)*
GWILI RAILWAY
L O

NEPTUNE (ST NICHOLAS)
WINDMILL FARM RAILWAY

NEWPORT *No. (W11)*
ISLE OF WIGHT STEAM RAILWAY
L O

'NICKEL MOND NO 1'
SWANSEA VALE RAILWAY
L O

NINIAN *No. (9)*
SNOWDON MOUNTAIN RAILWAY
L O

NIPPY
IRISH STEAM PRESERVATION SOC
L O

NITH *No. (DM1002)*
LEADHILLS & WANLOCKHEAD
L O

NO 1 *No. (1876)*
SITTINGBOURNE & KEMSLEY
S D

NORA *No. (5)*
PONTYPOOL & BLAENAVON RAILWAY
L S

ROLLING STOCK by NAME

Mr Humphries — Nora

ᴬᴬᵂ NORFOLK HERO *No. (3)*
WELLS & WALSINGHAM
🅛

ᴬᴬᵂ NORMA *No. (3770)*
CAMBRIAN RAILWAY SOCIETY

ᴬᴬᵂ NORMANDY *No. (96)*
BLUEBELL RAILWAY
🅛 🅞

ᴬᴬᵂ NORTH DOWNS *No. (7846)*
SPA VALLEY RAILWAY
🅛

ᴬᴬᵂ NORTH STAR
STEAM
🅛 🅢 🅓

ᴬᴬᵂ NORTHAMPTON *No. (7646)*
NORTHAMPTON & LAMPORT RAILWAY
🅛 🅞

ᴬᴬᵂ NORTHERN CHIEF
ROMNEY HYTHE & DYMCHURCH
🅛 🅞

ᴬᴬᵂ NORTHERN GAS BOARD NO 1 *No. (2142)*
BATTLEFIELD LINE
🅛 🅞

ᴬᴬᵂ NORTHERN ROCK
RAVENGLASS & ESKDALE
🅛 🅞

ᴬᴬᵂ NORTHIAM *No. (25)*
KENT & EAST SUSSEX RAILWAY
🅛 🅞

ᴬᴬᵂ NORWEGIAN *No. (376)*
KENT & EAST SUSSEX RAILWAY
🅛 🅞

ᴬᴬᵂ NORWOOD *No. (77)*
BOWES RAILWAY
🅛 🅢

ᴬᴬᵂ NUNLOW
KEIGHLEY & WORTH VALLEY
🅛

ᴬᴬᵂ NUTTY
WELSHPOOL & LLANFAIR

ᴬᴬᵂ OAK BANK OIL COMPANY NO 2
ALMOND VALLEY HERITAGE TRUST
🅛 🅢 🅓

ᴬᴬᵂ OCTAVIUS ATKINSON *No. (DS88)*
DERWENT VALLEY
🅛 🅞

ᴬᴬᵂ ODIN *No. (3)*
ABBEY LIGHT RAILWAY
🅛 🅞

ᴬᴬᵂ ODNEY MANOR *No. (7828)*
WEST SOMERSET RAILWAY
🅛 🅞

ᴬᴬᵂ OFFA *No. (10)*
MOORS VALLEY RAILWAY
🅛 🅞

ᴬᴬᵂ OLD RUBE
CONWY VALLEY
🅛 🅞

ᴬᴬᵂ OLIVE *No. (RDB998901)*
MIDDLETON RAILWAY
🅛 🅞

ᴬᴬᵂ OLIVER CROMWELL *No. (70013)*
NATIONAL RAILWAY MUSEUM
🅛 🅢 🅓

ᴬᴬᵂ OLIVER VELTON *No. (6)*
CAMBRIAN RAILWAY SOCIETY

ᴬᴬᵂ OLWEN *No. (7058)*
GWILI RAILWAY
🅛 🅞

₳₳₳ ONSLAUGHT *No. (D832)*
EAST LANCASHIRE RAILWAY

₳₳₳ ORFORDNESS *No. (6)*
EAST ANGLIA TRANSPORT MUSEUM
L **O**

₳₳₳ ORION *No. (5)*
WELSHPOOL & LLANFAIR
L **O**

₳₳₳ OSRAM
BUCKINGHAMSHIRE RLWY CTRE
L

₳₳₳ OWAIN GLYNDWR *No. (7)*
VALE OF RHEIDOL RAILWAY
L

₳₳₳ OWL
KIRKLEES LIGHT RAILWAY
L **O**

₳₳₳ PADARN *No. (6)*
SNOWDON MOUNTAIN RAILWAY
L

₳₳₳ PALMERSTON *No. (4)*
FFESTINIOG RAILWAY
L **O**

₳₳₳ PAMELA *No. (920)*
OLD KILN LIGHT RAILWAY
L

₳₳₳ PAMELA *No. (3840)*
VALE OF GLAMORGAN RAILWAY
L **O**

₳₳₳ PATHFINDER
WEST LANCASHIRE LIGHT RLWY
L

₳₳₳ PATRICIA *No. (68189)*
CALEDONIAN RAILWAY
L

₳₳₳ PATRICIA *No. (68189)*
CALEDONIAN RAILWAY
L **S** **D**

₳₳₳ PC ALLEN *No. (11)*
LEIGHTON BUZZARD RAILWAY
L **O** **D**

₳₳₳ PEARL 2
AMERTON RAILWAY
L **O**

₳₳₳ PECTIN *No. (1)*
YEOVIL RAILWAY CENTRE
L **O**

₳₳₳ PEDEMOURA
WELSH HIGHLAND RAILWAY
L

₳₳₳ PEER GYNT *No. (5865)*
BRESSINGHAM STEAM
L **S** **D**

₳₳₳ PELDON *No. (21295)*
AMBERLEY WORKING MUSEUM
L

₳₳₳ PENDENNIS CASTLE *No. (4079)*
DIDCOT RAILWAY CENTRE
L

₳₳₳ PENDER
MUSEUM OF SCIENCE & INDUSTRY
L **S** **D**

₳₳₳ PENINSULAR & ORIENTAL S N CO *No. (35006)*
GLOUCESTERSHIRE WARWICKSHIRE
L

₳₳₳ PENN GREEN
EAST ANGLIAN RAILWAY MUSEUM
L

ROLLING STOCK by NAME
Onslaught — Penn Green

PENYGHENT *No. (D8)*
PEAK RAIL
L

PEN-YR-ORSEDD
DEVON RAILWAY CENTRE
O

PERCY *No. (1738)*
SOUTH DEVON RAILWAY
L O

PERIS *No. (11)*
SNOWDON MOUNTAIN RAILWAY
L O

PET
NATIONAL RAILWAY MUSEUM
L

PETER *No. (2067)*
AMBERLEY WORKING MUSEUM
L

PETER *No. (2)*
BODMIN & WENFORD RAILWAY
L

PETER *No. (02003)*
SOUTH YORKSHIRE RAILWAY

PETER PAN *No. (114)*
LEIGHTON BUZZARD RAILWAY
L O

PHANTOM *No. (08 604)*
DIDCOT RAILWAY CENTRE
L

PHOENIX *No. (1)*
SOUTH TYNEDALE RAILWAY
L

PHOENIX
ULSTER FOLK & TRANSPORT
L S D

PIONEER *No. (D634)*
ARMLEY MILLS
L S

PIONEER *No. (12)*
MOORS VALLEY RAILWAY
L O

PITCHFORD HALL *No. (4953)*
TYSELEY LOCOMOTIVE WORKS

PITPO
ARMLEY MILLS
L S

PIXIE
CADEBY LIGHT RAILWAY
L

PIXIE
LEIGHTON BUZZARD RAILWAY
L O D

PLANET
DEVON RAILWAY CENTRE
L O

PLASSER TAMPER
WELSHPOOL & LLANFAIR

POLAR BEAR *No. (1781)*
AMBERLEY WORKING MUSEUM
L

PONTYBEREM *No. (2)*
DIDCOT RAILWAY CENTRE
L

POOH *No. (4)*
LAPPA VALLEY STEAM RAILWAY
L O

PORT LINE *No. (35027)*
SWANAGE RAILWAY
L O

PORTBURY *No. (34)*
BRISTOL HARBOUR RAILWAY
L **O**

PREMIER *No. (886)*
SITTINGBOURNE & KEMSLEY
L **S** **D**

PRESTONGRANGE *No. (7)*
PRESTONGRANGE INDUSTRIAL

PRIDE OF SUSSEX *No. (1556)*
KENT & EAST SUSSEX RAILWAY
L **O**

PRIMROSE NO 2
EMBSAY & BOLTON ABBEY RLWY
L

PRINCE *No. (2)*
FFESTINIOG RAILWAY
L **O**

PRINCE OF WALES *No. (9113)*
DIDCOT RAILWAY CENTRE
R

PRINCE OF WALES *No. (9)*
VALE OF RHEIDOL RAILWAY
L **O**

PRINCE WILLIAM *No. (5751)*
WINDMILL FARM RAILWAY
L **O**

PRINCESS *No. (1)*
FFESTINIOG RAILWAY
L **D**

PRINCESS *No. (14)*
LAKESIDE & HAVERTHWAITE RLWY
L **O**

PRINCESS ANNE
WINDMILL FARM RAILWAY
L **O**

PRINCESS ELIZABETH *No. (9118)*
DIDCOT RAILWAY CENTRE
R

PRINCESS ELIZABETH *No. (6201)*
EAST LANCASHIRE RAILWAY

PRINCESS MARGARET
SPA VALLEY RAILWAY
L **O**

PRINCESS MARGARET ROSE *No. (46203)*
MIDLAND RAILWAY CENTRE
L **S** **D**

PROGRESS
ARMLEY MILLS
L

PROGRESS *No. (1)*
BODMIN & WENFORD RAILWAY
L **O**

PROGRESS
SWANAGE RAILWAY
L

PROGRESS
TANFIELD RAILWAY

PUFFING BILLY
NATIONAL RAILWAY MUSEUM
L **S** **D**

QUEEN MARY *No. (9112)*
DIDCOT RAILWAY CENTRE
R

R H SMITH *No. (3)*
RPSI
L **O**

RACHEL
FOXFIELD STEAM RAILWAY
L

RACHEL *No.(9)*
LAKESIDE & HAVERTHWAITE RLWY
L

RAF STANBRIDGE *No.(28)*
LEIGHTON BUZZARD RAILWAY
L

RALPH *No.(7)*
SNOWDON MOUNTAIN RAILWAY
L

RAMILLIES *No.(50019)*
MID-NORFOLK RAILWAY
L O

RAVEN
WELSHPOOL & LLANFAIR

RAVENINGHAM HALL *No.(6960)*
GLOUCESTERSHIRE WARWICKSHIRE
L O

RED RUM *No.(34)*
LEIGHTON BUZZARD RAILWAY
L O D

REDLAND
AMBERLEY WORKING MUSEUM
L

REDLAND
BUCKINGHAMSHIRE RLWY CTRE
L

RENOWN *No.(50029)*
PONTYPOOL & BLAENAVON RAILWAY
L

REPTON *No.(30926)*
NORTH YORKSHIRE MOORS RAILWAY
L

REPULSE *No.(11)*
LAKESIDE & HAVERTHWAITE RLWY
L O

REPULSE *No.(50030)*
PONTYPOOL & BLAENAVON RAILWAY
L

RESIN
ARMLEY MILLS
L S

REVENGE
EMBSAY & BOLTON ABBEY RLWY
L

RHOS
NENE VALLEY RAILWAY
L S D

RICHARD III *No.(3)*
BATTLEFIELD LINE
L S

RICHARD TREVITHICK *No.(2354)*
SWINDON & CRICKLADE RAILWAY
L O

RICHBOROUGH CASTLE
EAST KENT LIGHT RAILWAY
O

RING HAW
NORTH NORFOLK RAILWAY
L O

RISHRA *No.(3)*
LEIGHTON BUZZARD RAILWAY
L O

RIVER CHURNET *No.(6)*
RUDYARD LAKE RAILWAY
L O

RIVER ESK
RAVENGLASS & ESKDALE
L O

RIVER IRT
RAVENGLASS & ESKDALE
L O

RIVER MITE
RAVENGLASS & ESKDALE
L **O**

RIVER YEO *No. (20188)*
YEOVIL RAILWAY CENTRE
L **O**

ROBERT
RUISLIP LIDO RAILWAY
L **O**

ROBERT HEATH NO 6 *No. (6)*
FOXFIELD STEAM RAILWAY
L **O**

ROBERT SNOOKS *No. (16)*
MOORS VALLEY RAILWAY
L **O**

ROBIN *No. (E318)*
NORTH YORKSHIRE MOORS RAILWAY
C

ROCK (THE)
IRCHESTER NARROW GAUGE MUSEUM
L

ROCKET
NATIONAL RAILWAY MUSEUM
L **O** **D**

ROCKET
NATIONAL RAILWAY MUSEUM
L **S** **D**

RODNEY *No. (50021)*
BO'NESS & KINNEIL RAILWAY
L

ROKER
FOXFIELD STEAM RAILWAY
L **S** **D**

ROLVENDEN *No. (24)*
KENT & EAST SUSSEX RAILWAY
L **O**

ROM RIVER
FOXFIELD STEAM RAILWAY
L **S** **D**

RON ROTHWELL *No. (DSRM1)*
NORTH YORKSHIRE MOORS RAILWAY
L

ROOD ASHTON HALL *No. (4965)*
TYSELEY LOCOMOTIVE WORKS

RORKE'S DRIFT
MUSEUM OF ARMY TRANSPORT
L **O** **S** **D**

RORY *No. (2)*
GIANTS CAUSEWAY & BUSHMILLS
L **O**

ROSENKAVALIER
BRESSINGHAM STEAM
L **S** **D**

ROTHERHAM
SOUTH YORKSHIRE RAILWAY

ROUGH PUP
NARROW GAUGE RAILWAY MUSEUM
L **D**

ROYAL ARTILLERYMAN (THE) *No. (45118)*
NORTHAMPTON & LAMPORT RAILWAY
L **O**

ROYAL SALOON *No. (9003)*
STEAM
C **S** **D**

ROYAL SCOT *No. (6100)*
BARLEYLANDS MINIATURE RAILWAY
L **S** **D**

ROYAL SCOT *No. (6100)*
BRESSINGHAM STEAM
L **S**

〰 ROYAL SCOT
SOUTH DOWNS LIGHT RAILWAY
🇱 🇴

〰 ROYAL TANK REGIMENT *No. (45041)*
MIDLAND RAILWAY CENTRE
🇱

〰 RUDYARD LADY *No. (5)*
RUDYARD LAKE RAILWAY
🇱 🇴

〰 RUPERT
NATIONAL TRAMWAY MUSEUM
🇱 🇴

〰 RUSSELL
FAIRBOURNE & BARMOUTH
🇱 🇴

〰 RUSSELL
WELSH HIGHLAND RAILWAY
🇱 🇴

〰 RUSTON
DEVON RAILWAY CENTRE
🇱 🇴

〰 SACCHARINE
ALFORD VALLEY RAILWAY
🇱 🇴

〰 SAD SAM
NOTTINGHAM TRANSPORT CTRE
🇱

〰 SALMON *No. (2139)*
SWINDON & CRICKLADE RAILWAY
🇱

〰 SAMMY
TEIFI VALLEY RAILWAY
🇱 🇴

〰 SAMPSON *No. (D3014)*
PAIGNTON & DARTMOUTH RAILWAY
🇱 🇴

〰 SAMSON
ROMNEY HYTHE & DYMCHURCH
🇱 🇴

〰 SAMUEL WHITBREAD
HOLLYBUSH GARDEN CENTRE
🇱 🇴

〰 SANDY RIVER *No. (7)*
EASTLEIGH LAKESIDE RAILWAY
🇱 🇴

〰 SANS PAREIL
NATIONAL RAILWAY MUSEUM
🇱

〰 SANSPARIEL
TIMOTHY HACKWORTH
🇱 🇴

〰 SAO DOMINGOS *No. (3)*
SOUTH TYNEDALE RAILWAY
🇱

〰 SAPPER *No. (5)*
MOORS VALLEY RAILWAY
🇱 🇴

〰 SAPPER *No. (WD132)*
SOUTH DEVON RAILWAY
🇱

〰 SARAH *No. (42)*
LEIGHTON BUZZARD RAILWAY
🇱 🇴 🇩

〰 SCALDWELL
AMBERLEY WORKING MUSEUM
🇱

〰 SCOOBY *No. (16)*
WELSHPOOL & LLANFAIR
🇱 🇴

〰 SCOTT
BUCKINGHAMSHIRE RLWY CTRE
🇱

SCOTTIE
SPA VALLEY RAILWAY
L O

SEA LION
GROUDLE GLEN RAILWAY
L

SEABREEZE
CLEETHORPES LIGHT RAILWAY
L

SENTINEL *No.(5)*
CHASEWATER RAILWAY
L O

SENTINEL
FOXFIELD STEAM RAILWAY
L S

SEZELA NO 4
LEIGHTON BUZZARD RAILWAY
L

SGT MURPHY
TEIFI VALLEY RAILWAY
L O

SHANE *No.(3)*
GIANTS CAUSEWAY & BUSHMILLS
L O

SHANNON *No.(5)*
DIDCOT RAILWAY CENTRE
L

SHARPTHORN *No.(4)*
BLUEBELL RAILWAY
S D

SHAW SAVILL *No.(35009)*
WATERCRESS LINE
L S

SHEEPBRIDGE NO 15
CHASEWATER RAILWAY
L S D

SHELAGH OF ESKDALE
RAVENGLASS & ESKDALE
L O

SHELL MEX *No.(7285)*
NORTH YORKSHIRE MOORS RAILWAY
W

SHERPA
FAIRBOURNE & BARMOUTH
L O

SHERWOOD FORESTER *No.(45060)*
BARROW HILL ROUNDHOUSE
L S

SHIRE LODGE *No.(327974)*
NIRT
L O

SHOLTO
TEIFI VALLEY RAILWAY
L

SIAM *No.(105)*
BREDGAR & WORMSHILL
L

SIAN
CONWY VALLEY
L O

SILVER JUBILEE *No.(2)*
WINDMILL FARM RAILWAY
L

SILVER SPOON *No.(11510)*
SEVERN VALLEY RAILWAY
L O

SIMPLEX *No.(1369)*
ARMLEY MILLS
L S D

SINGAPORE
RUTLAND RAILWAY MUSEUM

ROLLING STOCK by NAME

Scottie — Singapore

SIPHON G No. (2796)
DIDCOT RAILWAY CENTRE
R

SIR ALFRED WOOD No. (319294)
NIRT
L O

SIR ARCHIBALD SINCLAIR No. (34059)
BLUEBELL RAILWAY

SIR ARTHUR HEYWOOD No. (10)
EASTLEIGH LAKESIDE RAILWAY
L O

SIR BERKELEY No. (1210)
MIDDLETON RAILWAY
L

SIR CECIL A COCHRANE
TANFIELD RAILWAY
O

SIR CHARLES
SWANSEA INDUSTRIAL MUSEUM

SIR DREFALDWYN No. (10)
WELSHPOOL & LLANFAIR
L S

SIR EDWARD ELGAR No. (50007)
MIDLAND RAILWAY CENTRE
L O

SIR FREDERICK PILE No. (34058)
AVON VALLEY RAILWAY
L

SIR GOMER No. (1859)
BATTLEFIELD LINE
L O

SIR GYLES No. (764)
NORTHAMPTON & LAMPORT RAILWAY
L

SIR HAYDN No. (3)
TALYLLYN RAILWAY
L O

SIR HERBERT WALKER No. (E6003)
LAVENDER LINE
L O

SIR JAMES No. (21)
LAKESIDE & HAVERTHWAITE RLWY
L O

SIR JOHN No. (1914)
GWILI RAILWAY
L S

SIR LAMIEL No. (30777)
GREAT CENTRAL RAILWAY
L

SIR LAMIEL No. (777)
NATIONAL RAILWAY MUSEUM
L

SIR NIGEL GRESLEY No. (4498)
SOUTH DOWNS LIGHT RAILWAY
L O

SIR SAGRAMORE No. (771)
SOUTH DOWNS LIGHT RAILWAY
L O

SIR THOMAS
BUCKINGHAMSHIRE RLWY CTRE
L

SIR THOMAS ROYDEN
RUTLAND RAILWAY MUSEUM

SIR VINCENT
BUCKINGHAMSHIRE RLWY CTRE
L

SIR WALTER GOWER
ROYAL VICTORIA RAILWAY
L O

SIR WALTER RALEIGH
BICTON WOODLAND RAILWAY
L **O**

SLIEVE GULLION *No. (171)*
RPSI
L **O**

SLOUGH ESTATES NO 3
SWINDON & CRICKLADE RAILWAY
L **O**

SLOUGH ESTATES NO 5
EMBSAY & BOLTON ABBEY RLWY
L

SMITHY WOOD
ARMLEY MILLS
L

SNOWDON *No. (4)*
SNOWDON MOUNTAIN RAILWAY
L **O**

SNOWDOWN
EAST KENT LIGHT RAILWAY
L **O**

SOUTH DURHAM MALLEABLE NO 5 *No. (5)*
BEAMISH
L **S** **D**

SOUTH HETTON NO 69
EMBSAY & BOLTON ABBEY RLWY
L

SOUTHAM NO 2 *No. (D625)*
ARMLEY MILLS
L **S**

SOUTHERHAM *No. (2591)*
SPA VALLEY RAILWAY
L **O**

SOUTHERN MAID
ROMNEY HYTHE & DYMCHURCH
L **O**

SOVEREIGN
BO'NESS & KINNEIL RAILWAY
L **O**

SPARTAN *No. (3135)*
SPA VALLEY RAILWAY
L **O**

SPEEDY
SOUTH YORKSHIRE RAILWAY

SPIRIT O' FIFE
KEITH & DUFFTOWN RAILWAY
L **O**

SPIRIT OF ADVENTURE *No. (PG1)*
PERRYGROVE RAILWAY
L **O**

SPIRIT OF BANFFSHIRE *No. (51568)*
KEITH & DUFFTOWN RAILWAY
L **O**

SPIRIT OF SPEYSIDE *No. (53628)*
KEITH & DUFFTOWN RAILWAY
L **O**

SPITFIRE
BURE VALLEY RAILWAY
L **O**

SPITFIRE
EAST KENT LIGHT RAILWAY
L **O**

SPITFIRE
NORTH GLOUCESTERSHIRE RAILWAY
L

SPONDON NO 2
FOXFIELD STEAM RAILWAY
S **D**

ST DUNSTAN
EAST KENT LIGHT RAILWAY
L **S** **D**

ST IVEL *No. (W44019)*
NORTH YORKSHIRE MOORS RAILWAY
W

STAGSHAW
TANFIELD RAILWAY
L O

STAMFORD *No. (24)*
BLUEBELL RAILWAY
L

STAN SYMES *No. (D6515)*
SWANAGE RAILWAY
L O

STANHOPE
WEST LANCASHIRE LIGHT RLWY
L

STANTON *No. (24)*
MIDLAND RAILWAY CENTRE
L S D

STAR CONSTRUCTION
AMBERLEY WORKING MUSEUM
L

STEAM ELEPHANT
BEAMISH
L O D

STEPNEY *No. (55)*
BLUEBELL RAILWAY
L O

STOWE *No. (928)*
BLUEBELL RAILWAY
S D

SUPERB *No. (2624)*
SITTINGBOURNE & KEMSLEY
L O

SUPERIOR *No. (4034)*
GREAT WHIPSNADE RAILWAY
L O

SUTTON *No. (32650)*
KENT & EAST SUSSEX RAILWAY
L S D

SUTTON
ULSTER FOLK & TRANSPORT
L S D

SWANAGE *No. (34105)*
WATERCRESS LINE
L

SWANSCOMBE
BUCKINGHAMSHIRE RLWY CTRE
L

SWANSEA JACK *No. (393302)*
GWILI RAILWAY
L O

SWANSEA VALE *No. (9622)*
GWILI RAILWAY
L O S

SWIFTSURE *No. (2857)*
BODMIN & WENFORD RAILWAY
L O

SWORDFISH *No. (2138)*
SWINDON & CRICKLADE RAILWAY
L

SYBIL
LAUNCESTON STEAM RAILWAY
L

SYBILLA *No. (D7628)*
NORTH YORKSHIRE MOORS RAILWAY
L

T W LEWIS *No. (LM39)*
LEIGHTON BUZZARD RAILWAY
L

TALIESIN
FFESTINIOG RAILWAY
L O

ROLLING STOCK by NAME

St Ivel — Taliesin

TALOS *No. (3)*
MOORS VALLEY RAILWAY
L O

TALYLLYN *No. (1)*
TALYLLYN RAILWAY
L O

TAMWORTH CASTLE *No. (D7672)*
CHURNET VALLEY RAILWAY
L O

TARMAC
BUCKINGHAMSHIRE RLWY CTRE
L

TAW VALLEY *No. (34027)*
SEVERN VALLEY RAILWAY
L O

TAWD
WEST LANCASHIRE LIGHT RLWY
* L

TEES STORAGE
SCOTTISH RAILWAY CENTRE
L O

TELEMON
ROTHER VALLEY RAILWAY

TEVAN *No. (79933)*
DIDCOT RAILWAY CENTRE
W

THAKEHAM TILES NO 3
AMBERLEY WORKING MUSEUM
L

THAKEHAM TILES NO 4 *No. (4)*
AMBERLEY WORKING MUSEUM
L

THEODORA *No. (51)*
KENT & EAST SUSSEX RAILWAY
C

THOMAS
EMBSAY & BOLTON ABBEY RLWY
L

THOMAS *No. (1800)*
NENE VALLEY RAILWAY
L O

THOMAS
TELFORD STEAM RAILWAY
L O

THOMAS *No. (1)*
WATERCRESS LINE
L O

THOMAS BACH
LLANBERIS LAKE RAILWAY
L O

THOMAS EDMONDSON *No. (6)*
SOUTH TYNEDALE RAILWAY
L O

THOMAS II *No. (4)*
BEER HEIGHTS
L O

THOR
BROOKSIDE MINIATURE
L O

THORPENESS *No. (5)*
EAST ANGLIA TRANSPORT MUSEUM
L O

THUNDER
BURE VALLEY RAILWAY
L O

THUNDERSLEY *No. (80)*
NATIONAL RAILWAY MUSEUM
L S D

TIGER
BO'NESS & KINNEIL RAILWAY
L

Key: **L** Loco **R** Rolling Stock **W** Wagon **C** Coach **O** Operational **S** Static **D** On Display

ROLLING STOCK by NAME

Talos — Tiger

⌁⌁⌁ TINKERBELL *No. (4)*
MOORS VALLEY RAILWAY
L O

⌁⌁⌁ TINY
KEIGHLEY & WORTH VALLEY
L

⌁⌁⌁ TINY *No. (151)*
SOUTH DEVON RAILWAY
L S D

⌁⌁⌁ TINY TIM *No. (13)*
MOORS VALLEY RAILWAY
L O

⌁⌁⌁ TINY TIM *No. (13)*
SOUTH TYNEDALE RAILWAY
L S D

⌁⌁⌁ TIPPOCKETY *No. (88DS)*
NORTH NORFOLK RAILWAY
R

⌁⌁⌁ TITAN *No. (43)*
KENT & EAST SUSSEX RAILWAY
L O

⌁⌁⌁ TITAN *No. (D2192)*
PAIGNTON & DARTMOUTH RAILWAY
L O

⌁⌁⌁ TOAD *No. (37)*
CHASEWATER RAILWAY
L

⌁⌁⌁ TOBY
BATTLEFIELD LINE
L O

⌁⌁⌁ TOBY
BRESSINGHAM STEAM
L O

⌁⌁⌁ TOBY
NENE VALLEY RAILWAY
L

⌁⌁⌁ TOFFO
SOUTH YORKSHIRE RAILWAY

⌁⌁⌁ TOM ROLT *No. (7)*
TALYLLYN RAILWAY
L O

⌁⌁⌁ TONKA
FOXFIELD STEAM RAILWAY
L S D

⌁⌁⌁ TOPHAM
SPA VALLEY RAILWAY
L

⌁⌁⌁ TOTO
MANGAPPS RAILWAY MUSEUM
L D

⌁⌁⌁ TOWNSEND HOOK *No. (4)*
AMBERLEY WORKING MUSEUM
L

⌁⌁⌁ TRACTION *No. (20227)*
MIDLAND RAILWAY CENTRE
L O

⌁⌁⌁ TRAM ENGINE *No. (7)*
KIRKLEES LIGHT RAILWAY
O

⌁⌁⌁ TRECATTY *No. (421702)*
GWILI RAILWAY
L

⌁⌁⌁ TRECWN *No. (2390)*
ARMLEY MILLS
L S D

⌁⌁⌁ TRENT *No. (40)*
LEIGHTON BUZZARD RAILWAY
L

⌁⌁⌁ TRIUMPH *No. (500042)*
BODMIN & WENFORD RAILWAY
L O

TRIUMPH *No. (2511)*
SITTINGBOURNE & KEMSLEY
L **O**

TROJAN *No. (1340)*
DIDCOT RAILWAY CENTRE
L

TROJAN *No. (4588)*
PAIGNTON & DARTMOUTH RAILWAY
L

TULYAR *No. (55015)*
MIDLAND RAILWAY CENTRE
L

TWEEDLEDUM
SOUTH DOWNS LIGHT RAILWAY
L

TWIZELL *No. (3)*
BEAMISH
L

TWLL COED *No. (268878)*
LLANBERIS LAKE RAILWAY
L

TYPHOON
ROMNEY HYTHE & DYMCHURCH
L

TYRONE *No. (1)*
GIANTS CAUSEWAY & BUSHMILLS
L **O**

UGLY *No. (62)*
BODMIN & WENFORD RAILWAY
L **O**

UNICORN *No. (08060)*
CHOLSEY & WALLINGFORD RAILWAY
L **O**

UNION *No. (D571)*
ARMLEY MILLS
L **S** **D**

UNION OF SOUTH AFRICA *No. (60009)*
SEVERN VALLEY RAILWAY
L **O**

UNION PACIFIC
CONWY VALLEY
L **O**

UNIQUE *No. (2216)*
SITTINGBOURNE & KEMSLEY
L **S** **D**

UNITED MOLASSES *No. (6)*
NORTH YORKSHIRE MOORS RAILWAY
W

UNIVERSITY OF SOUTHAMPTON *No. (3221)*
EASTLEIGH LAKESIDE RAILWAY
L **O**

UPNOR *No. (199)*
SITTINGBOURNE & KEMSLEY
R

UPNOR CASTLE
WELSHPOOL & LLANFAIR

UPPINGHAM
RUTLAND RAILWAY MUSEUM

URANUS
CALEDONIAN RAILWAY
L **D**

URSULA
PERRYGROVE RAILWAY
L **O**

UTRILLAS
WEST LANCASHIRE LIGHT RLWY
L

V *No. (1)*
SOUTH TYNEDALE RAILWAY
C

ROLLING STOCK by NAME

Triumph — v

ROLLING STOCK by NAME

Vale of Ffestiniog — Waleswood

VALE OF FFESTINIOG
FFESTINIOG RAILWAY
L O

VALIANT No. (50015)
EAST LANCASHIRE RAILWAY

VANGUARD No. (5374)
NORTHAMPTON & LAMPORT RAILWAY
L

VAUCLAIN DANISH COMPOUND PACIFIC
No. (DSB996)
RAILWORLD
L S D

VELINHELI
LAUNCESTON STEAM RAILWAY
L O

VESTA No. (1223)
INDUSTRIAL RAILWAY MUSEUM
L S D

VICTOR No. (2996)
BATTLEFIELD LINE
L O

VICTOR No. (2091)
GREAT WESTERN RAILWAY MUSEUM
L

VICTOR No. (4160005)
GREAT WHIPSNADE RAILWAY
L

VICTOR No. (4182)
SITTINGBOURNE & KEMSLEY
L O

VICTORIA No. (2216)
BOWES RAILWAY
L

VICTORIA
MULL RAILWAY
L O

VICTORY No. (7)
BREDGAR & WORMSHILL
L

VICTORY
COLNE VALLEY RAILWAY
L

VICTORY
DERBY INDUSTRIAL MUSEUM
L S D

VICTORY No. (2201)
GWILI RAILWAY
L O

VIGILANT No. (287)
NIRT
L

VULCAN No. (4)
ABBEY LIGHT RAILWAY
L O

VULCAN
BARLEYLANDS MINIATURE RAILWAY
L O

VULCAN No. (828)
PEAK RAIL
L

WADEBRIDGE No. (34007)
BODMIN & WENFORD RAILWAY
L

WAGGONER No. (92)
MUSEUM OF ARMY TRANSPORT
L S D

WAINWRIGHT No. (DS238)
KENT & EAST SUSSEX RAILWAY
L O

WALESWOOD
BATTLEFIELD LINE
L

WALRUS
GROUDLE GLEN RAILWAY
L **S**

WARRINGTON *No. (68006)*
PEAK RAIL
L

WARRIOR *No. (4555)*
PAIGNTON & DARTMOUTH RAILWAY
L **O**

WARWICKSHIRE *No. (2047)*
SEVERN VALLEY RAILWAY
L **S** **D**

WAVERLEY
MULL RAILWAY
L **O**

WAVERLEY *No. (47701)*
TYSELEY LOCOMOTIVE WORKS

WEASEL *No. (2)*
WELLS & WALSINGHAM
L

WEE MAC (THE)
KEITH & DUFFTOWN RAILWAY
L **O**

WELLINGTON
TANFIELD RAILWAY
L

WELSH GUARDSMAN *No. (71516)*
GWILI RAILWAY
L **O**

WELSH PONY *No. (5)*
FFESTINIOG RAILWAY
L **D**

WELSH PONY
WEST LANCASHIRE LIGHT RLWY

WENDY *No. (2091)*
KEW BRIDGE STEAM MUSEUM
L **O**

WESTERN CAMPAIGNER *No. (D1010)*
WEST SOMERSET RAILWAY
L **O**

WESTERN CHAMPION *No. (D1015)*
SEVERN VALLEY RAILWAY
L **O**

WESTERN COURIER *No. (D1062)*
SEVERN VALLEY RAILWAY
L **O**

WESTERN LADY *No. (D1048)*
MIDLAND RAILWAY CENTRE
L

WESTERN PRIDE *No. (D1171)*
AVON VALLEY RAILWAY
L

WESTERN PRINCE *No. (D1041)*
EAST LANCASHIRE RAILWAY

WESTERN RANGER *No. (D1013)*
SEVERN VALLEY RAILWAY
L

WESTMINSTER *No. (1378)*
NORTHAMPTON & LAMPORT RAILWAY
L

WEYMSS COAL COMPANY NO 20
BO'NESS & KINNEIL RAILWAY
L

WHELDALE
EMBSAY & BOLTON ABBEY RLWY
L

WHIPPET QUICK
WINDMILL FARM RAILWAY
L **O**

ROLLING STOCK by NAME

Walrus — Whippet Quick

ROLLING STOCK by NAME

Whiston — Workhorse

WHISTON
FOXFIELD STEAM RAILWAY
L O

WHIT NO 4 *No. (S100)*
CHASEWATER RAILWAY
L O

WHITEHEAD
MIDLAND RAILWAY CENTRE
L O

WICKHAM TROLLEY
EMBSAY & BOLTON ABBEY RLWY
L O

WIGHTWICK HALL *No. (6989)*
BUCKINGHAMSHIRE RLWY CTRE
L

WILBERT THE FOREST ENGINE
DEAN FOREST RAILWAY
L

WILLIAM *No. (9599)*
BATTLEFIELD LINE
L S

WILLIAM BAKER *No. (4789)*
EASTLEIGH LAKESIDE RAILWAY
L O

WILLIAM COOKWORTHY *No. (37207)*
PLYM VALLEY RAILWAY
L

WILLIAM FRANCIS *No. (6841)*
BRESSINGHAM STEAM
L S D

WILLIAM MURDOCH
EAST ANGLIAN RAILWAY MUSEUM
L

WILLIAM RUFUS *No. (15)*
MOORS VALLEY RAILWAY
L O

WILLIAM STEWART TRIMBLE *No. (2361)*
BOWES RAILWAY
L O

WIMBLEBURY
FOXFIELD STEAM RAILWAY
L

WINDLE *No. (53)*
MIDDLETON RAILWAY
L

WINFIELD
EAST LANCASHIRE RAILWAY

WINSTON CHURCHILL *No. (34051)*
NATIONAL RAILWAY MUSEUM
L S D

WINSTON CHURCHILL
ROMNEY HYTHE & DYMCHURCH
L O

WISSINGTON
NORTH NORFOLK RAILWAY
L S D

WITHERSLACK HALL *No. (6990)*
GREAT CENTRAL RAILWAY
L O

WOLSTANTON NO 3 *No. (3)*
FOXFIELD STEAM RAILWAY
L

WOODBINE *No. (21442)*
SWINDON & CRICKLADE RAILWAY
L

WOOLMER
MUSEUM OF ARMY TRANSPORT
L S D

WORKHORSE *No. (2)*
PERRYGROVE RAILWAY
L O

🚂 WREN
NATIONAL RAILWAY MUSEUM
`L` `S` `D`

🚂 WROXHAM BROAD *No.(1)*
BURE VALLEY RAILWAY
`L` `O`

🚂 WYDDFA *No.(3)*
SNOWDON MOUNTAIN RAILWAY
`L` `O`

🚂 WYNNSTAY
WELSHPOOL & LLANFAIR

🚂 YELLOW PERIL *No.(747)*
AMERTON RAILWAY
`L`

🚂 YEO
FAIRBOURNE & BARMOUTH
`L` `O`

🚂 YETI *No.(10)*
SNOWDON MOUNTAIN RAILWAY
`L` `O`

🚂 YIMKIN *No.(26)*
LEIGHTON BUZZARD RAILWAY
`L`

🚂 YORK NO 1
EMBSAY & BOLTON ABBEY RLWY
`L`

🚂 ZEBEDEE *No.(1)*
LAPPA VALLEY STEAM RAILWAY
`L` `O`

🚂 ZEBEDEE *No.(7597)*
PEAK RAIL
`L`

🚂 ZEUS *No.(11)*
MOORS VALLEY RAILWAY
`L` `O`

ROLLING STOCK by NAME

Wren — Zeus

**Current Number
of the rolling stock**

SECTION 5B

*This section gives you details
where the current number of
the stock can be located, also
showing it's name and icons
displaying what type of stock
it is and it's status*

Type Icons:
  L - Loco
  R - Rolling Stock
  W - Wagon
  C - Coach

Status Icons:
  O - Operational
  S - Static
  D - On Display

**e.g. 02101, Gwili Railway,
    Nellie, LO**

Once you have located a
railway/museum using this
section you can then refer
to the railway or museum's
detailed profile in section 1.

No. 02003 *(Peter)*
SOUTH YORKSHIRE RAILWAY

No. 02101 *(Nellie)*
GWILI RAILWAY
L O

No. 03018
SOUTH YORKSHIRE RAILWAY

No. 03020
SOUTH YORKSHIRE RAILWAY

No. 03022
SWINDON & CRICKLADE RAILWAY
L O

No. 03027
PEAK RAIL
L

No. 03037
SOUTH YORKSHIRE RAILWAY

No. 03066
BARROW HILL ROUNDHOUSE
L S D

No. 03079
DERWENT VALLEY
L O

No. 03084
PEAK RAIL
L

No. 03094
BARROW HILL ROUNDHOUSE
L

No. 03099
SOUTH YORKSHIRE RAILWAY

No. 0314
BUCKINGHAMSHIRE RLWY CTRE
L

No. 03158 *(Margaret Anne)*
PEAK RAIL
L

No. 03180
SOUTH YORKSHIRE RAILWAY

No. 03197
SOUTH YORKSHIRE RAILWAY

No. 03399
MANGAPPS RAILWAY MUSEUM
L O D

No. 03938
BEAMISH
W

No. 042227
BARROW HILL ROUNDHOUSE
O

No. 05/576
ALMOND VALLEY HERITAGE TRUST
L O

No. 055
EAST ANGLIAN RAILWAY MUSEUM
W

No. 06003
BATTLEFIELD LINE
L

No. 064847
CHINNOR & PRINCES RISBOROUGH
W

No. 07012
SOUTH YORKSHIRE RAILWAY

No. 070863
SOUTH DEVON RAILWAY
W

ROLLING STOCK by NUMBER

02003 — 070863

No.076104
CHINNOR & PRINCES RISBOROUGH
W

No.08 604 *(Phantom)*
DIDCOT RAILWAY CENTRE
L

No.08022 *(Lion)*
CHOLSEY & WALLINGFORD RAILWAY
L O

No.08060 *(Unicorn)*
CHOLSEY & WALLINGFORD RAILWAY
L O

No.08123 *(George Mason)*
CHOLSEY & WALLINGFORD RAILWAY
L O

No.08216
SOUTH YORKSHIRE RAILWAY
L

No.083655
SPA VALLEY RAILWAY
R

No.08390
SOUTH YORKSHIRE RAILWAY
L

No.08443
BO'NESS & KINNEIL RAILWAY
L

No.08479
EAST LANCASHIRE RAILWAY

No.08556
NORTH YORKSHIRE MOORS RAILWAY
L

No.08590
MIDLAND RAILWAY CENTRE
L O

No.08631
TYSELEY LOCOMOTIVE WORKS

No.08707
SOUTH YORKSHIRE RAILWAY
L

No.08823
CHURNET VALLEY RAILWAY
L

No.08850
NORTH YORKSHIRE MOORS RAILWAY
L

No.08885
NOTTINGHAM TRANSPORT CTRE
L O

No.08937
DARTMOOR RAILWAY
L O

No.08944
EAST LANCASHIRE RAILWAY

No.1 *(Loweco)*
ABBEY LIGHT RAILWAY
L O

No.1 *(Locomotion)*
BEAMISH
L O D

No.1 *(Progress)*
BODMIN & WENFORD RAILWAY
L O

No.1 *(Lady Joan)*
BREDGAR & WORMSHILL
L O

No.1 *(Bronhilde)*
BREDGAR & WORMSHILL
L O

ROLLING STOCK by **NUMBER**

1—1

No. 1 *(Wroxham Broad)*
BURE VALLEY RAILWAY
L **O**

No. 1
CHASEWATER RAILWAY
L

No. 1 *(Konigswinter)*
CLEETHORPES LIGHT RAILWAY
L

No. 1
COLNE VALLEY RAILWAY
L

No. 1 *(Boris)*
DEVON RAILWAY CENTRE
L **O**

No. 1 *(Bonnie Prince Charlie)*
DIDCOT RAILWAY CENTRE
L

No. 1
DIDCOT RAILWAY CENTRE
W

No. 1
EAST LANCASHIRE RAILWAY

No. 1 *(MR Mercury)*
EAST LANCASHIRE RAILWAY

No. 1 *(Princess)*
FFESTINIOG RAILWAY
L **D**

No. 1 *(Boots No 1)*
FOXFIELD STEAM RAILWAY
L **S**

No. 1 *(Ironbridge No 1)*
FOXFIELD STEAM RAILWAY
L **S** **D**

No. 1 *(Tyrone)*
GIANTS CAUSEWAY & BUSHMILLS
L **O**

No. 1 *(Lady Augusta (The))*
HEATHERSLAW LIGHT RAILWAY
L **O**

No. 1 *(Gazelle)*
KENT & EAST SUSSEX RAILWAY
L **S** **D**

No. 1 *(Zebedee)*
LAPPA VALLEY STEAM RAILWAY
L **O**

No. 1 *(Bluebell)*
LEIGHTON BUZZARD RAILWAY
L

No. 1 *(Chaloner)*
LEIGHTON BUZZARD RAILWAY
L **O** **D**

No. 1 *(Locomotion)*
NATIONAL RAILWAY MUSEUM
L **S** **D**

No. 1
NATIONAL RAILWAY MUSEUM
R

No. 1
NORTH GLOUCESTERSHIRE RAILWAY
L

No. 1 *(Phoenix)*
SOUTH TYNEDALE RAILWAY
L

No. 1 *(v)*
SOUTH TYNEDALE RAILWAY
C

No. 1 *(Talyllyn)*
TALYLLYN RAILWAY
L **O**

ROLLING STOCK by NUMBER

1 — 1001

No.1
TALYLLYN RAILWAY
C

No.1
TANFIELD RAILWAY
O

No.1
TYSELEY LOCOMOTIVE WORKS

No.1
ULSTER FOLK & TRANSPORT
L S D

No.1
ULSTER FOLK & TRANSPORT
L S D

No.1 *(Thomas)*
WATERCRESS LINE
L O

No.1 *(Earl (The))*
WELSHPOOL & LLANFAIR
L O

No.1 *(Pectin)*
YEOVIL RAILWAY CENTRE
L O

No.10 *(Baguley)*
ABBEY LIGHT RAILWAY
L

No.10 *(Sir Arthur Heywood)*
EASTLEIGH LAKESIDE RAILWAY
L O

No.10 *(Mr Bill)*
GREAT WHIPSNADE RAILWAY
L O

No.10 *(G H Wood)*
ISLE OF MAN RAILWAY
L

No.10 *(Haydn Taylor)*
LEIGHTON BUZZARD RAILWAY
L O D

No.10 *(Offa)*
MOORS VALLEY RAILWAY
L O

No.10 *(Yeti)*
SNOWDON MOUNTAIN RAILWAY
L O

No.10 *(Naklo)*
SOUTH TYNEDALE RAILWAY
L

No.10 *(Bryn Eglwys)*
TALYLLYN RAILWAY
L O

No.10
TALYLLYN RAILWAY
C

No.10
TANFIELD RAILWAY

No.10
VALE OF RHEIDOL RAILWAY
L O

No.10 *(Douglas)*
WATERCRESS LINE
L O

No.10 *(Sir Drefaldwyn)*
WELSHPOOL & LLANFAIR
L S

No.1000
NATIONAL RAILWAY MUSEUM
L

No.1001 *(Monarch (The))*
EASTLEIGH LAKESIDE RAILWAY
L O

No. 1002
NATIONAL RAILWAY MUSEUM
C

No. 100377
DIDCOT RAILWAY CENTRE
W

No. 100677
BLUEBELL RAILWAY
W O

No. 100682
DIDCOT RAILWAY CENTRE
W

No. 100682
DIDCOT RAILWAY CENTRE

No. 100684
CHASEWATER RAILWAY
R

No. 100715
SOUTH DEVON RAILWAY
W

No. 1008
NATIONAL RAILWAY MUSEUM
L S D

No. 101
BOWES RAILWAY
L O

No. 101
DIDCOT RAILWAY CENTRE
W

No. 101 *(Joan)*
RHYL MINIATURE RAILWAY
L O

No. 1010
KENT & EAST SUSSEX RAILWAY
W

No. 10153
DIDCOT RAILWAY CENTRE
W

No. 101720
DIDCOT RAILWAY CENTRE
W

No. 101836
DIDCOT RAILWAY CENTRE
W

No. 101A
NENE VALLEY RAILWAY
L O

No. 102 *(Granville)*
BRESSINGHAM STEAM
L S D

No. 102
NATIONAL RAILWAY MUSEUM
L O

No. 10252
BATTLEFIELD LINE
L

No. 102833
BEAMISH
W

No. 1030
MANGAPPS RAILWAY MUSEUM
L O S

No. 1032
NATIONAL RAILWAY MUSEUM
R

No. 103584
PLYM VALLEY RAILWAY
W

No. 103686
KENT & EAST SUSSEX RAILWAY
W

ROLLING STOCK by NUMBER

1002 — 103686

No. 104
KENT & EAST SUSSEX RAILWAY
W

No. 104 *(Llanwern)*
PONTYPOOL & BLAENAVON RAILWAY
L O

No. 104
STRATHSPEY RAILWAY
R C O

No. 104700
SOUTH DEVON RAILWAY
W

No. 1049 *(Excelsior)*
GREAT WHIPSNADE RAILWAY
L O

No. 105 *(Siam)*
BREDGAR & WORMSHILL
L

No. 10509
DIDCOT RAILWAY CENTRE
R

No. 10517
GWILI RAILWAY
C

No. 1054
KEIGHLEY & WORTH VALLEY
L

No. 105599
DIDCOT RAILWAY CENTRE
W

No. 105742
DIDCOT RAILWAY CENTRE
W

No. 105860
DIDCOT RAILWAY CENTRE
W

No. 106
BLUEBELL RAILWAY
C

No. 106
PONTYPOOL & BLAENAVON RAILWAY
L

No. 1061
BLUEBELL RAILWAY
C

No. 107
KENT & EAST SUSSEX RAILWAY
W

No. 107
NORTH YORKSHIRE MOORS RAILWAY
W

No. 1077
BEAMISH
W

No. 1077
NORTH YORKSHIRE MOORS RAILWAY

No. 108207
SOUTH DEVON RAILWAY
W

No. 109
EXMOOR STEAM RAILWAY
L S D

No. 109
KENT & EAST SUSSEX RAILWAY
W

No. 109
NATIONAL RAILWAY MUSEUM
R

No. 109
STRATHSPEY RAILWAY
R C O

No.1098
BLUEBELL RAILWAY
C **O**

No.11 *(Baguley)*
ABBEY LIGHT RAILWAY
L

No.11 *(Meirionnydd)*
BALA LAKE RAILWAY
L **O**

No.11
BATTLEFIELD LINE
L

No.11
BUCKINGHAMSHIRE RLWY CTRE
L

No.11
CHASEWATER RAILWAY

No.11 *(Alfred Paget)*
CHASEWATER RAILWAY
L

No.11
EAST ANGLIAN RAILWAY MUSEUM
L

No.11
FOXFIELD STEAM RAILWAY
L **S** **O**

No.11 *(Maitland)*
ISLE OF MAN RAILWAY
L

No.11 *(Repulse)*
LAKESIDE & HAVERTHWAITE RLWY
L **O**

No.11
LEIGHTON BUZZARD RAILWAY
R **C** **O** **D**

No.11 *(PC Allen)*
LEIGHTON BUZZARD RAILWAY
L **O** **D**

No.11 *(Zeus)*
MOORS VALLEY RAILWAY
L **O**

No.11 *(Peris)*
SNOWDON MOUNTAIN RAILWAY
L **O**

No.11 *(Cumbria)*
SOUTH TYNEDALE RAILWAY
L **O**

No.11
TALYLLYN RAILWAY
C

No.11 *(Ferret)*
WELSHPOOL & LLANFAIR
L **S**

No.110 *(Burgundy)*
EAST SOMERSET RAILWAY
L

No.1101
BARROW HILL ROUNDHOUSE
W

No.1106
GWILI RAILWAY
C

No.1109
CHASEWATER RAILWAY
R

No.111
DIDCOT RAILWAY CENTRE
C

No.111
KENT & EAST SUSSEX RAILWAY
W **D**

〰 No. 11104
MANGAPPS RAILWAY MUSEUM
L O D

〰 No. 1111
DIDCOT RAILWAY CENTRE
R

〰 No. 1111
NORTH YORKSHIRE MOORS RAILWAY
C

〰 No. 1112
BARROW HILL ROUNDHOUSE
W

〰 No. 11152 *(Iron Mink)*
DIDCOT RAILWAY CENTRE
W

〰 No. 112
NATIONAL RAILWAY MUSEUM
R

〰 No. 11215
BATTLEFIELD LINE
L

〰 No. 1126 *(Barbouilleur)*
AMBERLEY WORKING MUSEUM
L

〰 No. 112843
DIDCOT RAILWAY CENTRE
W

〰 No. 1137
NORTH NORFOLK RAILWAY
R

〰 No. 114
KENT & EAST SUSSEX RAILWAY
W D

〰 No. 114 *(Peter Pan)*
LEIGHTON BUZZARD RAILWAY
L O

〰 No. 114762
SWANSEA VALE RAILWAY
R

〰 No. 115
EXMOOR STEAM RAILWAY
L S D

〰 No. 11506
EAST LANCASHIRE RAILWAY

〰 No. 11509 *(Alan)*
SEVERN VALLEY RAILWAY
L S

〰 No. 1151
KENT & EAST SUSSEX RAILWAY
W

〰 No. 11510 *(Silver Spoon)*
SEVERN VALLEY RAILWAY
L O

〰 No. 1152
EAST ANGLIAN RAILWAY MUSEUM
W

〰 No. 1159
DIDCOT RAILWAY CENTRE

〰 No. 116954
DIDCOT RAILWAY CENTRE
W

〰 No. 1170
BLUEBELL RAILWAY
C

〰 No. 1178
NENE VALLEY RAILWAY
L S D

〰 No. 117993
DIDCOT RAILWAY CENTRE
W

ROLLING STOCK by NUMBER

11104 — 117993

No. 118
BEAMISH
C

No. 118 *(Brussels)*
KEIGHLEY & WORTH VALLEY
L

No. 1184
BLUEBELL RAILWAY

No. 1184
DIDCOT RAILWAY CENTRE
R

No. 11916
BLUEBELL RAILWAY
W **O**

No. 12 *(Greenbat)*
ABBEY LIGHT RAILWAY
L **O**

No. 12 *(Chilmark)*
BALA LAKE RAILWAY
L

No. 12
BEER HEIGHTS
W

No. 12 *(Hutchinson)*
ISLE OF MAN RAILWAY
L

No. 12 *(Marcia)*
KENT & EAST SUSSEX RAILWAY
L **O**

No. 12
LEIGHTON BUZZARD RAILWAY
R **C** **O** **D**

No. 12
LEIGHTON BUZZARD RAILWAY
L

No. 12 *(Pioneer)*
MOORS VALLEY RAILWAY
L **O**

No. 12
NATIONAL RAILWAY MUSEUM
R

No. 12 *(George)*
SNOWDON MOUNTAIN RAILWAY
L **O**

No. 12 *(Chaka's Kraal No 6)*
SOUTH TYNEDALE RAILWAY
L

No. 12
TALYLLYN RAILWAY
C

No. 12 *(Joan)*
WELSHPOOL & LLANFAIR
L **S** **D**

No. 12 139 *(Neil D Barker)*
NORTH YORKSHIRE MOORS RAILWAY
L

No. 120
NATIONAL RAILWAY MUSEUM
L

No. 120116
CHASEWATER RAILWAY
W

No. 12049
WATERCRESS LINE
L **O**

No. 12074
SOUTH YORKSHIRE RAILWAY
L

No. 12077
MIDLAND RAILWAY CENTRE
L **O**

No. 12083
SOUTH YORKSHIRE RAILWAY
L

No. 12098
SOUTH YORKSHIRE RAILWAY

No. 12099
SEVERN VALLEY RAILWAY
L **O**

No. 121
KENT & EAST SUSSEX RAILWAY
W

No. 1210 *(Luton)*
ARMLEY MILLS
L **S** **D**

No. 1210 *(Sir Berkeley)*
MIDDLETON RAILWAY
L

No. 1211
STRATHSPEY RAILWAY
R **C** **S**

No. 12123
NATIONAL RAILWAY MUSEUM
R

No. 12131
NORTH NORFOLK RAILWAY
L

No. 1214
DERWENT VALLEY
C

No. 1217
NATIONAL RAILWAY MUSEUM
L

No. 1223 *(Vesta)*
INDUSTRIAL RAILWAY MUSEUM
L **S** **D**

No. 1240
SPA VALLEY RAILWAY
R

No. 1247
NATIONAL RAILWAY MUSEUM
L

No. 12514
SWANSEA VALE RAILWAY
L

No. 125814
SOUTH DEVON RAILWAY
W

No. 1264
GREAT CENTRAL RAILWAY
L **O**

No. 1275
NATIONAL RAILWAY MUSEUM
L

No. 1285
SOUTH DEVON RAILWAY
C

No. 1289
DIDCOT RAILWAY CENTRE
R

No. 129
NORTH NORFOLK RAILWAY
R

No. 129
NORTH NORFOLK RAILWAY
C

No. 129148
NORTH NORFOLK RAILWAY
W

No. 13
ALMOND VALLEY HERITAGE TRUST
L **S** **D**

No. 13 *(Arkle)*
LEIGHTON BUZZARD RAILWAY
L **O** **D**

No. 13 *(Tiny Tim)*
MOORS VALLEY RAILWAY
L **O**

No. 13 *(Tiny Tim)*
SOUTH TYNEDALE RAILWAY
L **S** **D**

No. 13
TALYLLYN RAILWAY
C

No. 13
TANFIELD RAILWAY
L

No. 130
EXMOOR STEAM RAILWAY
L **S** **D**

No. 13002
PLYM VALLEY RAILWAY
L **O**

No. 13018
CHINNOR & PRINCES RISBOROUGH
L **O**

No. 13029
TYSELEY LOCOMOTIVE WORKS

No. 1306 *(Mayflower)*
NENE VALLEY RAILWAY
L

No. 1309
BLUEBELL RAILWAY
C **O**

No. 1309 *(Henry De Lacy II)*
MIDDLETON RAILWAY
L

No. 131
NORTH YORKSHIRE MOORS RAILWAY
W

No. 1310
MIDDLETON RAILWAY
L **O**

No. 13180
NOTTINGHAM TRANSPORT CTRE
L **O**

No. 1319
BEAMISH
W

No. 13231
AVON VALLEY RAILWAY
C

No. 13245
SOUTH DOWNS LIGHT RAILWAY
L **O**

No. 13251
EAST ANGLIAN RAILWAY MUSEUM

No. 13254
NATIONAL RAILWAY MUSEUM
R

No. 1329
MIDDLETON RAILWAY
L

No. 13324
MANGAPPS RAILWAY MUSEUM
C

No. 1336
BLUEBELL RAILWAY
C

No. 1338
DIDCOT RAILWAY CENTRE
L **O**

ROLLING STOCK by NUMBER

13 — 1338

AW No. 1340 *(Trojan)*
DIDCOT RAILWAY CENTRE
L

AW No. 13436
CHINNOR & PRINCES RISBOROUGH
C

AW No. 13437
KEITH & DUFFTOWN RAILWAY
C

AW No. 13446
MID-NORFOLK RAILWAY
R

AW No. 135
EXMOOR STEAM RAILWAY
L S D

AW No. 135
KENT & EAST SUSSEX RAILWAY
W

AW No. 1357
DIDCOT RAILWAY CENTRE
R

AW No. 136
KENT & EAST SUSSEX RAILWAY
W

AW No. 1361
INDUSTRIAL RAILWAY MUSEUM
L S D

AW No. 1361
NORTH NORFOLK RAILWAY
R

AW No. 1363
DIDCOT RAILWAY CENTRE
L

AW No. 1365
BLUEBELL RAILWAY
C

AW No. 1367
DERWENT VALLEY
R

AW No. 1369 *(Simplex)*
ARMLEY MILLS
L S D

AW No. 1369
SOUTH DEVON RAILWAY
L O

AW No. 137
KENT & EAST SUSSEX RAILWAY
W

AW No. 1378
MUSEUM OF SCIENCE & INDUSTRY
L O D

AW No. 1378 *(Westminster)*
NORTHAMPTON & LAMPORT RAILWAY
L

AW No. 1380
MID-NORFOLK RAILWAY
R

AW No. 138C
MIDDLETON RAILWAY
L O

AW No. 1398 *(Lord Fisher)*
EAST SOMERSET RAILWAY
L O

AW No. 14
BEAMISH
L S D

AW No. 14
BUCKINGHAMSHIRE RLWY CTRE
L

AW No. 14 *(Charwelton)*
KENT & EAST SUSSEX RAILWAY
L

No. 14 *(Princess)*
LAKESIDE & HAVERTHWAITE RLWY
L **O**

No. 14
LEIGHTON BUZZARD RAILWAY
L

No. 14 *(Horton)*
MOORS VALLEY RAILWAY
L **O**

No. 14 *(Helen Kathryn)*
SOUTH TYNEDALE RAILWAY
L **O**

No. 14
TALYLLYN RAILWAY
C

No. 14
WELSHPOOL & LLANFAIR
L **O**

No. 14
WINDMILL FARM RAILWAY
L

No. 140
EMBSAY & BOLTON ABBEY RLWY
L **O**

No. 14024
CHASEWATER RAILWAY
C

No. 14031
AVON VALLEY RAILWAY
C

No. 14060
PEAK RAIL
R

No. 141108
MID-NORFOLK RAILWAY
L

No. 1420
SOUTH DEVON RAILWAY
L **O**

No. 14241
NATIONAL RAILWAY MUSEUM
R

No. 14351
MID-NORFOLK RAILWAY

No. 14352
MID-NORFOLK RAILWAY

No. 1438
APPLEBY-FRODINGHAM RAILWAY
L **O**

No. 1439
NATIONAL RAILWAY MUSEUM
L

No. 1450
GLOUCESTERSHIRE WARWICKSHIRE
L

No. 145428
DIDCOT RAILWAY CENTRE
W

No. 1456
BLUEBELL RAILWAY
C

No. 146
KENT & EAST SUSSEX RAILWAY
W

No. 1463
NATIONAL RAILWAY MUSEUM
L **S** **D**

No. 146366
DIDCOT RAILWAY CENTRE
W

No. 1464
BLUEBELL RAILWAY
C O

No. 146C *(Bunty)*
NORTHAMPTON & LAMPORT RAILWAY
L

No. 1470
CHASEWATER RAILWAY

No. 1476
NORTH NORFOLK RAILWAY
R

No. 1481
BLUEBELL RAILWAY
C

No. 1482
BLUEBELL RAILWAY
C O

No. 14901
BO'NESS & KINNEIL RAILWAY
L

No. 14901
TELFORD STEAM RAILWAY
C O

No. 15
CHASEWATER RAILWAY
W

No. 15 *(Caledonia)*
ISLE OF MAN RAILWAY
L

No. 15 *(Askham Hall)*
LAKESIDE & HAVERTHWAITE RLWY
L D

No. 15
LEIGHTON BUZZARD RAILWAY
L

No. 15 *(William Rufus)*
MOORS VALLEY RAILWAY
L O

No. 15
SOUTH TYNEDALE RAILWAY
L

No. 15
TALYLLYN RAILWAY
C

No. 1505 *(Ariadne)*
MUSEUM OF SCIENCE & INDUSTRY
L D

No. 151
KENT & EAST SUSSEX RAILWAY
W

No. 151 *(Tiny)*
SOUTH DEVON RAILWAY
L S D

No. 151
STRATHSPEY RAILWAY
R C S

No. 1510
NORTH NORFOLK RAILWAY
R

No. 1520
BLUEBELL RAILWAY
C

No. 15224
SPA VALLEY RAILWAY
L O

No. 153
BLUEBELL RAILWAY
R

No. 15354
MID-NORFOLK RAILWAY

No. 15396
MID-NORFOLK RAILWAY

No. 1556 *(Pride of Sussex)*
KENT & EAST SUSSEX RAILWAY
L **O**

No. 157
BLUEBELL RAILWAY

No. 15750
BLUEBELL RAILWAY
W **O**

No. 158
TANFIELD RAILWAY

No. 15829
GWILI RAILWAY
C

No. 15843
BLUEBELL RAILWAY
C **O**

No. 158A
MIDLAND RAILWAY CENTRE
L **S** **D**

No. 158A
NATIONAL RAILWAY MUSEUM
L

No. 159918
EAST ANGLIAN RAILWAY MUSEUM
W

No. 15997
NORTH NORFOLK RAILWAY
R

No. 16
HOLLYCOMBE STEAM COLLECTION
L

No. 16 *(Fluff)*
LAKESIDE & HAVERTHWAITE RLWY
L **D**

No. 16
LEIGHTON BUZZARD RAILWAY
L **O** **D**

No. 16 *(Robert Snooks)*
MOORS VALLEY RAILWAY
L **O**

No. 16
NORTH NORFOLK RAILWAY
R

No. 16
NORTH YORKSHIRE MOORS RAILWAY

No. 16
SOUTH TYNEDALE RAILWAY
L **D**

No. 16
TALYLLYN RAILWAY
C

No. 16
TANFIELD RAILWAY

No. 16 *(Scooby)*
WELSHPOOL & LLANFAIR
L **O**

No. 16
WEST SOMERSET RAILWAY
L **O**

No. 1600
NORTH NORFOLK RAILWAY
R

No. 1601 *(Matthew Murray)*
MIDDLETON RAILWAY
L **O**

ROLLING STOCK by NUMBER

15396 — 1601

ᴬᴬᴬ No. 16012
NORTHAMPTON & LAMPORT RAILWAY
C

ᴬᴬᴬ No. 1604 *(Alston)*
MID-SUFFOLK LIGHT RAILWAY
L **S**

ᴬᴬᴬ No. 1618
BLUEBELL RAILWAY
L **S** **D**

ᴬᴬᴬ No. 16190
NOTTINGHAM TRANSPORT CTRE
R

ᴬᴬᴬ No. 162
LEIGHTON BUZZARD RAILWAY
R **W** **O** **D**

ᴬᴬᴬ No. 1621
NATIONAL RAILWAY MUSEUM
L **S** **D**

ᴬᴬᴬ No. 16210
BLUEBELL RAILWAY
C **D**

ᴬᴬᴬ No. 1625
MIDDLETON RAILWAY
L

ᴬᴬᴬ No. 16263
BLUEBELL RAILWAY
C

ᴬᴬᴬ No. 163
KENT & EAST SUSSEX RAILWAY
W

ᴬᴬᴬ No. 163058
NORTH NORFOLK RAILWAY
R

ᴬᴬᴬ No. 16358
BLUEBELL RAILWAY
W **O**

ᴬᴬᴬ No. 1636 *(Fonmon)*
SPA VALLEY RAILWAY
L **O**

ᴬᴬᴬ No. 163748
SWANSEA VALE RAILWAY
R

ᴬᴬᴬ No. 1638
BLUEBELL RAILWAY
L

ᴬᴬᴬ No. 1638
KENT & EAST SUSSEX RAILWAY
L

ᴬᴬᴬ No. 16410
MIDLAND RAILWAY CENTRE
L

ᴬᴬᴬ No. 164686
NORTH NORFOLK RAILWAY
R

ᴬᴬᴬ No. 1647
NORTHAMPTON & LAMPORT RAILWAY
C

ᴬᴬᴬ No. 16631
EAST ANGLIAN RAILWAY MUSEUM
C

ᴬᴬᴬ No. 1666
NORTH YORKSHIRE MOORS RAILWAY
C

ᴬᴬᴬ No. 169
KENT & EAST SUSSEX RAILWAY
W

ᴬᴬᴬ No. 1697 *(John Alcock)*
MIDDLETON RAILWAY
L **O**

ᴬᴬᴬ No. 17 *(Damredub)*
LEIGHTON BUZZARD RAILWAY
L **O** **D**

No. 17 *(Hartfield)*
MOORS VALLEY RAILWAY
L **O**

No. 17
SOUTH TYNEDALE RAILWAY
L **O**

No. 17
STRATHSPEY RAILWAY
L

No. 17
TALYLLYN RAILWAY
C

No. 17
TANFIELD RAILWAY

No. 17055
NOTTINGHAM TRANSPORT CTRE
R

No. 171 *(Slieve Gullion)*
RPSI
L **O**

No. 1719 *(Lady Nan)*
EAST SOMERSET RAILWAY
L **O**

No. 172
NORTH YORKSHIRE MOORS RAILWAY
C

No. 173
NORTH YORKSHIRE MOORS RAILWAY
R

No. 1738 *(Percy)*
SOUTH DEVON RAILWAY
L **O**

No. 17391
BRISTOL HARBOUR RAILWAY
W **O** **D**

No. 174
NORTH YORKSHIRE MOORS RAILWAY
R

No. 17424
CHINNOR & PRINCES RISBOROUGH
W

No. 1748S
BLUEBELL RAILWAY
R **O**

No. 1748SM
BLUEBELL RAILWAY
R **O**

No. 175
BLUEBELL RAILWAY
O

No. 175
NORTH YORKSHIRE MOORS RAILWAY

No. 176 *(MS & L Tricomposite)*
VINTAGE CARRIAGES TRUST
C **O** **D**

No. 1776
ABBEY PUMPING STATION
L

No. 178
BLUEBELL RAILWAY
L

No. 1781 *(Polar Bear)*
AMBERLEY WORKING MUSEUM
L

No. 1782
NORTH YORKSHIRE MOORS RAILWAY

No. 1786 *(Courage)*
MIDDLETON RAILWAY
L **O**

No. 1788
BLUEBELL RAILWAY

No. 17898
EAST ANGLIAN RAILWAY MUSEUM
W

No. 179
NATIONAL RAILWAY MUSEUM
R

No. 17908
BLUEBELL RAILWAY
W

No. 18
AMBERLEY WORKING MUSEUM
L

No. 18 *(Lewin)*
BEAMISH
L S D

No. 18 *(Ifs & L Tramway Co)*
DIDCOT RAILWAY CENTRE
W

No. 18 *(Feanor)*
LEIGHTON BUZZARD RAILWAY
L O D

No. 18
TALYLLYN RAILWAY
C

No. 1800 *(Thomas)*
NENE VALLEY RAILWAY
L O

No. 1818
BLUEBELL RAILWAY
C O

No. 1827
FOXFIELD STEAM RAILWAY
L O

No. 1835
PEAK RAIL
R O

No. 1838
BLUEBELL RAILWAY
C O

No. 184
RPSI
L

No. 1845
CHINNOR & PRINCES RISBOROUGH
C

No. 185 *(David Payne)*
DARLINGTON RAILWAY PRES SOC
L S D

No. 1857
SWINDON & CRICKLADE RAILWAY
L

No. 1859 *(Sir Gomer)*
BATTLEFIELD LINE
L O

No. 186
NATIONAL RAILWAY MUSEUM
R

No. 186
RPSI
L

No. 1867
AVON VALLEY RAILWAY
C

No. 1868 *(Columbine)*
NATIONAL RAILWAY MUSEUM
L

No. 1876 *(No 1)*
SITTINGBOURNE & KEMSLEY
S D

No. 1877 *(Chevallier)*
GREAT WHIPSNADE RAILWAY
L **S**

No. 18798
CHINNOR & PRINCES RISBOROUGH
R

No. 1882 *(Mirvale)*
MIDDLETON RAILWAY
L **S**

No. 1883 *(Menelaeus)*
CALEDONIAN RAILWAY
L

No. 1888 *(Elizabeth)*
ARMLEY MILLS
L **S** **D**

No. 19
BODMIN & WENFORD RAILWAY
L **O**

No. 19
BO'NESS & KINNEIL RAILWAY
L

No. 19
EAST ANGLIAN RAILWAY MUSEUM
C

No. 19
SOUTH TYNEDALE RAILWAY
W

No. 19
TALYLLYN RAILWAY
C

No. 190
DIDCOT RAILWAY CENTRE
R

No. 1914 *(Sir John)*
GWILI RAILWAY
L **S**

No. 1925 *(Caliban)*
LAKESIDE & HAVERTHWAITE RLWY

No. 19305
GWILI RAILWAY
R

No. 1933
AVON VALLEY RAILWAY
C

No. 1940 *(Henbury)*
BRISTOL HARBOUR RAILWAY
L **O**

No. 1941
DIDCOT RAILWAY CENTRE
R

No. 196 *(Chattenden)*
SITTINGBOURNE & KEMSLEY
R

No. 1970
PEAK RAIL

No. 197266
NATIONAL RAILWAY MUSEUM
W

No. 19764
CAVAN & LEITRIM RAILWAY
R **S** **D**

No. 19765
CAVAN & LEITRIM RAILWAY
R **S** **D**

No. 19818
DIDCOT RAILWAY CENTRE
W

No. 1987
BLUEBELL RAILWAY
C

ROLLING STOCK by NUMBER

1877 — 1987

ROLLING STOCK by NUMBER

199 — 2

No. 199 *(Upnor)*
SITTINGBOURNE & KEMSLEY
R

No. 1994 *(Eastleigh)*
EASTLEIGH LAKESIDE RAILWAY
L O

No. 2 *(Atlas)*
ABBEY LIGHT RAILWAY
L O

No. 2
AMBERLEY WORKING MUSEUM
L

No. 2 *(Edwin Hulse)*
AVON VALLEY RAILWAY
L

No. 2 *(Bicton)*
BICTON WOODLAND RAILWAY
L O

No. 2 *(Peter)*
BODMIN & WENFORD RAILWAY
L

No. 2 *(Katie)*
BREDGAR & WORMSHILL
L O

No. 2
CHURNET VALLEY RAILWAY
L S D

No. 2 *(Arnold J Rimmer)*
CLEETHORPES LIGHT RAILWAY
L

No. 2 *(Pontyberem)*
DIDCOT RAILWAY CENTRE
L

No. 2
EAST ANGLIA TRANSPORT MUSEUM
L O

No. 2
EAST ANGLIAN RAILWAY MUSEUM
W

No. 2 *(Prince)*
FFESTINIOG RAILWAY
L O

No. 2 *(Meaford No 2)*
FOXFIELD STEAM RAILWAY
L O

No. 2 *(Florence No 2)*
FOXFIELD STEAM RAILWAY
L

No. 2 *(Andrew)*
GARTELL LIGHT RAILWAY

No. 2 *(Rory)*
GIANTS CAUSEWAY & BUSHMILLS
L O

No. 2 *(Clive)*
HEATHERSLAW LIGHT RAILWAY
L O

No. 2
IRISH STEAM PRESERVATION SOC
L O

No. 2 *(Muffin)*
LAPPA VALLEY STEAM RAILWAY
L O

No. 2 *(Dundee Gas Works Loco)*
NARROW GAUGE RAILWAY MUSEUM
L O

No. 2
NATIONAL RAILWAY MUSEUM
R

No. 2 *(Bauxite)*
NATIONAL RAILWAY MUSEUM
L

No.2
NORTH GLOUCESTERSHIRE RAILWAY
L

No.2
NORTH YORKSHIRE MOORS RAILWAY
R

No.2
NORTH YORKSHIRE MOORS RAILWAY
L

No.2 *(Workhorse)*
PERRYGROVE RAILWAY
L O

No.2 *(Ivor)*
ROYAL VICTORIA RAILWAY
L

No.2 *(Mildred)*
RUDYARD LAKE RAILWAY
L O

No.2 *(Enid)*
SNOWDON MOUNTAIN RAILWAY
L O

No.2
SOUTH TYNEDALE RAILWAY
C O

No.2 *(May)*
SWANAGE RAILWAY
L O

No.2 *(Dolgoch)*
TALYLLYN RAILWAY
L O

No.2
TALYLLYN RAILWAY
C

No.2
TANFIELD RAILWAY
L O

No.2
TANFIELD RAILWAY
L

No.2
ULSTER FOLK & TRANSPORT
L S D

No.2 *(Blanche)*
ULSTER FOLK & TRANSPORT
L S D

No.2
ULSTER FOLK & TRANSPORT
L S D

No.2 *(Weasel)*
WELLS & WALSINGHAM
L

No.2 *(Countess)*
WELSHPOOL & LLANFAIR
L

No.2 *(Silver Jubilee)*
WINDMILL FARM RAILWAY
L

No.20
ALMOND VALLEY HERITAGE TRUST
L

No.20
BOWES RAILWAY
L

No.20
CADEBY LIGHT RAILWAY
L

No.20
KENT & EAST SUSSEX RAILWAY
L

No.20
LAKESIDE & HAVERTHWAITE RLWY
L O D

ROLLING STOCK by NUMBER

2 — 20

No. 20
LAKESIDE & HAVERTHWAITE RLWY

No. 20
LEIGHTON BUZZARD RAILWAY
W **S**

No. 20
SOUTH TYNEDALE RAILWAY

No. 20
TALYLLYN RAILWAY
C

No. 20
ULSTER FOLK & TRANSPORT
L **S** **D**

No. 200 *(Lodge Hill)*
SITTINGBOURNE & KEMSLEY
R

No. 2002
GWILI RAILWAY
W

No. 2003 *(John Blenkinsop)*
MIDDLETON RAILWAY
L

No. 2005 *(King George)*
KERR MINIATURE RAILWAY
O

No. 20055
DERWENT VALLEY

No. 20056
BARROW HILL ROUNDHOUSE
L **O**

No. 20087
EAST LANCASHIRE RAILWAY

No. 2009
GWILI RAILWAY
W

No. 20096
BARROW HILL ROUNDHOUSE
L **S**

No. 201
SPA VALLEY RAILWAY
R

No. 201
STRATHSPEY RAILWAY
R

No. 20135
BARROW HILL ROUNDHOUSE
L

No. 2016
SOUTH DEVON RAILWAY
W

No. 20188
WATERCRESS LINE
L **O**

No. 20188 *(River Yeo)*
YEOVIL RAILWAY CENTRE
L **O**

No. 20205
MIDLAND RAILWAY CENTRE
L

No. 20214
LAKESIDE & HAVERTHWAITE RLWY
L **O**

No. 20227 *(Traction)*
MIDLAND RAILWAY CENTRE
L **O**

No. 203031 *(Braich)*
LLANBERIS LAKE RAILWAY
L

No. 204 *(Four Elms)*
SITTINGBOURNE & KEMSLEY
R

No. 2044
MANGAPPS RAILWAY MUSEUM
L O S

No. 21 *(Sir James)*
LAKESIDE & HAVERTHWAITE RLWY
L D

No. 2047 *(Warwickshire)*
SEVERN VALLEY RAILWAY
L S D

No. 21 *(Festoon)*
LEIGHTON BUZZARD RAILWAY
L

No. 2067 *(Peter)*
AMBERLEY WORKING MUSEUM
L

No. 21
NORTHAMPTON & LAMPORT RAILWAY
L

No. 20685 *(Cement)*
ARMLEY MILLS
L S

No. 21
TALYLLYN RAILWAY
C

No. 207103 *(Idris)*
GWILI RAILWAY
L O

No. 21
TANFIELD RAILWAY

No. 2080
PEAK RAIL
C

No. 21027
EAST ANGLIAN RAILWAY MUSEUM

No. 2085 *(Foleshill)*
PALLOT STEAM MUSEUM
L S D

No. 2103
MIDDLETON RAILWAY
L O

No. 2087
NIRT
L O

No. 2104
NORTHAMPTON & LAMPORT RAILWAY
L O S D

No. 2091 *(Victor)*
GREAT WESTERN RAILWAY MUSEUM
L

No. 21187
GWILI RAILWAY
C

No. 2091 *(Wendy)*
KEW BRIDGE STEAM MUSEUM
L O

No. 21249
LAVENDER LINE
C

No. 20C
CAVAN & LEITRIM RAILWAY
R

No. 2126
NATIONAL WATERWAYS MUSEUM
S D

No. 21
CHASEWATER RAILWAY
L

No. 21271
BLUEBELL RAILWAY
C

No. 21274
NATIONAL RAILWAY MUSEUM
R

No. 2129 *(Kestrel)*
PALLOT STEAM MUSEUM
L O

No. 21295 *(Peldon)*
AMBERLEY WORKING MUSEUM
L

No. 2138 *(Swordfish)*
SWINDON & CRICKLADE RAILWAY
L

No. 2139 *(Salmon)*
SWINDON & CRICKLADE RAILWAY
L

No. 214 *(Gladstone)*
NATIONAL RAILWAY MUSEUM
L S D

No. 2142 *(Northern Gas Board No 1)*
BATTLEFIELD LINE
L O

No. 2142
TELFORD STEAM RAILWAY
L O

No. 21442 *(Woodbine)*
SWINDON & CRICKLADE RAILWAY
L

No. 2180
SOUTH DEVON RAILWAY
C

No. 2186
BLUEBELL RAILWAY

No. 219
BLUEBELL RAILWAY

No. 21C123 *(Blackmoor Vale)*
BLUEBELL RAILWAY
L O

No. 22
BOWES RAILWAY
L O

No. 22
DIDCOT RAILWAY CENTRE

No. 22
LAKESIDE & HAVERTHWAITE RLWY

No. 22
LEIGHTON BUZZARD RAILWAY
L

No. 22
SOUTH TYNEDALE RAILWAY
R W O

No. 22
TALYLLYN RAILWAY
C

No. 220
GWILI RAILWAY
C

No. 2201 *(Victory)*
GWILI RAILWAY
L O

No. 2202
DIDCOT RAILWAY CENTRE
R

No. 2210
PEAK RAIL
W

No. 2216 *(Victoria)*
BOWES RAILWAY
L

ROLLING STOCK by NUMBER

21274 — 2216

No. 2216 *(Unique)*
SITTINGBOURNE & KEMSLEY
L **S** **D**

No. 2234
NATIONAL RAILWAY MUSEUM

No. 223700
ABBEY PUMPING STATION
L **O**

No. 2238
NORTH YORKSHIRE MOORS RAILWAY
L

No. 2253
NORTH YORKSHIRE MOORS RAILWAY
L

No. 22624
MANGAPPS RAILWAY MUSEUM
C **D**

No. 2276
BLUEBELL RAILWAY

No. 228
NOTTINGHAM TRANSPORT CTRE
R

No. 229
BLUEBELL RAILWAY
O

No. 23
AMBERLEY WORKING MUSEUM
L

No. 23
EAST ANGLIAN RAILWAY MUSEUM
L **O**

No. 23 *(Holman F Stephens)*
KENT & EAST SUSSEX RAILWAY
L

No. 23
LEIGHTON BUZZARD RAILWAY
L

No. 23
LONDON TRANSPORT MUSEUM
L **S** **D**

No. 23
TALYLLYN RAILWAY
C

No. 230142
NORTH YORKSHIRE MOORS RAILWAY

No. 23053
NOTTINGHAM TRANSPORT CTRE
W

No. 231
DIDCOT RAILWAY CENTRE
R

No. 231 *(Merlin)*
KEIGHLEY & WORTH VALLEY
L **O**

No. 2315 *(Lady Ingrid)*
SPA VALLEY RAILWAY
L **O**

No. 2317
SPA VALLEY RAILWAY
R

No. 2325
MANGAPPS RAILWAY MUSEUM
L **O** **D**

No. 2333 *(David)*
LAKESIDE & HAVERTHWAITE RLWY
L **O**

No. 2338
KENT & EAST SUSSEX RAILWAY
W

ROLLING STOCK by NUMBER

2216 — 2338

No. 23387
WELSH HIGHLAND RAILWAY
L O

No. 23389 *(Eryri)*
WELSH HIGHLAND RAILWAY
L O

No. 2352
MUSEUM OF SCIENCE & INDUSTRY
L D

No. 2354 *(Richard Trevithick)*
SWINDON & CRICKLADE RAILWAY
L O

No. 2356
BLUEBELL RAILWAY
C

No. 2356
DIDCOT RAILWAY CENTRE
W

No. 2361 *(William Stewart Trimble)*
BOWES RAILWAY
L O

No. 2370
NORTH NORFOLK RAILWAY
L

No. 23791
NORTH YORKSHIRE MOORS RAILWAY
R

No. 2387 *(Brookes No 1)*
MIDDLETON RAILWAY
L O

No. 23890
NORTH YORKSHIRE MOORS RAILWAY

No. 2390 *(Trecwn)*
ARMLEY MILLS
L S D

No. 2392
NORTH YORKSHIRE MOORS RAILWAY
L

No. 23956
NORTH YORKSHIRE MOORS RAILWAY

No. 24 *(Stamford)*
BLUEBELL RAILWAY
L

No. 24
BO'NESS & KINNEIL RAILWAY
L

No. 24
CLEETHORPES LIGHT RAILWAY
L

No. 24 *(Rolvenden)*
KENT & EAST SUSSEX RAILWAY
L O

No. 24
LEIGHTON BUZZARD RAILWAY
L

No. 24 *(Stanton)*
MIDLAND RAILWAY CENTRE
L S D

No. 24
SOUTH TYNEDALE RAILWAY
R W O

No. 24
WEST SOMERSET RAILWAY
L

No. 2408
MID-NORFOLK RAILWAY
R W

No. 24081
GLOUCESTERSHIRE WARWICKSHIRE
L O

No. 24082
EAST ANGLIAN RAILWAY MUSEUM
R

No. 2409 *(King George)*
GLOUCESTERSHIRE WARWICKSHIRE
L **O**

No. 24109
NORTH YORKSHIRE MOORS RAILWAY

No. 242
BRISTOL HARBOUR RAILWAY
L

No. 242688 *(Muffin)*
NIRT

No. 24376 *(Hercules)*
GREAT WHIPSNADE RAILWAY
L **O**

No. 24376
SPA VALLEY RAILWAY
R

No. 245
NATIONAL RAILWAY MUSEUM
L

No. 2450 *(J T Daly)*
PALLOT STEAM MUSEUM
L **S** **D**

No. 246 *(Morayshire)*
BO'NESS & KINNEIL RAILWAY
L

No. 246
ULSTER FOLK & TRANSPORT
L **S** **D**

No. 2462
BLUEBELL RAILWAY
O

No. 2472 *(Alpha)*
SITTINGBOURNE & KEMSLEY
L **S** **D**

No. 24823
GWILI RAILWAY
C

No. 24825
GWILI RAILWAY
C

No. 24843
GWILI RAILWAY
C

No. 24959
EAST ANGLIAN RAILWAY MUSEUM
O

No. 25 *(Northiam)*
KENT & EAST SUSSEX RAILWAY
L **O**

No. 25
LEIGHTON BUZZARD RAILWAY
L

No. 25
LEIGHTON BUZZARD RAILWAY
L

No. 25 *(Derwent)*
NATIONAL RAILWAY MUSEUM
L

No. 25
TANFIELD RAILWAY

No. 2500
NATIONAL RAILWAY MUSEUM
L

No. 25035 *(Castell Dinas Bran)*
NORTHAMPTON & LAMPORT RAILWAY
L

ROLLING STOCK by NUMBER

24082 — 25035

No. 25040
AVON VALLEY RAILWAY
C

No. 25067
BARROW HILL ROUNDHOUSE
L **S**

No. 25083
CALEDONIAN RAILWAY
L **D**

No. 251
NATIONAL RAILWAY MUSEUM
L **S** **D**

No. 2511
DIDCOT RAILWAY CENTRE
R

No. 2511 *(Triumph)*
SITTINGBOURNE & KEMSLEY
L **D**

No. 2515
BLUEBELL RAILWAY
C **D**

No. 2516
NATIONAL RAILWAY MUSEUM
L

No. 2516 *(Dean Goods)*
STEAM
L **S** **D**

No. 252 *(E B Wilson)*
ARMLEY MILLS

No. 252
NORTH NORFOLK RAILWAY
R

No. 2526
BLUEBELL RAILWAY
C

No. 25265 *(Harlech Castle)*
GREAT CENTRAL RAILWAY
L **D**

No. 25299
AVON VALLEY RAILWAY
C

No. 2531
BLUEBELL RAILWAY

No. 25313
LLANGOLLEN RAILWAY
L **D**

No. 2536
NORTH NORFOLK RAILWAY
R

No. 2553
BARROW HILL ROUNDHOUSE
L **D**

No. 25728
BLUEBELL RAILWAY
C **D**

No. 25735
AVON VALLEY RAILWAY
C

No. 25769
BLUEBELL RAILWAY
C **D**

No. 2589 *(Harry)*
BARROW HILL ROUNDHOUSE
L **D**

No. 2591 *(Southerham)*
SPA VALLEY RAILWAY
L **D**

No. 25972
AVON VALLEY RAILWAY
C

ROLLING STOCK by NUMBER

25040 — 25972

No. 2599
AVON VALLEY RAILWAY
C

No. 26
BUCKINGHAMSHIRE RLWY CTRE
L

No. 26 *(Yimkin)*
LEIGHTON BUZZARD RAILWAY
L

No. 26004
BO'NESS & KINNEIL RAILWAY
L

No. 26007
BARROW HILL ROUNDHOUSE
L

No. 26010
NORTHAMPTON & LAMPORT RAILWAY
L

No. 26011
BARROW HILL ROUNDHOUSE
L S D

No. 26014
PEAK RAIL
C

No. 26025
PEAK RAIL
C

No. 26035
CALEDONIAN RAILWAY
L D

No. 26038
SOUTH YORKSHIRE RAILWAY
L

No. 26043
PEAK RAIL
C O

No. 26049
PEAK RAIL
C O

No. 2613 *(Brookfield)*
MANGAPPS RAILWAY MUSEUM
L O D

No. 2624 *(Superb)*
SITTINGBOURNE & KEMSLEY
L O

No. 263
BLUEBELL RAILWAY
S D

No. 263
DIDCOT RAILWAY CENTRE
W

No. 263278
SOUTH DEVON RAILWAY
W

No. 2648 *(Linda)*
BATTLEFIELD LINE
L

No. 2659
CAVAN & LEITRIM RAILWAY
L O

No. 2667
WELSH HIGHLAND RAILWAY
L

No. 2670 *(Lamport No 3)*
BATTLEFIELD LINE
L O

No. 2671
DIDCOT RAILWAY CENTRE
W

No. 2678 *(Knowle)*
KENT & EAST SUSSEX RAILWAY
L O

⚞⚟ No.268878 *(Twll Coed)*
LLANBERIS LAKE RAILWAY
L

⚞⚟ No.269
MID-NORFOLK RAILWAY
R

⚞⚟ No.27
AMBERLEY WORKING MUSEUM
L

⚞⚟ No.27
BLUEBELL RAILWAY
L

⚞⚟ No.27
LEIGHTON BUZZARD RAILWAY
L

⚞⚟ No.27 *(Lough Erne)*
RPSI
L

⚞⚟ No.270
BLUEBELL RAILWAY
R

⚞⚟ No.2700
NATIONAL RAILWAY MUSEUM
L

⚞⚟ No.2700
NATIONAL RAILWAY MUSEUM
L

⚞⚟ No.27000 *(Electra)*
MIDLAND RAILWAY CENTRE
R S D

⚞⚟ No.2702 *(Matthew Murray)*
MIDDLETON RAILWAY
L

⚞⚟ No.27024
CALEDONIAN RAILWAY
L O

⚞⚟ No.27043
STRATHSPEY RAILWAY
R C

⚞⚟ No.2705 *(Beatrice)*
EMBSAY & BOLTON ABBEY RLWY
L

⚞⚟ No.27093
NATIONAL RAILWAY MUSEUM
R

⚞⚟ No.2716 *(Esso)*
NORTH YORKSHIRE MOORS RAILWAY
W

⚞⚟ No.2723
STRATHSPEY RAILWAY
R C

⚞⚟ No.2745
GWILI RAILWAY
W

⚞⚟ No.2749
SPA VALLEY RAILWAY
C

⚞⚟ No.276
SOUTH DEVON RAILWAY
C

⚞⚟ No.27654 *(Dylan Thomas)*
GWILI RAILWAY
L

⚞⚟ No.2766
BODMIN & WENFORD RAILWAY
L S

⚞⚟ No.2773
BLUEBELL RAILWAY
W

⚞⚟ No.27878
GWILI RAILWAY
L

No. 27914
SWANSEA VALE RAILWAY
L

No. 2796 *(Siphon G)*
DIDCOT RAILWAY CENTRE
R

No. 28 *(Bardon)*
GREAT CENTRAL RAILWAY
L O

No. 28
LEIGHTON BUZZARD RAILWAY
L D

No. 28 *(RAF Stanbridge)*
LEIGHTON BUZZARD RAILWAY
L

No. 28
NATIONAL RAILWAY MUSEUM
L

No. 2807
GLOUCESTERSHIRE WARWICKSHIRE
L

No. 281266
COLNE VALLEY RAILWAY
L

No. 2818
NATIONAL RAILWAY MUSEUM
L

No. 282328
GWILI RAILWAY

No. 283 *(Charles)*
INDUSTRIAL RAILWAY MUSEUM
L D

No. 28361
NATIONAL RAILWAY MUSEUM
R

No. 284235
NATIONAL RAILWAY MUSEUM

No. 2856
VINTAGE CARRIAGES TRUST
C O D

No. 2857 *(Swiftsure)*
BODMIN & WENFORD RAILWAY
L O

No. 2862
DIDCOT RAILWAY CENTRE
W

No. 287 *(Vigilant)*
NIRT
L

No. 2870 *(City of London)*
WINDMILL FARM RAILWAY
L O

No. 287664
NOTTINGHAM TRANSPORT CTRE
R

No. 28918
GWILI RAILWAY
W

No. 29 *(Creepy)*
LEIGHTON BUZZARD RAILWAY
L O D

No. 29
NORTH YORKSHIRE MOORS RAILWAY
L

No. 290
DIDCOT RAILWAY CENTRE
R

No. 2911
NATIONAL RAILWAY MUSEUM
R

ROLLING STOCK by NUMBER

27914 — 2911

ROLLING STOCK by NUMBER

292030 — 3

No. 292030 *(Glaslyn)*
WELSH HIGHLAND RAILWAY
L O

No. 2944 *(Hotspur)*
SPA VALLEY RAILWAY
L

No. 295
NORTH NORFOLK RAILWAY
R

No. 295516
DERWENT VALLEY
R

No. 29663
MIDLAND RAILWAY CENTRE

No. 29666
MIDLAND RAILWAY CENTRE

No. 29670
MIDLAND RAILWAY CENTRE

No. 2968
SEVERN VALLEY RAILWAY
L

No. 297147
BRISTOL HARBOUR RAILWAY
W O D

No. 298
NATIONAL RAILWAY MUSEUM
L

No. 2987
NATIONAL RAILWAY MUSEUM

No. 29896
NATIONAL RAILWAY MUSEUM
R

No. 299 *(Hodbarrow)*
ARMLEY MILLS
L S

No. 2996 *(Victor)*
BATTLEFIELD LINE
L O

No. 2999 *(Lady of Legend)*
DIDCOT RAILWAY CENTRE
L

No. 3 *(Odin)*
ABBEY LIGHT RAILWAY
L O

No. 3 *(Holy War)*
BALA LAKE RAILWAY
L O

No. 3 *(Richard III)*
BATTLEFIELD LINE
L S

No. 3 *(Twizell)*
BEAMISH
L

No. 3 *(Dickie)*
BEER HEIGHTS
L O

No. 3 *(Baxter)*
BLUEBELL RAILWAY
L

No. 3 *(Lec)*
BODMIN & WENFORD RAILWAY
L O

No. 3 *(Harrogate)*
BREDGAR & WORMSHILL
L O

No. 3 *(2nd Air Division USAAF)*
BURE VALLEY RAILWAY
L O

No. 3
CAMBRIAN RAILWAY SOCIETY
L

No. 3 *(Colin McAndrew)*
CHASEWATER RAILWAY
L S D

No. 3
DOWNPATRICK & ARDGLASS
L O

No. 3 *(Francis Henry Lloyd)*
EASTLEIGH LAKESIDE RAILWAY
L O

No. 3 *(Wolstanton No 3)*
FOXFIELD STEAM RAILWAY
L

No. 3 *(Marston, Thompson & Evershed Limited No 3)*
FOXFIELD STEAM RAILWAY
L

No. 3 *(Shane)*
GIANTS CAUSEWAY & BUSHMILLS
L O

No. 3 *(Bodiam)*
KENT & EAST SUSSEX RAILWAY
L

No. 3 *(Gladiator)*
LAPPA VALLEY STEAM RAILWAY
L O

No. 3
LEIGHTON BUZZARD RAILWAY
R C O D

No. 3 *(Rishra)*
LEIGHTON BUZZARD RAILWAY
L D

No. 3 *(Talos)*
MOORS VALLEY RAILWAY
L O

No. 3 *(Coppernob)*
NATIONAL RAILWAY MUSEUM
L

No. 3
NORTH GLOUCESTERSHIRE RAILWAY
L

No. 3
NORTH YORKSHIRE MOORS RAILWAY
L

No. 3
PLYM VALLEY RAILWAY
L O

No. 3 *(Maurice the Major)*
ROYAL VICTORIA RAILWAY
L

No. 3 *(R H Smith)*
RPSI
L O

No. 3 *(Wyddfa)*
SNOWDON MOUNTAIN RAILWAY
L O

No. 3 *(Sao Domingos)*
SOUTH TYNEDALE RAILWAY
L

No. 3
SOUTH TYNEDALE RAILWAY
C

No. 3 *(Sir Haydn)*
TALYLLYN RAILWAY
L O

No. 3
TALYLLYN RAILWAY
C

No. 3
TANFIELD RAILWAY

ROLLING STOCK by NUMBER

3 — 3

No. 3
TANFIELD RAILWAY

No. 3
TANFIELD RAILWAY

No. 3
TELFORD STEAM RAILWAY

No. 3 *(Norfolk Hero)*
WELLS & WALSINGHAM
L

No. 30
LEIGHTON BUZZARD RAILWAY
L O D

No. 30
ULSTER FOLK & TRANSPORT
L S D

No. 30004
BLUEBELL RAILWAY

No. 30064
BLUEBELL RAILWAY
L S D

No. 30072
KEIGHLEY & WORTH VALLEY
L

No. 301580
CHASEWATER RAILWAY
O

No. 3020 *(Cornwall)*
RAILWAY AGE
L O

No. 3030
DIDCOT RAILWAY CENTRE
W

No. 3037
SOUTH DEVON RAILWAY
W

No. 304470
MID-SUFFOLK LIGHT RAILWAY
L O

No. 30499
WATERCRESS LINE
L S D

No. 3050 *(Gelert)*
WELSH HIGHLAND RAILWAY
L O

No. 3051
AVON VALLEY RAILWAY
C

No. 3058 *(Alfred)*
BODMIN & WENFORD RAILWAY
L O

No. 30587
SOUTH DEVON RAILWAY
L

No. 3060
GWILI RAILWAY
C

No. 3061 *(Empress)*
MANGAPPS RAILWAY MUSEUM
L D

No. 30777 *(Sir Lamiel)*
GREAT CENTRAL RAILWAY
L

No. 308
EAST ANGLIAN RAILWAY MUSEUM

No. 3089
AVON VALLEY RAILWAY
C

No. 30926 *(Repton)*
NORTH YORKSHIRE MOORS RAILWAY
L

No. 31 *(Hamburg)*
KEIGHLEY & WORTH VALLEY
L

No. 31
LEIGHTON BUZZARD RAILWAY
L **S** **D**

No. 31
NATIONAL RAILWAY MUSEUM
R

No. 31
SOUTH TYNEDALE RAILWAY
W

No. 3101
AMBERLEY WORKING MUSEUM
L

No. 311
BLUEBELL RAILWAY
O

No. 311
NATIONAL RAILWAY MUSEUM
R

No. 31105
TYSELEY LOCOMOTIVE WORKS

No. 31106
TYSELEY LOCOMOTIVE WORKS

No. 31108
MIDLAND RAILWAY CENTRE
L **O**

No. 31128
TYSELEY LOCOMOTIVE WORKS

No. 3116
BLUEBELL RAILWAY
C **O**

No. 31186
TYSELEY LOCOMOTIVE WORKS

No. 31190
TYSELEY LOCOMOTIVE WORKS

No. 3121
BODMIN & WENFORD RAILWAY
L **S**

No. 31235
MID-NORFOLK RAILWAY
L **O**

No. 312433
SWANSEA VALE RAILWAY
L **O**

No. 31271
MIDLAND RAILWAY CENTRE
L **S** **D**

No. 31289
TYSELEY LOCOMOTIVE WORKS

No. 31301
TYSELEY LOCOMOTIVE WORKS

No. 3135 *(Spartan)*
SPA VALLEY RAILWAY
L **O**

No. 3138 *(Hutnik)*
APPLEBY-FRODINGHAM RAILWAY
L **O**

No. 31415
TYSELEY LOCOMOTIVE WORKS

No. 31422
TYSELEY LOCOMOTIVE WORKS

No. 31452
TYSELEY LOCOMOTIVE WORKS

ROLLING STOCK by NUMBER

30926 — 31452

No. 31459
TYSELEY LOCOMOTIVE WORKS

No. 31462
TYSELEY LOCOMOTIVE WORKS

No. 31467
EAST LANCASHIRE RAILWAY

No. 31468
TYSELEY LOCOMOTIVE WORKS

No. 31524
TYSELEY LOCOMOTIVE WORKS

No. 31526
TYSELEY LOCOMOTIVE WORKS

No. 31549
TYSELEY LOCOMOTIVE WORKS

No. 3157
MUSEUM OF SCIENCE & INDUSTRY
L **D**

No. 316
DIDCOT RAILWAY CENTRE
R

No. 3180 *(Antwerp)*
NORTH YORKSHIRE MOORS RAILWAY
L

No. 31806
WATERCRESS LINE
L **S**

No. 31874
WATERCRESS LINE
L

No. 319294 *(Sir Alfred Wood)*
NIRT
L **D**

No. 32 *(Gothenburg)*
EAST LANCASHIRE RAILWAY

No. 32
LEIGHTON BUZZARD RAILWAY
L

No. 32
TANFIELD RAILWAY

No. 320
BLUEBELL RAILWAY
C

No. 3205
SOUTH DEVON RAILWAY
L **D**

No. 3211
COLNE VALLEY RAILWAY
L

No. 3217 *(Earl of Berkeley)*
BLUEBELL RAILWAY
L

No. 322
CAMBRIAN RAILWAY SOCIETY
L

No. 3221 *(University of Southampton)*
EASTLEIGH LAKESIDE RAILWAY
L **D**

No. 323 *(Bluebell)*
BLUEBELL RAILWAY
L **S** **D**

No. 32337
DIDCOT RAILWAY CENTRE
W

No. 32338
DIDCOT RAILWAY CENTRE
W

No. 32518
EAST ANGLIAN RAILWAY MUSEUM
W

♨♨ No. 326
NATIONAL RAILWAY MUSEUM
R

♨♨ No. 32650 *(Sutton)*
KENT & EAST SUSSEX RAILWAY
L S D

♨♨ No. 3267
NATIONAL RAILWAY MUSEUM
R

♨♨ No. 3270 *(Carpenter)*
CHOLSEY & WALLINGFORD RAILWAY
L O

♨♨ No. 327904 *(Acorn)*
INDUSTRIAL RAILWAY MUSEUM
L O D

♨♨ No. 327974 *(Shire Lodge)*
NIRT
L O

♨♨ No. 328
BLUEBELL RAILWAY
C

♨♨ No. 3291
NORTH YORKSHIRE MOORS RAILWAY

♨♨ No. 32975
BLUEBELL RAILWAY
O

♨♨ No. 3299
DIDCOT RAILWAY CENTRE
R

♨♨ No. 33
BLUEBELL RAILWAY
C

♨♨ No. 33
LEIGHTON BUZZARD RAILWAY
L

♨♨ No. 33
MANGAPPS RAILWAY MUSEUM
S

♨♨ No. 33 *(George Edwards)*
PRESTONGRANGE INDUSTRIAL

♨♨ No. 33
SOUTH TYNEDALE RAILWAY
R W O

♨♨ No. 33001
NATIONAL RAILWAY MUSEUM
L

♨♨ No. 33003
STRATHSPEY RAILWAY
R C

♨♨ No. 33026 *(Eastleigh)*
TYSELEY LOCOMOTIVE WORKS

♨♨ No. 33048
WEST SOMERSET RAILWAY
L O

♨♨ No. 33056 *(Burma Star)*
CHURNET VALLEY RAILWAY
L

♨♨ No. 33063
EAST KENT LIGHT RAILWAY
L O

♨♨ No. 33065
EAST KENT LIGHT RAILWAY
L O

♨♨ No. 33102
CHURNET VALLEY RAILWAY
L O

♨♨ No. 33103
TYSELEY LOCOMOTIVE WORKS

♨♨ No. 33117
EAST LANCASHIRE RAILWAY

ROLLING STOCK by NUMBER 326 — 33117

No. 33201
MIDLAND RAILWAY CENTRE
L O

No. 33203 *(Earl Mountbatten of Burma)*
SOUTH YORKSHIRE RAILWAY

No. 334
PLYM VALLEY RAILWAY
W S D

No. 3346
BLUEBELL RAILWAY
W

No. 3363
BLUEBELL RAILWAY
C

No. 3395
NORTH NORFOLK RAILWAY
R

No. 34 *(Portbury)*
BRISTOL HARBOUR RAILWAY
L O

No. 34 *(Red Rum)*
LEIGHTON BUZZARD RAILWAY
L O D

No. 34007 *(Wadebridge)*
BODMIN & WENFORD RAILWAY
L

No. 34016 *(Bodmin)*
WATERCRESS LINE
L O

No. 34027 *(Taw Valley)*
SEVERN VALLEY RAILWAY
L O

No. 34028 *(Eddystone)*
SWANAGE RAILWAY
L

No. 3403
GWILI RAILWAY
W

No. 34039 *(Boscastle)*
GREAT CENTRAL RAILWAY
L

No. 34046 *(Braughton)*
WEST SOMERSET RAILWAY
L

No. 3405
BUCKINGHAMSHIRE RLWY CTRE
L S

No. 34051 *(Winston Churchill)*
NATIONAL RAILWAY MUSEUM
L S D

No. 34058 *(Sir Frederick Pile)*
AVON VALLEY RAILWAY
L

No. 34059 *(Sir Archibald Sinclair)*
BLUEBELL RAILWAY

No. 34072 *(257 Squadron)*
SWANAGE RAILWAY
L O

No. 34073 *(249 Squadron)*
WATERCRESS LINE
L S

No. 34081 *(92 Squadron)*
NENE VALLEY RAILWAY
L O

No. 34092 *(City of Wells)*
KEIGHLEY & WORTH VALLEY
L

No. 34101 *(Hartland)*
NORTH YORKSHIRE MOORS RAILWAY
L

⚒ No. 34105 *(Swanage)*
WATERCRESS LINE
L

⚒ No. 34111
AVON VALLEY RAILWAY
C

⚒ No. 3442 *(Great Marquess (The))*
SEVERN VALLEY RAILWAY
L

⚒ No. 34495
NORTH NORFOLK RAILWAY
R

⚒ No. 3453
NORTH YORKSHIRE MOORS RAILWAY
C

⚒ No. 34531
AVON VALLEY RAILWAY
C

⚒ No. 3463
NATIONAL RAILWAY MUSEUM
R

⚒ No. 34699
BARROW HILL ROUNDHOUSE
C

⚒ No. 347
MANGAPPS RAILWAY MUSEUM
C

⚒ No. 34712
NORTHAMPTON & LAMPORT RAILWAY
C

⚒ No. 35
BLUEBELL RAILWAY
C

⚒ No. 35 *(Binky)*
LEIGHTON BUZZARD RAILWAY
L

⚒ No. 35
TANFIELD RAILWAY
O

⚒ No. 35005 *(Canadian Pacific)*
WATERCRESS LINE
L **O**

⚒ No. 35006 *(Peninsular & Oriental S N Co)*
GLOUCESTERSHIRE WARWICKSHIRE
L

⚒ No. 35009 *(Shaw Savill)*
WATERCRESS LINE
L **S**

⚒ No. 35010 *(Blue Star)*
COLNE VALLEY RAILWAY
L

⚒ No. 35012
GWILI RAILWAY
C

⚒ No. 35018 *(British India Line)*
WATERCRESS LINE
L **S**

⚒ No. 35025 *(Brocklebank Line)*
GREAT CENTRAL RAILWAY
L

⚒ No. 35027 *(Port Line)*
SWANAGE RAILWAY
L **O**

⚒ No. 35029 *(Ellerman Lines)*
NATIONAL RAILWAY MUSEUM
L **S** **D**

⚒ No. 35174
AVON VALLEY RAILWAY
C

⚒ No. 35193
PEAK RAIL
C

ROLLING STOCK by NUMBER

34105 — 35193

No. 35251
CHASEWATER RAILWAY
R

No. 35255
AVON VALLEY RAILWAY
C O

No. 35337
CHINNOR & PRINCES RISBOROUGH
C

No. 35380
GWILI RAILWAY
W

No. 354068 *(Kinnerley)*
WELSH HIGHLAND RAILWAY
L O

No. 35420
SOUTH DEVON RAILWAY
W

No. 35448
BLUEBELL RAILWAY
C O

No. 35468
NATIONAL RAILWAY MUSEUM
R

No. 35481
AVON VALLEY RAILWAY
C

No. 3554
VINTAGE CARRIAGES TRUST
C O D

No. 357488
NOTTINGHAM TRANSPORT CTRE
R

No. 357771
NOTTINGHAM TRANSPORT CTRE
R

No. 35798
GWILI RAILWAY
W

No. 358 *(Minnie)*
MANGAPPS RAILWAY MUSEUM
L S D

No. 35831
CHASEWATER RAILWAY
R

No. 35883
CHINNOR & PRINCES RISBOROUGH
W

No. 3598
NATIONAL RAILWAY MUSEUM
R

No. 36
EMBSAY & BOLTON ABBEY RLWY
L O

No. 36 *(Caravan)*
LEIGHTON BUZZARD RAILWAY
L

No. 3650
DIDCOT RAILWAY CENTRE
L S

No. 3672 *(Dame Vera Lynn)*
NORTH YORKSHIRE MOORS RAILWAY
L

No. 368
BLUEBELL RAILWAY
C

No. 3687
BLUEBELL RAILWAY
C

No. 3690
SPA VALLEY RAILWAY
R

No. 3697
NORTH YORKSHIRE MOORS RAILWAY
W

No. 37 *(Toad)*
CHASEWATER RAILWAY
L

No. 37 *(Invincible)*
ISLE OF WIGHT STEAM RAILWAY
L O

No. 37
LEIGHTON BUZZARD RAILWAY
L

No. 37
SOUTH TYNEDALE RAILWAY
R W O

No. 37003
EAST ANGLIAN RAILWAY MUSEUM
L

No. 37038
EAST LANCASHIRE RAILWAY

No. 37075
GREAT CENTRAL RAILWAY
L O

No. 3717 *(City of Truro)*
NATIONAL RAILWAY MUSEUM
L

No. 3719
SITTINGBOURNE & KEMSLEY
S D

No. 37190
MIDLAND RAILWAY CENTRE
L O

No. 37197
EAST LANCASHIRE RAILWAY

No. 37207 *(William Cookworthy)*
PLYM VALLEY RAILWAY
L

No. 37215 *(Clydebridge)*
GLOUCESTERSHIRE WARWICKSHIRE
L O

No. 3724
BLUEBELL RAILWAY
C

No. 3738
DIDCOT RAILWAY CENTRE
L O

No. 3745
AVON VALLEY RAILWAY
C O

No. 3746
AVON VALLEY RAILWAY
C

No. 3749
AVON VALLEY RAILWAY
C

No. 3755
DIDCOT RAILWAY CENTRE
R

No. 3756
DIDCOT RAILWAY CENTRE
R

No. 376 *(Norwegian)*
KENT & EAST SUSSEX RAILWAY
L O

No. 377 *(King Haakon VII)*
BRESSINGHAM STEAM
L S D

No. 3770 *(Norma)*
CAMBRIAN RAILWAY SOCIETY

ROLLING STOCK by NUMBER

3697 — 3770

No. 3777 *(Josiah Wedgwood)*
CHURNET VALLEY RAILWAY
L

No. 3779
EAST ANGLIAN RAILWAY MUSEUM
O

No. 3792
NATIONAL RAILWAY MUSEUM
R

No. 3794 *(Cumbria)*
LAKESIDE & HAVERTHWAITE RLWY
L O

No. 38
ALMOND VALLEY HERITAGE TRUST
L O

No. 38
EMBSAY & BOLTON ABBEY RLWY
L O

No. 38 *(Ajax)*
ISLE OF WIGHT STEAM RAILWAY
L

No. 38 *(Harry Barnett)*
LEIGHTON BUZZARD RAILWAY
L O D

No. 38
TANFIELD RAILWAY
O

No. 38
TANFIELD RAILWAY

No. 38
TELFORD STEAM RAILWAY
C S

No. 3801
BLUEBELL RAILWAY

No. 3802
BODMIN & WENFORD RAILWAY
L

No. 3803
SOUTH DEVON RAILWAY
L

No. 3809
NORTH NORFOLK RAILWAY
L

No. 381
MANGAPPS RAILWAY MUSEUM
C

No. 3814
NORTH YORKSHIRE MOORS RAILWAY
L

No. 3815
AVON VALLEY RAILWAY
C

No. 3822
DIDCOT RAILWAY CENTRE
L

No. 3825
PEAK RAIL
C

No. 384 *(Kestrel)*
HOLLYBUSH GARDEN CENTRE
L O

No. 3840 *(Pamela)*
VALE OF GLAMORGAN RAILWAY
L O

No. 3845
SWINDON & CRICKLADE RAILWAY
L

No. 385
MIDDLETON RAILWAY
L

No. 3850
WEST SOMERSET RAILWAY
L

No. 387
BLUEBELL RAILWAY
C O

No. 39
DARLINGTON RAILWAY PRES SOC
L S D

No. 39
EAST SOMERSET RAILWAY
L O

No. 39
SOUTH TYNEDALE RAILWAY
R W O

No. 3900002
MIDDLETON RAILWAY
L

No. 3900011 *(Dinmor)*
CAVAN & LEITRIM RAILWAY
L O

No. 393302 *(Swansea Jack)*
GWILI RAILWAY
L O

No. 394
BLUEBELL RAILWAY
C O

No. 395
NATIONAL RAILWAY MUSEUM
R

No. 395305 *(Ivor)*
NIRT
L

No. 396
NATIONAL RAILWAY MUSEUM
R

No. 39617
BLUEBELL RAILWAY
W

No. 3967 *(Hylton)*
NIRT
L O

No. 398
BLUEBELL RAILWAY
C

No. 3991
AVON VALLEY RAILWAY
C

No. 3BG *(Guinness)*
RPSI
L

No. 3D *(Hem Heath)*
CHASEWATER RAILWAY
L O

No. 4 *(Vulcan)*
ABBEY LIGHT RAILWAY
L O

No. 4 *(Thakeham Tiles No 4)*
AMBERLEY WORKING MUSEUM
L

No. 4 *(Townsend Hook)*
AMBERLEY WORKING MUSEUM
L

No. 4 *(Thomas II)*
BEER HEIGHTS
L O

No. 4 *(Clinton)*
BICTON WOODLAND RAILWAY
L O

No. 4 *(Sharpthorn)*
BLUEBELL RAILWAY
S D

ROLLING STOCK by NUMBER

3850 — 4

No. 4 *(Armistice)*
BREDGAR & WORMSHILL
L **O**

No. 4 *(Asbestos)*
CHASEWATER RAILWAY
L

No. 4
CHASEWATER RAILWAY
R

No. 4
EAST ANGLIA TRANSPORT MUSEUM
L **O**

No. 4 *(Palmerston)*
FFESTINIOG RAILWAY
L **O**

No. 4 *(Meenglas)*
FOYLE VALLEY RAILWAY CENTRE
L

No. 4
IRISH STEAM PRESERVATION SOC
L **O**

No. 4 *(Loch)*
ISLE OF MAN RAILWAY
L

No. 4 *(Pooh)*
LAPPA VALLEY STEAM RAILWAY
L **O**

No. 4 *(Doll)*
LEIGHTON BUZZARD RAILWAY
L **O**

No. 4 *(Tinkerbell)*
MOORS VALLEY RAILWAY
L **O**

No. 4
NATIONAL RAILWAY MUSEUM

No. 4 *(Isambard Kingdom Brunel)*
ROYAL VICTORIA RAILWAY
L **O**

No. 4
RPSI
L **O**

No. 4 *(Snowdon)*
SNOWDON MOUNTAIN RAILWAY
L **O**

No. 4 *(Naworth)*
SOUTH TYNEDALE RAILWAY
L **O**

No. 4
STEAM
L **S** **D**

No. 4 *(Edward Thomas)*
TALYLLYN RAILWAY
L **O**

No. 4
TANFIELD RAILWAY

No. 4 *(Blue Pacific)*
WINDMILL FARM RAILWAY
L

No. 40
COLNE VALLEY RAILWAY
L

No. 40
KENT & EAST SUSSEX RAILWAY
L **O**

No. 40 *(Trent)*
LEIGHTON BUZZARD RAILWAY
L

No. 40
NORTH YORKSHIRE MOORS RAILWAY

No. 40
SOUTH TYNEDALE RAILWAY
R **W** **O**

No. 40012 *(Aureol)*
MIDLAND RAILWAY CENTRE
L **O**

No. 40013 *(Andania)*
MIDLAND RAILWAY CENTRE
L

No. 4002
EAST LANCASHIRE RAILWAY

No. 4003 *(Lode Star)*
NATIONAL RAILWAY MUSEUM
L **S** **D**

No. 4007
COLNE VALLEY RAILWAY
L

No. 40118
TYSELEY LOCOMOTIVE WORKS

No. 402
BLUEBELL RAILWAY
W

No. 40232
SWANSEA VALE RAILWAY
R

No. 4027
NATIONAL RAILWAY MUSEUM
L **S** **D**

No. 4034 *(Superior)*
GREAT WHIPSNADE RAILWAY
L **O**

No. 4035
AVON VALLEY RAILWAY
C

No. 40353
SWANSEA VALE RAILWAY
R

No. 404
BLUEBELL RAILWAY
R **O**

No. 405
GWILI RAILWAY
W

No. 4058
AVON VALLEY RAILWAY
C

No. 4073 *(Caerphilly Castle)*
NATIONAL RAILWAY MUSEUM
L **S** **D**

No. 4079 *(Pendennis Castle)*
DIDCOT RAILWAY CENTRE
L

No. 4089
NATIONAL RAILWAY MUSEUM
L

No. 41
KENT & EAST SUSSEX RAILWAY
L **O**

No. 41
LEIGHTON BUZZARD RAILWAY
L

No. 411453
NOTTINGHAM TRANSPORT CTRE
W

No. 412
BLUEBELL RAILWAY
C

No. 4121
TYSELEY LOCOMOTIVE WORKS

ROLLING STOCK by NUMBER

40 — 4121

AAW No. 41241
KEIGHLEY & WORTH VALLEY
L

AAW No. 41298
BUCKINGHAMSHIRE RLWY CTRE
L

AAW No. 41312
WATERCRESS LINE
L O

AAW No. 41313
BUCKINGHAMSHIRE RLWY CTRE
L

AAW No. 4141
LLANGOLLEN RAILWAY
L O

AAW No. 4144
DIDCOT RAILWAY CENTRE
L

AAW No. 416
DIDCOT RAILWAY CENTRE
R

AAW No. 4160
WEST SOMERSET RAILWAY
L O

AAW No. 4160004 *(Hector)*
GREAT WHIPSNADE RAILWAY
L O

AAW No. 4160005 *(Victor)*
GREAT WHIPSNADE RAILWAY
L

AAW No. 41723 *(Coral A)*
DIDCOT RAILWAY CENTRE
W

AAW No. 4182 *(Victor)*
SITTINGBOURNE & KEMSLEY
L O

AAW No. 41873
SOUTH DEVON RAILWAY
W

AAW No. 419
BLUEBELL RAILWAY
R O

AAW No. 419
BO'NESS & KINNEIL RAILWAY
L O

AAW No. 41934 *(Crocodile F)*
DIDCOT RAILWAY CENTRE
W

AAW No. 41946
GWILI RAILWAY
W

AAW No. 42
ALMOND VALLEY HERITAGE TRUST
L O

AAW No. 42
BO'NESS & KINNEIL RAILWAY
L

AAW No. 42
CADEBY LIGHT RAILWAY
L

AAW No. 42 *(Sarah)*
LEIGHTON BUZZARD RAILWAY
L O D

AAW No. 42
WELSH HIGHLAND RAILWAY
C

AAW No. 4202
CAVAN & LEITRIM RAILWAY
W S D

AAW No. 42073
LAKESIDE & HAVERTHWAITE RLWY
L O

No. 42085
LAKESIDE & HAVERTHWAITE RLWY
L

No. 421220
NORTH NORFOLK RAILWAY
W

No. 42155
GWILI RAILWAY
W

No. 421702 *(Trecatty)*
GWILI RAILWAY
L

No. 4219 *(Melior)*
SITTINGBOURNE & KEMSLEY
L O

No. 42193 *(Hydra D)*
DIDCOT RAILWAY CENTRE
W

No. 4220001
NIRT
L

No. 4220033 *(Lois)*
NIRT
L O

No. 42223
SOUTH DEVON RAILWAY
W

No. 42239 *(Grain)*
DIDCOT RAILWAY CENTRE
W

No. 4227
BLUEBELL RAILWAY
C

No. 42271 *(Loriot L)*
DIDCOT RAILWAY CENTRE
W

No. 4248
STEAM
L S D

No. 427 *(Buffs (The))*
EAST KENT LIGHT RAILWAY
L O

No. 427
VINTAGE CARRIAGES TRUST
C O D

No. 4270
SWANSEA VALE RAILWAY
L

No. 42765
EAST LANCASHIRE RAILWAY

No. 4279
BLUEBELL RAILWAY
C O

No. 43 *(Titan)*
KENT & EAST SUSSEX RAILWAY
L O

No. 43
LEIGHTON BUZZARD RAILWAY
L O D

No. 43106
SEVERN VALLEY RAILWAY
L

No. 43157
EAST ANGLIAN RAILWAY MUSEUM
C

No. 43264
MANGAPPS RAILWAY MUSEUM
C

No. 43289
EAST SOMERSET RAILWAY
C

ROLLING STOCK by NUMBER

42085 — 43289

No. 435403 *(Edward Lloyd)*
SITTINGBOURNE & KEMSLEY
L **O**

No. 43567
NORTH YORKSHIRE MOORS RAILWAY

No. 436
GWILI RAILWAY
W

No. 4388
FOXFIELD STEAM RAILWAY

No. 43909
BLUEBELL RAILWAY
C **O**

No. 43924
KEIGHLEY & WORTH VALLEY
L

No. 43949
DIDCOT RAILWAY CENTRE
W

No. 44
CHASEWATER RAILWAY

No. 44
LEIGHTON BUZZARD RAILWAY
L **S** **D**

No. 44
SOUTH YORKSHIRE RAILWAY

No. 44
TANFIELD RAILWAY

No. 44 *(Cagney)*
WINDMILL FARM RAILWAY
L

No. 44027
MIDLAND RAILWAY CENTRE
L

No. 44052 *(Alister)*
KEW BRIDGE STEAM MUSEUM
L **O**

No. 441 *(Barber)*
ARMLEY MILLS
L **S**

No. 44123
AVON VALLEY RAILWAY
L

No. 441427 *(Coed Gorau)*
LLANBERIS LAKE RAILWAY
L

No. 442
BLUEBELL RAILWAY

No. 4430
BLUEBELL RAILWAY
O

No. 4441
BLUEBELL RAILWAY
C

No. 44422
CHURNET VALLEY RAILWAY
L

No. 4444
BLUEBELL RAILWAY
C

No. 44551
NORTHAMPTON & LAMPORT RAILWAY
W

No. 44611
BLUEBELL RAILWAY
W

No. 4468 *(Mallard)*
NATIONAL RAILWAY MUSEUM
L

No. 4472 *(Flying Scotsman)*
BRESSINGHAM STEAM
L

No. 4472 *(Flying Scotsman)*
WINDMILL FARM RAILWAY
L

No. 44767 *(George Stephenson)*
NORTH YORKSHIRE MOORS RAILWAY
L

No. 44806 *(Black 5 Magpie)*
LLANGOLLEN RAILWAY
L O

No. 44842
BEAMISH
W

No. 4492
SOUTH DEVON RAILWAY
W

No. 44932
MIDLAND RAILWAY CENTRE
L

No. 4498 *(Sir Nigel Gresley)*
SOUTH DOWNS LIGHT RAILWAY
L O

No. 45 *(Colwyn)*
NORTHAMPTON & LAMPORT RAILWAY
L

No. 45021
STRATHSPEY RAILWAY
R C O

No. 4503
NORTH YORKSHIRE MOORS RAILWAY
W

No. 45041 *(Royal Tank Regiment)*
MIDLAND RAILWAY CENTRE
L

No. 45049
NATIONAL RAILWAY MUSEUM
L S D

No. 45053
NATIONAL RAILWAY MUSEUM

No. 45060 *(Sherwood Forester)*
BARROW HILL ROUNDHOUSE
L S

No. 45110
GREAT WESTERN RAILWAY MUSEUM
L S

No. 45110
SEVERN VALLEY RAILWAY
L O

No. 45118 *(Royal Artilleryman (The))*
NORTHAMPTON & LAMPORT RAILWAY
L O

No. 45132
WATERCRESS LINE
L O D

No. 45133
MIDLAND RAILWAY CENTRE
L O

No. 45163
COLNE VALLEY RAILWAY
L

No. 451901 *(Llanelli)*
LLANBERIS LAKE RAILWAY
L

No. 45231
GREAT CENTRAL RAILWAY
L

No. 45293
COLNE VALLEY RAILWAY
L

ROLLING STOCK by NUMBER

4472 — 45293

ROLLING STOCK by NUMBER

45337 — 46258

No. 45337
EAST LANCASHIRE RAILWAY

No. 45379
NOTTINGHAM TRANSPORT CTRE
L

No. 45407
EAST LANCASHIRE RAILWAY

No. 45428 *(Eric Treacy)*
NORTH YORKSHIRE MOORS RAILWAY
L

No. 45491
MIDLAND RAILWAY CENTRE
L

No. 4553
DIDCOT RAILWAY CENTRE
G

No. 4555 *(Warrior)*
PAIGNTON & DARTMOUTH RAILWAY
L O

No. 45596 *(Bahamas)*
KEIGHLEY & WORTH VALLEY
L

No. 4561
NORTH YORKSHIRE MOORS RAILWAY
W

No. 4561
WEST SOMERSET RAILWAY
L D

No. 4566
SEVERN VALLEY RAILWAY
L

No. 4588 *(Trojan)*
PAIGNTON & DARTMOUTH RAILWAY
L

No. 459515 *(Iris)*
CHINNOR & PRINCES RISBOROUGH
L

No. 46
LEIGHTON BUZZARD RAILWAY
L D

No. 46
SOUTH TYNEDALE RAILWAY
R W O

No. 4601
BLUEBELL RAILWAY

No. 46010
LLANGOLLEN RAILWAY
L O

No. 46045
MIDLAND RAILWAY CENTRE
L O

No. 4606
GWILI RAILWAY
W

No. 461
RPSI
L

No. 46152
BEAMISH
W

No. 46203 *(Princess Margaret Rose)*
MIDLAND RAILWAY CENTRE
L S O

No. 4623
PEAK RAIL
G

No. 46258 *(City of Westminster)*
SOUTH DOWNS LIGHT RAILWAY
L O

No. 46428
EAST LANCASHIRE RAILWAY

No. 46441
EAST LANCASHIRE RAILWAY

No. 46443
SEVERN VALLEY RAILWAY
L O

No. 46447
BUCKINGHAMSHIRE RLWY CTRE
L

No. 465
VINTAGE CARRIAGES TRUST

No. 46512 *(E V Cooper, Engineer)*
STRATHSPEY RAILWAY
L O

No. 46521
SEVERN VALLEY RAILWAY
L S

No. 47
LEIGHTON BUZZARD RAILWAY
L

No. 47
SOUTH YORKSHIRE RAILWAY

No. 47
TANFIELD RAILWAY

No. 47105
GLOUCESTERSHIRE WARWICKSHIRE
L O

No. 47105
GLOUCESTERSHIRE WARWICKSHIRE
L O

No. 47107
GWILI RAILWAY
W

No. 47160 *(Cunarder)*
SWANAGE RAILWAY

No. 47279
KEIGHLEY & WORTH VALLEY
L O

No. 47298
LLANGOLLEN RAILWAY
L O

No. 472E
MANGAPPS RAILWAY MUSEUM
C

No. 473 *(Birch Grove)*
BLUEBELL RAILWAY
L O

No. 47324
EAST LANCASHIRE RAILWAY

No. 47357
MIDLAND RAILWAY CENTRE
L O

No. 47383
SEVERN VALLEY RAILWAY
L O

No. 47401
MIDLAND RAILWAY CENTRE
L O

No. 47406
GREAT CENTRAL RAILWAY
L

No. 47445
MIDLAND RAILWAY CENTRE
L S

No. 47449
LLANGOLLEN RAILWAY
L O

ROLLING STOCK by NUMBER

46428 — 47449

No. 474558
BLUEBELL RAILWAY
W

No. 47488
TYSELEY LOCOMOTIVE WORKS

No. 47493
EAST SOMERSET RAILWAY
L

No. 47493
SPA VALLEY RAILWAY
L

No. 47493
SPA VALLEY RAILWAY
L

No. 47564
MIDLAND RAILWAY CENTRE
L S

No. 47588
BLUEBELL RAILWAY
W O

No. 47643
BO'NESS & KINNEIL RAILWAY
L

No. 47701 *(Waverley)*
TYSELEY LOCOMOTIVE WORKS

No. 47703
TYSELEY LOCOMOTIVE WORKS

No. 47709
TYSELEY LOCOMOTIVE WORKS

No. 4771 *(Green Arrow)*
NATIONAL RAILWAY MUSEUM
L

No. 47710
TYSELEY LOCOMOTIVE WORKS

No. 47712
TYSELEY LOCOMOTIVE WORKS

No. 4779
CHINNOR & PRINCES RISBOROUGH
C

No. 4789 *(William Baker)*
EASTLEIGH LAKESIDE RAILWAY
L O

No. 47923
GWILI RAILWAY
W

No. 48
BLUEBELL RAILWAY
C

No. 48
KENT & EAST SUSSEX RAILWAY
L O

No. 48 *(Macnamara)*
LEIGHTON BUZZARD RAILWAY
L O O

No. 480222
BLUEBELL RAILWAY
W

No. 4807
NORTH NORFOLK RAILWAY
W

No. 48173
AVON VALLEY RAILWAY
L

No. 4830
LAVENDER LINE
C

No. 48304
GWILI RAILWAY
W

✻ No. 48305
  CHURNET VALLEY RAILWAY
  L

✻ No. 48305
  GREAT CENTRAL RAILWAY
  L **O**

✻ No. 48306
  SWANSEA VALE RAILWAY
  R

✻ No. 48325
  GWILI RAILWAY
  W

✻ No. 484
  DIDCOT RAILWAY CENTRE
  R

✻ No. 48431
  KEIGHLEY & WORTH VALLEY
  L

✻ No. 485
  NATIONAL RAILWAY MUSEUM
  L **S**

✻ No. 4866
  DIDCOT RAILWAY CENTRE
  L

✻ No. 48773
  SEVERN VALLEY RAILWAY
  L **O**

✻ No. 488
  BLUEBELL RAILWAY
  L **S** **D**

✻ No. 49
  LEIGHTON BUZZARD RAILWAY
  L

✻ No. 49
  TANFIELD RAILWAY
  O

✻ No. 490
  NATIONAL RAILWAY MUSEUM
  L

✻ No. 49004
  PLYM VALLEY RAILWAY
  R

✻ No. 49006
  NATIONAL RAILWAY MUSEUM
  R

✻ No. 49018
  BLUEBELL RAILWAY
  W

✻ No. 4906
  GWILI RAILWAY
  C

✻ No. 4920
  NATIONAL RAILWAY MUSEUM
  R

✻ No. 4920 *(Dumbleton Hall)*
  SOUTH DEVON RAILWAY
  L

✻ No. 4922
  BLUEBELL RAILWAY
  C

✻ No. 4930 *(Hagley Hall)*
  SEVERN VALLEY RAILWAY
  L **S** **D**

✻ No. 494
  BLUEBELL RAILWAY
  C

✻ No. 4941
  BLUEBELL RAILWAY
  C **O**

✻ No. 4953 *(Pitchford Hall)*
  TYSELEY LOCOMOTIVE WORKS

ROLLING STOCK by NUMBER

48305 — 4953

No. 4957
BLUEBELL RAILWAY
C O

No. 4965 *(Rood Ashton Hall)*
TYSELEY LOCOMOTIVE WORKS

No. 4974
PEAK RAIL
C O

No. 497753
MID-NORFOLK RAILWAY
R

No. 5
ABBEY LIGHT RAILWAY
L O

No. 5 *(Maid Marian)*
BALA LAKE RAILWAY
L O

No. 5 *(South Durham Malleable No 5)*
BEAMISH
L S D

No. 5 *(Linda)*
BEER HEIGHTS
L O

No. 5 *(Bredgar)*
BREDGAR & WORMSHILL

No. 5
BURE VALLEY RAILWAY
L O

No. 5
CAVAN & LEITRIM RAILWAY
R

No. 5 *(Sentinel)*
CHASEWATER RAILWAY
L O

No. 5 *(Alan Meaden)*
CORRIS RAILWAY MUSEUM

No. 5 *(Shannon)*
DIDCOT RAILWAY CENTRE
L

No. 5 *(Thorpeness)*
EAST ANGLIA TRANSPORT MUSEUM
L O

No. 5 *(Welsh Pony)*
FFESTINIOG RAILWAY
L D

No. 5 *(Alison)*
GARTELL LIGHT RAILWAY

No. 5 *(Elf)*
LEIGHTON BUZZARD RAILWAY
L O D

No. 5
LEIGHTON BUZZARD RAILWAY
R C O D

No. 5 *(John Hampden)*
LONDON TRANSPORT MUSEUM
L S D

No. 5 *(Sapper)*
MOORS VALLEY RAILWAY
L O

No. 5 *(Lord Ashfield)*
MUSEUM OF SCIENCE & INDUSTRY
L D

No. 5
NATIONAL RAILWAY MUSEUM
L S D

No. 5 *(Isibutu)*
NORTH GLOUCESTERSHIRE RAILWAY
L

No. 5
NORTH YORKSHIRE MOORS RAILWAY
L

No. 5 *(Nora)*
PONTYPOOL & BLAENAVON RAILWAY
L **S**

No. 5 *(Claude the Colonel)*
ROYAL VICTORIA RAILWAY
L **O**

No. 5 *(Rudyard Lady)*
RUDYARD LAKE RAILWAY
L **O**

No. 5 *(Moel Siabod)*
SNOWDON MOUNTAIN RAILWAY
L **O**

No. 5
SOUTH TYNEDALE RAILWAY
C **O**

No. 5
TALYLLYN RAILWAY
C

No. 5 *(Midlander)*
TALYLLYN RAILWAY
L **O**

No. 5
TRALEE & DINGLE RAILWAY
L **O**

No. 5 *(James)*
WATERCRESS LINE
L **O**

No. 5 *(Orion)*
WELSHPOOL & LLANFAIR
L **O**

No. 50 *(Commander B)*
HOLLYCOMBE STEAM COLLECTION
L **O**

No. 50
LEIGHTON BUZZARD RAILWAY
L

No. 5000
NATIONAL RAILWAY MUSEUM
L

No. 500042 *(Triumph)*
BODMIN & WENFORD RAILWAY
L **O**

No. 50007 *(Sir Edward Elgar)*
MIDLAND RAILWAY CENTRE
L **O**

No. 5001
NORTHAMPTON & LAMPORT RAILWAY
C

No. 50015 *(Valiant)*
EAST LANCASHIRE RAILWAY

No. 50019
MIDLAND RAILWAY CENTRE
L **O**

No. 50019 *(Ramillies)*
MID-NORFOLK RAILWAY
L **O**

No. 50021 *(Rodney)*
BO'NESS & KINNEIL RAILWAY
L

No. 50023 *(Howe)*
BARROW HILL ROUNDHOUSE
L **S**

No. 50027 *(Lion)*
NORTH YORKSHIRE MOORS RAILWAY
L

No. 50029 *(Renown)*
PONTYPOOL & BLAENAVON RAILWAY
L

ROLLING STOCK by NUMBER

5 — 50029

ROLLING STOCK by NUMBER

50030 — 51

⚙ No. 50030 *(Repulse)*
PONTYPOOL & BLAENAVON RAILWAY
🟦

⚙ No. 50043 *(Eagle)*
PONTYPOOL & BLAENAVON RAILWAY
🟦

⚙ No. 501
TANFIELD RAILWAY

⚙ No. 501
WEST SOMERSET RAILWAY
🟦 🟥

⚙ No. 501348
KENT & EAST SUSSEX RAILWAY
⬜

⚙ No. 5025
STRATHSPEY RAILWAY
🟦

⚙ No. 503
BOWES RAILWAY

⚙ No. 5034
BLUEBELL RAILWAY
🟧

⚙ No. 50413
WEST SOMERSET RAILWAY
🟦

⚙ No. 50416
MIDLAND RAILWAY CENTRE
🟦

⚙ No. 5043 *(Earl of Mount Edgcumbe)*
TYSELEY LOCOMOTIVE WORKS

⚙ No. 5051 *(Earl Bathurst)*
DIDCOT RAILWAY CENTRE
🟦 🟥

⚙ No. 506
NATIONAL RAILWAY MUSEUM
🟦 🟧 🟦

⚙ No. 506
WATERCRESS LINE
🟦 🟧

⚙ No. 506190 *(Cecil the Colossi)*
BLUEBELL RAILWAY
⬜

⚙ No. 506327
SOUTH DEVON RAILWAY
⬜

⚙ No. 5080 *(Defiant)*
TYSELEY LOCOMOTIVE WORKS

⚙ No. 5081
DERWENT VALLEY
⬜

⚙ No. 5085
DIDCOT RAILWAY CENTRE
🟥

⚙ No. 50899
BLUEBELL RAILWAY
⬜

⚙ No. 509
VINTAGE CARRIAGES TRUST
🟩 🟧

⚙ No. 50928
KEIGHLEY & WORTH VALLEY
🟦 🟧

⚙ No. 51 *(Theodora)*
KENT & EAST SUSSEX RAILWAY
🟩

⚙ No. 51
SOUTH TYNEDALE RAILWAY
🟥 ⬜ 🟧

No. 51000
EAST SOMERSET RAILWAY
C

No. 51073
MID-NORFOLK RAILWAY
L

No. 51131
BATTLEFIELD LINE

No. 51135
SWANSEA VALE RAILWAY
L O

No. 51148
SWANSEA VALE RAILWAY
L O

No. 512
WEST SOMERSET RAILWAY
L D

No. 51218
KEIGHLEY & WORTH VALLEY
L O

No. 51285
EAST LANCASHIRE RAILWAY

No. 513212
SOUTH DEVON RAILWAY
W

No. 51346
NORTH NORFOLK RAILWAY
R

No. 51352
WEST SOMERSET RAILWAY
L O

No. 51360
MID-NORFOLK RAILWAY
L

No. 51376
WEST SOMERSET RAILWAY
L O

No. 51388
NORTH NORFOLK RAILWAY
R

No. 5139 *(Goliath)*
PAIGNTON & DARTMOUTH RAILWAY
L O

No. 51402
NORTHAMPTON & LAMPORT RAILWAY
L O

No. 514207
NORTH NORFOLK RAILWAY
W

No. 514765
NORTH NORFOLK RAILWAY
R

No. 5156 *(Ayrshire Yeomanry)*
SOUTH DOWNS LIGHT RAILWAY
L O

No. 51565
KEIGHLEY & WORTH VALLEY
L O

No. 51566
PEAK RAIL
R

No. 51568 *(Spirit of Banffshire)*
KEITH & DUFFTOWN RAILWAY
L O

No. 51572
MID-NORFOLK RAILWAY
L O

No. 51616
GREAT CENTRAL RAILWAY

ROLLING STOCK by NUMBER

51622 — 52012

No. 51622
GREAT CENTRAL RAILWAY
L

No. 5164
SEVERN VALLEY RAILWAY
L

No. 516537
DERWENT VALLEY
W

No. 5166
PEAK RAIL
C

No. 51663
WEST SOMERSET RAILWAY
L O

No. 516673
DIDCOT RAILWAY CENTRE
W

No. 51769
NORTH NORFOLK RAILWAY
C O

No. 51769
NORTH NORFOLK RAILWAY
R

No. 51813
EAST LANCASHIRE RAILWAY

No. 51842
EAST LANCASHIRE RAILWAY

No. 51852
WEST SOMERSET RAILWAY
L O

No. 51886
BUCKINGHAMSHIRE RLWY CTRE
L

No. 51887
WEST SOMERSET RAILWAY
L

No. 51899
BUCKINGHAMSHIRE RLWY CTRE
L

No. 51914
DEAN FOREST RAILWAY
L O

No. 5193
PLYM VALLEY RAILWAY
O

No. 5193
WEST SOMERSET RAILWAY

No. 51937
PEAK RAIL
R

No. 51947
BODMIN & WENFORD RAILWAY
L S

No. 5197
CHURNET VALLEY RAILWAY
L O

No. 51993 *(Mrs Slocombe)*
CALEDONIAN RAILWAY
L R

No. 52 *(Barbara)*
KENT & EAST SUSSEX RAILWAY
C

No. 52
SOUTH TYNEDALE RAILWAY
R W O

No. 52012 *(Mr Humphries)*
CALEDONIAN RAILWAY
R

No. 52029
LAKESIDE & HAVERTHWAITE RLWY

No. 52044
KEIGHLEY & WORTH VALLEY
L O

No. 52061
SWANSEA VALE RAILWAY

No. 52077
LAKESIDE & HAVERTHWAITE RLWY
L O

No. 5209
NOTTINGHAM TRANSPORT CTRE
W

No. 52256
NORTH NORFOLK RAILWAY
R

No. 5229
NORTHAMPTON & LAMPORT RAILWAY
C O

No. 523
NORTH NORFOLK RAILWAY
R

No. 52322
EAST LANCASHIRE RAILWAY

No. 5235
PEAK RAIL
R O

No. 52361
NORTHAMPTON & LAMPORT RAILWAY
L

No. 526 *(Hawarden)*
INDUSTRIAL RAILWAY MUSEUM
L S D

No. 5260
ABBEY PUMPING STATION
L

No. 5267
DIDCOT RAILWAY CENTRE
R

No. 5268
DIDCOT RAILWAY CENTRE
R

No. 5272 *(Haulwen)*
GWILI RAILWAY
L

No. 53 *(Windle)*
MIDDLETON RAILWAY
L

No. 53
SOUTH TYNEDALE RAILWAY
R W O

No. 5305
GREAT CENTRAL RAILWAY
L

No. 53083
NORTH NORFOLK RAILWAY
W

No. 5318
NORTH NORFOLK RAILWAY
R

No. 5322
DIDCOT RAILWAY CENTRE
L S

No. 53556
SOUTH YORKSHIRE RAILWAY
R

No. 536
DIDCOT RAILWAY CENTRE
R

ROLLING STOCK by NUMBER

53628 — 55223

No. 53628 *(Spirit of Speyside)*
KEITH & DUFFTOWN RAILWAY
L **O**

No. 5374 *(Vanguard)*
NORTHAMPTON & LAMPORT RAILWAY
L

No. 53808
SOMERSET & DORSET RAILWAY
L

No. 53808
WEST SOMERSET RAILWAY
L

No. 53809
MIDLAND RAILWAY CENTRE
L

No. 53933
PEAK RAIL
R

No. 541
BLUEBELL RAILWAY
L **S** **D**

No. 54279
VALE OF GLAMORGAN RAILWAY
R **O**

No. 54287
MANGAPPS RAILWAY MUSEUM
C **D**

No. 5455
NATIONAL RAILWAY MUSEUM
R

No. 5474
EAST ANGLIAN RAILWAY MUSEUM
W

No. 5474
SOUTH DEVON RAILWAY
L **S** **D**

No. 5498
BLUEBELL RAILWAY
R

No. 55 *(Stepney)*
BLUEBELL RAILWAY
L **O**

No. 55006
MID-NORFOLK RAILWAY
L

No. 55006
MID-NORFOLK RAILWAY
L **O**

No. 55015 *(Tulyar)*
MIDLAND RAILWAY CENTRE
L

No. 550179
SOUTH DEVON RAILWAY
W

No. 55023
CHINNOR & PRINCES RISBOROUGH
L **O**

No. 55026
SWANSEA VALE RAILWAY
L

No. 55034
TYSELEY LOCOMOTIVE WORKS

No. 550472
SOUTH DEVON RAILWAY
W

No. 55167
NORTH NORFOLK RAILWAY
R

No. 55223
RAILWORLD

No. 5526
SOUTH DEVON RAILWAY
L

No. 553
EAST ANGLIAN RAILWAY MUSEUM
O D

No. 5536
MID-NORFOLK RAILWAY
R

No. 5538
VALE OF GLAMORGAN RAILWAY
L D

No. 5541
DEAN FOREST RAILWAY
L O

No. 5542
BLUEBELL RAILWAY
W

No. 5542
WEST SOMERSET RAILWAY
L

No. 5546
BLUEBELL RAILWAY
C

No. 55490
BLUEBELL RAILWAY
W

No. 55508
MID-NORFOLK RAILWAY

No. 5552
BODMIN & WENFORD RAILWAY
L

No. 55528
MID-NORFOLK RAILWAY

No. 5553
TYSELEY LOCOMOTIVE WORKS

No. 5572
DIDCOT RAILWAY CENTRE
L

No. 5580
MIDLAND RAILWAY CENTRE
L O

No. 5593 *(Kolhapur)*
TYSELEY LOCOMOTIVE WORKS

No. 55966
MIDLAND RAILWAY CENTRE
L O

No. 55976
MIDLAND RAILWAY CENTRE
L O

No. 55993
BLUEBELL RAILWAY
W O

No. 56
NOTTINGHAM TRANSPORT CTRE
L

No. 56006
MIDLAND RAILWAY CENTRE
L O

No. 56097
WEST SOMERSET RAILWAY

No. 56121
EAST LANCASHIRE RAILWAY

No. 56169
WEST SOMERSET RAILWAY

No. 56171
MIDLAND RAILWAY CENTRE
L

ROLLING STOCK by NUMBER

5526 — 56171

No. 5619
TELFORD STEAM RAILWAY
L **D**

No. 56224
MID-NORFOLK RAILWAY
O

No. 56290
BLUEBELL RAILWAY
W

No. 563
NATIONAL RAILWAY MUSEUM
L **S** **D**

No. 56301
MID-NORFOLK RAILWAY
D

No. 5637
EAST SOMERSET RAILWAY
L

No. 5637
SWINDON & CRICKLADE RAILWAY
L **O**

No. 56400
DIDCOT RAILWAY CENTRE
W

No. 5643
LAKESIDE & HAVERTHWAITE RLWY
L

No. 5644
BLUEBELL RAILWAY
C

No. 56492
DEAN FOREST RAILWAY
L **O**

No. 56495
KENT & EAST SUSSEX RAILWAY
W

No. 565
DIDCOT RAILWAY CENTRE
R

No. 568001
EAST KENT LIGHT RAILWAY
R **C**

No. 56856
NORTH YORKSHIRE MOORS RAILWAY

No. 5690 *(Leander)*
EAST LANCASHIRE RAILWAY

No. 5699 *(Galatea)*
TYSELEY LOCOMOTIVE WORKS

No. 570027
BLUEBELL RAILWAY
W

No. 5706
BLUEBELL RAILWAY
W

No. 5751 *(Prince William)*
WINDMILL FARM RAILWAY
L **O**

No. 5759
EAST KENT LIGHT RAILWAY
R **C**

No. 5764
SEVERN VALLEY RAILWAY
L **O**

No. 5768
BLUEBELL RAILWAY
C

No. 577 *(Mary)*
MIDDLETON RAILWAY
L **O**

No. 577
NORTH YORKSHIRE MOORS RAILWAY
W

No. 5775
KEIGHLEY & WORTH VALLEY
L

No. 5786
SOUTH DEVON RAILWAY
L **O**

No. 5787
DIDCOT RAILWAY CENTRE
R

No. 57889
BLUEBELL RAILWAY
W **O**

No. 57949
BLUEBELL RAILWAY
W **O**

No. 57A
NATIONAL RAILWAY MUSEUM
R

No. 58
NORTH YORKSHIRE MOORS RAILWAY

No. 5820
KEIGHLEY & WORTH VALLEY
L

No. 5865 *(Peer Gynt)*
BRESSINGHAM STEAM
L **S** **D**

No. 587511
SOUTH DEVON RAILWAY
W

No. 59
KENT & EAST SUSSEX RAILWAY
C

No. 59
NATIONAL RAILWAY MUSEUM
R

No. 590
BLUEBELL RAILWAY
W

No. 5900 *(Hinderton Hall)*
DIDCOT RAILWAY CENTRE
L **S**

No. 59119
SOUTH DEVON RAILWAY
W

No. 592
BLUEBELL RAILWAY
L **S** **D**

No. 592433
SOUTH DEVON RAILWAY
W

No. 59252
BLUEBELL RAILWAY
W

No. 59276
GREAT CENTRAL RAILWAY
L

No. 59305
BLUEBELL RAILWAY
W

No. 59387
PEAK RAIL
R

No. 594
SOUTH DEVON RAILWAY
C

No. 59408
SOUTH DEVON RAILWAY
W

ROLLING STOCK by NUMBER

577 — 59408

ROLLING STOCK by NUMBER

59505 — 6

No. 59505
WEST SOMERSET RAILWAY
L O

No. 59511
LAVENDER LINE
C

No. 59516
NORTH NORFOLK RAILWAY
R

No. 5952 *(Cogan Hall)*
CAMBRIAN RAILWAY SOCIETY

No. 5952
DIDCOT RAILWAY CENTRE
R

No. 59575
MID-NORFOLK RAILWAY
C

No. 59609
MIDLAND RAILWAY CENTRE
L O

No. 5967 *(Bickmarsh Hall)*
PONTYPOOL & BLAENAVON RAILWAY
L S

No. 59678
WEST SOMERSET RAILWAY
L O

No. 59685
BLUEBELL RAILWAY
W

No. 59701
EAST LANCASHIRE RAILWAY

No. 59761
BUCKINGHAMSHIRE RLWY CTRE
L

No. 5987
NATIONAL RAILWAY MUSEUM
R

No. 6 *(Druid)*
ABBEY LIGHT RAILWAY
L O

No. 6 *(Monty)*
AMBERLEY WORKING MUSEUM
L

No. 6 *(Jimmy)*
BEER HEIGHTS
L O

No. 6
BO'NESS & KINNEIL RAILWAY
L

No. 6 *(Eigiau)*
BREDGAR & WORMSHILL
L O

No. 6
BREDGAR & WORMSHILL
L S

No. 6 *(Blickling Hall)*
BURE VALLEY RAILWAY
L O

No. 6 *(Oliver Velton)*
CAMBRIAN RAILWAY SOCIETY

No. 6
CHASEWATER RAILWAY
L S D

No. 6
CLEETHORPES LIGHT RAILWAY
L

No. 6 *(Orfordness)*
EAST ANGLIA TRANSPORT MUSEUM
L O

No. 6 *(Robert Heath No 6)*
FOXFIELD STEAM RAILWAY
L **O**

No. 6 *(Columbkille)*
FOYLE VALLEY RAILWAY CENTRE
L

No. 6 *(Mr G)*
GARTELL LIGHT RAILWAY
L

No. 6
MIDDLETON RAILWAY
L

No. 6 *(Medea)*
MOORS VALLEY RAILWAY
L **O**

No. 6 *(United Molasses)*
NORTH YORKSHIRE MOORS RAILWAY
W

No. 6 *(River Churnet)*
RUDYARD LAKE RAILWAY
L **O**

No. 6 *(Padarn)*
SNOWDON MOUNTAIN RAILWAY
L

No. 6
SOUTH TYNEDALE RAILWAY
C **O**

No. 6 *(Thomas Edmondson)*
SOUTH TYNEDALE RAILWAY
L **D**

No. 6 *(Douglas)*
TALYLLYN RAILWAY
L **O**

No. 6
TALYLLYN RAILWAY
C

No. 6
TANFIELD RAILWAY

No. 6
TANFIELD RAILWAY

No. 60
BLUEBELL RAILWAY
C

No. 600
BLUEBELL RAILWAY

No. 600 *(Gordon)*
SEVERN VALLEY RAILWAY
L

No. 6000 *(King George V)*
STEAM
L **S** **D**

No. 60009 *(Union of South Africa)*
SEVERN VALLEY RAILWAY
L **O**

No. 60019 *(Bittern)*
WATERCRESS LINE
L

No. 60101
MANGAPPS RAILWAY MUSEUM
C

No. 6023 *(King Edward II)*
DIDCOT RAILWAY CENTRE
L

No. 6024 *(King Edward I)*
DIDCOT RAILWAY CENTRE
L **O**

No. 603
BLUEBELL RAILWAY
C

ROLLING STOCK by NUMBER

6 — 603

ROLLING STOCK by NUMBER

60532 — 6263

No. 60532 *(Blue Peter)*
NORTH YORKSHIRE MOORS RAILWAY
L

No. 606 *(Alan George)*
TEIFI VALLEY RAILWAY
L O

No. 607
NATIONAL RAILWAY MUSEUM
L

No. 61
NORTHAMPTON & LAMPORT RAILWAY
W

No. 610 *(General Lord Robertson)*
AVON VALLEY RAILWAY
L

No. 6100 *(Royal Scot)*
BARLEYLANDS MINIATURE RAILWAY
L S D

No. 6100 *(Royal Scot)*
BRESSINGHAM STEAM
L S

No. 6106
DIDCOT RAILWAY CENTRE
L

No. 61264
GREAT CENTRAL RAILWAY

No. 613
BOWES RAILWAY
L O

No. 614 *(Bear)*
SITTINGBOURNE & KEMSLEY
L S D

No. 61553
EAST ANGLIAN RAILWAY MUSEUM
C

No. 61572
NORTH NORFOLK RAILWAY
L O

No. 61742
DARTMOOR RAILWAY
C

No. 61743
DARTMOOR RAILWAY
C

No. 62 *(Ugly)*
BODMIN & WENFORD RAILWAY
L O

No. 62
TANFIELD RAILWAY

No. 62005
NORTH YORKSHIRE MOORS RAILWAY
L

No. 6201 *(Princess Elizabeth)*
EAST LANCASHIRE RAILWAY

No. 621
STRATHSPEY RAILWAY
R C S

No. 623
BLUEBELL RAILWAY
C

No. 6233 *(Duchess of Sutherland)*
MIDLAND RAILWAY CENTRE
L O

No. 626
SITTINGBOURNE & KEMSLEY
R

No. 6263
BOWES RAILWAY
L O

No. 63
KENT & EAST SUSSEX RAILWAY
C

No. 63
NOTTINGHAM TRANSPORT CTRE
L

No. 63066
DIDCOT RAILWAY CENTRE
W

No. 63078
SOUTH DEVON RAILWAY
W

No. 631 *(Carroll)*
MIDDLETON RAILWAY
L O

No. 63101
KENT & EAST SUSSEX RAILWAY
W

No. 633 *(Lord Granby)*
ARMLEY MILLS
L S

No. 633
SITTINGBOURNE & KEMSLEY
R

No. 6335 *(Charlotte)*
LEADHILLS & WANLOCKHEAD
L

No. 63601
GREAT CENTRAL RAILWAY
L O

No. 63875
MANGAPPS RAILWAY MUSEUM
C

No. 641
NORTH YORKSHIRE MOORS RAILWAY
C

No. 641
SITTINGBOURNE & KEMSLEY
C

No. 6412
WEST SOMERSET RAILWAY
L O

No. 6435 *(Ajax)*
PAIGNTON & DARTMOUTH RAILWAY
L O

No. 645 *(American GP40)*
HOLLYBUSH GARDEN CENTRE
L C

No. 647
SITTINGBOURNE & KEMSLEY
R

No. 649
NORTH YORKSHIRE MOORS RAILWAY

No. 64994
BEAMISH
W

No. 65
BLUEBELL RAILWAY

No. 65
BUCKINGHAMSHIRE RLWY CTRE
L

No. 65
DERWENT VALLEY
L O

No. 65 *(Maunsell)*
KENT & EAST SUSSEX RAILWAY
L O

No. 6515
SOUTH DEVON RAILWAY
C

ROLLING STOCK by NUMBER

63 — 6515

₩₩ No. 653
BLUEBELL RAILWAY

₩₩ No. 65451
EAST LANCASHIRE RAILWAY

₩₩ No. 65462
NORTH NORFOLK RAILWAY
L

₩₩ No. 655
SITTINGBOURNE & KEMSLEY
R

₩₩ No. 656
NENE VALLEY RAILWAY
L S D

₩₩ No. 657
SITTINGBOURNE & KEMSLEY
R

₩₩ No. 6575
BLUEBELL RAILWAY
C

₩₩ No. 658
SITTINGBOURNE & KEMSLEY
R

₩₩ No. 659
SITTINGBOURNE & KEMSLEY
R

₩₩ No. 66
BUCKINGHAMSHIRE RLWY CTRE
L

₩₩ No. 66 *(Aerolite)*
NATIONAL RAILWAY MUSEUM
L

₩₩ No. 660
SITTINGBOURNE & KEMSLEY
R

₩₩ No. 66071
BLUEBELL RAILWAY
W

₩₩ No. 661
BLUEBELL RAILWAY
C

₩₩ No. 6619
NORTH YORKSHIRE MOORS RAILWAY
L

₩₩ No. 662 *(Martello)*
BRESSINGHAM STEAM
L S D

₩₩ No. 6686
BLUEBELL RAILWAY
C O

₩₩ No. 6697
DIDCOT RAILWAY CENTRE
L

₩₩ No. 67 *(Ken)*
SOUTH YORKSHIRE RAILWAY

₩₩ No. 672 *(Fenchurch)*
BLUEBELL RAILWAY
L O

₩₩ No. 673 *(Maude)*
BO'NESS & KINNEIL RAILWAY
L

₩₩ No. 673
NATIONAL RAILWAY MUSEUM
L

₩₩ No. 676
BLUEBELL RAILWAY
C

₩₩ No. 68
CHASEWATER RAILWAY

No. 68
KENT & EAST SUSSEX RAILWAY
C

No. 680 *(Jacob)*
BEAMISH
L

No. 68003
MID-NORFOLK RAILWAY
R

No. 68005
EMBSAY & BOLTON ABBEY RLWY
L O

No. 68006 *(Warrington)*
PEAK RAIL
L

No. 68009
NORTH NORFOLK RAILWAY
L

No. 68011 *(Errol Lonsdale)*
SOUTH DEVON RAILWAY
L O

No. 68012 *(Blackie)*
LAVENDER LINE
L O

No. 68012 *(Duke (The))*
PEAK RAIL
L

No. 68072
COLNE VALLEY RAILWAY
L

No. 68077
KEIGHLEY & WORTH VALLEY
L

No. 68088
NOTTINGHAM TRANSPORT CTRE
L O

No. 68153
MIDDLETON RAILWAY
L

No. 68189 *(Patricia)*
CALEDONIAN RAILWAY
L

No. 68189 *(Patricia)*
CALEDONIAN RAILWAY
L S D

No. 6824
DIDCOT RAILWAY CENTRE
C

No. 6839
AVON VALLEY RAILWAY
C

No. 684 *(Jack)*
ARMLEY MILLS
L O

No. 6841 *(William Francis)*
BRESSINGHAM STEAM
L S D

No. 6843
NORTH NORFOLK RAILWAY
R

No. 6843
NORTH NORFOLK RAILWAY
C

No. 68494
NORTH YORKSHIRE MOORS RAILWAY
R

No. 68500
NOTTINGHAM TRANSPORT CTRE
R O

No. 686 *(Lady Armaghdale (The))*
SEVERN VALLEY RAILWAY
L

ROLLING STOCK by NUMBER

68 — 686

No. 68645
GWILI RAILWAY

No. 68684
DIDCOT RAILWAY CENTRE
[W]

No. 68777
SOUTH DEVON RAILWAY
[W]

No. 69
KENT & EAST SUSSEX RAILWAY
[C]

No. 69023
NORTH YORKSHIRE MOORS RAILWAY
[L]

No. 69310
DARTMOOR RAILWAY
[C]

No. 695
NOTTINGHAM TRANSPORT CTRE
[R]

No. 69523
GREAT CENTRAL RAILWAY
[L]

No. 6960 *(Raveningham Hall)*
GLOUCESTERSHIRE WARWICKSHIRE
[L] [O]

No. 6989 *(Wightwick Hall)*
BUCKINGHAMSHIRE RLWY CTRE
[L]

No. 6990 *(Witherslack Hall)*
GREAT CENTRAL RAILWAY
[L] [O]

No. 6998 *(Burton Agnes Hall)*
DIDCOT RAILWAY CENTRE
[L]

No. 7
ABBEY LIGHT RAILWAY
[L]

No. 7 *(Mr P)*
BEER HEIGHTS
[L] [O]

No. 7
BO'NESS & KINNEIL RAILWAY
[L]

No. 7 *(Victory)*
BREDGAR & WORMSHILL
[L]

No. 7
BUCKINGHAMSHIRE RLWY CTRE
[L]

No. 7 *(Barclay)*
CALEDONIAN RAILWAY
[L] [O]

No. 7 *(Fleet)*
CHASEWATER RAILWAY
[L] [O]

No. 7 *(Sandy River)*
EASTLEIGH LAKESIDE RAILWAY
[L] [O]

No. 7 *(Tram Engine)*
KIRKLEES LIGHT RAILWAY
[O]

No. 7
LAKESIDE & HAVERTHWAITE RLWY

No. 7 *(Falcon)*
LEIGHTON BUZZARD RAILWAY
[L] [O] [D]

No. 7
LEIGHTON BUZZARD RAILWAY
[R] [C] [O] [D]

No. 7 *(Aelfred)*
MOORS VALLEY RAILWAY
L **O**

No. 7 *(Prestongrange)*
PRESTONGRANGE INDUSTRIAL

No. 7 *(Merlin)*
RUDYARD LAKE RAILWAY
L **O**

No. 7 *(Ralph)*
SNOWDON MOUNTAIN RAILWAY
L

No. 7
SOUTH DEVON RAILWAY
C

No. 7
SOUTH TYNEDALE RAILWAY
R

No. 7
TALYLLYN RAILWAY
C

No. 7 *(Tom Rolt)*
TALYLLYN RAILWAY
L **O**

No. 7 *(Owain Glyndwr)*
VALE OF RHEIDOL RAILWAY
L

No. 7 *(Chattenden)*
WELSHPOOL & LLANFAIR
L **O**

No. 70 *(Caledonia)*
HOLLYCOMBE STEAM COLLECTION
L **O**

No. 70000 *(Britannia)*
BARLEYLANDS MINIATURE RAILWAY
L **O**

No. 70013 *(Oliver Cromwell)*
NATIONAL RAILWAY MUSEUM
L **S** **D**

No. 700320
BRISTOL HARBOUR RAILWAY
W **O** **D**

No. 701 *(Franklin D Roosevelt)*
WATERCRESS LINE
L

No. 7029 *(Clun Castle)*
TYSELEY LOCOMOTIVE WORKS

No. 70335 *(Macaw B)*
DIDCOT RAILWAY CENTRE
W

No. 705
EAST SOMERSET RAILWAY
L **O**

No. 7058 *(Olwen)*
GWILI RAILWAY
L **O**

No. 70621
NORTH NORFOLK RAILWAY
R

No. 7069
GLOUCESTERSHIRE WARWICKSHIRE
L

No. 7080
CHASEWATER RAILWAY
S **D**

No. 7090
SOUTH DEVON RAILWAY
C

No. 71000 *(Duke of Gloucester)*
EAST LANCASHIRE RAILWAY

ROLLING STOCK by NUMBER

7 — 71000

No. 7151
AVON VALLEY RAILWAY
L O

No. 71516 *(Welsh Guardsman)*
GWILI RAILWAY
L O

No. 7173
NENE VALLEY RAILWAY
L S D

No. 719
BLUEBELL RAILWAY
R

No. 72
KENT & EAST SUSSEX RAILWAY
C

No. 7200
BUCKINGHAMSHIRE RLWY CTRE
L

No. 7202
DIDCOT RAILWAY CENTRE
L

No. 7229
EAST LANCASHIRE RAILWAY

No. 7285
DIDCOT RAILWAY CENTRE

No. 7285 *(Shell Mex)*
NORTH YORKSHIRE MOORS RAILWAY
W

No. 73
KENT & EAST SUSSEX RAILWAY
C

No. 73004
LAVENDER LINE
L

No. 7303
SOUTH DEVON RAILWAY
W

No. 73050 *(City of Peterborough)*
NENE VALLEY RAILWAY
L

No. 730767
SPA VALLEY RAILWAY
R

No. 73082 *(Camelot)*
BLUEBELL RAILWAY
L O

No. 73096
WATERCRESS LINE
L

No. 73129
MIDLAND RAILWAY CENTRE
L

No. 7313
DIDCOT RAILWAY CENTRE

No. 73156
EAST LANCASHIRE RAILWAY

No. 7325
SEVERN VALLEY RAILWAY
L D

No. 732744
CHASEWATER RAILWAY

No. 7330
ALMOND VALLEY HERITAGE TRUST
L O

No. 737
NATIONAL RAILWAY MUSEUM
L

No. 7371
DIDCOT RAILWAY CENTRE

No. 7372
DIDCOT RAILWAY CENTRE

No. 7377
SOUTH DEVON RAILWAY
C

No. 74 *(Dunluce Castle)*
ULSTER FOLK & TRANSPORT
L S D

No. 740
LEIGHTON BUZZARD RAILWAY
L D

No. 741574
SOUTH DEVON RAILWAY
W

No. 743010
SOUTH DEVON RAILWAY
W

No. 743031
SOUTH DEVON RAILWAY
W

No. 745
DIDCOT RAILWAY CENTRE
W

No. 746
AMERTON RAILWAY
L O

No. 747 *(Yellow Peril)*
AMERTON RAILWAY
L

No. 75
KENT & EAST SUSSEX RAILWAY
C

No. 75006
NENE VALLEY RAILWAY
L O

No. 75014
EAST LANCASHIRE RAILWAY

No. 75014 *(Braveheart)*
NORTH YORKSHIRE MOORS RAILWAY
L

No. 7502
MANGAPPS RAILWAY MUSEUM
L O

No. 75027
BLUEBELL RAILWAY
L O

No. 75069
SEVERN VALLEY RAILWAY
L

No. 75078
KEIGHLEY & WORTH VALLEY
L

No. 75079 *(City of Plymouth)*
PLYM VALLEY RAILWAY
L

No. 75080
SOUTH DOWNS LIGHT RAILWAY
L O

No. 752
DIDCOT RAILWAY CENTRE
W

No. 752
KEIGHLEY & WORTH VALLEY
L

No. 7522
KENT & EAST SUSSEX RAILWAY
W

No. 755094
NORTH NORFOLK RAILWAY
R

ROLLING STOCK by NUMBER

7372 — 755094

No. 756939
NORTH NORFOLK RAILWAY
R

No. 7597
BODMIN & WENFORD RAILWAY
L

No. 7597 *(Zebedee)*
PEAK RAIL
L

No. 7598
BLUEBELL RAILWAY
C

No. 76
NATIONAL RAILWAY MUSEUM
R

No. 76017
WATERCRESS LINE
L S

No. 76077
GLOUCESTERSHIRE WARWICKSHIRE
L

No. 76079
EAST LANCASHIRE RAILWAY

No. 764 *(Sir Gyles)*
NORTHAMPTON & LAMPORT RAILWAY
L

No. 7646 *(Northampton)*
NORTHAMPTON & LAMPORT RAILWAY
L O

No. 766158
SOUTH DEVON RAILWAY
W

No. 7663
LLANGOLLEN RAILWAY
L O

No. 7663
PEAK RAIL
C

No. 769
NORTH NORFOLK RAILWAY
R

No. 77 *(Norwood)*
BOWES RAILWAY
L S

No. 77
BRECON MOUNTAIN RAILWAY

No. 7705
VALE OF GLAMORGAN RAILWAY
L

No. 771 *(Sir Sagramore)*
SOUTH DOWNS LIGHT RAILWAY
L O

No. 7714
SEVERN VALLEY RAILWAY
L O

No. 7715
BUCKINGHAMSHIRE RLWY CTRE
L O

No. 77172
EAST LANCASHIRE RAILWAY

No. 772584
PEAK RAIL
R

No. 7752
TYSELEY LOCOMOTIVE WORKS

No. 7754
LLANGOLLEN RAILWAY
L O

No. 7760
TYSELEY LOCOMOTIVE WORKS

No.777 *(Sir Lamiel)*
NATIONAL RAILWAY MUSEUM
L

No.778
LEIGHTON BUZZARD RAILWAY
L D

No.778436
SOUTH DEVON RAILWAY
W

No.78018 *(Borough of Darlington)*
DARLINGTON RAILWAY PRES SOC
L

No.78019
GREAT CENTRAL RAILWAY
L

No.7802 *(Bradley Manor)*
SEVERN VALLEY RAILWAY
L O

No.78022
KEIGHLEY & WORTH VALLEY
L

No.78059
BLUEBELL RAILWAY
L

No.7808 *(Cookham Manor)*
DIDCOT RAILWAY CENTRE
L

No.7812 *(Erlestoke Manor)*
SEVERN VALLEY RAILWAY
L

No.7819 *(Hinton Manor)*
SEVERN VALLEY RAILWAY
L S

No.7820 *(Dinmore Manor)*
WEST SOMERSET RAILWAY
L O

No.7821 *(Ditcheat Manor)*
CAMBRIAN RAILWAY SOCIETY

No.7822 *(Foxcote Manor)*
LLANGOLLEN RAILWAY
L O

No.782625
NORTH YORKSHIRE MOORS RAILWAY

No.782670
NORTH YORKSHIRE MOORS RAILWAY

No.7827 *(Lydham Manor)*
PAIGNTON & DARTMOUTH RAILWAY
L

No.7828
NATIONAL RAILWAY MUSEUM
R

No.7828 *(Odney Manor)*
WEST SOMERSET RAILWAY
L O

No.7846 *(North Downs)*
SPA VALLEY RAILWAY
L

No.786393
SOUTH DEVON RAILWAY
W

No.7864
BLUEBELL RAILWAY
C

No.79
NORTH YORKSHIRE MOORS RAILWAY
C

No.790 *(Hardwicke)*
NATIONAL RAILWAY MUSEUM
L S D

ROLLING STOCK by NUMBER

777 — 790

No.79008
GWILI RAILWAY
[W]

No.79018
MIDLAND RAILWAY CENTRE
[L]

No.7903 *(Foremarke Hall)*
SWINDON & CRICKLADE RAILWAY
[L]

No.7931
CHINNOR & PRINCES RISBOROUGH
[G]

No.7953
SWANSEA VALE RAILWAY

No.79612
MIDLAND RAILWAY CENTRE
[L]

No.7976
DIDCOT RAILWAY CENTRE

No.798
NATIONAL RAILWAY MUSEUM
[R]

No.799
NATIONAL RAILWAY MUSEUM
[R]

No.799
NOTTINGHAM TRANSPORT CTRE
[R]

No.79933 *(Tevan)*
DIDCOT RAILWAY CENTRE
[W]

No.79962
KEIGHLEY & WORTH VALLEY
[L]

No.79964
KEIGHLEY & WORTH VALLEY
[L] [O]

No.7999 *(A J Hill)*
NORTH NORFOLK RAILWAY
[L]

No.79999
EAST ANGLIAN RAILWAY MUSEUM
[L]

No.8 *(Hudson GoGo)*
ABBEY LIGHT RAILWAY
[L]

No.8 *(Gem)*
BEER HEIGHTS
[L] [O]

No.8
BREDGAR & WORMSHILL
[L]

No.8
CAMBRIAN RAILWAY SOCIETY
[L]

No.8
DERWENT VALLEY
[L] [O]

No.8
EMBSAY & BOLTON ABBEY RLWY
[L]

No.8
LAKESIDE & HAVERTHWAITE RLWY

No.8
LEIGHTON BUZZARD RAILWAY
[R] [G] [O] [D]

No.8
LEIGHTON BUZZARD RAILWAY
[L]

ROLLING STOCK by NUMBER

79008 — 8

No. 8
PONTYPOOL & BLAENAVON RAILWAY
L

No. 8
RUDYARD LAKE RAILWAY
W O

No. 8 *(Eryri)*
SNOWDON MOUNTAIN RAILWAY
L O

No. 8 *(Merseysider)*
TALYLLYN RAILWAY
L

No. 8
TALYLLYN RAILWAY
C

No. 8 *(Llwelyn)*
VALE OF RHEIDOL RAILWAY
L O

No. 8 *(Dougal)*
WELSHPOOL & LLANFAIR
L O

No. 80 *(Beaudesert)*
LEIGHTON BUZZARD RAILWAY
L O D

No. 80 *(Thundersley)*
NATIONAL RAILWAY MUSEUM
L S D

No. 800
NATIONAL RAILWAY MUSEUM
R

No. 800 *(Maedb)*
ULSTER FOLK & TRANSPORT
L S D

No. 80002
KEIGHLEY & WORTH VALLEY
L

No. 80064
BLUEBELL RAILWAY
L S D

No. 80079
SEVERN VALLEY RAILWAY
L O

No. 80080
MIDLAND RAILWAY CENTRE
L D

No. 80097
EAST LANCASHIRE RAILWAY

No. 80098
MIDLAND RAILWAY CENTRE
L O

No. 801
NATIONAL RAILWAY MUSEUM
R

No. 80100
BLUEBELL RAILWAY
L S

No. 80105
BO'NESS & KINNEIL RAILWAY
L

No. 80135
NORTH YORKSHIRE MOORS RAILWAY
L

No. 80136
CHURNET VALLEY RAILWAY
L O

No. 80151
BLUEBELL RAILWAY
L

No. 80212
BARROW HILL ROUNDHOUSE
C

ROLLING STOCK by NUMBER

80214 — 825

No. 80214
MID-NORFOLK RAILWAY
R

No. 80217
NORTH YORKSHIRE MOORS RAILWAY
C

No. 80224
DIDCOT RAILWAY CENTRE
R

No. 80257
BARROW HILL ROUNDHOUSE
C

No. 804 *(Alco 660HP American Switcher)*
RAILWORLD
L S D

No. 80501
CHINNOR & PRINCES RISBOROUGH
C

No. 806
BLUEBELL RAILWAY
C

No. 80659
NATIONAL RAILWAY MUSEUM
C

No. 80668
DIDCOT RAILWAY CENTRE
W

No. 80746
GWILI RAILWAY
W

No. 80789
DIDCOT RAILWAY CENTRE
W

No. 81
BEAMISH
W

No. 8112
BLUEBELL RAILWAY
W

No. 81295
KEITH & DUFFTOWN RAILWAY
C

No. 813
BLUEBELL RAILWAY
W

No. 814
DIDCOT RAILWAY CENTRE
R

No. 81547
GWILI RAILWAY
R

No. 818
BEAMISH
C

No. 82 *(Boxhill)*
NATIONAL RAILWAY MUSEUM
L

No. 820
FOXFIELD STEAM RAILWAY
L O

No. 820
NATIONAL RAILWAY MUSEUM
R

No. 82008
BARROW HILL ROUNDHOUSE
L S D

No. 8249
SOUTH DEVON RAILWAY
C

No. 825
NORTH YORKSHIRE MOORS RAILWAY
L

No. 8274
GLOUCESTERSHIRE WARWICKSHIRE
L

No. 828 *(Vulcan)*
PEAK RAIL
L

No. 828
STRATHSPEY RAILWAY
L

No. 84554
PEAK RAIL
C

No. 847
BLUEBELL RAILWAY
L S D

No. 85
IRCHESTER NARROW GAUGE MUSEUM
L O

No. 85
KEIGHLEY & WORTH VALLEY
L O

No. 85
KENT & EAST SUSSEX RAILWAY
C

No. 85 *(Merlin)*
RPSI
L O

No. 850 *(Lord Nelson)*
NATIONAL RAILWAY MUSEUM
L

No. 85121
SWANSEA VALE RAILWAY
R

No. 85189
SWANSEA VALE RAILWAY
R

No. 85192
SWANSEA VALE RAILWAY
R

No. 85630
NORTH YORKSHIRE MOORS RAILWAY
R

No. 859
INDUSTRIAL RAILWAY MUSEUM
L S D

No. 86
IRCHESTER NARROW GAUGE MUSEUM
L O

No. 86
KENT & EAST SUSSEX RAILWAY
C

No. 8624
PEAK RAIL
L

No. 865
ARMLEY MILLS
L

No. 87
EXMOOR STEAM RAILWAY
L S D

No. 87
IRCHESTER NARROW GAUGE MUSEUM
L S D

No. 87
NATIONAL RAILWAY MUSEUM
L

No. 87
NORTH NORFOLK RAILWAY
R

No. 87004
CADEBY LIGHT RAILWAY
L

ROLLING STOCK by NUMBER

8274 — 87004

✦✦✦ No. 87008
CADEBY LIGHT RAILWAY
L

✦✦✦ No. 87009
CADEBY LIGHT RAILWAY
L

✦✦✦ No. 87051
CADEBY LIGHT RAILWAY
L

✦✦✦ No. 876
BEAMISH
L S D

✦✦✦ No. 87720
BLUEBELL RAILWAY

✦✦✦ No. 87782
BLUEBELL RAILWAY
W

✦✦✦ No. 885
NORTH YORKSHIRE MOORS RAILWAY

✦✦✦ No. 886 *(Premier)*
SITTINGBOURNE & KEMSLEY
L S D

✦✦✦ No. 887
EMBSAY & BOLTON ABBEY RLWY
L O

✦✦✦ No. 887
NORTH YORKSHIRE MOORS RAILWAY

✦✦✦ No. 88DS *(Tippockety)*
NORTH NORFOLK RAILWAY
R

✦✦✦ No. 89
BLUEBELL RAILWAY

✦✦✦ No. 9 *(Muir Hill)*
ABBEY LIGHT RAILWAY
L

✦✦✦ No. 9
BEER HEIGHTS
L

✦✦✦ No. 9
BUCKINGHAMSHIRE RLWY CTRE
L

✦✦✦ No. 9 *(Rachel)*
LAKESIDE & HAVERTHWAITE RLWY
L

✦✦✦ No. 9
LEIGHTON BUZZARD RAILWAY
R C O D

✦✦✦ No. 9 *(Madge)*
LEIGHTON BUZZARD RAILWAY
L

✦✦✦ No. 9 *(Jason)*
MOORS VALLEY RAILWAY
L O

✦✦✦ No. 9 *(Ninian)*
SNOWDON MOUNTAIN RAILWAY
L O

✦✦✦ No. 9
SOUTH TYNEDALE RAILWAY
L O

✦✦✦ No. 9
STRATHSPEY RAILWAY
L O

✦✦✦ No. 9
TALYLLYN RAILWAY
C

✦✦✦ No. 9 *(Alf)*
TALYLLYN RAILWAY
L O

✦✦✦ No. 9
TANFIELD RAILWAY

No. 9 *(Prince of Wales)*
VALE OF RHEIDOL RAILWAY
L **O**

No. 9002
DIDCOT RAILWAY CENTRE

No. 9003 *(Royal Saloon)*
STEAM
C **S** **D**

No. 9006
NATIONAL RAILWAY MUSEUM
R

No. 9007
NATIONAL RAILWAY MUSEUM
R

No. 901
NATIONAL RAILWAY MUSEUM
L **S** **D**

No. 901
NATIONAL RAILWAY MUSEUM
R

No. 901
NORTH YORKSHIRE MOORS RAILWAY
L

No. 902502
NATIONAL RAILWAY MUSEUM

No. 904093
NORTH NORFOLK RAILWAY
R

No. 90773
KEIGHLEY & WORTH VALLEY
L

No. 90775
NORTH YORKSHIRE MOORS RAILWAY
L

No. 9083
DIDCOT RAILWAY CENTRE

No. 91
MIDDLETON RAILWAY
L **O**

No. 91
NORTH NORFOLK RAILWAY
R

No. 91
SPA VALLEY RAILWAY
R

No. 910
NATIONAL RAILWAY MUSEUM
L

No. 9102
NORTHAMPTON & LAMPORT RAILWAY
C

No. 9105
PEAK RAIL
R

No. 9111
SOUTH DEVON RAILWAY
C

No. 9112 *(Queen Mary)*
DIDCOT RAILWAY CENTRE
R

No. 9113 *(Prince of Wales)*
DIDCOT RAILWAY CENTRE
R

No. 9118 *(Princess Elizabeth)*
DIDCOT RAILWAY CENTRE
R

No. 9135
NATIONAL RAILWAY MUSEUM
R

ROLLING STOCK by NUMBER

9 — 9135

© *HCC* Publishing Ltd

Key: **L** Loco **R** Rolling Stock **W** Wagon **C** Coach **O** Operational **S** Static **D** On Display

Section 5b. 413

ROLLING STOCK by **NUMBER**

92 — 92943

No. 92
BLUEBELL RAILWAY
R

No. 92
DIDCOT RAILWAY CENTRE
R

No. 92 *(Florence)*
EASTLEIGH LAKESIDE RAILWAY
L O

No. 92 *(Waggoner)*
MUSEUM OF ARMY TRANSPORT
L S D

No. 920 *(Pamela)*
OLD KILN LIGHT RAILWAY
L

No. 92035
SOUTH DEVON RAILWAY
W

No. 9208
AVON VALLEY RAILWAY
C

No. 92092
SOUTH DEVON RAILWAY
W

No. 92134
CHURNET VALLEY RAILWAY
L

No. 92158
PEAK RAIL
C

No. 92203 *(Black Prince)*
BARLEYLANDS MINIATURE RAILWAY
L O

No. 92203 *(Black Prince)*
GLOUCESTERSHIRE WARWICKSHIRE
L

No. 92207 *(Morning Star)*
EAST LANCASHIRE RAILWAY

No. 92212
GREAT CENTRAL RAILWAY

No. 92214
MIDLAND RAILWAY CENTRE
L S D

No. 92219
MIDLAND RAILWAY CENTRE
L

No. 92220 *(Evening Star)*
NATIONAL RAILWAY MUSEUM
L S D

No. 92240
BLUEBELL RAILWAY
L O

No. 9241
EAST SOMERSET RAILWAY
C

No. 925
NATIONAL RAILWAY MUSEUM
L

No. 926 *(Leader)*
SITTINGBOURNE & KEMSLEY
L O

No. 928 *(Stowe)*
BLUEBELL RAILWAY
S D

No. 929 *(Alexandra)*
LAKESIDE & HAVERTHWAITE RLWY
L D

No. 92943
DIDCOT RAILWAY CENTRE
W

No. 93
DIDCOT RAILWAY CENTRE
L

No. 93183
PEAK RAIL
R

No. 933
DIDCOT RAILWAY CENTRE
R

No. 93545
NORTH YORKSHIRE MOORS RAILWAY
R

No. 9365 *(Belvedere)*
NIRT
L S D

No. 9369 *(Musketeer)*
NIRT
L D

No. 93813
NORTH YORKSHIRE MOORS RAILWAY
R

No. 9394
PEAK RAIL
R

No. 9400
NATIONAL RAILWAY MUSEUM
L

No. 9400
STEAM
L S D

No. 94058
BARROW HILL ROUNDHOUSE
C

No. 94062
NORTHAMPTON & LAMPORT RAILWAY
W

No. 94071
NORTHAMPTON & LAMPORT RAILWAY
W

No. 9410
CHINNOR & PRINCES RISBOROUGH

No. 94240
CHASEWATER RAILWAY
R

No. 9449 *(Blue Circle)*
BLUEBELL RAILWAY

No. 945 *(Annie)*
LAVENDER LINE
L

No. 945
NORTH YORKSHIRE MOORS RAILWAY

No. 9466
BUCKINGHAMSHIRE RLWY CTRE
L O

No. 948
NATIONAL RAILWAY MUSEUM
R

No. 94835
DIDCOT RAILWAY CENTRE
W

No. 949
BLUEBELL RAILWAY
C

No. 950
BLUEBELL RAILWAY
C

No. 950344
SOUTH DEVON RAILWAY
W

ROLLING STOCK by NUMBER

93 — 950344

ROLLING STOCK by NUMBER

950592 — 9681

No. 950592
DIDCOT RAILWAY CENTRE
W

No. 95156
SWANSEA VALE RAILWAY
R

No. 95199
BARROW HILL ROUNDHOUSE
C

No. 9520
DIDCOT RAILWAY CENTRE
R

No. 952282
NOTTINGHAM TRANSPORT CTRE
R

No. 953640
SOUTH DEVON RAILWAY
W

No. 957
BLUEBELL RAILWAY
L

No. 957
MANGAPPS RAILWAY MUSEUM
C

No. 95861
BEAMISH
W

No. 95979
SOUTH DEVON RAILWAY
W

No. 9599 *(William)*
BATTLEFIELD LINE
L S

No. 96 *(Normandy)*
BLUEBELL RAILWAY
L O

No. 9600
TYSELEY LOCOMOTIVE WORKS

No. 960209
NATIONAL RAILWAY MUSEUM

No. 9604
BLUEBELL RAILWAY
W O

No. 9622 *(Swansea Vale)*
GWILI RAILWAY
L O S

No. 96302
GWILI RAILWAY
W

No. 9631
NATIONAL RAILWAY MUSEUM
R

No. 9635
DIDCOT RAILWAY CENTRE
R

No. 9642
DEAN FOREST RAILWAY
L O

No. 9642
SWANSEA VALE RAILWAY

No. 9653
NATIONAL RAILWAY MUSEUM
R

No. 9654
NATIONAL RAILWAY MUSEUM
R

No. 9681
DEAN FOREST RAILWAY
L

No. 96835
SOUTH DEVON RAILWAY
W

No. 969
NORTH NORFOLK RAILWAY
R

No. 971
BLUEBELL RAILWAY
C **O**

No. 975
DIDCOT RAILWAY CENTRE
R

No. 9752
BLUEBELL RAILWAY
W

No. 975496
EAST ANGLIAN RAILWAY MUSEUM
S **D**

No. 97650
LINCOLNSHIRE WOLDS RAILWAY

No. 977019
NOTTINGHAM TRANSPORT CTRE
R

No. 984176
SOUTH DEVON RAILWAY
W

No. 984872
SOUTH DEVON RAILWAY
W

No. 9872 *(Auld Reekie)*
KERR MINIATURE RAILWAY
O

No. 98799
NORTH YORKSHIRE MOORS RAILWAY
R

No. 990 *(Henry Oakley)*
NATIONAL RAILWAY MUSEUM
L **S** **D**

No. 99204 *(Bullion Van)*
PEAK RAIL
C

No. 993247
SOUTH DEVON RAILWAY
W

No. 993471
SOUTH DEVON RAILWAY
W

No. 993710
SOUTH DEVON RAILWAY
W

No. 99625
BARROW HILL ROUNDHOUSE
O

No. 9998 *(Elouise)*
OLD KILN LIGHT RAILWAY
L **O**

No. AB354
LAVENDER LINE
L

No. AD3088
KENT & EAST SUSSEX RAILWAY
W

No. ADB904148
NORTH NORFOLK RAILWAY
R

No. ADB904149
NORTH NORFOLK RAILWAY
R

No. ADB965204
MANGAPPS RAILWAY MUSEUM
R

ROLLING STOCK by NUMBER

96835 — ADB965204

⚙ No. ADB975455
NORTH YORKSHIRE MOORS RAILWAY
R

⚙ No. ADB975472
KENT & EAST SUSSEX RAILWAY
W

⚙ No. ADB975672
NATIONAL RAILWAY MUSEUM

⚙ No. ADB975758
KEITH & DUFFTOWN RAILWAY
C

⚙ No. ADB975814
BARROW HILL ROUNDHOUSE
C

⚙ No. ADB977383
MID-NORFOLK RAILWAY
R

⚙ No. ADB999074
NORTHAMPTON & LAMPORT RAILWAY
W

⚙ No. ADE230943
PEAK RAIL

⚙ No. ADE320883
NORTH NORFOLK RAILWAY
R

⚙ No. ADE330102
NORTH YORKSHIRE MOORS RAILWAY

⚙ No. ADE330107
NORTH YORKSHIRE MOORS RAILWAY

⚙ No. ADE941751
NORTH YORKSHIRE MOORS RAILWAY

⚙ No. ADE941753
PEAK RAIL
W

⚙ No. ADM40252
BARROW HILL ROUNDHOUSE
O **D**

⚙ No. ADM40252
PEAK RAIL
R

⚙ No. ADM40294
PEAK RAIL
R

⚙ No. ADM47
MANGAPPS RAILWAY MUSEUM
R

⚙ No. ADRC95223
PEAK RAIL
W **O**

⚙ No. ADS61024
NORTH YORKSHIRE MOORS RAILWAY
W

⚙ No. AMW144
EAST ANGLIAN RAILWAY MUSEUM
L

⚙ No. B021172
NORTHAMPTON & LAMPORT RAILWAY
W

⚙ No. B234830
NORTH YORKSHIRE MOORS RAILWAY
W

⚙ No. B274600
CHASEWATER RAILWAY
W

⚙ No. B291264
DERWENT VALLEY
R

⚙ No. B316711
CHASEWATER RAILWAY
W

No. B3192 *(Express Dairy)*
NORTH YORKSHIRE MOORS RAILWAY
W

No. B415776
NORTH YORKSHIRE MOORS RAILWAY
W

No. B418444
NORTH YORKSHIRE MOORS RAILWAY
W

No. B419025
NORTH YORKSHIRE MOORS RAILWAY
W

No. B428991
NORTH YORKSHIRE MOORS RAILWAY
W

No. B431861
NORTH YORKSHIRE MOORS RAILWAY
W

No. B445025
NORTH YORKSHIRE MOORS RAILWAY
W

No. B451885
NORTH YORKSHIRE MOORS RAILWAY
W

No. B452670
NORTH YORKSHIRE MOORS RAILWAY
W

No. B458525
BLUEBELL RAILWAY
W **O**

No. B460168
KENT & EAST SUSSEX RAILWAY
W

No. B460575
KENT & EAST SUSSEX RAILWAY
W

No. B461224
BLUEBELL RAILWAY
W **O**

No. B47757
CHASEWATER RAILWAY
W

No. B483720
KENT & EAST SUSSEX RAILWAY
W

No. B503877
CHINNOR & PRINCES RISBOROUGH
W

No. B560
SPA VALLEY RAILWAY
R

No. B68231
EAST ANGLIAN RAILWAY MUSEUM
W

No. B73006
MID-NORFOLK RAILWAY
W

No. B741161
CHASEWATER RAILWAY
W

No. B741620
NORTH YORKSHIRE MOORS RAILWAY
W

No. B741748
MID-NORFOLK RAILWAY
R **W**

No. B745522
EAST ANGLIAN RAILWAY MUSEUM
W

No. B749678
CHASEWATER RAILWAY
W

ROLLING STOCK by NUMBER

B3192 — B749678

⚅ No. B753473
NORTH YORKSHIRE MOORS RAILWAY

⚅ No. B755340
NORTH YORKSHIRE MOORS RAILWAY

⚅ No. B760651
EAST ANGLIAN RAILWAY MUSEUM
W

⚅ No. B761349
BLUEBELL RAILWAY
W

⚅ No. B762112
NORTH YORKSHIRE MOORS RAILWAY

⚅ No. B771448
NORTH YORKSHIRE MOORS RAILWAY

⚅ No. B772972
BLUEBELL RAILWAY
W

⚅ No. B778771
NOTTINGHAM TRANSPORT CTRE
R

⚅ No. B779761
NOTTINGHAM TRANSPORT CTRE
R

⚅ No. B781763
NORTH YORKSHIRE MOORS RAILWAY

⚅ No. B782111
NOTTINGHAM TRANSPORT CTRE
R

⚅ No. B782274
NORTH YORKSHIRE MOORS RAILWAY

⚅ No. B782523
NORTH YORKSHIRE MOORS RAILWAY

⚅ No. B783071
NORTH NORFOLK RAILWAY
R

⚅ No. B786655
NORTH YORKSHIRE MOORS RAILWAY

⚅ No. B853043
NORTH YORKSHIRE MOORS RAILWAY

⚅ No. B874076
RAILWORLD

⚅ No. B894178
NORTH YORKSHIRE MOORS RAILWAY

⚅ No. B900427
KENT & EAST SUSSEX RAILWAY
W

⚅ No. B900910
BRISTOL HARBOUR RAILWAY
W **0** **D**

⚅ No. B900920
BLUEBELL RAILWAY
W

⚅ No. B900935
NORTH YORKSHIRE MOORS RAILWAY
W

⚅ No. B904134
BLUEBELL RAILWAY
W **0**

⚅ No. B904147
CHASEWATER RAILWAY
0

⚅ No. B904152
NORTH YORKSHIRE MOORS RAILWAY
W

⚅ No. B904551
NORTH YORKSHIRE MOORS RAILWAY
W

⚅ No. B905100
NORTH YORKSHIRE MOORS RAILWAY
W

　　　　　　　　　　　　　　　　© *HCC* Publishing Ltd

No. B905112
KEITH & DUFFTOWN RAILWAY
W

No. B91762
EAST ANGLIAN RAILWAY MUSEUM
W

No. B927541
MID-NORFOLK RAILWAY
R

No. B932267
NORTH YORKSHIRE MOORS RAILWAY
W

No. B933122
NORTH YORKSHIRE MOORS RAILWAY
W

No. B934279
NORTH YORKSHIRE MOORS RAILWAY
W

No. B934280
NORTH YORKSHIRE MOORS RAILWAY
W

No. B934281
NORTH YORKSHIRE MOORS RAILWAY
W

No. B934386
NORTH YORKSHIRE MOORS RAILWAY
W

No. B935493
NORTHAMPTON & LAMPORT RAILWAY
W

No. B940007
NORTH NORFOLK RAILWAY
R

No. B940081
NORTH YORKSHIRE MOORS RAILWAY
W

No. B943064
GWILI RAILWAY
W

No. B945798
CHINNOR & PRINCES RISBOROUGH
W

No. B950003
PEAK RAIL
R

No. B95007
GWILI RAILWAY
W

No. B950567
MID-NORFOLK RAILWAY
R

No. B951144
DERWENT VALLEY
R

No. B951771
EAST ANGLIAN RAILWAY MUSEUM
W

No. B951805
NORTHAMPTON & LAMPORT RAILWAY
W O

No. B953231
BARROW HILL ROUNDHOUSE
R

No. B953691
KEITH & DUFFTOWN RAILWAY
W

No. B953827
CHASEWATER RAILWAY
R

No. B954215
BARROW HILL ROUNDHOUSE
R

ROLLING STOCK by NUMBER

B905112 — B954215

No. B954353
NOTTINGHAM TRANSPORT CTRE
R

No. B954819
KEITH & DUFFTOWN RAILWAY
W

No. B954854
NORTH YORKSHIRE MOORS RAILWAY
R

No. B955225
NORTH YORKSHIRE MOORS RAILWAY
R

No. B983904
PEAK RAIL
O

No. B993076
PEAK RAIL
W

No. B993736
CHASEWATER RAILWAY
R

No. BP060174
CHINNOR & PRINCES RISBOROUGH
W

No. C1
BLUEBELL RAILWAY
L S D

No. CDM700704
EAST ANGLIAN RAILWAY MUSEUM
W

No. D1010 ***(Western Campaigner)***
WEST SOMERSET RAILWAY
L O

No. D1013 ***(Western Ranger)***
SEVERN VALLEY RAILWAY
L

No. D1015 ***(Western Champion)***
SEVERN VALLEY RAILWAY
L O

No. D1041 ***(Western Prince)***
EAST LANCASHIRE RAILWAY

No. D1048 ***(Western Lady)***
MIDLAND RAILWAY CENTRE
L

No. D1062 ***(Western Courier)***
SEVERN VALLEY RAILWAY
L O

No. D1171 ***(Western Pride)***
AVON VALLEY RAILWAY
L

No. D123
GREAT CENTRAL RAILWAY
L O

No. D1501 ***(Gateshead)***
EAST LANCASHIRE RAILWAY

No. D1516
MIDLAND RAILWAY CENTRE
L S D

No. D1705
GREAT CENTRAL RAILWAY
L O

No. D2023
KENT & EAST SUSSEX RAILWAY
L O

No. D2024
KENT & EAST SUSSEX RAILWAY
L S

No. D2051
NORTH NORFOLK RAILWAY
L

No. D2059
ISLE OF WIGHT STEAM RAILWAY
L **O**

No. D2062
EAST LANCASHIRE RAILWAY

No. D2063
NORTH NORFOLK RAILWAY
L

No. D2069
GLOUCESTERSHIRE WARWICKSHIRE

No. D2072
LAKESIDE & HAVERTHWAITE RLWY
L **O**

No. D2089
MANGAPPS RAILWAY MUSEUM
L **O**

No. D2118
SOUTH YORKSHIRE RAILWAY

No. D2119
WEST SOMERSET RAILWAY
L **O**

No. D2133
WEST SOMERSET RAILWAY
L **O**

No. D2134
SOUTH YORKSHIRE RAILWAY

No. D2138
MIDLAND RAILWAY CENTRE
L **O**

No. D2139
SOUTH YORKSHIRE RAILWAY

No. D2178
GWILI RAILWAY
L **O**

No. D2192 *(Titan)*
PAIGNTON & DARTMOUTH RAILWAY
L **O**

No. D2199
SOUTH YORKSHIRE RAILWAY

No. D2203
EMBSAY & BOLTON ABBEY RLWY
L **O**

No. D2207
NORTH YORKSHIRE MOORS RAILWAY
L

No. D2229
SOUTH YORKSHIRE RAILWAY

No. D2246 *(Bluebell)*
SOUTH YORKSHIRE RAILWAY

No. D226
KEIGHLEY & WORTH VALLEY
L **O**

No. D2267
NORTH NORFOLK RAILWAY
L **S** **D**

No. D2271
WEST SOMERSET RAILWAY
L **O**

No. D2272 *(Alfie)*
SOUTH YORKSHIRE RAILWAY

No. D2279
EAST ANGLIAN RAILWAY MUSEUM
L **O**

No. D2280
NORTH NORFOLK RAILWAY
L

No. D2284
SOUTH YORKSHIRE RAILWAY

No. D2298
BUCKINGHAMSHIRE RLWY CTRE
🔳

No. D2302
SOUTH YORKSHIRE RAILWAY

No. D2310
SOUTH YORKSHIRE RAILWAY

No. D2324 *(Judith)*
SOUTH YORKSHIRE RAILWAY

No. D2334
CHURNET VALLEY RAILWAY
🔳🔳

No. D2337 *(Dorothy)*
SOUTH YORKSHIRE RAILWAY
🔳

No. D2511
KEIGHLEY & WORTH VALLEY
🔳🔳

No. D2554
ISLE OF WIGHT STEAM RAILWAY
🔳🔳

No. D2587
SOUTH YORKSHIRE RAILWAY

No. D2767
EAST LANCASHIRE RAILWAY

No. D2774
EAST LANCASHIRE RAILWAY

No. D2854
SOUTH YORKSHIRE RAILWAY

No. D2866
SOUTH YORKSHIRE RAILWAY

No. D2867
SOUTH YORKSHIRE RAILWAY

No. D2868
SOUTH YORKSHIRE RAILWAY

No. D2953
SOUTH YORKSHIRE RAILWAY

No. D2957
SEVERN VALLEY RAILWAY
🔳🔳

No. D2961
SEVERN VALLEY RAILWAY
🔳🔳

No. D2994
AVON VALLEY RAILWAY
🔳🔳

No. D3000
SOUTH YORKSHIRE RAILWAY
🔳

No. D3014 *(Sampson)*
PAIGNTON & DARTMOUTH RAILWAY
🔳🔳

No. D3019 *(Gwyneth)*
SOUTH YORKSHIRE RAILWAY
🔳

No. D3022
SEVERN VALLEY RAILWAY
🔳🔳

No. D3023
SOUTH YORKSHIRE RAILWAY
🔳

No. D3059 *(Brechin City)*
CALEDONIAN RAILWAY
🔳

No. D306 *(Atlantic Conveyor)*
NENE VALLEY RAILWAY
🔳🔳

No. D3101
GREAT CENTRAL RAILWAY
🔲 🔲 🔲

No. D3167
LINCOLNSHIRE WOLDS RAILWAY
🔲

No. D3174 *(Dover Castle)*
KENT & EAST SUSSEX RAILWAY
🔲 🔲

No. D3232
EAST LANCASHIRE RAILWAY

No. D3336
KEIGHLEY & WORTH VALLEY
🔲 🔲

No. D335
EAST LANCASHIRE RAILWAY

No. D3358
WATERCRESS LINE
🔲 🔲

No. D3420
CHURNET VALLEY RAILWAY
🔲 🔲

No. D345
EAST LANCASHIRE RAILWAY

No. D3452
BODMIN & WENFORD RAILWAY
🔲 🔲

No. D3462
WEST SOMERSET RAILWAY
🔲 🔲

No. D3476
COLNE VALLEY RAILWAY
🔲

No. D3489 *(Colonel Tomline)*
SPA VALLEY RAILWAY
🔲 🔲

No. D3559
BODMIN & WENFORD RAILWAY
🔲 🔲

No. D3586
SEVERN VALLEY RAILWAY
🔲 🔲

No. D3594
STRATHSPEY RAILWAY
🔲

No. D3605
STRATHSPEY RAILWAY
🔲 🔲

No. D39
LEIGHTON BUZZARD RAILWAY
🔲 🔲 🔲 🔲 🔲

No. D3935
NORTH NORFOLK RAILWAY
🔲

No. D4 *(Great Gable)*
MIDLAND RAILWAY CENTRE
🔲 🔲

No. D4067
GREAT CENTRAL RAILWAY
🔲 🔲

No. D4092 *(Christine)*
SOUTH YORKSHIRE RAILWAY
🔲

No. D4279 *(Arthur Wright)*
GREAT CENTRAL RAILWAY
🔲

No. D5032 *(Helen Turner)*
NORTH YORKSHIRE MOORS RAILWAY
🔲

ROLLING STOCK by NUMBER

D3101 — D5032

No. D5054
EAST LANCASHIRE RAILWAY

No. D5061
NORTH YORKSHIRE MOORS RAILWAY
L

No. D5207
NORTH NORFOLK RAILWAY
L O

No. D5207
NORTH NORFOLK RAILWAY
L O

No. D5209
KEIGHLEY & WORTH VALLEY
L O

No. D5301
LAKESIDE & HAVERTHWAITE RLWY
L O D

No. D5314
CALEDONIAN RAILWAY
L O

No. D5325
STRATHSPEY RAILWAY
L O

No. D5351
BO'NESS & KINNEIL RAILWAY
L

No. D5353
WATERCRESS LINE
L

No. D5386
NORTH NORFOLK RAILWAY
L O

No. D5401
NORTHAMPTON & LAMPORT RAILWAY
L

No. D5410
SEVERN VALLEY RAILWAY
L O

No. D5518
BATTLEFIELD LINE
L O

No. D5600
EAST LANCASHIRE RAILWAY

No. D570283
NORTH NORFOLK RAILWAY
R

No. D5705
EAST LANCASHIRE RAILWAY

No. D571 *(Union)*
ARMLEY MILLS
L S D

No. D5830
GREAT CENTRAL RAILWAY
L O

No. D5905 *(Baby Deltie)*
MARKEATON PARK LIGHT RAILWAY
L

No. D625 *(Southam No 2)*
ARMLEY MILLS
L S

No. D634 *(Pioneer)*
ARMLEY MILLS
L S

No. D6353 *(Joe Brown)*
WINDMILL FARM RAILWAY
L O

No. D6515 *(Stan Symes)*
SWANAGE RAILWAY
L O

No. D6525 *(Captain Bill Smith RNR)*
WATERCRESS LINE
L **O**

No. D6527
BODMIN & WENFORD RAILWAY
L **O**

No. D6570 *(Ashford)*
KENT & EAST SUSSEX RAILWAY
L **O**

No. D6593
WATERCRESS LINE
L **O**

No. D6732 *(Mirage)*
NORTH NORFOLK RAILWAY
L **O**

No. D697
NIRT
L **O**

No. D7017
WEST SOMERSET RAILWAY
L **O**

No. D7018
WEST SOMERSET RAILWAY
L

No. D7029
SEVERN VALLEY RAILWAY
L

No. D7062 *(Artic Prince)*
ROYAL VICTORIA RAILWAY
L **O**

No. D7076
EAST LANCASHIRE RAILWAY

No. D7523
WEST SOMERSET RAILWAY
L **O**

No. D7535 *(Hercules)*
PAIGNTON & DARTMOUTH RAILWAY
L **O**

No. D7541 *(Diana (The))*
NORTH YORKSHIRE MOORS RAILWAY
L

No. D7585
BO'NESS & KINNEIL RAILWAY
L

No. D7628 *(Sybilla)*
NORTH YORKSHIRE MOORS RAILWAY
L

No. D7629
GREAT CENTRAL RAILWAY
L **O**

No. D7629
NORTHAMPTON & LAMPORT RAILWAY
L

No. D7633
SEVERN VALLEY RAILWAY
L **O**

No. D7671
MIDLAND RAILWAY CENTRE
L **O**

No. D7672 *(Tamworth Castle)*
CHURNET VALLEY RAILWAY
L **O**

No. D8 *(Penyghent)*
PEAK RAIL
L

No. D8001
MIDLAND RAILWAY CENTRE
L **O**

No. D8020
BO'NESS & KINNEIL RAILWAY
L

ROLLING STOCK by NUMBER

D6525 — D8020

No. D8031
KEIGHLEY & WORTH VALLEY
L **O**

No. D8048
BATTLEFIELD LINE

No. D8069
MID-NORFOLK RAILWAY
L **O**

No. D8098
GREAT CENTRAL RAILWAY
L **O**

No. D8137
GLOUCESTERSHIRE WARWICKSHIRE
L **O**

No. D8154
CHURNET VALLEY RAILWAY
L **O**

No. D8166
BODMIN & WENFORD RAILWAY
L **O**

No. D8197
BODMIN & WENFORD RAILWAY
L **S**

No. D821 *(Cornwall)*
SEVERN VALLEY RAILWAY
L **O**

No. D832 *(Onslaught)*
EAST LANCASHIRE RAILWAY

No. D8526 *(Bill Caddick)*
VALE OF GLAMORGAN RAILWAY
L **O**

No. D8568 *(Clayton)*
CHINNOR & PRINCES RISBOROUGH
L

No. D9009 *(Alycidon)*
NORTH YORKSHIRE MOORS RAILWAY
L

No. D9500
SOUTH YORKSHIRE RAILWAY

No. D950173
PEAK RAIL
R

No. D9502
SOUTH YORKSHIRE RAILWAY
L

No. D950885
PEAK RAIL
R

No. D9516
NENE VALLEY RAILWAY
L **O**

No. D9520
NOTTINGHAM TRANSPORT CTRE
L **O**

No. D9523
NENE VALLEY RAILWAY
L **O**

No. D9526
WEST SOMERSET RAILWAY
L

No. D9531
EAST LANCASHIRE RAILWAY

No. D9539
GLOUCESTERSHIRE WARWICKSHIRE
L **O**

No. D99 *(3rd Carabinier)*
EAST LANCASHIRE RAILWAY

No. DB74007
NATIONAL RAILWAY MUSEUM
C

No. DB784455
NOTTINGHAM TRANSPORT CTRE
R

No. DB787163
BARROW HILL ROUNDHOUSE
W

No. DB787287
BARROW HILL ROUNDHOUSE
W

No. DB946060
NORTH YORKSHIRE MOORS RAILWAY
W

No. DB950133
NORTH NORFOLK RAILWAY
R

No. DB965082
SOUTH TYNEDALE RAILWAY
L **W** **O**

No. DB977241
BARROW HILL ROUNDHOUSE
O **D**

No. DB983103
BLUEBELL RAILWAY
W **O**

No. DB983586
NOTTINGHAM TRANSPORT CTRE
W

No. DB983908
CHASEWATER RAILWAY
R

No. DB983914
GWILI RAILWAY
W

No. DB984082
BLUEBELL RAILWAY
W **O**

No. DB984506
BLUEBELL RAILWAY
W **O**

No. DB986179
PEAK RAIL
W

No. DB986419
BLUEBELL RAILWAY
W **O**

No. DB986591
BLUEBELL RAILWAY
W **O**

No. DB987403
BLUEBELL RAILWAY
W **O**

No. DB988395
BLUEBELL RAILWAY
W **O**

No. DB989104
KENT & EAST SUSSEX RAILWAY
W

No. DB991391
BLUEBELL RAILWAY
W **O**

No. DB992780
BLUEBELL RAILWAY
W **O**

No. DB993039
NOTTINGHAM TRANSPORT CTRE
W

No. DB993126
GWILI RAILWAY
W

ROLLING STOCK by NUMBER

DB74007 — DB993126

Key: **L** Loco **R** Rolling Stock **W** Wagon **C** Coach **O** Operational **S** Static **D** On Display

No. DB993210
BLUEBELL RAILWAY
W **O**

No. DB993217
BLUEBELL RAILWAY
W **O**

No. DB993348
BLUEBELL RAILWAY
W **O**

No. DB993597
NOTTINGHAM TRANSPORT CTRE
W

No. DB993605
KENT & EAST SUSSEX RAILWAY
W

No. DB993620
KENT & EAST SUSSEX RAILWAY
W

No. DB993632
CHASEWATER RAILWAY
R

No. DB993768
PEAK RAIL
R

No. DB993874
NOTTINGHAM TRANSPORT CTRE
R

No. DB993894
NORTH YORKSHIRE MOORS RAILWAY

No. DB994107
MID-NORFOLK RAILWAY
R

No. DB994256
PEAK RAIL
W

No. DB994271
NOTTINGHAM TRANSPORT CTRE
R **O**

No. DB994275
NORTH YORKSHIRE MOORS RAILWAY
W

No. DB994441
KENT & EAST SUSSEX RAILWAY
W

No. DB994457
KENT & EAST SUSSEX RAILWAY
W

No. DB996406
PEAK RAIL
W

No. DB996761
SWANSEA VALE RAILWAY
R

No. DB996996
KEITH & DUFFTOWN RAILWAY
W

No. DB998017
BARROW HILL ROUNDHOUSE
W

No. DB999044
PEAK RAIL

No. DE2524
NORTH YORKSHIRE MOORS RAILWAY

No. DE301559
NORTH YORKSHIRE MOORS RAILWAY
R

No. DE320651
MANGAPPS RAILWAY MUSEUM
C

No. DE320709
NATIONAL RAILWAY MUSEUM
R

No. DE320779
MANGAPPS RAILWAY MUSEUM
C

No. DE320803
MANGAPPS RAILWAY MUSEUM
O **D**

No. DE320952
NATIONAL RAILWAY MUSEUM

No. DE330152
NORTH YORKSHIRE MOORS RAILWAY

No. DE331153
NATIONAL RAILWAY MUSEUM

No. DE58033
NORTH YORKSHIRE MOORS RAILWAY

No. DE632802
NORTH YORKSHIRE MOORS RAILWAY
R

No. DE900566
NATIONAL RAILWAY MUSEUM

No. DE900572
NORTH YORKSHIRE MOORS RAILWAY

No. DH16
EAST LANCASHIRE RAILWAY

No. DL26
DIDCOT RAILWAY CENTRE
L

No. DM01836M
CHASEWATER RAILWAY
C **S** **D**

No. DM1002 *(Nith)*
LEADHILLS & WANLOCKHEAD
L **O**

No. DM411245
BLUEBELL RAILWAY
W

No. DM730687
BARROW HILL ROUNDHOUSE
R

No. DM732331
SWANSEA VALE RAILWAY
R

No. DMBS51365
PLYM VALLEY RAILWAY
L **O**

No. DMS51407
PLYM VALLEY RAILWAY
L **O**

No. DRB4W
NORTH NORFOLK RAILWAY
R

No. DRS81139
PEAK RAIL
W **O**

No. DRT80169
BODMIN & WENFORD RAILWAY
O

No. DS 62002
BLUEBELL RAILWAY
W

No. DS 62864
BLUEBELL RAILWAY
W

No. DS1385
CHASEWATER RAILWAY
R

No. DS165
DERWENT VALLEY
L **O**

ROLLING STOCK by NUMBER

DE320709 — DS165

No. DS169
CHASEWATER RAILWAY
R

No. DS1749
NORTH NORFOLK RAILWAY
R

No. DS1749
NORTH NORFOLK RAILWAY
R

No. DS1770
KENT & EAST SUSSEX RAILWAY
W

No. DS238 *(Wainwright)*
KENT & EAST SUSSEX RAILWAY
L **O**

No. DS3141
KENT & EAST SUSSEX RAILWAY
W

No. DS36
CHASEWATER RAILWAY
R

No. DS451
KENT & EAST SUSSEX RAILWAY
W

No. DS48 *(Jim)*
DERWENT VALLEY
L

No. DS61976
BARROW HILL ROUNDHOUSE
O

No. DS62014
NOTTINGHAM TRANSPORT CTRE
W

No. DS62058
NORTH YORKSHIRE MOORS RAILWAY
W

No. DS62064
NORTH YORKSHIRE MOORS RAILWAY
W

No. DS62862
KENT & EAST SUSSEX RAILWAY
O

No. DS64752
NORTH YORKSHIRE MOORS RAILWAY
W

No. DS70003
KENT & EAST SUSSEX RAILWAY
W

No. DS70165
MANGAPPS RAILWAY MUSEUM
S

No. DS70278
CHASEWATER RAILWAY
W

No. DS8 PMV
GWILI RAILWAY
W

No. DS830
GREAT CENTRAL RAILWAY
L **O**

No. DS88 *(Octavius Atkinson)*
DERWENT VALLEY
L **O**

No. DS88 *(Cynthia)*
PEAK RAIL
L

No. DSB996 *(Vauclain Danish Compound Pacific)*
RAILWORLD
L **S** **D**

₳₥₮ No. DSRM1 *(Ron Rothwell)*
NORTH YORKSHIRE MOORS RAILWAY
L

₳₥₮ No. DSRM2
NORTH YORKSHIRE MOORS RAILWAY
L

₳₥₮ No. DW103310
NORTH YORKSHIRE MOORS RAILWAY
W

₳₥₮ No. DW150351
SWANSEA VALE RAILWAY
R

₳₥₮ No. DW35403
BARROW HILL ROUNDHOUSE
R

₳₥₮ No. DX68051
PEAK RAIL
R

₳₥₮ No. E1
BEAMISH
L S

₳₥₮ No. E10525
NORTH NORFOLK RAILWAY
R

₳₥₮ No. E1104 *(Jessie)*
BATTLEFIELD LINE
C

₳₥₮ No. E110E
NORTH YORKSHIRE MOORS RAILWAY
C

₳₥₮ No. E1299
NORTH YORKSHIRE MOORS RAILWAY

₳₥₮ No. E13043
NORTH YORKSHIRE MOORS RAILWAY
R

₳₥₮ No. E1308
NORTH YORKSHIRE MOORS RAILWAY
R

₳₥₮ No. E1322
NORTH YORKSHIRE MOORS RAILWAY

₳₥₮ No. E15745
NORTH YORKSHIRE MOORS RAILWAY

₳₥₮ No. E16156
NORTH YORKSHIRE MOORS RAILWAY

₳₥₮ No. E1623
NORTH YORKSHIRE MOORS RAILWAY

₳₥₮ No. E1693
NOTTINGHAM TRANSPORT CTRE
R

₳₥₮ No. E1823
NORTH YORKSHIRE MOORS RAILWAY

₳₥₮ No. E18477E
NORTH YORKSHIRE MOORS RAILWAY
C

₳₥₮ No. E18488
NORTH YORKSHIRE MOORS RAILWAY

₳₥₮ No. E187774
NORTH YORKSHIRE MOORS RAILWAY
R

₳₥₮ No. E2
BEAMISH
L S D

₳₥₮ No. E21100
NORTH YORKSHIRE MOORS RAILWAY

₳₥₮ No. E21103
NORTH NORFOLK RAILWAY
R

₳₥₮ No. E21214
SPA VALLEY RAILWAY
C

ROLLING STOCK by NUMBER

DSRM1 — E21214

No. E217315
NORTH YORKSHIRE MOORS RAILWAY
W

No. E230908
NORTH YORKSHIRE MOORS RAILWAY
W

No. E246710
NORTH YORKSHIRE MOORS RAILWAY
R

No. E24804
NORTH YORKSHIRE MOORS RAILWAY

No. E24808
NORTH YORKSHIRE MOORS RAILWAY
C

No. E24984
NORTH YORKSHIRE MOORS RAILWAY

No. E25700
NORTH YORKSHIRE MOORS RAILWAY

No. E25845
SPA VALLEY RAILWAY
R

No. E269004
NORTH YORKSHIRE MOORS RAILWAY
W

No. E269379
NORTH YORKSHIRE MOORS RAILWAY
W

No. E273885
NORTH YORKSHIRE MOORS RAILWAY

No. E274006
NORTH YORKSHIRE MOORS RAILWAY
W

No. E3003
BARROW HILL ROUNDHOUSE
L S D

No. E3035
BARROW HILL ROUNDHOUSE
L S D

No. E3036
BARROW HILL ROUNDHOUSE
L S D

No. E3061
BARROW HILL ROUNDHOUSE
L D

No. E307005
NORTH YORKSHIRE MOORS RAILWAY
W

No. E3095
NOTTINGHAM TRANSPORT CTRE
R D

No. E318 *(Robin)*
NORTH YORKSHIRE MOORS RAILWAY
C

No. E327 *(Garnet)*
NORTH YORKSHIRE MOORS RAILWAY
C

No. E328
NORTH YORKSHIRE MOORS RAILWAY
C

No. E34557
NORTH YORKSHIRE MOORS RAILWAY
C

No. E35089
NORTH YORKSHIRE MOORS RAILWAY

No. E3860
NORTH YORKSHIRE MOORS RAILWAY
C

No. E3868
NORTH NORFOLK RAILWAY
R

No. E3872
NORTH YORKSHIRE MOORS RAILWAY
C

No. E3948
NORTH YORKSHIRE MOORS RAILWAY
C

No. E4286
NORTH YORKSHIRE MOORS RAILWAY
C

No. E4290
NORTH YORKSHIRE MOORS RAILWAY
C

No. E43034
NORTH NORFOLK RAILWAY
R

No. E43041
NORTH NORFOLK RAILWAY
R

No. E43046
NATIONAL RAILWAY MUSEUM
R

No. E43357
NORTH NORFOLK RAILWAY
R

No. E43359
NORTH NORFOLK RAILWAY
R

No. E4455
NORTH YORKSHIRE MOORS RAILWAY

No. E4521
NORTH NORFOLK RAILWAY
R

No. E4597
NORTH YORKSHIRE MOORS RAILWAY

No. E46147
NORTH NORFOLK RAILWAY
R

No. E4641
EAST SOMERSET RAILWAY
C

No. E4651
NORTH NORFOLK RAILWAY
R

No. E4828
SPA VALLEY RAILWAY
R

No. E4839
NORTH YORKSHIRE MOORS RAILWAY

No. E4990
NORTH YORKSHIRE MOORS RAILWAY

No. E6003 *(Sir Herbert Walker)*
LAVENDER LINE
L O

No. E70687
NORTH YORKSHIRE MOORS RAILWAY
R

No. E70692E
MANGAPPS RAILWAY MUSEUM
C D

No. E765W
EAST ANGLIAN RAILWAY MUSEUM
W

No. E79960
NORTH NORFOLK RAILWAY
L R O

No. E80796
NORTH YORKSHIRE MOORS RAILWAY
C

ROLLING STOCK by NUMBER

E3872 — E80796

No. E828 *(Harry A Frith)*
SWANAGE RAILWAY
L **O**

No. E86129
NOTTINGHAM TRANSPORT CTRE
R

No. E86639
NORTH YORKSHIRE MOORS RAILWAY
R

No. E9066E
MANGAPPS RAILWAY MUSEUM
G **S**

No. E9115E
MANGAPPS RAILWAY MUSEUM
G

No. E9235
NORTH YORKSHIRE MOORS RAILWAY
G

No. E9267
NORTH YORKSHIRE MOORS RAILWAY

No. E9389
NOTTINGHAM TRANSPORT CTRE
R

No. E94464
NORTH NORFOLK RAILWAY
R

No. E94597
MID-NORFOLK RAILWAY
R

No. ED 2
NORTH YORKSHIRE MOORS RAILWAY

No. ED 5
NORTH YORKSHIRE MOORS RAILWAY

No. ED1
NORTH YORKSHIRE MOORS RAILWAY

No. ED10
IRCHESTER NARROW GAUGE MUSEUM
L **O**

No. ED16
NORTH YORKSHIRE MOORS RAILWAY
L

No. F38
LEIGHTON BUZZARD RAILWAY
R **G** **O** **D**

No. HE6347 *(Clyde)*
LEADHILLS & WANLOCKHEAD
L **O**

No. HW402
MID-NORFOLK RAILWAY
R

No. HW426
NORTH NORFOLK RAILWAY
R

No. HW429
NORTH NORFOLK RAILWAY
R

No. KD1
RHYL MINIATURE RAILWAY
L

No. KDB733694
KENT & EAST SUSSEX RAILWAY
W

No. KDB740487
NORTH NORFOLK RAILWAY
W

No. KDB740699
PEAK RAIL
W

No. KDB740918
NORTH NORFOLK RAILWAY
W

No. KDB741895
KENT & EAST SUSSEX RAILWAY
W

No. KDB768358
PEAK RAIL
R

No. KDB771392
PEAK RAIL
R

No. KDB784652
PEAK RAIL
R

No. KDB932502
KENT & EAST SUSSEX RAILWAY
W

No. KDS13
PEAK RAIL
R

No. L5
NORTH GLOUCESTERSHIRE RAILWAY
L

No. LM39 *(T W Lewis)*
LEIGHTON BUZZARD RAILWAY
L

No. LP202
NORTH YORKSHIRE MOORS RAILWAY
W

No. M1295M
PEAK RAIL

No. M13092
NORTHAMPTON & LAMPORT RAILWAY
C

No. M1501M
PEAK RAIL

No. M16168
NOTTINGHAM TRANSPORT CTRE
R

No. M2
TANFIELD RAILWAY
L

No. M21240
NORTH YORKSHIRE MOORS RAILWAY

No. M24576
NORTHAMPTON & LAMPORT RAILWAY
C

No. M26012
NORTH NORFOLK RAILWAY
R

No. M27001M
PEAK RAIL

No. M27109M
PEAK RAIL
R

No. M288824
NORTH YORKSHIRE MOORS RAILWAY
R

No. M300045
NORTH YORKSHIRE MOORS RAILWAY
R

No. M324
NORTH YORKSHIRE MOORS RAILWAY
C

No. M33655
NOTTINGHAM TRANSPORT CTRE
W

No. M34368
SPA VALLEY RAILWAY
C

ROLLING STOCK by NUMBER

KDB741895 — M34368

ROLLING STOCK by **NUMBER**

M35062 — M732170

No. M35062
NORTHAMPTON & LAMPORT RAILWAY
W **O**

No. M37326
NORTHAMPTON & LAMPORT RAILWAY
W

No. M3805
NORTH YORKSHIRE MOORS RAILWAY
C

No. M3919
NORTHAMPTON & LAMPORT RAILWAY
C

No. M401732
NOTTINGHAM TRANSPORT CTRE
W

No. M405032
EAST ANGLIAN RAILWAY MUSEUM
W

No. M4425
NORTH YORKSHIRE MOORS RAILWAY
C

No. M44408
NORTH YORKSHIRE MOORS RAILWAY

No. M476325
NORTHAMPTON & LAMPORT RAILWAY
W

No. M479157
NORTH YORKSHIRE MOORS RAILWAY
W

No. M4843
NORTH NORFOLK RAILWAY
R

No. M492136
NOTTINGHAM TRANSPORT CTRE
W

No. M499227
NORTHAMPTON & LAMPORT RAILWAY
W

No. M5000
NORTH YORKSHIRE MOORS RAILWAY

No. M500348
NOTTINGHAM TRANSPORT CTRE
R

No. M51548, FN128
KENT & EAST SUSSEX RAILWAY
W

No. M52054
BODMIN & WENFORD RAILWAY
L **O**

No. M6720M
PEAK RAIL

No. M6815M
PEAK RAIL
R

No. M691576
NOTTINGHAM TRANSPORT CTRE
W

No. M691793
NOTTINGHAM TRANSPORT CTRE
R

No. M726631
NORTH NORFOLK RAILWAY
W

No. M730003
NORTHAMPTON & LAMPORT RAILWAY
W

No. M732170
NORTH YORKSHIRE MOORS RAILWAY
R

No. M81033
NORTH NORFOLK RAILWAY
R

No. M81156
EAST SOMERSET RAILWAY
C

No. M81269
NORTH NORFOLK RAILWAY
R

No. M84031
NORTHAMPTON & LAMPORT RAILWAY
C

No. M9125M
PEAK RAIL

No. M9205M
PEAK RAIL
R

No. M9225
NORTHAMPTON & LAMPORT RAILWAY
C O

No. M93226
MID-NORFOLK RAILWAY
R

No. M93887
PLYM VALLEY RAILWAY

No. M93927
PLYM VALLEY RAILWAY
W

No. M9396
SWANSEA VALE RAILWAY
C

No. M94109
MANGAPPS RAILWAY MUSEUM
S

No. M9414
SPA VALLEY RAILWAY
C

No. MDHB 32
KEIGHLEY & WORTH VALLEY
L O

No. MLR740 *(Indian Railways Hill Engine)*
RAILWORLD

No. MNR291
MID-NORFOLK RAILWAY
R W

No. MOD4122
SOUTH DEVON RAILWAY
W

No. NCO102
SWANSEA VALE RAILWAY
R

No. NE239666
DERWENT VALLEY
W

No. NE539249
DERWENT VALLEY
W

No. NER108635
BEAMISH
W

No. NER92189
BEAMISH
W

No. NGB4404
LEIGHTON BUZZARD RAILWAY
R W O D

No. P6687
BO'NESS & KINNEIL RAILWAY
L

ROLLING STOCK by NUMBER

M81033 — P6687

ROLLING STOCK by NUMBER

PG1 — S2439S

No. PG1 *(Spirit of Adventure)*
PERRYGROVE RAILWAY
L O

No. PWM3769
AVON VALLEY RAILWAY
L O

No. PWM651
NORTHAMPTON & LAMPORT RAILWAY
L

No. QWAG
GREAT CENTRAL RAILWAY
L S D

No. RDB975874
NATIONAL RAILWAY MUSEUM

No. RDB998901 *(Olive)*
MIDDLETON RAILWAY
L O

No. RS1083
BLUEBELL RAILWAY
R

No. RS12
MIDLAND RAILWAY CENTRE
L S D

No. RS9
MIDLAND RAILWAY CENTRE
L S D

No. S100 *(Whit No 4)*
CHASEWATER RAILWAY
L D

No. S1000
EAST SOMERSET RAILWAY

No. S11179S
NATIONAL RAILWAY MUSEUM
R

No. S11530
KENT & EAST SUSSEX RAILWAY
W

No. S14036
NORTH YORKSHIRE MOORS RAILWAY
W

No. S1439
EAST ANGLIAN RAILWAY MUSEUM
W

No. S1563
NOTTINGHAM TRANSPORT CTRE
R

No. S16204
PLYM VALLEY RAILWAY
G

No. S1770S
CHASEWATER RAILWAY
R

No. S1834
NORTHAMPTON & LAMPORT RAILWAY
W

No. S1874S
BARROW HILL ROUNDHOUSE
O

No. S1874S
NOTTINGHAM TRANSPORT CTRE
R

No. S2195
MANGAPPS RAILWAY MUSEUM
R

No. S2239S
SPA VALLEY RAILWAY
R

No. S2439S
NORTHAMPTON & LAMPORT RAILWAY
W

No. S2530
NORTH YORKSHIRE MOORS RAILWAY

No. S272
NOTTINGHAM TRANSPORT CTRE
R

No. S2735
MANGAPPS RAILWAY MUSEUM
O D

No. S31875
MANGAPPS RAILWAY MUSEUM
C

No. S4035S
NORTH YORKSHIRE MOORS RAILWAY

No. S4409
DIDCOT RAILWAY CENTRE
W

No. S56541
PLYM VALLEY RAILWAY
R

No. S5916, FN155
KENT & EAST SUSSEX RAILWAY
W

No. S62861
CHASEWATER RAILWAY
R

No. S8143S
NATIONAL RAILWAY MUSEUM
R

No. SC1100
NATIONAL RAILWAY MUSEUM
R

No. SC16191
NORTH YORKSHIRE MOORS RAILWAY

No. SC3798
NORTH YORKSHIRE MOORS RAILWAY
C

No. SC3801
NORTH YORKSHIRE MOORS RAILWAY
C

No. SC4207
NORTH YORKSHIRE MOORS RAILWAY
C

No. SC4252
NORTH YORKSHIRE MOORS RAILWAY
C

No. SC88339E
NORTH YORKSHIRE MOORS RAILWAY

No. SUK067024
PEAK RAIL
W

No. V47
CADEBY LIGHT RAILWAY
L S D

No. W1009
NORTHAMPTON & LAMPORT RAILWAY
W

No. W11 *(Newport)*
ISLE OF WIGHT STEAM RAILWAY
L O

No. W112835
NORTH YORKSHIRE MOORS RAILWAY
R

No. W13252
NATIONAL RAILWAY MUSEUM
R

No. W13487
SPA VALLEY RAILWAY
C

ROLLING STOCK by NUMBER

S2530 — W13487

No. W17293
NORTHAMPTON & LAMPORT RAILWAY
W

No. W18591
PLYM VALLEY RAILWAY
C

No. W2009W
MANGAPPS RAILWAY MUSEUM
R

No. W225
SOUTH DEVON RAILWAY
C

No. W2336W
CHASEWATER RAILWAY
R

No. W24 *(Calbourne)*
ISLE OF WIGHT STEAM RAILWAY
L O

No. W240
SOUTH DEVON RAILWAY
C

No. W25508
NORTH YORKSHIRE MOORS RAILWAY

No. W297W
NORTHAMPTON & LAMPORT RAILWAY
C

No. W34945
PLYM VALLEY RAILWAY
C

No. W35148
NORTH NORFOLK RAILWAY
R

No. W4198
NORTH YORKSHIRE MOORS RAILWAY
C

No. W44019 *(St Ivel)*
NORTH YORKSHIRE MOORS RAILWAY
W

No. W46137
SWANSEA VALE RAILWAY
C

No. W4728
NORTH YORKSHIRE MOORS RAILWAY

No. W4786
NORTH YORKSHIRE MOORS RAILWAY

No. W4817
NORTH YORKSHIRE MOORS RAILWAY

No. W48339
NORTHAMPTON & LAMPORT RAILWAY
W

No. W4907
EAST SOMERSET RAILWAY
C

No. W51370
CHASEWATER RAILWAY
O

No. W51372
CHASEWATER RAILWAY
O

No. W51412
CHASEWATER RAILWAY
O

No. W55001
NORTHAMPTON & LAMPORT RAILWAY
L

No. W55003
NORTHAMPTON & LAMPORT RAILWAY
L O

No. W59444
CHASEWATER RAILWAY
O

No. W59603
CHASEWATER RAILWAY
O

No. W8 *(Freshwater)*
ISLE OF WIGHT STEAM RAILWAY
L **O**

No. W80974
NORTH YORKSHIRE MOORS RAILWAY
C

No. W9274
NORTH YORKSHIRE MOORS RAILWAY

No. W94034
BARROW HILL ROUNDHOUSE
C

No. W9485
NORTHAMPTON & LAMPORT RAILWAY
W

No. W95166
DERWENT VALLEY
R

No. WD132 *(Sapper)*
SOUTH DEVON RAILWAY
L

No. WD190
COLNE VALLEY RAILWAY
L

No. WD70031 *(Grumpy)*
AVON VALLEY RAILWAY
L

No. WD75133
SOUTH YORKSHIRE RAILWAY

No. WGB4015
PEAK RAIL
R

No. WGB4041
CHINNOR & PRINCES RISBOROUGH
W

No. WR537
NATIONAL RAILWAY MUSEUM
C

No. YD43
COLNE VALLEY RAILWAY
L

ROLLING STOCK by NUMBER

W59444 — YD43

Rolling Stock by Type

SECTION 5C

This section shows type of stock and where it can be located

e.g. 3 Plank Wagon, North Yorkshire Moors Railway

Once you have located a railway/museum using this section you can then refer to the railway or museum's detailed profile in section 1.

2 COMP FIRST CLASS
TALYLLYN RAILWAY

2 PLANK WAGON
CAVAN & LEITRIM RAILWAY

2 SALOONS
TALYLLYN RAILWAY

3 COMP & GUARD
TALYLLYN RAILWAY

3 COMP & WHEELCHAIR
TALYLLYN RAILWAY

3 COMP CLOSED
TALYLLYN RAILWAY

3 COMP OPEN SIDE
TALYLLYN RAILWAY

3 COMPARTMENT OPEN
ROYAL VICTORIA RAILWAY

3 PLANK DROP SIDE BALLAST WAGON
BLUEBELL RAILWAY

3 PLANK GOODS WAGON
NORTHAMPTON & LAMPORT RAILWAY

3 PLANK OPEN WAGON
PLYM VALLEY RAILWAY

3 PLANK WAGON
NORTH YORKSHIRE MOORS RAILWAY

4 COMP & GUARD
TALYLLYN RAILWAY

4 PLANK OPEN WAGON
CHASEWATER RAILWAY

PLYM VALLEY RAILWAY

4 SEAT BOGIE OPEN COACHES
BEER HEIGHTS

4W CHASSIS
SOUTH TYNEDALE RAILWAY

4W COMPOSITE
DIDCOT RAILWAY CENTRE

4W HOPPER WAGON
SOUTH TYNEDALE RAILWAY

4W SKIP
SOUTH TYNEDALE RAILWAY

4W THIRD
DIDCOT RAILWAY CENTRE

4W WAGON
SOUTH TYNEDALE RAILWAY

4WPM
CHASEWATER RAILWAY

5 COMP CLOSED
TALYLLYN RAILWAY

5 PLANK OPEN
BLUEBELL RAILWAY

EAST ANGLIAN RAILWAY MUSEUM

NOTTINGHAM TRANSPORT CTRE

SOUTH DEVON RAILWAY

5 PLANK OPEN HIGH BAR
BLUEBELL RAILWAY

5 PLANK WAGON
NORTH NORFOLK RAILWAY

NORTH YORKSHIRE MOORS RAILWAY

NOTTINGHAM TRANSPORT CTRE

ROYAL VICTORIA RAILWAY

6 COMP CLOSED
TALYLLYN RAILWAY

6 COMP CLOSED COMP
TALYLLYN RAILWAY

6 COUPLED
BOWES RAILWAY

6 PLANK OPEN HIGH BAR
BLUEBELL RAILWAY

6W DRINKING WATER TANK WAGON
DIDCOT RAILWAY CENTRE

6W MILK TANK WAGON
DIDCOT RAILWAY CENTRE

6W TRI COMPOSITE
DIDCOT RAILWAY CENTRE

6W VAN (BZ)
NORTH YORKSHIRE MOORS RAILWAY

7 PLANK OPEN WAGON
BLUEBELL RAILWAY

PLYM VALLEY RAILWAY

8 PLANK OPEN GOODS
BLUEBELL RAILWAY

ALL STEEL BOGIE WAGON
SOUTH TYNEDALE RAILWAY

AUSTRIAN FERRY WAGONS
PEAK RAIL

ROLLING STOCK by TYPE

2 Comp First Class — Austrian Ferry Wagons

AUTO COACH

AM NORTH YORKSHIRE MOORS RAILWAY

AUTO TRAILER

AM DIDCOT RAILWAY CENTRE

AM SOUTH DEVON RAILWAY

B12

AM NORTH NORFOLK RAILWAY

BALLAST BRAKE

AM NORTH YORKSHIRE MOORS RAILWAY

BALLAST HOPPER

AM KENT & EAST SUSSEX RAILWAY

AM MID-NORFOLK RAILWAY

AM NORTH NORFOLK RAILWAY

AM NORTH YORKSHIRE MOORS RAILWAY

BALLAST HOPPER WAGON

AM NORTHAMPTON & LAMPORT RAILWAY

BALLAST PACKER

AM NORTH YORKSHIRE MOORS RAILWAY

BALLAST PLOUGH BRAKE

AM NATIONAL RAILWAY MUSEUM

BALLAST PLOUGH VAN

AM CHASEWATER RAILWAY

BALLAST WAGON

AM DIDCOT RAILWAY CENTRE

AM HEATHERSLAW LIGHT RAILWAY

AM PEAK RAIL

BANANA VAN

AM DIDCOT RAILWAY CENTRE

AM KENT & EAST SUSSEX RAILWAY

BAR CAR

AM ROMNEY HYTHE & DYMCHURCH

BE

AM ALMOND VALLEY HERITAGE TRUST

AM AMBERLEY WORKING MUSEUM

AM ARMLEY MILLS

AM SOUTH TYNEDALE RAILWAY

AM TANFIELD RAILWAY

AM WEST LANCASHIRE LIGHT RLWY

BIRDCAGE BRAKE VAN

AM BLUEBELL RAILWAY

BLACK FIVE

AM SEVERN VALLEY RAILWAY

BLOATER VAN

AM GWILI RAILWAY

BLUE SPOT FISH VAN

AM BLUEBELL RAILWAY

BOGIE BALLAST WAGON

AM NOTTINGHAM TRANSPORT CTRE

BOGIE BOLSTER

AM BLUEBELL RAILWAY

AM GWILI RAILWAY

AM KENT & EAST SUSSEX RAILWAY

AM MID-NORFOLK RAILWAY

AM NORTH NORFOLK RAILWAY

AM NORTH YORKSHIRE MOORS RAILWAY

AM SOUTH DEVON RAILWAY

AM SWANSEA VALE RAILWAY

BOGIE BOLSTER FLAT WAGON

AM KENT & EAST SUSSEX RAILWAY

BOGIE BOLSTER WAGON

AM DERWENT VALLEY

AM DIDCOT RAILWAY CENTRE

BOGIE DROPSIDE WAGON

AM LEIGHTON BUZZARD RAILWAY

BOGIE FLAT WAGON

AM SOUTH TYNEDALE RAILWAY

BOGIE MATCH WAGON

AM KENT & EAST SUSSEX RAILWAY

BOGIE MILK CHURN VAN

AM DIDCOT RAILWAY CENTRE

BOGIE RAIL WAGON

AM KEITH & DUFFTOWN RAILWAY

BOGIE SCENERY VAN

AM BLUEBELL RAILWAY

BOGIE TUBE WAGON

AM PLYM VALLEY RAILWAY

BOGIE VACUUM BRAKE VAN

AM BLUEBELL RAILWAY

BOGIE WAGON

AM BRISTOL HARBOUR RAILWAY

BOGIE WELL WAGON

AM BLUEBELL RAILWAY

AM DIDCOT RAILWAY CENTRE

AM SOUTH TYNEDALE RAILWAY

BOOTH CAR

- GWILI RAILWAY

BOX VAN

- CAVAN & LEITRIM RAILWAY
- CHASEWATER RAILWAY
- DERWENT VALLEY
- GWILI RAILWAY
- KENT & EAST SUSSEX RAILWAY
- NORTH YORKSHIRE MOORS RAILWAY
- PEAK RAIL
- SOUTH DEVON RAILWAY

BOX WAGON

- MID-NORFOLK RAILWAY

BRAKE

- KIRKLEES LIGHT RAILWAY

BRAKE BOGIE THIRD

- CHASEWATER RAILWAY

BRAKE COMPOSITE

- BLUEBELL RAILWAY
- DIDCOT RAILWAY CENTRE

BRAKE COMPOSITE CORRIDOR

- AVON VALLEY RAILWAY
- BLUEBELL RAILWAY
- EAST ANGLIAN RAILWAY MUSEUM
- GWILI RAILWAY
- KENT & EAST SUSSEX RAILWAY
- LAVENDER LINE
- NORTH NORFOLK RAILWAY
- NORTH YORKSHIRE MOORS RAILWAY
- PEAK RAIL
- SOUTH DEVON RAILWAY
- SPA VALLEY RAILWAY

BRAKE FIRST CORRIDOR

- AVON VALLEY RAILWAY
- CHASEWATER RAILWAY
- NOTTINGHAM TRANSPORT CTRE

BRAKE GANGWAYED

- EAST SOMERSET RAILWAY
- NORTH NORFOLK RAILWAY
- PEAK RAIL

BRAKE GANGWAYED (Z)

- BLUEBELL RAILWAY
- NORTH NORFOLK RAILWAY

BRAKE SECOND

- BLUEBELL RAILWAY
- EAST ANGLIAN RAILWAY MUSEUM
- EAST SOMERSET RAILWAY
- NORTH NORFOLK RAILWAY
- SWANSEA VALE RAILWAY

BRAKE SECOND CORRIDOR

- AVON VALLEY RAILWAY
- BARROW HILL ROUNDHOUSE
- BLUEBELL RAILWAY
- EAST ANGLIAN RAILWAY MUSEUM
- GWILI RAILWAY
- NORTH NORFOLK RAILWAY
- NORTH YORKSHIRE MOORS RAILWAY
- NORTHAMPTON & LAMPORT RAILWAY
- PEAK RAIL
- PLYM VALLEY RAILWAY
- SPA VALLEY RAILWAY

BRAKE SECOND OPEN

- AVON VALLEY RAILWAY
- EAST SOMERSET RAILWAY
- KENT & EAST SUSSEX RAILWAY
- MID-NORFOLK RAILWAY
- NORTH YORKSHIRE MOORS RAILWAY
- NORTHAMPTON & LAMPORT RAILWAY
- NOTTINGHAM TRANSPORT CTRE
- PEAK RAIL
- SPA VALLEY RAILWAY

BRAKE STOWAGE VAN

- DIDCOT RAILWAY CENTRE

BRAKE THIRD

- BLUEBELL RAILWAY
- DIDCOT RAILWAY CENTRE
- GWILI RAILWAY
- NORTH YORKSHIRE MOORS RAILWAY
- SPA VALLEY RAILWAY
- STRATHSPEY RAILWAY

BRAKE THIRD COMPOSITE
- NORTH YORKSHIRE MOORS RAILWAY

BRAKE THIRD CORRIDOR
- BLUEBELL RAILWAY
- NORTH NORFOLK RAILWAY
- NORTH YORKSHIRE MOORS RAILWAY
- SOUTH DEVON RAILWAY

BRAKE THIRD LAVATORY
- NORTH YORKSHIRE MOORS RAILWAY

BRAKE THIRD OPEN
- NORTH YORKSHIRE MOORS RAILWAY

BRAKE THIRD PULLMAN
- NORTH YORKSHIRE MOORS RAILWAY

BRAKE VAN
- BARROW HILL ROUNDHOUSE
- BLUEBELL RAILWAY
- CHASEWATER RAILWAY
- DERWENT VALLEY
- DIDCOT RAILWAY CENTRE
- EAST ANGLIAN RAILWAY MUSEUM
- GWILI RAILWAY
- KEITH & DUFFTOWN RAILWAY
- KENT & EAST SUSSEX RAILWAY
- MID-NORFOLK RAILWAY
- NORTH NORFOLK RAILWAY
- NORTH YORKSHIRE MOORS RAILWAY
- NORTHAMPTON & LAMPORT RAILWAY
- NOTTINGHAM TRANSPORT CTRE
- OLD KILN LIGHT RAILWAY
- PEAK RAIL
- PLYM VALLEY RAILWAY
- SOUTH DEVON RAILWAY
- SOUTH TYNEDALE RAILWAY
- SPA VALLEY RAILWAY
- SWANSEA VALE RAILWAY

BT
- DIDCOT RAILWAY CENTRE

BTO
- EAST ANGLIAN RAILWAY MUSEUM

BUFFET CAR
- EAST ANGLIAN RAILWAY MUSEUM
- NORTH YORKSHIRE MOORS RAILWAY

BY
- GWILI RAILWAY
- NORTH NORFOLK RAILWAY

CAFETERIA CAR
- KEITH & DUFFTOWN RAILWAY

CATTLE VAN
- EAST ANGLIAN RAILWAY MUSEUM
- MANGAPPS RAILWAY MUSEUM

CATTLE WAGON
- NORTH YORKSHIRE MOORS RAILWAY

CHINA CLAY WAGON
- DIDCOT RAILWAY CENTRE

CINEMA COACH
- NOTTINGHAM TRANSPORT CTRE

CLERESTORY ROOFED CARRIAGE
- NOTTINGHAM TRANSPORT CTRE

CLOSED
- SITTINGBOURNE & KEMSLEY

COAL HOPPER WAGON
- NORTH YORKSHIRE MOORS RAILWAY

COAL WAGON
- DERWENT VALLEY
- DIDCOT RAILWAY CENTRE

COMPARTMENT COACH
- DERWENT VALLEY
- SOUTH TYNEDALE RAILWAY

COMPOSITE
- BLUEBELL RAILWAY
- DIDCOT RAILWAY CENTRE

COMPOSITE BRAKE
- CHASEWATER RAILWAY

COMPOSITE CORRIDOR
- BLUEBELL RAILWAY
- GWILI RAILWAY
- KENT & EAST SUSSEX RAILWAY
- NORTH NORFOLK RAILWAY
- NORTH YORKSHIRE MOORS RAILWAY
- NORTHAMPTON & LAMPORT RAILWAY
- NOTTINGHAM TRANSPORT CTRE
- PEAK RAIL

PLYM VALLEY RAILWAY

COMPOSITE DINER CLERESTORY

DIDCOT RAILWAY CENTRE

COMPOSITE LAVATORY

NORTH NORFOLK RAILWAY

NORTH YORKSHIRE MOORS RAILWAY

COMPRESSOR WAGON

SOUTH TYNEDALE RAILWAY

CONVERTIBLE HOPPER VAN

DIDCOT RAILWAY CENTRE

COVERED CARRIAGE TRUCK

BLUEBELL RAILWAY

CHASEWATER RAILWAY

DIDCOT RAILWAY CENTRE

EAST ANGLIAN RAILWAY MUSEUM

MANGAPPS RAILWAY MUSEUM

MID-NORFOLK RAILWAY

NORTH NORFOLK RAILWAY

NORTH YORKSHIRE MOORS RAILWAY

NORTHAMPTON & LAMPORT RAILWAY

NOTTINGHAM TRANSPORT CTRE

SPA VALLEY RAILWAY

COVERED GOODS VAN

BLUEBELL RAILWAY

KENT & EAST SUSSEX RAILWAY

LEIGHTON BUZZARD RAILWAY

NORTHAMPTON & LAMPORT RAILWAY

PEAK RAIL

CRANE

GWILI RAILWAY

HEATHERSLAW LIGHT RAILWAY

SWANSEA VALE RAILWAY

CRANE MATCH WAGON

KENT & EAST SUSSEX RAILWAY

CRANE RUNNER

NORTH NORFOLK RAILWAY

NORTH YORKSHIRE MOORS RAILWAY

PEAK RAIL

CRANE TANK

BO'NESS & KINNEIL RAILWAY

DE

CALEDONIAN RAILWAY

CHURNET VALLEY RAILWAY

DIDCOT RAILWAY CENTRE

NORTH NORFOLK RAILWAY

SOUTH YORKSHIRE RAILWAY

WATERCRESS LINE

DH

ALMOND VALLEY HERITAGE TRUST

AMERTON RAILWAY

AVON VALLEY RAILWAY

BATTLEFIELD LINE

BEER HEIGHTS

BODMIN & WENFORD RAILWAY

BO'NESS & KINNEIL RAILWAY

BOWES RAILWAY

BUCKINGHAMSHIRE RLWY CTRE

BURE VALLEY RAILWAY

CAMBRIAN RAILWAY SOCIETY

CHASEWATER RAILWAY

CHINNOR & PRINCES RISBOROUGH

CHURNET VALLEY RAILWAY

EAST ANGLIAN RAILWAY MUSEUM

EAST LANCASHIRE RAILWAY

FFESTINIOG RAILWAY

FOXFIELD STEAM RAILWAY

GARTELL LIGHT RAILWAY

HEATHERSLAW LIGHT RAILWAY

KIRKLEES LIGHT RAILWAY

LEIGHTON BUZZARD RAILWAY

MIDDLETON RAILWAY

MOORS VALLEY RAILWAY

NENE VALLEY RAILWAY

NIRT

NORTH YORKSHIRE MOORS RAILWAY

NORTHAMPTON & LAMPORT RAILWAY

NOTTINGHAM TRANSPORT CTRE

PEAK RAIL

PONTYPOOL & BLAENAVON RAILWAY

ROLLING STOCK by TYPE

Composite Corridor — DH

ROLLING STOCK by TYPE

DH — DM

ᴧᴧᴧ ROYAL VICTORIA RAILWAY	ᴧᴧᴧ CADEBY LIGHT RAILWAY
ᴧᴧᴧ RUISLIP LIDO RAILWAY	ᴧᴧᴧ CALEDONIAN RAILWAY
ᴧᴧᴧ SCOTTISH RAILWAY CENTRE	ᴧᴧᴧ CAMBRIAN RAILWAY SOCIETY
ᴧᴧᴧ SNOWDON MOUNTAIN RAILWAY	ᴧᴧᴧ CHASEWATER RAILWAY
ᴧᴧᴧ SOUTH YORKSHIRE RAILWAY	ᴧᴧᴧ CHURNET VALLEY RAILWAY
ᴧᴧᴧ SWANSEA VALE RAILWAY	ᴧᴧᴧ CLEETHORPES LIGHT RAILWAY
ᴧᴧᴧ TANFIELD RAILWAY	ᴧᴧᴧ CORRIS RAILWAY MUSEUM
ᴧᴧᴧ WEST SOMERSET RAILWAY	ᴧᴧᴧ DARLINGTON RAILWAY PRES SOC
ᴧᴧᴧ WESTON PARK RAILWAY	ᴧᴧᴧ DERWENT VALLEY
ᴧᴧᴧ WINDMILL FARM RAILWAY	ᴧᴧᴧ DEVON RAILWAY CENTRE

DH CRANE

ᴧᴧᴧ SWANSEA VALE RAILWAY

DIESEL CRANE

ᴧᴧᴧ KENT & EAST SUSSEX RAILWAY

ᴧᴧᴧ PEAK RAIL

DINING CAR

ᴧᴧᴧ NATIONAL RAILWAY MUSEUM

DINING THIRD

ᴧᴧᴧ BLUEBELL RAILWAY

DIRECTORS SALOON

ᴧᴧᴧ BLUEBELL RAILWAY

ᴧᴧᴧ NORTH NORFOLK RAILWAY

DM

ᴧᴧᴧ ABBEY PUMPING STATION	ᴧᴧᴧ DIDCOT RAILWAY CENTRE
ᴧᴧᴧ ALDERNEY RAILWAY	ᴧᴧᴧ EAST ANGLIA TRANSPORT MUSEUM
ᴧᴧᴧ ALMOND VALLEY HERITAGE TRUST	ᴧᴧᴧ EAST LANCASHIRE RAILWAY
ᴧᴧᴧ AMBERLEY WORKING MUSEUM	ᴧᴧᴧ EMBSAY & BOLTON ABBEY RLWY
ᴧᴧᴧ AMERTON RAILWAY	ᴧᴧᴧ EXMOOR STEAM RAILWAY
ᴧᴧᴧ ARMLEY MILLS	ᴧᴧᴧ FFESTINIOG RAILWAY
ᴧᴧᴧ AVON VALLEY RAILWAY	ᴧᴧᴧ FOXFIELD STEAM RAILWAY
ᴧᴧᴧ BALA LAKE RAILWAY	ᴧᴧᴧ GREAT CENTRAL RAILWAY
ᴧᴧᴧ BARROW HILL ROUNDHOUSE	ᴧᴧᴧ GWILI RAILWAY
ᴧᴧᴧ BATTLEFIELD LINE	ᴧᴧᴧ HOLLYCOMBE STEAM COLLECTION
ᴧᴧᴧ BICTON WOODLAND RAILWAY	ᴧᴧᴧ IRCHESTER NARROW GAUGE MUSEUM
ᴧᴧᴧ BODMIN & WENFORD RAILWAY	ᴧᴧᴧ IRISH STEAM PRESERVATION SOC
ᴧᴧᴧ BO'NESS & KINNEIL RAILWAY	ᴧᴧᴧ ISLE OF WIGHT STEAM RAILWAY
ᴧᴧᴧ BOWES RAILWAY	ᴧᴧᴧ KEIGHLEY & WORTH VALLEY
ᴧᴧᴧ BRESSINGHAM STEAM	ᴧᴧᴧ KEITH & DUFFTOWN RAILWAY
ᴧᴧᴧ BUCKINGHAMSHIRE RLWY CTRE	ᴧᴧᴧ LAKESIDE & HAVERTHWAITE RLWY
ᴧᴧᴧ BURE VALLEY RAILWAY	ᴧᴧᴧ LAUNCESTON STEAM RAILWAY
	ᴧᴧᴧ LAVENDER LINE
	ᴧᴧᴧ LEIGHTON BUZZARD RAILWAY
	ᴧᴧᴧ MIDDLETON RAILWAY
	ᴧᴧᴧ MIDLAND RAILWAY CENTRE
	ᴧᴧᴧ MID-SUFFOLK LIGHT RAILWAY
	ᴧᴧᴧ MUSEUM OF ARMY TRANSPORT
	ᴧᴧᴧ NATIONAL TRAMWAY MUSEUM
	ᴧᴧᴧ NIRT
	ᴧᴧᴧ NORTH GLOUCESTERSHIRE RAILWAY
	ᴧᴧᴧ NORTH NORFOLK RAILWAY
	ᴧᴧᴧ NORTH YORKSHIRE MOORS RAILWAY

- NORTHAMPTON & LAMPORT RAILWAY
- PERRYGROVE RAILWAY
- PRESTONGRANGE INDUSTRIAL
- RHYL MINIATURE RAILWAY
- ROTHER VALLEY RAILWAY
- RUISLIP LIDO RAILWAY
- SCOTTISH RAILWAY CENTRE
- SITTINGBOURNE & KEMSLEY
- SOUTH TYNEDALE RAILWAY
- SOUTH YORKSHIRE RAILWAY
- SPA VALLEY RAILWAY
- SWANAGE RAILWAY
- SWANSEA VALE RAILWAY
- SWINDON & CRICKLADE RAILWAY
- TANFIELD RAILWAY
- WELSHPOOL & LLANFAIR
- WEST SOMERSET RAILWAY
- WINDMILL FARM RAILWAY

DMC
- PEAK RAIL

DMS
- CHASEWATER RAILWAY
- NORTHAMPTON & LAMPORT RAILWAY
- SWANSEA VALE RAILWAY

DMU
- KENT & EAST SUSSEX RAILWAY
- NORTH NORFOLK RAILWAY
- SOUTH YORKSHIRE RAILWAY
- SWANSEA VALE RAILWAY
- VALE OF GLAMORGAN RAILWAY

DOCK TANK
- BLUEBELL RAILWAY

DOGFISH
- CHASEWATER RAILWAY
- GWILI RAILWAY
- SOUTH DEVON RAILWAY

DOGFISH BALLAST HOPPER
- BLUEBELL RAILWAY
- MID-NORFOLK RAILWAY
- NORTHAMPTON & LAMPORT RAILWAY

- PEAK RAIL

DOGFISH BALLAST WAGON
- NOTTINGHAM TRANSPORT CTRE

DORMITORY COACH
- DIDCOT RAILWAY CENTRE

DOUBLE BOLSTER WAGON
- KENT & EAST SUSSEX RAILWAY

DRIVING MOTOR BRAKE SECOND
- BUCKINGHAMSHIRE RLWY CTRE
- CHASEWATER RAILWAY
- MIDLAND RAILWAY CENTRE
- MID-NORFOLK RAILWAY
- NORTHAMPTON & LAMPORT RAILWAY
- PEAK RAIL
- SWANSEA VALE RAILWAY

DROP SIDE BALLAST WAGON
- BLUEBELL RAILWAY

DROP SIDE PLATE WAGON
- NORTHAMPTON & LAMPORT RAILWAY

DROP SIDE WAGON
- BLUEBELL RAILWAY
- KENT & EAST SUSSEX RAILWAY
- LEIGHTON BUZZARD RAILWAY

DROPSIDE ENGINEERS WAGON
- BLUEBELL RAILWAY

DS
- NORTHAMPTON & LAMPORT RAILWAY

DYNAMOMETER CARRIAGE
- SOUTH DEVON RAILWAY

EXPRESS FREIGHT VAN
- DIDCOT RAILWAY CENTRE

F
- DARLINGTON RAILWAY CENTRE
- EAST LANCASHIRE RAILWAY
- EAST SOMERSET RAILWAY
- GREAT CENTRAL RAILWAY
- LAKESIDE & HAVERTHWAITE RLWY
- MIDLAND RAILWAY CENTRE
- MUSEUM OF SCIENCE & INDUSTRY
- NORTH NORFOLK RAILWAY
- SPA VALLEY RAILWAY

ROLLING STOCK by TYPE

DM — F

ROLLING STOCK by TYPE

Ferry Van — Great Eastern Coach Body

FERRY VAN
ꙮ **SPA VALLEY RAILWAY**

FIRST
ꙮ **BLUEBELL RAILWAY**

FIRST & SECOND COMPOSITE
ꙮ **NATIONAL RAILWAY MUSEUM**

FIRST CORRIDOR
ꙮ **AVON VALLEY RAILWAY**
ꙮ **KEITH & DUFFTOWN RAILWAY**
ꙮ **MID-NORFOLK RAILWAY**
ꙮ **SPA VALLEY RAILWAY**

FIRST DINER
ꙮ **DIDCOT RAILWAY CENTRE**

FIRST OPEN
ꙮ **AVON VALLEY RAILWAY**
ꙮ **BLUEBELL RAILWAY**
ꙮ **NOTTINGHAM TRANSPORT CTRE**

FIRST SLEEPER
ꙮ **BLUEBELL RAILWAY**
ꙮ **DIDCOT RAILWAY CENTRE**

FISH VAN
ꙮ **BARROW HILL ROUNDHOUSE**
ꙮ **DIDCOT RAILWAY CENTRE**
ꙮ **EAST ANGLIAN RAILWAY MUSEUM**
ꙮ **PEAK RAIL**
ꙮ **PLYM VALLEY RAILWAY**

FLAME PROOF DIESEL
ꙮ **SOUTH TYNEDALE RAILWAY**

FLAT BOGIE
ꙮ **ROYAL VICTORIA RAILWAY**

FLAT BOGIE BOLSTER
ꙮ **EAST ANGLIAN RAILWAY MUSEUM**

FLAT TRUCK
ꙮ **NORTH YORKSHIRE MOORS RAILWAY**

FLAT WAGON
ꙮ **BARROW HILL ROUNDHOUSE**
ꙮ **CHASEWATER RAILWAY**
ꙮ **LEIGHTON BUZZARD RAILWAY**
ꙮ **MID-NORFOLK RAILWAY**
ꙮ **NORTH NORFOLK RAILWAY**
ꙮ **NOTTINGHAM TRANSPORT CTRE**

ꙮ **ROYAL VICTORIA RAILWAY**

FRUIT VAN
ꙮ **DIDCOT RAILWAY CENTRE**
ꙮ **GWILI RAILWAY**
ꙮ **NORTH NORFOLK RAILWAY**

FULL BRAKE
ꙮ **BLUEBELL RAILWAY**

FULL BRAKE (BG)
ꙮ **NORTH YORKSHIRE MOORS RAILWAY**

FULL THIRD
ꙮ **CHASEWATER RAILWAY**

FULLY CLOSED
ꙮ **HEATHERSLAW LIGHT RAILWAY**

FULLY OPEN
ꙮ **HEATHERSLAW LIGHT RAILWAY**

FZ
ꙮ **NORTH NORFOLK RAILWAY**

GANGWAYED BOGIE LUGGAGE VAN
ꙮ **BLUEBELL RAILWAY**

GANGWAYED BRAKE
ꙮ **NORTHAMPTON & LAMPORT RAILWAY**

GANGWAYED BRAKE SECOND
ꙮ **NORTH NORFOLK RAILWAY**

GANGWAYED SALOON COACH
ꙮ **SOUTH TYNEDALE RAILWAY**

GENERAL UTILITY VAN
ꙮ **MID-NORFOLK RAILWAY**
ꙮ **NORTH YORKSHIRE MOORS RAILWAY**
ꙮ **NOTTINGHAM TRANSPORT CTRE**
ꙮ **PEAK RAIL**
ꙮ **PLYM VALLEY RAILWAY**

GENERATOR COACH
ꙮ **BARROW HILL ROUNDHOUSE**

GH
ꙮ **CLEETHORPES LIGHT RAILWAY**

GOODS BRAKE VAN
ꙮ **BRISTOL HARBOUR RAILWAY**

GOODS VAN
ꙮ **NORTH YORKSHIRE MOORS RAILWAY**

GREAT EASTERN COACH BODY
ꙮ **MID-NORFOLK RAILWAY**

GUARDS VAN

🚂 **BARROW HILL ROUNDHOUSE**

🚂 **TALYLLYN RAILWAY**

HAND CRANE

🚂 **BLUEBELL RAILWAY**

🚂 **NORTH NORFOLK RAILWAY**

HOPPER TIPPING WAGON

🚂 **SOUTH TYNEDALE RAILWAY**

HOPPER WAGON

🚂 **NOTTINGHAM TRANSPORT CTRE**

INGOT CARRIER

🚂 **NORTH YORKSHIRE MOORS RAILWAY**

INSPECTION CAR

🚂 **CAVAN & LEITRIM RAILWAY**

INSPECTION SALOON

🚂 **NORTH YORKSHIRE MOORS RAILWAY**

IRON BODIED VAN

🚂 **DIDCOT RAILWAY CENTRE**

IRON MINK

🚂 **SOUTH DEVON RAILWAY**

IRONSTONE HOPPER

🚂 **NORTH YORKSHIRE MOORS RAILWAY**

🚂 **NOTTINGHAM TRANSPORT CTRE**

KITCHEN BUFFET

🚂 **BLUEBELL RAILWAY**

KITCHEN BUFFET UNCLASSIFIED

🚂 **GWILI RAILWAY**

KITCHEN CAR

🚂 **KEITH & DUFFTOWN RAILWAY**

🚂 **NATIONAL RAILWAY MUSEUM**

LAVATORY BRAKE THIRD

🚂 **BLUEBELL RAILWAY**

LAVATORY THIRD

🚂 **BLUEBELL RAILWAY**

LONDON UNDERGROUND TUBE CAR

🚂 **MANGAPPS RAILWAY MUSEUM**

LOWMAC

🚂 **CHASEWATER RAILWAY**

🚂 **EAST ANGLIAN RAILWAY MUSEUM**

🚂 **KEITH & DUFFTOWN RAILWAY**

🚂 **NORTH NORFOLK RAILWAY**

🚂 **NORTH YORKSHIRE MOORS RAILWAY**

🚂 **PEAK RAIL**

🚂 **SOUTH DEVON RAILWAY**

LUGGAGE COMPOSITE

🚂 **NORTH YORKSHIRE MOORS RAILWAY**

LUGGAGE VAN

🚂 **MID-NORFOLK RAILWAY**

MACHINERY WAGON

🚂 **BLUEBELL RAILWAY**

MATCH TRUCK

🚂 **NATIONAL RAILWAY MUSEUM**

MATCH WAGON

🚂 **KENT & EAST SUSSEX RAILWAY**

🚂 **NORTH NORFOLK RAILWAY**

MATCH WAGON FOR HAND CRANE

🚂 **BLUEBELL RAILWAY**

MEAT VAN

🚂 **DIDCOT RAILWAY CENTRE**

MEDICAL EXAMINATION CARRIAGE

🚂 **MUSEUM OF SCIENCE & INDUSTRY**

MEDICAL OFFICERS COACH

🚂 **DIDCOT RAILWAY CENTRE**

MESS VAN

🚂 **DIDCOT RAILWAY CENTRE**

MILK TANK

🚂 **BLUEBELL RAILWAY**

🚂 **SOUTH DEVON RAILWAY**

MILK VAN

🚂 **BLUEBELL RAILWAY**

MINERAL OPEN

🚂 **GWILI RAILWAY**

MINERAL WAGON

🚂 **CHASEWATER RAILWAY**

🚂 **NORTH YORKSHIRE MOORS RAILWAY**

🚂 **SOUTH DEVON RAILWAY**

MINIATURE BUFFET

🚂 **NORTH YORKSHIRE MOORS RAILWAY**

🚂 **PEAK RAIL**

MINK A VAN

🚂 **GWILI RAILWAY**

MISCELLANEOUS VAN

🚂 **EAST ANGLIAN RAILWAY MUSEUM**

MN

WATERCRESS LINE

MOTOR CAR VAN

DIDCOT RAILWAY CENTRE

N7

NORTH NORFOLK RAILWAY

NCB

BO'NESS & KINNEIL RAILWAY

OBSERVATION CAR

BLUEBELL RAILWAY

OIL TANK WAGON

DIDCOT RAILWAY CENTRE

EAST ANGLIAN RAILWAY MUSEUM

OPEN

KIRKLEES LIGHT RAILWAY

SITTINGBOURNE & KEMSLEY

OPEN CARRIAGE TRUCK

BLUEBELL RAILWAY

OPEN GOODS WAGON

BLUEBELL RAILWAY

NORTH YORKSHIRE MOORS RAILWAY

OPEN HIGH BAR

BLUEBELL RAILWAY

OPEN HOPPER

EAST ANGLIAN RAILWAY MUSEUM

OPEN MINERAL WAGON

EAST ANGLIAN RAILWAY MUSEUM

OPEN SALOON BRAKE

NOTTINGHAM TRANSPORT CTRE

OPEN SHEET BAR WAGON

EAST ANGLIAN RAILWAY MUSEUM

OPEN THIRD

EAST ANGLIAN RAILWAY MUSEUM

OPEN TOURIST SALOON

NOTTINGHAM TRANSPORT CTRE

OPEN WAGON

BRISTOL HARBOUR RAILWAY

DIDCOT RAILWAY CENTRE

KENT & EAST SUSSEX RAILWAY

NORTHAMPTON & LAMPORT RAILWAY

PALLET VAN

GWILI RAILWAY

PEAK RAIL

PALVAN

NORTH YORKSHIRE MOORS RAILWAY

NOTTINGHAM TRANSPORT CTRE

PANNIER TANK

DEAN FOREST RAILWAY

LAPPA VALLEY STEAM RAILWAY

PARCELS TRAIN BRAKE VAN

SOUTH DEVON RAILWAY

PARCELS VAN

DERWENT VALLEY

PEAK RAIL

PASSENGER BRAKE

CHASEWATER RAILWAY

DIDCOT RAILWAY CENTRE

EAST ANGLIAN RAILWAY MUSEUM

PASSENGER FRUIT VAN

CHASEWATER RAILWAY

DIDCOT RAILWAY CENTRE

PASSENGER LUGGAGE VAN

BLUEBELL RAILWAY

PEAT WAGON

LEIGHTON BUZZARD RAILWAY

PERMANENT WAY TROLLEY

SOUTH TYNEDALE RAILWAY

PICNIC SALOON

BUCKINGHAMSHIRE RLWY CTRE

PIPE WAGON

CHASEWATER RAILWAY

KENT & EAST SUSSEX RAILWAY

MID-NORFOLK RAILWAY

NORTH NORFOLK RAILWAY

PIPEFIT

NORTH YORKSHIRE MOORS RAILWAY

PLANK DROPSIDE

KENT & EAST SUSSEX RAILWAY

PLANK OPEN WAGON

KENT & EAST SUSSEX RAILWAY

PLANK PIPE WAGON

PEAK RAIL

PLANK WAGON

KENT & EAST SUSSEX RAILWAY

PLANK WOODEN MINERAL WAGON

- PEAK RAIL

PLATE WAGON

- DERWENT VALLEY
- KENT & EAST SUSSEX RAILWAY
- NORTH NORFOLK RAILWAY
- NORTH YORKSHIRE MOORS RAILWAY

PM

- AMBERLEY WORKING MUSEUM
- BEAMISH
- CADEBY LIGHT RAILWAY
- NORTH GLOUCESTERSHIRE RAILWAY

PMV

- NORTH NORFOLK RAILWAY
- NORTHAMPTON & LAMPORT RAILWAY
- NOTTINGHAM TRANSPORT CTRE
- SPA VALLEY RAILWAY

POOLEY VAN

- SWANSEA VALE RAILWAY

PULLMAN BT

- BLUEBELL RAILWAY

PULLMAN FIRST KITCHEN

- BLUEBELL RAILWAY
- NORTH YORKSHIRE MOORS RAILWAY

PULLMAN FIRST PARLOUR

- NORTH YORKSHIRE MOORS RAILWAY

PULLMAN THIRD

- BLUEBELL RAILWAY

QRA RE RAILING VAN

- MID-NORFOLK RAILWAY

RAIL CRANE

- BRISTOL HARBOUR RAILWAY
- NORTH YORKSHIRE MOORS RAILWAY

RAILBUS

- DOWNPATRICK & ARDGLASS
- EMBSAY & BOLTON ABBEY RLWY
- KEIGHLEY & WORTH VALLEY

RAILCAR

- KENT & EAST SUSSEX RAILWAY

RB

- NORTH NORFOLK RAILWAY

RECTANK BOGIE WAGON

- NOTTINGHAM TRANSPORT CTRE

RESTAURANT BUFFET

- NORTH NORFOLK RAILWAY

RESTAURANT BUFFET REFURBISHED

- NORTH YORKSHIRE MOORS RAILWAY
- NORTHAMPTON & LAMPORT RAILWAY
- NOTTINGHAM TRANSPORT CTRE

RESTAURANT CAR

- STRATHSPEY RAILWAY

RESTAURANT FIRST

- NORTH YORKSHIRE MOORS RAILWAY

RESTAURANT MINIATURE BUFFET

- AVON VALLEY RAILWAY
- BLUEBELL RAILWAY
- KENT & EAST SUSSEX RAILWAY

RESTAURANT PANTRY CAR

- MANGAPPS RAILWAY MUSEUM

RESTAURANT UNCLASSIFIED

- KENT & EAST SUSSEX RAILWAY

RESTAURANT UNCLASSIFIED (BUFFET)

- AVON VALLEY RAILWAY
- BLUEBELL RAILWAY

RIDING VAN

- NORTH YORKSHIRE MOORS RAILWAY

ROAD VAN

- BLUEBELL RAILWAY

RT

- WEST LANCASHIRE LIGHT RLWY

SADDLE TANK

- BOWES RAILWAY
- COLNE VALLEY RAILWAY
- DARLINGTON RAILWAY CENTRE
- DOWNPATRICK & ARDGLASS
- EAST ANGLIAN RAILWAY MUSEUM
- EMBSAY & BOLTON ABBEY RLWY
- GREAT WESTERN RAILWAY MUSEUM
- IRCHESTER NARROW GAUGE MUSEUM
- KENT & EAST SUSSEX RAILWAY
- KIRKLEES LIGHT RAILWAY
- MUSEUM OF ARMY TRANSPORT

ROLLING STOCK by TYPE

Plank Wooden Mineral Wagon — Saddle Tank

NORTH NORFOLK RAILWAY

NORTHAMPTON & LAMPORT RAILWAY

RUISLIP LIDO RAILWAY

SOMERSET & DORSET RAILWAY

SPA VALLEY RAILWAY

SWINDON & CRICKLADE RAILWAY

SALOON

BLUEBELL RAILWAY

BUCKINGHAMSHIRE RLWY CTRE

SOUTH DEVON RAILWAY

SCENERY VAN

GWILI RAILWAY

SECOND

BLUEBELL RAILWAY

SECOND COMPARTMENT COACH

EAST SOMERSET RAILWAY

SECOND CORRIDOR

AVON VALLEY RAILWAY

BLUEBELL RAILWAY

EAST ANGLIAN RAILWAY MUSEUM

GWILI RAILWAY

KENT & EAST SUSSEX RAILWAY

NORTH NORFOLK RAILWAY

NORTH YORKSHIRE MOORS RAILWAY

NORTHAMPTON & LAMPORT RAILWAY

PEAK RAIL

PLYM VALLEY RAILWAY

SPA VALLEY RAILWAY

SWANSEA VALE RAILWAY

SECOND OPEN

BLUEBELL RAILWAY

NORTH YORKSHIRE MOORS RAILWAY

PEAK RAIL

SPA VALLEY RAILWAY

SECOND SALOON BRAKE

BLUEBELL RAILWAY

SELF PROPELLED CRANE

SPA VALLEY RAILWAY

SEMI OPEN

HEATHERSLAW LIGHT RAILWAY

KIRKLEES LIGHT RAILWAY

SITTINGBOURNE & KEMSLEY

SEMI OPEN BRAKE

GWILI RAILWAY

SEMI OPEN BRAKE THIRD

BLUEBELL RAILWAY

SEMI OPEN BRAKE THIRD WITH COUPE

BLUEBELL RAILWAY

SEMI ROYAL SALOON

BLUEBELL RAILWAY

SHARK BALLAST PLOUGH

BLUEBELL RAILWAY

CHASEWATER RAILWAY

SHARK BRAKE VAN

PEAK RAIL

SOUTH DEVON RAILWAY

SHARK PLOUGH BRAKE

NOTTINGHAM TRANSPORT CTRE

SHOC VAN

EAST SOMERSET RAILWAY

NORTH YORKSHIRE MOORS RAILWAY

SOUTH DEVON RAILWAY

SHOC WAGON

NORTH YORKSHIRE MOORS RAILWAY

SHUNTER

BRISTOL HARBOUR RAILWAY

CHOLSEY & WALLINGFORD RAILWAY

DERWENT VALLEY

DIDCOT RAILWAY CENTRE

EAST ANGLIAN RAILWAY MUSEUM

EMBSAY & BOLTON ABBEY RLWY

LINCOLNSHIRE WOLDS RAILWAY

NORTH NORFOLK RAILWAY

PEAK RAIL

PLYM VALLEY RAILWAY

SOUTH DEVON RAILWAY

SHUNTING CRANE

PLYM VALLEY RAILWAY

SHUNTING ENGINE

BRISTOL HARBOUR RAILWAY

SIDE TANK

- DOWNPATRICK & ARDGLASS
- EAST ANGLIAN RAILWAY MUSEUM
- SPA VALLEY RAILWAY
- SWINDON & CRICKLADE RAILWAY

SLATE WAGON

- LEIGHTON BUZZARD RAILWAY

SLEEPER

- BLUEBELL RAILWAY
- NORTH YORKSHIRE MOORS RAILWAY

SLEEPER FIRST

- NORTH YORKSHIRE MOORS RAILWAY

SLEEPER WAGON

- BLUEBELL RAILWAY
- SOUTH DEVON RAILWAY

SLEEPING CAR

- GWILI RAILWAY
- PEAK RAIL
- STRATHSPEY RAILWAY

SLIP COACH

- SOUTH DEVON RAILWAY

SNOW PLOUGH

- NORTH YORKSHIRE MOORS RAILWAY

SPECIAL CATTLE VAN

- DIDCOT RAILWAY CENTRE

SPECIAL SALOON

- DIDCOT RAILWAY CENTRE

SPECIAL TRAFFICS VAN

- DIDCOT RAILWAY CENTRE

ST

- BATTLEFIELD LINE
- BRISTOL HARBOUR RAILWAY

STAFF & TOOL VAN

- CHASEWATER RAILWAY
- KENT & EAST SUSSEX RAILWAY

STANDARD BRAKE VAN

- PEAK RAIL

STEAM BREAKDOWN CRANE

- NATIONAL RAILWAY MUSEUM

STEAM CRANE

- BLUEBELL RAILWAY
- BODMIN & WENFORD RAILWAY

- BURE VALLEY RAILWAY
- DERWENT VALLEY
- KENT & EAST SUSSEX RAILWAY
- NORTH NORFOLK RAILWAY
- PEAK RAIL
- SWANSEA VALE RAILWAY
- VALE OF GLAMORGAN RAILWAY

STEAM HEAT VAN

- NORTH YORKSHIRE MOORS RAILWAY

STEAM RAILMOTOR

- DIDCOT RAILWAY CENTRE

STEEL BODIED OPEN

- KENT & EAST SUSSEX RAILWAY

STEEL BODIED WAGON

- KENT & EAST SUSSEX RAILWAY

STORES WAGON

- DIDCOT RAILWAY CENTRE

SUPER SALOON

- DIDCOT RAILWAY CENTRE
- SOUTH DEVON RAILWAY

SUPER SALOON KITCHEN

- DIDCOT RAILWAY CENTRE

SUPPORT COACH

- DIDCOT RAILWAY CENTRE
- NORTH YORKSHIRE MOORS RAILWAY

SZ

- NORTH NORFOLK RAILWAY

TANK WAGON

- CHASEWATER RAILWAY
- DERWENT VALLEY
- DIDCOT RAILWAY CENTRE
- KENT & EAST SUSSEX RAILWAY
- MID-NORFOLK RAILWAY
- NORTH YORKSHIRE MOORS RAILWAY
- NORTHAMPTON & LAMPORT RAILWAY
- NOTTINGHAM TRANSPORT CTRE
- PEAK RAIL
- RAILWORLD

TANKER

- GWILI RAILWAY
- NORTH NORFOLK RAILWAY

ROLLING STOCK by TYPE

Side Tank — Tanker

ROLLING STOCK by TYPE

Tar Tank Wagon — Van

TAR TANK WAGON

- DIDCOT RAILWAY CENTRE
- GWILI RAILWAY
- NORTHAMPTON & LAMPORT RAILWAY
- SOUTH DEVON RAILWAY
- SWANSEA VALE RAILWAY

TC

- MIDLAND RAILWAY CENTRE

TCL

- BUCKINGHAMSHIRE RLWY CTRE
- LAVENDER LINE

TENCH WAGON

- MID-NORFOLK RAILWAY

THIRD

- BLUEBELL RAILWAY
- NATIONAL RAILWAY MUSEUM

THIRD BRAKE

- BLUEBELL RAILWAY
- EAST ANGLIAN RAILWAY MUSEUM
- NATIONAL RAILWAY MUSEUM

THIRD CORRIDOR

- BLUEBELL RAILWAY
- NORTH NORFOLK RAILWAY
- NORTH YORKSHIRE MOORS RAILWAY
- PEAK RAIL

THIRD OPEN

- BLUEBELL RAILWAY
- NATIONAL RAILWAY MUSEUM
- NORTH YORKSHIRE MOORS RAILWAY
- PEAK RAIL

TOOL VAN

- BLUEBELL RAILWAY
- NORTH YORKSHIRE MOORS RAILWAY

TOURIST SECOND

- CHASEWATER RAILWAY

TOURIST SECOND OPEN

- AVON VALLEY RAILWAY
- EAST ANGLIAN RAILWAY MUSEUM
- EAST SOMERSET RAILWAY
- GWILI RAILWAY
- KENT & EAST SUSSEX RAILWAY

- LAVENDER LINE
- MID-NORFOLK RAILWAY
- NORTH NORFOLK RAILWAY
- NORTH YORKSHIRE MOORS RAILWAY
- NORTHAMPTON & LAMPORT RAILWAY
- PEAK RAIL
- SOUTH DEVON RAILWAY

TOURIST THIRD OPEN

- NORTH NORFOLK RAILWAY
- NORTH YORKSHIRE MOORS RAILWAY

TPO

- NATIONAL RAILWAY MUSEUM

TRAILER BUFFET

- MID-NORFOLK RAILWAY

TRAILER SECOND LAVATORY

- CHASEWATER RAILWAY
- PEAK RAIL

TRAM ENGINE

- NATIONAL TRAMWAY MUSEUM

TRAVELLING POST OFFICE

- BLUEBELL RAILWAY

TUBE WAGON

- KENT & EAST SUSSEX RAILWAY
- MID-NORFOLK RAILWAY
- NORTHAMPTON & LAMPORT RAILWAY
- NOTTINGHAM TRANSPORT CTRE
- SOUTH DEVON RAILWAY

TZ

- NORTH NORFOLK RAILWAY

UNCLASSED BRAKE

- BLUEBELL RAILWAY

UNDERGROUND COAL WAGON

- LEIGHTON BUZZARD RAILWAY

UNFITTED VAN

- EAST ANGLIAN RAILWAY MUSEUM

VAN

- BARROW HILL ROUNDHOUSE
- BLUEBELL RAILWAY
- BRISTOL HARBOUR RAILWAY
- DIDCOT RAILWAY CENTRE
- KENT & EAST SUSSEX RAILWAY

NN **NORTH NORFOLK RAILWAY**

NN **NORTH YORKSHIRE MOORS RAILWAY**

NN **NOTTINGHAM TRANSPORT CTRE**

NN **SWANSEA VALE RAILWAY**

VAN GUARD SHUNTER

NN **PLYM VALLEY RAILWAY**

VENTILATED BOX VAN

NN **DERWENT VALLEY**

NN **NORTHAMPTON & LAMPORT RAILWAY**

VENTILATED LUGGAGE VAN

NN **BLUEBELL RAILWAY**

VENTILATED VAN

NN **BARROW HILL ROUNDHOUSE**

NN **BUCKINGHAMSHIRE RLWY CTRE**

NN **EAST ANGLIAN RAILWAY MUSEUM**

NN **KENT & EAST SUSSEX RAILWAY**

NN **PLYM VALLEY RAILWAY**

VESTIBULE THIRD

NN **BUCKINGHAMSHIRE RLWY CTRE**

WEED KILLER WAGON

NN **SOUTH TYNEDALE RAILWAY**

WELL TANK

NN **BRECON MOUNTAIN RAILWAY**

NN **IRISH STEAM PRESERVATION SOC**

NN **SOUTH TYNEDALE RAILWAY**

WELL WAGON

NN **DIDCOT RAILWAY CENTRE**

WELTROL BOGIE TROLLEY

NN **KENT & EAST SUSSEX RAILWAY**

WICKHAM TROLLEY

NN **MID-NORFOLK RAILWAY**

NN **PEAK RAIL**

YARD SHUNTER

NN **PEAK RAIL**

ROLLING STOCK by TYPE

Van — Yard Shunter

Rolling Stock by Class

SECTION 5D

This section shows the Class of stock and where it can be located

e.g. 02, Bluebell Railway

Once you have located a railway/museum using this section you can then refer to the railway or museum's detailed profile in section 1.

0

KENT & EAST SUSSEX RAILWAY

01

BLUEBELL RAILWAY

EAST LANCASHIRE RAILWAY

SOUTH YORKSHIRE RAILWAY

02

BLUEBELL RAILWAY

ISLE OF WIGHT STEAM RAILWAY

SOUTH YORKSHIRE RAILWAY

0298

BUCKINGHAMSHIRE RLWY CTRE

03

BARROW HILL ROUNDHOUSE

DERWENT VALLEY

EAST LANCASHIRE RAILWAY

GLOUCESTERSHIRE WARWICKSHIRE

GWILI RAILWAY

ISLE OF WIGHT STEAM RAILWAY

LAKESIDE & HAVERTHWAITE RLWY

MANGAPPS RAILWAY MUSEUM

MIDLAND RAILWAY CENTRE

NORTH NORFOLK RAILWAY

PEAK RAIL

SOUTH YORKSHIRE RAILWAY

SWINDON & CRICKLADE RAILWAY

WEST SOMERSET RAILWAY

04

BATTLEFIELD LINE

BLUEBELL RAILWAY

BUCKINGHAMSHIRE RLWY CTRE

CHURNET VALLEY RAILWAY

EAST ANGLIAN RAILWAY MUSEUM

EMBSAY & BOLTON ABBEY RLWY

GLOUCESTERSHIRE WARWICKSHIRE

GREAT CENTRAL RAILWAY

NATIONAL RAILWAY MUSEUM

NORTH NORFOLK RAILWAY

NORTH YORKSHIRE MOORS RAILWAY

PLYM VALLEY RAILWAY

SOUTH YORKSHIRE RAILWAY

WEST SOMERSET RAILWAY

0415

BLUEBELL RAILWAY

05

FOYLE VALLEY RAILWAY CENTRE

ISLE OF WIGHT STEAM RAILWAY

SOUTH YORKSHIRE RAILWAY

06

BATTLEFIELD LINE

07

AVON VALLEY RAILWAY

SOUTH YORKSHIRE RAILWAY

08

BODMIN & WENFORD RAILWAY

BO'NESS & KINNEIL RAILWAY

CALEDONIAN RAILWAY

CHOLSEY & WALLINGFORD RAILWAY

CHURNET VALLEY RAILWAY

DARTMOOR RAILWAY

DEAN FOREST RAILWAY

DIDCOT RAILWAY CENTRE

EAST LANCASHIRE RAILWAY

GREAT CENTRAL RAILWAY

KEIGHLEY & WORTH VALLEY

KENT & EAST SUSSEX RAILWAY

LINCOLNSHIRE WOLDS RAILWAY

MIDLAND RAILWAY CENTRE

NORTH NORFOLK RAILWAY

NORTH YORKSHIRE MOORS RAILWAY

NOTTINGHAM TRANSPORT CTRE

PLYM VALLEY RAILWAY

SEVERN VALLEY RAILWAY

ROLLING STOCK by CLASS

0 — 08

🚂 SOUTH YORKSHIRE RAILWAY	🚂 SEVERN VALLEY RAILWAY
🚂 TYSELEY LOCOMOTIVE WORKS	🚂 SOUTH YORKSHIRE RAILWAY
🚂 WATERCRESS LINE	🚂 WATERCRESS LINE
🚂 WEST SOMERSET RAILWAY	**110**

10

🚂 BODMIN & WENFORD RAILWAY

🚂 EAST LANCASHIRE RAILWAY

🚂 COLNE VALLEY RAILWAY

🚂 LAKESIDE & HAVERTHWAITE RLWY

🚂 GREAT CENTRAL RAILWAY

111

🚂 SOUTH YORKSHIRE RAILWAY

🚂 MID-NORFOLK RAILWAY

🚂 SPA VALLEY RAILWAY

114

100

🚂 MIDLAND RAILWAY CENTRE

🚂 MID-NORFOLK RAILWAY

115

101

🚂 BUCKINGHAMSHIRE RLWY CTRE

🚂 WEST SOMERSET RAILWAY

🚂 SPA VALLEY RAILWAY

103

🚂 WEST SOMERSET RAILWAY

🚂 WEST SOMERSET RAILWAY

104

116

🚂 SOUTH YORKSHIRE RAILWAY

🚂 SWANSEA VALE RAILWAY

105

117

🚂 EAST LANCASHIRE RAILWAY

🚂 MID-NORFOLK RAILWAY

107

🚂 NORTH NORFOLK RAILWAY

🚂 CALEDONIAN RAILWAY

🚂 NORTHAMPTON & LAMPORT RAILWAY

🚂 EMBSAY & BOLTON ABBEY RLWY

🚂 PLYM VALLEY RAILWAY

🚂 LAKESIDE & HAVERTHWAITE RLWY

🚂 WEST SOMERSET RAILWAY

108

119

🚂 BODMIN & WENFORD RAILWAY

🚂 MID-NORFOLK RAILWAY

🚂 DEAN FOREST RAILWAY

12

🚂 KEIGHLEY & WORTH VALLEY

🚂 SPA VALLEY RAILWAY

🚂 KEITH & DUFFTOWN RAILWAY

120

🚂 KENT & EAST SUSSEX RAILWAY

🚂 GREAT CENTRAL RAILWAY

🚂 MID-NORFOLK RAILWAY

121

🚂 SWANSEA VALE RAILWAY

🚂 SWANSEA VALE RAILWAY

🚂 VALE OF GLAMORGAN RAILWAY

🚂 TYSELEY LOCOMOTIVE WORKS

11

122

🚂 MIDLAND RAILWAY CENTRE

🚂 MID-NORFOLK RAILWAY

🚂 NORTH NORFOLK RAILWAY

🚂 NORTHAMPTON & LAMPORT RAILWAY

🚂 NORTH YORKSHIRE MOORS RAILWAY

127

🚂 GREAT CENTRAL RAILWAY

🚂 MIDLAND RAILWAY CENTRE

1361

🚂 DIDCOT RAILWAY CENTRE

13DL

MMT LEIGHTON BUZZARD RAILWAY

13HP

MMT WEST LANCASHIRE LIGHT RLWY

14

MMT EAST LANCASHIRE RAILWAY

MMT GLOUCESTERSHIRE WARWICKSHIRE

MMT KENT & EAST SUSSEX RAILWAY

MMT NENE VALLEY RAILWAY

MMT NOTTINGHAM TRANSPORT CTRE

MMT SOUTH YORKSHIRE RAILWAY

MMT WEST SOMERSET RAILWAY

140

MMT KEITH & DUFFTOWN RAILWAY

141

MMT MID-NORFOLK RAILWAY

14XX

MMT GLOUCESTERSHIRE WARWICKSHIRE

165

MMT NORTHAMPTON & LAMPORT RAILWAY

16XX

MMT KENT & EAST SUSSEX RAILWAY

20

MMT BARROW HILL ROUNDHOUSE

MMT BATTLEFIELD LINE

MMT BODMIN & WENFORD RAILWAY

MMT EAST LANCASHIRE RAILWAY

MMT GLOUCESTERSHIRE WARWICKSHIRE

MMT GREAT CENTRAL RAILWAY

MMT KEIGHLEY & WORTH VALLEY

MMT LAKESIDE & HAVERTHWAITE RLWY

MMT MIDLAND RAILWAY CENTRE

MMT MID-NORFOLK RAILWAY

MMT WATERCRESS LINE

MMT YEOVIL RAILWAY CENTRE

20DL

MMT LEIGHTON BUZZARD RAILWAY

20HP

MMT WEST LANCASHIRE LIGHT RLWY

21C

MMT KENT & EAST SUSSEX RAILWAY

21HP

MMT WEST LANCASHIRE LIGHT RLWY

24

MMT EAST LANCASHIRE RAILWAY

MMT NORTH YORKSHIRE MOORS RAILWAY

25

MMT BARROW HILL ROUNDHOUSE

MMT CALEDONIAN RAILWAY

MMT CHURNET VALLEY RAILWAY

MMT GREAT CENTRAL RAILWAY

MMT MIDLAND RAILWAY CENTRE

MMT NORTH NORFOLK RAILWAY

MMT NORTH YORKSHIRE MOORS RAILWAY

MMT SEVERN VALLEY RAILWAY

MMT WEST SOMERSET RAILWAY

2511

MMT NORTHAMPTON & LAMPORT RAILWAY

26

MMT BARROW HILL ROUNDHOUSE

MMT CALEDONIAN RAILWAY

MMT LAKESIDE & HAVERTHWAITE RLWY

MMT NORTHAMPTON & LAMPORT RAILWAY

MMT SOUTH YORKSHIRE RAILWAY

MMT STRATHSPEY RAILWAY

27

MMT CALEDONIAN RAILWAY

MMT EAST LANCASHIRE RAILWAY

MMT NORTH NORFOLK RAILWAY

MMT NORTHAMPTON & LAMPORT RAILWAY

MMT SEVERN VALLEY RAILWAY

MMT WATERCRESS LINE

28

MMT EAST LANCASHIRE RAILWAY

ROLLING STOCK by CLASS

13DL — 28

ROLLING STOCK by CLASS

2884 — 42

2884
- BODMIN & WENFORD RAILWAY
- DIDCOT RAILWAY CENTRE
- NORTH YORKSHIRE MOORS RAILWAY

28HP
- WEST LANCASHIRE LIGHT RLWY

28XX
- GLOUCESTERSHIRE WARWICKSHIRE

2F
- KEIGHLEY & WORTH VALLEY

2MT
- BUCKINGHAMSHIRE RLWY CTRE
- EAST LANCASHIRE RAILWAY
- GREAT CENTRAL RAILWAY
- KEIGHLEY & WORTH VALLEY

3
- EAST LANCASHIRE RAILWAY
- EAST SOMERSET RAILWAY
- GREAT CENTRAL RAILWAY
- MIDLAND RAILWAY CENTRE
- SPA VALLEY RAILWAY

30DL
- LEIGHTON BUZZARD RAILWAY

30HP
- WEST LANCASHIRE LIGHT RLWY

31
- BATTLEFIELD LINE
- EAST LANCASHIRE RAILWAY
- GREAT CENTRAL RAILWAY
- MIDLAND RAILWAY CENTRE
- MID-NORFOLK RAILWAY
- TYSELEY LOCOMOTIVE WORKS

32XX
- BLUEBELL RAILWAY

33
- BODMIN & WENFORD RAILWAY
- CHURNET VALLEY RAILWAY
- EAST LANCASHIRE RAILWAY

- KENT & EAST SUSSEX RAILWAY
- MIDLAND RAILWAY CENTRE
- SOUTH YORKSHIRE RAILWAY
- SWANAGE RAILWAY
- TYSELEY LOCOMOTIVE WORKS
- WATERCRESS LINE
- WEST SOMERSET RAILWAY

35
- EAST LANCASHIRE RAILWAY
- WEST SOMERSET RAILWAY

37
- EAST ANGLIAN RAILWAY MUSEUM
- EAST LANCASHIRE RAILWAY
- GLOUCESTERSHIRE WARWICKSHIRE
- GREAT CENTRAL RAILWAY
- MIDLAND RAILWAY CENTRE
- NORTH NORFOLK RAILWAY
- PLYM VALLEY RAILWAY

40
- EAST LANCASHIRE RAILWAY
- MIDLAND RAILWAY CENTRE
- NENE VALLEY RAILWAY
- TYSELEY LOCOMOTIVE WORKS

4073/CASTLE
- DIDCOT RAILWAY CENTRE

40DL
- LEIGHTON BUZZARD RAILWAY

40HP
- WEST LANCASHIRE LIGHT RLWY

411
- DARTMOOR RAILWAY

415
- MID-NORFOLK RAILWAY

419
- MID-NORFOLK RAILWAY

42
- EAST LANCASHIRE RAILWAY

4200
SWANSEA VALE RAILWAY

422
DARTMOOR RAILWAY

4300
DIDCOT RAILWAY CENTRE

43XX
SEVERN VALLEY RAILWAY

44
MIDLAND RAILWAY CENTRE

PEAK RAIL

45
EAST LANCASHIRE RAILWAY

GREAT CENTRAL RAILWAY

NORTHAMPTON & LAMPORT RAILWAY

WATERCRESS LINE

4575
BODMIN & WENFORD RAILWAY

DIDCOT RAILWAY CENTRE

TYSELEY LOCOMOTIVE WORKS

45XX
SEVERN VALLEY RAILWAY

47
BROOKSIDE MINIATURE

EAST LANCASHIRE RAILWAY

GLOUCESTERSHIRE WARWICKSHIRE

GREAT CENTRAL RAILWAY

MIDLAND RAILWAY CENTRE

TYSELEY LOCOMOTIVE WORKS

48
IRCHESTER NARROW GAUGE MUSEUM

4800
DIDCOT RAILWAY CENTRE

4900/HALL
DIDCOT RAILWAY CENTRE

49XX
SEVERN VALLEY RAILWAY

4F
AVON VALLEY RAILWAY

CHURNET VALLEY RAILWAY

KEIGHLEY & WORTH VALLEY

MIDLAND RAILWAY CENTRE

NATIONAL RAILWAY MUSEUM

4MT
CHURNET VALLEY RAILWAY

EAST LANCASHIRE RAILWAY

MIDLAND RAILWAY CENTRE

NORTH YORKSHIRE MOORS RAILWAY

WATERCRESS LINE

50
BARROW HILL ROUNDHOUSE

BODMIN & WENFORD RAILWAY

BO'NESS & KINNEIL RAILWAY

EAST LANCASHIRE RAILWAY

MIDLAND RAILWAY CENTRE

MID-NORFOLK RAILWAY

NORTH YORKSHIRE MOORS RAILWAY

PONTYPOOL & BLAENAVON RAILWAY

SEVERN VALLEY RAILWAY

504
EAST LANCASHIRE RAILWAY

5101
DIDCOT RAILWAY CENTRE

TYSELEY LOCOMOTIVE WORKS

51XX
SEVERN VALLEY RAILWAY

52
EAST LANCASHIRE RAILWAY

MIDLAND RAILWAY CENTRE

NENE VALLEY RAILWAY

WEST SOMERSET RAILWAY

52 WESTERN
SEVERN VALLEY RAILWAY

55
MIDLAND RAILWAY CENTRE

NORTH YORKSHIRE MOORS RAILWAY

ROLLING STOCK by CLASS

5600 — 9F

5600
- DIDCOT RAILWAY CENTRE

56XX
- EAST SOMERSET RAILWAY
- NORTH YORKSHIRE MOORS RAILWAY
- SWINDON & CRICKLADE RAILWAY

5700
- BUCKINGHAMSHIRE RLWY CTRE
- DIDCOT RAILWAY CENTRE
- SWANSEA VALE RAILWAY
- TYSELEY LOCOMOTIVE WORKS

57XX
- SEVERN VALLEY RAILWAY

59
- WESTON PARK RAILWAY

5MT
- BO'NESS & KINNEIL RAILWAY
- EAST LANCASHIRE RAILWAY
- GREAT CENTRAL RAILWAY
- MIDLAND RAILWAY CENTRE
- NENE VALLEY RAILWAY
- NORTH YORKSHIRE MOORS RAILWAY
- NOTTINGHAM TRANSPORT CTRE
- WATERCRESS LINE

6000/KING
- DIDCOT RAILWAY CENTRE

60HP
- WEST LANCASHIRE LIGHT RLWY

6100
- DIDCOT RAILWAY CENTRE

64
- NENE VALLEY RAILWAY

68HP
- WEST LANCASHIRE LIGHT RLWY

6959
- DIDCOT RAILWAY CENTRE

7200
- BUCKINGHAMSHIRE RLWY CTRE
- DIDCOT RAILWAY CENTRE

EAST LANCASHIRE RAILWAY

73
- LAVENDER LINE

7800/MANOR
- DIDCOT RAILWAY CENTRE

78XX
- SEVERN VALLEY RAILWAY

7F
- MIDLAND RAILWAY CENTRE
- SOMERSET & DORSET RAILWAY
- WEST SOMERSET RAILWAY

81
- BARROW HILL ROUNDHOUSE

82
- BARROW HILL ROUNDHOUSE

83
- BARROW HILL ROUNDHOUSE

84
- BARROW HILL ROUNDHOUSE

85
- BARROW HILL ROUNDHOUSE

88
- NORTHAMPTON & LAMPORT RAILWAY

8F
- AVON VALLEY RAILWAY
- CHURNET VALLEY RAILWAY
- GLOUCESTERSHIRE WARWICKSHIRE
- KEIGHLEY & WORTH VALLEY
- PEAK RAIL

8P
- EAST LANCASHIRE RAILWAY
- MIDLAND RAILWAY CENTRE

9400
- BUCKINGHAMSHIRE RLWY CTRE

9F
- BLUEBELL RAILWAY
- CHURNET VALLEY RAILWAY
- EAST LANCASHIRE RAILWAY
- GLOUCESTERSHIRE WARWICKSHIRE

♨ MIDLAND RAILWAY CENTRE

A

♨ HEATHERSLAW LIGHT RAILWAY

♨ LONDON TRANSPORT MUSEUM

A1 TERRIER

♨ BLUEBELL RAILWAY

A1X TERRIER

♨ BLUEBELL RAILWAY

♨ ISLE OF WIGHT STEAM RAILWAY

♨ KENT & EAST SUSSEX RAILWAY

A2

♨ NORTH YORKSHIRE MOORS RAILWAY

A4

♨ SEVERN VALLEY RAILWAY

♨ WATERCRESS LINE

A5

♨ LAKESIDE & HAVERTHWAITE RLWY

ALBION

♨ RHYL MINIATURE RAILWAY

AUSTERITY

♨ CHURNET VALLEY RAILWAY

♨ COLNE VALLEY RAILWAY

♨ NORTH NORFOLK RAILWAY

♨ SEVERN VALLEY RAILWAY

♨ VALE OF GLAMORGAN RAILWAY

B

♨ NORTH YORKSHIRE MOORS RAILWAY

B1

♨ GREAT CENTRAL RAILWAY

♨ NENE VALLEY RAILWAY

B12

♨ NORTH NORFOLK RAILWAY

B4

♨ BLUEBELL RAILWAY

BARETTO

♨ SITTINGBOURNE & KEMSLEY

BATTLE OF BRITAIN

♨ NENE VALLEY RAILWAY

BB

♨ WATERCRESS LINE

BRAZIL

♨ SITTINGBOURNE & KEMSLEY

C

♨ BLUEBELL RAILWAY

♨ NORTH YORKSHIRE MOORS RAILWAY

CASTLE

♨ TYSELEY LOCOMOTIVE WORKS

COLLIER

♨ NATIONAL RAILWAY MUSEUM

D49

♨ BO'NESS & KINNEIL RAILWAY

E

♨ DARLINGTON RAILWAY PRES SOC

♨ NATIONAL TRAMWAY MUSEUM

♨ RAILWORLD

E1

♨ EAST SOMERSET RAILWAY

E4

♨ BLUEBELL RAILWAY

GL

♨ MUSEUM OF SCIENCE & INDUSTRY

H

♨ BLUEBELL RAILWAY

♨ MIDDLETON RAILWAY

HALL

♨ CAMBRIAN RAILWAY SOCIETY

♨ GREAT CENTRAL RAILWAY

♨ GREAT WESTERN RAILWAY MUSEUM

♨ PONTYPOOL & BLAENAVON RAILWAY

♨ TYSELEY LOCOMOTIVE WORKS

INDUSTRIAL

♨ BRISTOL HARBOUR RAILWAY

♨ BURE VALLEY RAILWAY

♨ GLOUCESTERSHIRE WARWICKSHIRE

♨ GREAT CENTRAL RAILWAY

♨ NENE VALLEY RAILWAY

♨ NORTHAMPTON & LAMPORT RAILWAY

ROLLING STOCK by CLASS

9F — Industrial

ROLLING STOCK by CLASS

J — U

J

🚂 DOWNPATRICK & ARDGLASS

J15

🚂 NORTH NORFOLK RAILWAY

🚂 RPSI

J72

🚂 NORTH YORKSHIRE MOORS RAILWAY

J94

🚂 GWILI RAILWAY

🚂 KEIGHLEY & WORTH VALLEY

🚂 WATERCRESS LINE

JUBILEE

🚂 EAST LANCASHIRE RAILWAY

🚂 KEIGHLEY & WORTH VALLEY

🚂 TYSELEY LOCOMOTIVE WORKS

K1

🚂 NORTH YORKSHIRE MOORS RAILWAY

K2

🚂 RPSI

K4

🚂 SEVERN VALLEY RAILWAY

KING

🚂 DIDCOT RAILWAY CENTRE

KING ARTHUR

🚂 GREAT CENTRAL RAILWAY

KITCHENER

🚂 ISLE OF WIGHT STEAM RAILWAY

MANOR

🚂 CAMBRIAN RAILWAY SOCIETY

🚂 WEST SOMERSET RAILWAY

MN

🚂 WATERCRESS LINE

'MODIFIED HALL'

🚂 BUCKINGHAMSHIRE RLWY CTRE

MOUNTAIN

🚂 ROMNEY HYTHE & DYMCHURCH

N

🚂 WATERCRESS LINE

NG15

🚂 EXMOOR STEAM RAILWAY

NGG16

🚂 EXMOOR STEAM RAILWAY

P

🚂 BLUEBELL RAILWAY

🚂 BUCKINGHAMSHIRE RLWY CTRE

🚂 KENT & EAST SUSSEX RAILWAY

PACIFIC

🚂 KERR MINIATURE RAILWAY

PRINCESS

🚂 EAST LANCASHIRE RAILWAY

Q

🚂 BLUEBELL RAILWAY

Q1

🚂 BLUEBELL RAILWAY

🚂 NATIONAL RAILWAY MUSEUM

Q6

🚂 NORTH YORKSHIRE MOORS RAILWAY

Q7

🚂 NATIONAL RAILWAY MUSEUM

🚂 NORTH YORKSHIRE MOORS RAILWAY

S15

🚂 BLUEBELL RAILWAY

🚂 WATERCRESS LINE

S260

🚂 WATERCRESS LINE

SAINT

🚂 DIDCOT RAILWAY CENTRE

SCHOOLS

🚂 NORTH YORKSHIRE MOORS RAILWAY

THIRD CLASS

🚂 BLUEBELL RAILWAY

🚂 EAST ANGLIAN RAILWAY MUSEUM

🚂 NORTH YORKSHIRE MOORS RAILWAY

🚂 NOTTINGHAM TRANSPORT CTRE

TKH

🚂 APPLEBY-FRODINGHAM RAILWAY

U

🚂 BLUEBELL RAILWAY

🚂 WATERCRESS LINE

USA

🚂 **BLUEBELL RAILWAY**

V

🚂 **BLUEBELL RAILWAY**

WC

🚂 **BLUEBELL RAILWAY**

🚂 **WATERCRESS LINE**

ZB

🚂 **BURE VALLEY RAILWAY**

ROLLING STOCK by CLASS

USA — ZB

SECTION 5E

This section shows the Origin of stock and where it can be located

e.g. BR, Great Central Railway

Once you have located a railway/museum using this section you can then refer to the railway or museum's detailed profile in section 1.

STEAM
RAILWAY

ADAMS

🚂 **MANGAPPS RAILWAY MUSEUM**

ALEXANDER DOCKS & RAILWAY CO

🚂 **DIDCOT RAILWAY CENTRE**

AMALGAMATED ROADSTONE CORP

🚂 **LEIGHTON BUZZARD RAILWAY**

APPLEBY FRODINGHAM STEELWORKS

🚂 **DARLINGTON RAILWAY PRES SOC**

ARMY

🚂 **SEVERN VALLEY RAILWAY**

ARNOLD NATHAN LTD

🚂 **LEIGHTON BUZZARD RAILWAY**

ASSOCIATED PORTLAND CEMENT MFRS

🚂 **LEIGHTON BUZZARD RAILWAY**

BAC RAILWAY (LARNE)

🚂 **GIANTS CAUSEWAY & BUSHMILLS**

BEAMISH WAGON WAY

🚂 **BEAMISH**

BEESTEN UDC

🚂 **KEW BRIDGE STEAM MUSEUM**

BELFAST & CO DOWN RAILWAY

🚂 **ULSTER FOLK & TRANSPORT**

BLUECIRCLE RAILWAY

🚂 **GIANTS CAUSEWAY & BUSHMILLS**

BNM RAILWAY (PORTARLINGTON)

🚂 **GIANTS CAUSEWAY & BUSHMILLS**

BR

🚂 **AVON VALLEY RAILWAY**

🚂 **BARROW HILL ROUNDHOUSE**

🚂 **BATTLEFIELD LINE**

🚂 **BLUEBELL RAILWAY**

🚂 **BODMIN & WENFORD RAILWAY**

🚂 **BO'NESS & KINNEIL RAILWAY**

🚂 **BRISTOL HARBOUR RAILWAY**

🚂 **BUCKINGHAMSHIRE RLWY CTRE**

🚂 **CALEDONIAN RAILWAY**

🚂 **CHASEWATER RAILWAY**

🚂 **CHURNET VALLEY RAILWAY**

🚂 **DARLINGTON RAILWAY PRES SOC**

🚂 **DARTMOOR RAILWAY**

🚂 **DERWENT VALLEY**

🚂 **DIDCOT RAILWAY CENTRE**

🚂 **EAST ANGLIAN RAILWAY MUSEUM**

🚂 **EAST KENT LIGHT RAILWAY**

🚂 **EAST LANCASHIRE RAILWAY**

🚂 **EAST SOMERSET RAILWAY**

🚂 **GLOUCESTERSHIRE WARWICKSHIRE**

🚂 **GREAT CENTRAL RAILWAY**

🚂 **GWILI RAILWAY**

🚂 **ISLE OF WIGHT STEAM RAILWAY**

🚂 **KEIGHLEY & WORTH VALLEY**

🚂 **KEITH & DUFFTOWN RAILWAY**

🚂 **KENT & EAST SUSSEX RAILWAY**

🚂 **LAKESIDE & HAVERTHWAITE RLWY**

🚂 **LEIGHTON BUZZARD RAILWAY**

🚂 **LLANGOLLEN RAILWAY**

🚂 **MANGAPPS RAILWAY MUSEUM**

🚂 **MIDLAND RAILWAY CENTRE**

🚂 **MID-NORFOLK RAILWAY**

🚂 **NATIONAL RAILWAY MUSEUM**

🚂 **NENE VALLEY RAILWAY**

🚂 **NORTH NORFOLK RAILWAY**

🚂 **NORTHAMPTON & LAMPORT RAILWAY**

🚂 **NOTTINGHAM TRANSPORT CTRE**

🚂 **PEAK RAIL**

🚂 **PONTYPOOL & BLAENAVON RAILWAY**

🚂 **RAILWORLD**

🚂 **SEVERN VALLEY RAILWAY**

🚂 **SOUTH DEVON RAILWAY**

🚂 **SOUTH DOWNS LIGHT RAILWAY**

🚂 **SOUTH TYNEDALE RAILWAY**

🚂 **SOUTH YORKSHIRE RAILWAY**

🚂 **SPA VALLEY RAILWAY**

🚂 **STRATHSPEY RAILWAY**

🚂 **SWANAGE RAILWAY**

🚂 **SWANSEA VALE RAILWAY**

🚂 **TELFORD STEAM RAILWAY**

🚂 **TYSELEY LOCOMOTIVE WORKS**

🚂 **VALE OF GLAMORGAN RAILWAY**

🚂 **VINTAGE CARRIAGES TRUST**

ROLLING STOCK by ORIGIN

Adams — BR

WATERCRESS LINE

WEST SOMERSET RAILWAY

YEOVIL RAILWAY CENTRE

BR
FORD MOTOR CO.

NORTH NORFOLK RAILWAY

BRCW

EAST LANCASHIRE RAILWAY

LAKESIDE & HAVERTHWAITE RLWY

BRITISH ALUMINIUM CO

ULSTER FOLK & TRANSPORT

BRITISH COAL

LEIGHTON BUZZARD RAILWAY

BRITISH INDUSTRIAL SAND LTD

LEIGHTON BUZZARD RAILWAY

BRITISH STEEL

RAILWORLD

BRITISH SUGAR CORPORATION

SEVERN VALLEY RAILWAY

BROOMFIELD BRICKWORKS

LEIGHTON BUZZARD RAILWAY

BRW

PAIGNTON & DARTMOUTH RAILWAY

BURY PORT & GWENDRAETH VALLEY RLWY

DIDCOT RAILWAY CENTRE

BUTTERLEY BRICK CO

LEIGHTON BUZZARD RAILWAY

CALCUTTA CORPORATION

LEIGHTON BUZZARD RAILWAY

CALEDONIAN RAILWAY

STRATHSPEY RAILWAY

CAMEROON DEVELOPMENT CORP

LEIGHTON BUZZARD RAILWAY

CARDIFF RAILWAY

DIDCOT RAILWAY CENTRE

CCWR

CHASEWATER RAILWAY

CEGB

MANGAPPS RAILWAY MUSEUM

CENTRAL RAILWAY, INDIA

LEIGHTON BUZZARD RAILWAY

CLEVELAND BRIDGE ENGINEERING

DARLINGTON RAILWAY PRES SOC

CO DONEGAL RAILWAY JOINT COMMITTEE

ULSTER FOLK & TRANSPORT

COMMONWEALTH SMELTING

LEIGHTON BUZZARD RAILWAY

CONSETT IRON CO

BEAMISH

CORRIS RAILWAY

TALYLLYN RAILWAY

COWAN, LEITRIM & RUSCOMMON RLY

ULSTER FOLK & TRANSPORT

DANISH STATE RAILWAY

RAILWORLD

DARLINGTON CHEMICAL & INSULATING CO

DARLINGTON RAILWAY PRES SOC

DARLINGTON CHEMICAL AND INSULATING CO

DARLINGTON RAILWAY PRES SOC

DB

NENE VALLEY RAILWAY

DEVON COUNTY COUNCIL

LEIGHTON BUZZARD RAILWAY

DEVONPORT DOCKYARD

PLYM VALLEY RAILWAY

DINORWIC QUARRY

KEW BRIDGE STEAM MUSEUM

LEIGHTON BUZZARD RAILWAY

DORKING LIME

BEAMISH

DSB

NENE VALLEY RAILWAY

EAST COAST JOINT STOCK

VINTAGE CARRIAGES TRUST

EATON HALL

PERRYGROVE RAILWAY

ECLIPSE PEAT CO LTD

LEIGHTON BUZZARD RAILWAY

EDMUND NUTTALL CONTRACTORS

VINTAGE CARRIAGES TRUST

ELY PAPER MILLS - CARDIFF

VALE OF GLAMORGAN RAILWAY

FAR INGS TILERIES

LEIGHTON BUZZARD RAILWAY

FETHERLEYS BRICKWORKS

LEIGHTON BUZZARD RAILWAY

ROLLING STOCK by ORIGIN

BR — Fetherleys Brickworks

FORD MOTOR CO
NNR NORTH NORFOLK RAILWAY

GAS BOARD
NNR BEAMISH

GCR
NNR DERWENT VALLEY

NNR NOTTINGHAM TRANSPORT CTRE

GEORGE GARSIDE (SAND) LTD
NNR LEIGHTON BUZZARD RAILWAY

GER
NNR CHASEWATER RAILWAY

NNR MANGAPPS RAILWAY MUSEUM

NNR NORTH NORFOLK RAILWAY

GERMAN MILITARY
NNR WELSHPOOL & LLANFAIR

GNR
NNR BLUEBELL RAILWAY

NNR MANGAPPS RAILWAY MUSEUM

NNR NORTH NORFOLK RAILWAY

NNR RPSI

GREAT NORTHERN RAILWAY, IRELAND
NNR ULSTER FOLK & TRANSPORT

GROUDLE GLEN
NNR AMBERLEY WORKING MUSEUM

GSR
NNR ULSTER FOLK & TRANSPORT

GUARD BRIDGE PAPER CO
NNR LEIGHTON BUZZARD RAILWAY

GUINNESS RAILWAY
NNR ULSTER FOLK & TRANSPORT

GWR
NNR ARMLEY MILLS

NNR BLUEBELL RAILWAY

NNR BUCKINGHAMSHIRE RLWY CTRE

NNR CAMBRIAN RAILWAY SOCIETY

NNR CHASEWATER RAILWAY

NNR DERWENT VALLEY

NNR DIDCOT RAILWAY CENTRE

NNR EAST LANCASHIRE RAILWAY

NNR GLOUCESTERSHIRE WARWICKSHIRE

NNR GREAT WESTERN RAILWAY MUSEUM

NNR GWILI RAILWAY

NNR KEIGHLEY & WORTH VALLEY

NNR KENT & EAST SUSSEX RAILWAY

NNR LLANGOLLEN RAILWAY

NNR MUSEUM OF SCIENCE & INDUSTRY

NNR NATIONAL RAILWAY MUSEUM

NNR NOTTINGHAM TRANSPORT CTRE

NNR PAIGNTON & DARTMOUTH RAILWAY

NNR PONTYPOOL & BLAENAVON RAILWAY

NNR SEVERN VALLEY RAILWAY

NNR SOUTH DEVON RAILWAY

NNR STEAM

NNR SWANSEA VALE RAILWAY

NNR TELFORD STEAM RAILWAY

NNR TYSELEY LOCOMOTIVE WORKS

HALL & CO
NNR LEIGHTON BUZZARD RAILWAY

HAMMILL BRICK CO
NNR LEIGHTON BUZZARD RAILWAY

HARTON COAL CO
NNR BEAMISH

HEATHERSLAW LIGHT RAILWAY
NNR HEATHERSLAW LIGHT RAILWAY

HETTON COLLIERY
NNR BEAMISH

HIGHLAND RAILWAY
NNR STRATHSPEY RAILWAY

HOLLANDS MOSS PEAT CO LTD
NNR LEIGHTON BUZZARD RAILWAY

ISLE OF MAN RAILWAY
NNR ISLE OF MAN RAILWAY

JACOBS AINTREE
NNR BEAMISH

JOSEPH ARNOLD & SONS LTD
NNR LEIGHTON BUZZARD RAILWAY

L & NW
NNR CHASEWATER RAILWAY

LBSCR
NNR BLUEBELL RAILWAY

LCDR
NNR BLUEBELL RAILWAY

ROLLING STOCK by ORIGIN

Ford Motor Co — LCDR

ROLLING STOCK by ORIGIN

Leighton Buzzard Railway — Mersey Ironworks

LEIGHTON BUZZARD RAILWAY
- LEIGHTON BUZZARD RAILWAY

LEISURERAIL LTD
- HOLLYBUSH GARDEN CENTRE

LIVERPOOL & MANCHESTER RAILWAY
- TIMOTHY HACKWORTH

LMR
- PEAK RAIL

LMS
- AVON VALLEY RAILWAY
- BARROW HILL ROUNDHOUSE
- BLUEBELL RAILWAY
- BO'NESS & KINNEIL RAILWAY
- BRESSINGHAM STEAM
- BRISTOL HARBOUR RAILWAY
- BUCKINGHAMSHIRE RLWY CTRE
- DERWENT VALLEY
- EAST ANGLIAN RAILWAY MUSEUM
- EAST LANCASHIRE RAILWAY
- EAST SOMERSET RAILWAY
- GLOUCESTERSHIRE WARWICKSHIRE
- GWILI RAILWAY
- KEIGHLEY & WORTH VALLEY
- KENT & EAST SUSSEX RAILWAY
- LLANGOLLEN RAILWAY
- MUSEUM OF SCIENCE & INDUSTRY
- NOTTINGHAM TRANSPORT CTRE
- PEAK RAIL
- SEVERN VALLEY RAILWAY
- SOUTH DEVON RAILWAY
- SOUTH DOWNS LIGHT RAILWAY
- STRATHSPEY RAILWAY
- SWANSEA VALE RAILWAY
- TYSELEY LOCOMOTIVE WORKS

LMS & BR
- SPA VALLEY RAILWAY

LMS & NCC
- ULSTER FOLK & TRANSPORT

LMS & TURKISH STATE RAILWAYS
- GLOUCESTERSHIRE WARWICKSHIRE

LMSR
- CHASEWATER RAILWAY

LNER
- DERWENT VALLEY
- EAST ANGLIAN RAILWAY MUSEUM
- GREAT CENTRAL RAILWAY
- KEIGHLEY & WORTH VALLEY
- MANGAPPS RAILWAY MUSEUM
- NENE VALLEY RAILWAY
- NORTH NORFOLK RAILWAY
- NOTTINGHAM TRANSPORT CTRE
- SEVERN VALLEY RAILWAY
- SOUTH DEVON RAILWAY
- SOUTH DOWNS LIGHT RAILWAY
- STRATHSPEY RAILWAY
- WATERCRESS LINE

LNWR
- BLUEBELL RAILWAY
- KEIGHLEY & WORTH VALLEY
- MID-NORFOLK RAILWAY

LONDON BRIGHTON & SOUTH COAST RAILWAY
- BLUEBELL RAILWAY

LONDONDERRY PORT & HARBOUR COMMISSIONERS
- ULSTER FOLK & TRANSPORT

LSWR
- BLUEBELL RAILWAY
- BRESSINGHAM STEAM
- BUCKINGHAMSHIRE RLWY CTRE
- GREAT WESTERN RAILWAY MUSEUM
- WATERCRESS LINE

LT
- MANGAPPS RAILWAY MUSEUM

M & C
- CHASEWATER RAILWAY

MANCHESTER SHIP CANAL
- SEVERN VALLEY RAILWAY
- VALE OF GLAMORGAN RAILWAY

MATHERAN LIGHT RAILWAY
- RAILWORLD

MERSEY IRONWORKS
- SEVERN VALLEY RAILWAY

METROPOLITAN

VINTAGE CARRIAGES TRUST

METROPOLITAN RAILWAY/LONDON TRANSPORT

SPA VALLEY RAILWAY

MINISTRY OF DEFENCE

LEIGHTON BUZZARD RAILWAY

OLD KILN LIGHT RAILWAY

MOTOR RAIL

PERRYGROVE RAILWAY

MOWT

BLUEBELL RAILWAY

MR

BARROW HILL ROUNDHOUSE

BLUEBELL RAILWAY

KEIGHLEY & WORTH VALLEY

MS & L

CHASEWATER RAILWAY

VINTAGE CARRIAGES TRUST

NATIONAL COAL BOARD

INDUSTRIAL RAILWAY MUSEUM

LEIGHTON BUZZARD RAILWAY

VALE OF GLAMORGAN RAILWAY

NBR

BO'NESS & KINNEIL RAILWAY

NCB

CHASEWATER RAILWAY

DERWENT VALLEY

MANGAPPS RAILWAY MUSEUM

SOUTH DOWNS LIGHT RAILWAY

SOUTH TYNEDALE RAILWAY

STRATHSPEY RAILWAY

SWANSEA VALE RAILWAY

NER

BEAMISH

CHASEWATER RAILWAY

DERWENT VALLEY

MANGAPPS RAILWAY MUSEUM

NORTH WALES NARROW GAUGE

BARLEYLANDS MINIATURE RAILWAY

NORTHERN GAS BOARD

BATTLEFIELD LINE

NSB

BRESSINGHAM STEAM

OAKLEY SLATE QUARRY

LEIGHTON BUZZARD RAILWAY

OXTED GREYSTONE LIME CO

LEIGHTON BUZZARD RAILWAY

PADARN RAILWAY

INDUSTRIAL RAILWAY MUSEUM

PARKHILL MINE

LEIGHTON BUZZARD RAILWAY

PATENT SHAFT STEELWORKS

SEVERN VALLEY RAILWAY

PENRHYN SLATE QUARRY

OLD KILN LIGHT RAILWAY

PEN-YR-ORSEDD QUARRY

LEIGHTON BUZZARD RAILWAY

PKP, POLISH STATE RAILWAYS

APPLEBY-FRODINGHAM RAILWAY

POLISH RAILWAYS

LEIGHTON BUZZARD RAILWAY

SPA VALLEY RAILWAY

PORT STEWART TRAMWAY

ULSTER FOLK & TRANSPORT

PORTUGUESE FORESTRY COMMISSION

OLD KILN LIGHT RAILWAY

PRENTON BRICK & TILE CO LTD

LEIGHTON BUZZARD RAILWAY

RAILCAR SERVICES

DARLINGTON RAILWAY PRES SOC

REDLAND FLETTONS LTD

LEIGHTON BUZZARD RAILWAY

RFS INDUSTRIES

MANGAPPS RAILWAY MUSEUM

RICHARDSONS MOSS LITTER CO LTD

LEIGHTON BUZZARD RAILWAY

ROYAL AIR FORCE

TALYLLYN RAILWAY

ROYAL ORDNANCE

LEIGHTON BUZZARD RAILWAY

RSH

MANGAPPS RAILWAY MUSEUM

PEAK RAIL

ROLLING STOCK by ORIGIN

Metropolitan — RSH

RUGBY PORTLNAD CEMENT
- SEVERN VALLEY RAILWAY

SAR
- BUCKINGHAMSHIRE RLWY CTRE

SEAHAM HARBOUR
- BEAMISH

SECR
- BLUEBELL RAILWAY
- WATERCRESS LINE

SER
- BLUEBELL RAILWAY

SEVERN TRENT WATER AUTHORITY
- LEIGHTON BUZZARD RAILWAY

SEZELA SUGAR ESTATE
- LEIGHTON BUZZARD RAILWAY

SKINNINGROVE STEEL WORKS
- MANGAPPS RAILWAY MUSEUM

SL & NCR
- RPSI

SOLVAY
- LEIGHTON BUZZARD RAILWAY

SOUTH EASTERN & CHATHAM RAILWAY
- BLUEBELL RAILWAY

SOUTH EASTERN RAILWAY
- BLUEBELL RAILWAY

SOUTH HETTON COLLIERY
- TIMOTHY HACKWORTH

SPRINGFIELD TILERIES
- LEIGHTON BUZZARD RAILWAY

SR
- AVON VALLEY RAILWAY
- BLUEBELL RAILWAY
- CHASEWATER RAILWAY
- GLOUCESTERSHIRE WARWICKSHIRE
- KEIGHLEY & WORTH VALLEY
- NOTTINGHAM TRANSPORT CTRE
- SEVERN VALLEY RAILWAY
- SOUTH DOWNS LIGHT RAILWAY
- SPA VALLEY RAILWAY
- SWANAGE RAILWAY
- VINTAGE CARRIAGES TRUST
- WATERCRESS LINE

ST ALBANS SAND & GRAVEL CO
- LEIGHTON BUZZARD RAILWAY

STANDARD BOTTLE CO
- LEIGHTON BUZZARD RAILWAY

STAVELEY IRON & STEEL LTD
- LEIGHTON BUZZARD RAILWAY

STEWARTS & LLOYDS
- LEIGHTON BUZZARD RAILWAY

STOCKTON & DARLINGTON RAILWAY
- BEAMISH

SUGAR CANE, ANTIGUA
- WELSHPOOL & LLANFAIR

TALYLLYN RAILWAY
- TALYLLYN RAILWAY

USATC
- TYSELEY LOCOMOTIVE WORKS
- WATERCRESS LINE

VIP PETROLEUM
- RAILWORLD

VULCAN FOUNDRY
- PEAK RAIL

W R CUNIS
- LEIGHTON BUZZARD RAILWAY

WALLSEND COLLIERY
- BEAMISH

WAR DEPARTMENT LIGHT RAILWAYS
- BEAMISH
- BLUEBELL RAILWAY
- LEIGHTON BUZZARD RAILWAY
- ULSTER FOLK & TRANSPORT

WEST KENT MAIN SEWERAGE BOARD
- LEIGHTON BUZZARD RAILWAY

WESTON REGION STYLE
- ROYAL VICTORIA RAILWAY

WEYMSS PRIVATE RAILWAY
- STRATHSPEY RAILWAY

WHESIDE ENGINEERING LTD
- DARLINGTON RAILWAY PRES SOC

WOODHAM BRICK CO LTD
- LEIGHTON BUZZARD RAILWAY

WYLAM COLLIERY
- NATIONAL RAILWAY MUSEUM

Rolling Stock by Wheel Arrangement

SECTION 5F

This section shows the Wheel Arrangement of stock and where it can be located

e.g. 0-4-0, Abbey Light Railway

Once you have located a railway/museum using this section you can then refer to the railway or museum's detailed profile in section 1.

0-2-2

AWT NATIONAL RAILWAY MUSEUM

0-2-2WT

AWT BLUEBELL RAILWAY

0-4-0

AWT ABBEY LIGHT RAILWAY

AWT ARMLEY MILLS

AWT BARROW HILL ROUNDHOUSE

AWT BEAMISH

AWT BICTON WOODLAND RAILWAY

AWT BO'NESS & KINNEIL RAILWAY

AWT BOWES RAILWAY

AWT BREDGAR & WORMSHILL

AWT BRISTOL HARBOUR RAILWAY

AWT CALEDONIAN RAILWAY

AWT CHOLSEY & WALLINGFORD RAILWAY

AWT DARLINGTON RAILWAY CENTRE

AWT DARLINGTON RAILWAY PRES SOC

AWT DOWNPATRICK & ARDGLASS

AWT EAST ANGLIAN RAILWAY MUSEUM

AWT EAST KENT LIGHT RAILWAY

AWT EMBSAY & BOLTON ABBEY RLWY

AWT FAIRBOURNE & BARMOUTH

AWT FOXFIELD STEAM RAILWAY

AWT GIANTS CAUSEWAY & BUSHMILLS

AWT GREAT WESTERN RAILWAY MUSEUM

AWT GREAT WHIPSNADE RAILWAY

AWT GROUDLE GLEN RAILWAY

AWT INDUSTRIAL RAILWAY MUSEUM

AWT IRISH STEAM PRESERVATION SOC

AWT KEITH & DUFFTOWN RAILWAY

AWT KENT & EAST SUSSEX RAILWAY

AWT KEW BRIDGE STEAM MUSEUM

AWT KIRKLEES LIGHT RAILWAY

AWT LAKESIDE & HAVERTHWAITE RLWY

AWT LLANBERIS LAKE RAILWAY

AWT MANGAPPS RAILWAY MUSEUM

AWT MARKEATON PARK LIGHT RAILWAY

AWT NARROW GAUGE RAILWAY MUSEUM

AWT NATIONAL RAILWAY MUSEUM

AWT NIRT

AWT NORTHAMPTON & LAMPORT RAILWAY

AWT NOTTINGHAM TRANSPORT CTRE

AWT PALLOT STEAM MUSEUM

AWT PLYM VALLEY RAILWAY

AWT ROMNEY HYTHE & DYMCHURCH

AWT SEVERN VALLEY RAILWAY

AWT SOMERSET & DORSET RAILWAY

AWT SOUTH DOWNS LIGHT RAILWAY

AWT SOUTH TYNEDALE RAILWAY

AWT TALYLLYN RAILWAY

AWT TEIFI VALLEY RAILWAY

AWT TELFORD STEAM RAILWAY

AWT TIMOTHY HACKWORTH

AWT ULSTER FOLK & TRANSPORT

AWT WELSHPOOL & LLANFAIR

0-4-0 - 0-4-0

AWT SOUTH DOWNS LIGHT RAILWAY

0-4-0 + 0-4-0T

AWT BRESSINGHAM STEAM

0-4-0 DM

AWT BURE VALLEY RAILWAY

AWT CADEBY LIGHT RAILWAY

0-4-0 PM

AWT CADEBY LIGHT RAILWAY

0-4-0 ST

AWT CADEBY LIGHT RAILWAY

AWT CALEDONIAN RAILWAY

0-4-0BE

AWT AMBERLEY WORKING MUSEUM

AWT ARMLEY MILLS

0-4-0CT

AWT MIDLAND RAILWAY CENTRE

AWT TANFIELD RAILWAY

0-4-0DE

AWT BO'NESS & KINNEIL RAILWAY

AWT CHASEWATER RAILWAY

AWT GREAT CENTRAL RAILWAY

AWT GWILI RAILWAY

ROLLING STOCK by WHEEL ARRANGEMENT

0-2-2 — 0-4-0DE

ROLLING STOCK by WHEEL ARRANGEMENT

0-4-0DE — 0-4-0PE

MIDDLETON RAILWAY	DERWENT VALLEY
MIDLAND RAILWAY CENTRE	DEVON RAILWAY CENTRE
NENE VALLEY RAILWAY	EAST LANCASHIRE RAILWAY
NOTTINGHAM TRANSPORT CTRE	EMBSAY & BOLTON ABBEY RLWY
SOUTH YORKSHIRE RAILWAY	FFESTINIOG RAILWAY
TANFIELD RAILWAY	FOXFIELD STEAM RAILWAY
WEST SOMERSET RAILWAY	GREAT CENTRAL RAILWAY

0-4-0DH

BODMIN & WENFORD RAILWAY	HOLLYCOMBE STEAM COLLECTION
BO'NESS & KINNEIL RAILWAY	KEIGHLEY & WORTH VALLEY
BOWES RAILWAY	LAKESIDE & HAVERTHWAITE RLWY
CAMBRIAN RAILWAY SOCIETY	LAVENDER LINE
CHASEWATER RAILWAY	LEIGHTON BUZZARD RAILWAY
CHURNET VALLEY RAILWAY	MIDDLETON RAILWAY
EAST LANCASHIRE RAILWAY	MIDLAND RAILWAY CENTRE
MIDDLETON RAILWAY	MID-SUFFOLK LIGHT RAILWAY
NENE VALLEY RAILWAY	MUSEUM OF ARMY TRANSPORT
NIRT	NIRT
NORTH YORKSHIRE MOORS RAILWAY	NORTH YORKSHIRE MOORS RAILWAY
NORTHAMPTON & LAMPORT RAILWAY	PEAK RAIL
SCOTTISH RAILWAY CENTRE	PERRYGROVE RAILWAY
SNOWDON MOUNTAIN RAILWAY	ROTHER VALLEY RAILWAY
SOUTH YORKSHIRE RAILWAY	SCOTTISH RAILWAY CENTRE
SWANSEA VALE RAILWAY	SITTINGBOURNE & KEMSLEY
TANFIELD RAILWAY	SOUTH YORKSHIRE RAILWAY

0-4-0DM

ALDERNEY RAILWAY	SPA VALLEY RAILWAY
ALMOND VALLEY HERITAGE TRUST	SWANAGE RAILWAY
AMBERLEY WORKING MUSEUM	SWINDON & CRICKLADE RAILWAY
AMERTON RAILWAY	TANFIELD RAILWAY
ARMLEY MILLS	WELSHPOOL & LLANFAIR

0-4-0F

AVON VALLEY RAILWAY	BODMIN & WENFORD RAILWAY
BATTLEFIELD LINE	BUCKINGHAMSHIRE RLWY CTRE
BODMIN & WENFORD RAILWAY	MIDLAND RAILWAY CENTRE
BOWES RAILWAY	NATIONAL RAILWAY MUSEUM
BUCKINGHAMSHIRE RLWY CTRE	NATIONAL WATERWAYS MUSEUM
CAMBRIAN RAILWAY SOCIETY	SITTINGBOURNE & KEMSLEY
CHASEWATER RAILWAY	SWANSEA INDUSTRIAL MUSEUM

0-4-0PE

DARLINGTON RAILWAY PRES SOC	TYSELEY LOCOMOTIVE WORKS

0-4-0PM

🚂 **BEAMISH**

0-40ST

🚂 **LAKESIDE & HAVERTHWAITE RLWY**

0-4-0ST

🚂 AMBERLEY WORKING MUSEUM
🚂 AMERTON RAILWAY
🚂 APPLEBY-FRODINGHAM RAILWAY
🚂 ARMLEY MILLS
🚂 BALA LAKE RAILWAY
🚂 BATTLEFIELD LINE
🚂 BEAMISH
🚂 BODMIN & WENFORD RAILWAY
🚂 BO'NESS & KINNEIL RAILWAY
🚂 BRESSINGHAM STEAM
🚂 BUCKINGHAMSHIRE RLWY CTRE
🚂 CALEDONIAN RAILWAY
🚂 CAMBRIAN RAILWAY SOCIETY
🚂 CHASEWATER RAILWAY
🚂 DERBY INDUSTRIAL MUSEUM
🚂 DERWENT VALLEY
🚂 DIDCOT RAILWAY CENTRE
🚂 EAST LANCASHIRE RAILWAY
🚂 EAST SOMERSET RAILWAY
🚂 EMBSAY & BOLTON ABBEY RLWY
🚂 GWILI RAILWAY
🚂 HOLLYCOMBE STEAM COLLECTION
🚂 KEIGHLEY & WORTH VALLEY
🚂 KEW BRIDGE STEAM MUSEUM
🚂 LAKESIDE & HAVERTHWAITE RLWY
🚂 LAUNCESTON STEAM RAILWAY
🚂 LAVENDER LINE
🚂 LEIGHTON BUZZARD RAILWAY
🚂 LINCOLNSHIRE WOLDS RAILWAY
🚂 MIDDLETON RAILWAY
🚂 MIDLAND RAILWAY CENTRE
🚂 NATIONAL RAILWAY MUSEUM
🚂 NORTH GLOUCESTERSHIRE RAILWAY
🚂 NORTHAMPTON & LAMPORT RAILWAY

🚂 OLD KILN LIGHT RAILWAY
🚂 PEAK RAIL
🚂 PLYM VALLEY RAILWAY
🚂 PONTYPOOL & BLAENAVON RAILWAY
🚂 RPSI
🚂 RUTLAND RAILWAY MUSEUM
🚂 SITTINGBOURNE & KEMSLEY
🚂 SOUTH YORKSHIRE RAILWAY
🚂 SWANAGE RAILWAY
🚂 SWANSEA VALE RAILWAY
🚂 SWINDON & CRICKLADE RAILWAY
🚂 TANFIELD RAILWAY
🚂 TELFORD STEAM RAILWAY
🚂 TIMOTHY HACKWORTH
🚂 TYSELEY LOCOMOTIVE WORKS
🚂 VALE OF GLAMORGAN RAILWAY
🚂 VINTAGE CARRIAGES TRUST
🚂 WEST LANCASHIRE LIGHT RLWY
🚂 WEST SOMERSET RAILWAY
🚂 YEOVIL RAILWAY CENTRE

0-4-0STT

🚂 FFESTINIOG RAILWAY

0-4-0T

🚂 AMBERLEY WORKING MUSEUM
🚂 BLUEBELL RAILWAY
🚂 BO'NESS & KINNEIL RAILWAY
🚂 BRESSINGHAM STEAM
🚂 BUCKINGHAMSHIRE RLWY CTRE
🚂 ISLE OF WIGHT STEAM RAILWAY
🚂 KENT & EAST SUSSEX RAILWAY
🚂 LEIGHTON BUZZARD RAILWAY
🚂 MIDDLETON RAILWAY
🚂 MOORS VALLEY RAILWAY
🚂 NOTTINGHAM TRANSPORT CTRE
🚂 ROYAL VICTORIA RAILWAY
🚂 SOUTH DEVON RAILWAY
🚂 SOUTH TYNEDALE RAILWAY
🚂 SPA VALLEY RAILWAY
🚂 TANFIELD RAILWAY

ROLLING STOCK by WHEEL ARRANGEMENT

0-4-0PM — 0-4-0T

ROLLING STOCK by WHEEL ARRANGEMENT

0-4-0T — 0-4-2WT

- TYSELEY LOCOMOTIVE WORKS
- ULSTER FOLK & TRANSPORT
- WEST LANCASHIRE LIGHT RLWY

0-4-0TG

- NIRT

0-4-0TT

- MOORS VALLEY RAILWAY

0-4-0VB

- BEAMISH
- NATIONAL TRAMWAY MUSEUM

0-4-0VBT

- CLEETHORPES LIGHT RAILWAY
- DIDCOT RAILWAY CENTRE
- MIDDLETON RAILWAY
- NENE VALLEY RAILWAY

0-4-0VCT

- BEAMISH

0-4-0VG

- BEAMISH

0-4-0VRT

- LEIGHTON BUZZARD RAILWAY

0-4-0WE

- ARMLEY MILLS

0-4-0WT

- AMBERLEY WORKING MUSEUM
- ARMLEY MILLS
- BEAMISH
- BUCKINGHAMSHIRE RLWY CTRE
- DIDCOT RAILWAY CENTRE
- GIANTS CAUSEWAY & BUSHMILLS
- HOLLYCOMBE STEAM COLLECTION
- LEADHILLS & WANLOCKHEAD
- LEIGHTON BUZZARD RAILWAY
- MIDDLETON RAILWAY
- NORTH GLOUCESTERSHIRE RAILWAY
- TALYLLYN RAILWAY
- TANFIELD RAILWAY

0-4-2

- BEER HEIGHTS
- BREDGAR & WORMSHILL
- BROOKSIDE MINIATURE

- GREAT WESTERN RAILWAY MUSEUM
- GREAT WHIPSNADE RAILWAY
- HEATHERSLAW LIGHT RAILWAY
- HOLLYBUSH GARDEN CENTRE
- NATIONAL RAILWAY MUSEUM
- RAVENGLASS & ESKDALE
- SOUTH DOWNS LIGHT RAILWAY
- SOUTH TYNEDALE RAILWAY
- WELSH HIGHLAND RAILWAY

0-4-2DH

- MOORS VALLEY RAILWAY

0-4-2DM

- RHYL MINIATURE RAILWAY

0-4-2IST

- AMERTON RAILWAY

0-4-2ST

- PRESTONGRANGE INDUSTRIAL
- SITTINGBOURNE & KEMSLEY
- TALYLLYN RAILWAY
- TANFIELD RAILWAY

0-4-2ST & TENDER

- BEER HEIGHTS

0-4-2T

- ALFORD VALLEY RAILWAY
- CAVAN & LEITRIM RAILWAY
- CONWY VALLEY
- DIDCOT RAILWAY CENTRE
- EXMOOR STEAM RAILWAY
- GARTELL LIGHT RAILWAY
- GLOUCESTERSHIRE WARWICKSHIRE
- GROUDLE GLEN RAILWAY
- MARKEATON PARK LIGHT RAILWAY
- MOORS VALLEY RAILWAY
- NORTH GLOUCESTERSHIRE RAILWAY
- SNOWDON MOUNTAIN RAILWAY
- SOUTH DEVON RAILWAY
- TALYLLYN RAILWAY
- WEST LANCASHIRE LIGHT RLWY

0-4-2WT

- KENT & EAST SUSSEX RAILWAY

0-4-4T

- BLUEBELL RAILWAY
- BO'NESS & KINNEIL RAILWAY
- FFESTINIOG RAILWAY
- ISLE OF WIGHT STEAM RAILWAY
- NATIONAL RAILWAY MUSEUM

0-6-0

- ARMLEY MILLS
- AVON VALLEY RAILWAY
- BARROW HILL ROUNDHOUSE
- BEAMISH
- BLUEBELL RAILWAY
- BO'NESS & KINNEIL RAILWAY
- BOWES RAILWAY
- BREDGAR & WORMSHILL
- BRISTOL HARBOUR RAILWAY
- CALEDONIAN RAILWAY
- CHURNET VALLEY RAILWAY
- DARLINGTON RAILWAY PRES SOC
- EAST ANGLIAN RAILWAY MUSEUM
- EAST KENT LIGHT RAILWAY
- EAST LANCASHIRE RAILWAY
- EAST SOMERSET RAILWAY
- EASTLEIGH LAKESIDE RAILWAY
- ELSECAR HERITAGE CENTRE
- EMBSAY & BOLTON ABBEY RLWY
- FOXFIELD STEAM RAILWAY
- GLOUCESTERSHIRE WARWICKSHIRE
- GREAT WHIPSNADE RAILWAY
- INDUSTRIAL RAILWAY MUSEUM
- IRCHESTER NARROW GAUGE MUSEUM
- ISLE OF MAN RAILWAY
- KEIGHLEY & WORTH VALLEY
- KEITH & DUFFTOWN RAILWAY
- KENT & EAST SUSSEX RAILWAY
- KERR MINIATURE RAILWAY
- LAPPA VALLEY STEAM RAILWAY
- LLANGOLLEN RAILWAY
- MANGAPPS RAILWAY MUSEUM

- MIDLAND RAILWAY CENTRE
- MUSEUM OF SCIENCE & INDUSTRY
- NATIONAL RAILWAY MUSEUM
- NIRT
- NORTH NORFOLK RAILWAY
- NORTH YORKSHIRE MOORS RAILWAY
- NORTHAMPTON & LAMPORT RAILWAY
- NOTTINGHAM TRANSPORT CTRE
- PAIGNTON & DARTMOUTH RAILWAY
- PALLOT STEAM MUSEUM
- RPSI
- SEVERN VALLEY RAILWAY
- SOUTH DEVON RAILWAY
- SOUTH DOWNS LIGHT RAILWAY
- SOUTH TYNEDALE RAILWAY
- SPA VALLEY RAILWAY
- STEAM
- STRATHSPEY RAILWAY
- SWINDON & CRICKLADE RAILWAY
- TIMOTHY HACKWORTH
- VALE OF GLAMORGAN RAILWAY
- VALE OF RHEIDOL RAILWAY
- WATERCRESS LINE
- WELLS & WALSINGHAM
- WELSH HIGHLAND RAILWAY

0-6-0 ST

- CALEDONIAN RAILWAY

0-6-0DE

- AVON VALLEY RAILWAY
- BO'NESS & KINNEIL RAILWAY
- CALEDONIAN RAILWAY
- CHINNOR & PRINCES RISBOROUGH
- CHURNET VALLEY RAILWAY
- DARTMOOR RAILWAY
- DIDCOT RAILWAY CENTRE
- EAST LANCASHIRE RAILWAY
- GREAT CENTRAL RAILWAY
- KEIGHLEY & WORTH VALLEY
- MIDLAND RAILWAY CENTRE

ROLLING STOCK by WHEEL ARRANGEMENT

0-4-4T — 0-6-0DE

ROLLING STOCK by WHEEL ARRANGEMENT

0-6-0DE — 0-6-0ST

∿∿ NENE VALLEY RAILWAY	∿∿ MIDLAND RAILWAY CENTRE
∿∿ NORTH NORFOLK RAILWAY	∿∿ NORTH NORFOLK RAILWAY
∿∿ NORTH YORKSHIRE MOORS RAILWAY	∿∿ NORTH YORKSHIRE MOORS RAILWAY
∿∿ SOUTH YORKSHIRE RAILWAY	∿∿ PEAK RAIL
∿∿ STRATHSPEY RAILWAY	∿∿ SOUTH YORKSHIRE RAILWAY
∿∿ TYSELEY LOCOMOTIVE WORKS	∿∿ SWANSEA VALE RAILWAY
∿∿ WATERCRESS LINE	∿∿ SWINDON & CRICKLADE RAILWAY
∿∿ WEST SOMERSET RAILWAY	∿∿ WELSHPOOL & LLANFAIR

0-6-0DH

∿∿ BO'NESS & KINNEIL RAILWAY	∿∿ WEST SOMERSET RAILWAY

0-6-0MF

∿∿ BOWES RAILWAY	∿∿ BOWES RAILWAY
∿∿ BUCKINGHAMSHIRE RLWY CTRE	

0-6-0F

∿∿ CHINNOR & PRINCES RISBOROUGH	∿∿ LAKESIDE & HAVERTHWAITE RLWY
∿∿ EAST LANCASHIRE RAILWAY	∿∿ NORTH NORFOLK RAILWAY
∿∿ FFESTINIOG RAILWAY	∿∿ TANFIELD RAILWAY
∿∿ NENE VALLEY RAILWAY	

0-6-0PT

∿∿ NOTTINGHAM TRANSPORT CTRE	∿∿ BUCKINGHAMSHIRE RLWY CTRE
∿∿ PEAK RAIL	∿∿ DIDCOT RAILWAY CENTRE
∿∿ PONTYPOOL & BLAENAVON RAILWAY	∿∿ KEIGHLEY & WORTH VALLEY
∿∿ SOUTH YORKSHIRE RAILWAY	∿∿ KENT & EAST SUSSEX RAILWAY
∿∿ TANFIELD RAILWAY	∿∿ NATIONAL RAILWAY MUSEUM
∿∿ WEST SOMERSET RAILWAY	∿∿ SEVERN VALLEY RAILWAY

0-6-0DM

∿∿ ARMLEY MILLS	∿∿ SWANSEA VALE RAILWAY
∿∿ AVON VALLEY RAILWAY	∿∿ TYSELEY LOCOMOTIVE WORKS
∿∿ BARROW HILL ROUNDHOUSE	∿∿ WEST SOMERSET RAILWAY

0-6-0ST

∿∿ BATTLEFIELD LINE	∿∿ AMBERLEY WORKING MUSEUM
∿∿ BUCKINGHAMSHIRE RLWY CTRE	∿∿ ARMLEY MILLS
∿∿ CAMBRIAN RAILWAY SOCIETY	∿∿ AVON VALLEY RAILWAY
∿∿ CHASEWATER RAILWAY	∿∿ BATTLEFIELD LINE
∿∿ CHURNET VALLEY RAILWAY	∿∿ BLUEBELL RAILWAY
∿∿ DERWENT VALLEY	∿∿ BODMIN & WENFORD RAILWAY
∿∿ DIDCOT RAILWAY CENTRE	∿∿ BUCKINGHAMSHIRE RLWY CTRE
∿∿ EAST LANCASHIRE RAILWAY	∿∿ CAMBRIAN RAILWAY SOCIETY
∿∿ GWILI RAILWAY	∿∿ DIDCOT RAILWAY CENTRE
∿∿ ISLE OF WIGHT STEAM RAILWAY	∿∿ EMBSAY & BOLTON ABBEY RLWY
∿∿ KEIGHLEY & WORTH VALLEY	∿∿ GLOUCESTERSHIRE WARWICKSHIRE
∿∿ LAKESIDE & HAVERTHWAITE RLWY	∿∿ GWILI RAILWAY
∿∿ MIDDLETON RAILWAY	∿∿ KEIGHLEY & WORTH VALLEY

<table>
<tr><td>🚂 KENT & EAST SUSSEX RAILWAY</td><td>🚂 CHASEWATER RAILWAY</td></tr>
<tr><td>🚂 LAKESIDE & HAVERTHWAITE RLWY</td><td>🚂 CHURNET VALLEY RAILWAY</td></tr>
<tr><td>🚂 LAVENDER LINE</td><td>🚂 DERWENT VALLEY</td></tr>
<tr><td>🚂 LINCOLNSHIRE WOLDS RAILWAY</td><td>🚂 EAST LANCASHIRE RAILWAY</td></tr>
<tr><td>🚂 MIDDLETON RAILWAY</td><td>🚂 EAST SOMERSET RAILWAY</td></tr>
<tr><td>🚂 MID-SUFFOLK LIGHT RAILWAY</td><td>🚂 EMBSAY & BOLTON ABBEY RLWY</td></tr>
<tr><td>🚂 MUSEUM OF ARMY TRANSPORT</td><td>🚂 GREAT CENTRAL RAILWAY</td></tr>
<tr><td>🚂 NATIONAL RAILWAY MUSEUM</td><td>🚂 IRCHESTER NARROW GAUGE MUSEUM</td></tr>
<tr><td>🚂 NENE VALLEY RAILWAY</td><td>🚂 ISLE OF WIGHT STEAM RAILWAY</td></tr>
<tr><td>🚂 NORTH NORFOLK RAILWAY</td><td>🚂 KEIGHLEY & WORTH VALLEY</td></tr>
<tr><td>🚂 NORTH YORKSHIRE MOORS RAILWAY</td><td>🚂 KENT & EAST SUSSEX RAILWAY</td></tr>
<tr><td>🚂 NORTHAMPTON & LAMPORT RAILWAY</td><td>🚂 LEIGHTON BUZZARD RAILWAY</td></tr>
<tr><td>🚂 NOTTINGHAM TRANSPORT CTRE</td><td>🚂 MIDDLETON RAILWAY</td></tr>
<tr><td>🚂 PEAK RAIL</td><td>🚂 MIDLAND RAILWAY CENTRE</td></tr>
<tr><td>🚂 PONTYPOOL & BLAENAVON RAILWAY</td><td>🚂 NATIONAL RAILWAY MUSEUM</td></tr>
<tr><td>🚂 RPSI</td><td>🚂 NENE VALLEY RAILWAY</td></tr>
<tr><td>🚂 SCOTTISH RAILWAY CENTRE</td><td>🚂 NORTH YORKSHIRE MOORS RAILWAY</td></tr>
<tr><td>🚂 SEVERN VALLEY RAILWAY</td><td>🚂 NORTHAMPTON & LAMPORT RAILWAY</td></tr>
<tr><td>🚂 SOUTH YORKSHIRE RAILWAY</td><td>🚂 PEAK RAIL</td></tr>
<tr><td>🚂 SPA VALLEY RAILWAY</td><td>🚂 PERRYGROVE RAILWAY</td></tr>
<tr><td>🚂 STRATHSPEY RAILWAY</td><td>🚂 RAILWORLD</td></tr>
<tr><td>🚂 SWANSEA INDUSTRIAL MUSEUM</td><td>🚂 SEVERN VALLEY RAILWAY</td></tr>
<tr><td>🚂 SWANSEA VALE RAILWAY</td><td>🚂 SOUTH DEVON RAILWAY</td></tr>
<tr><td>🚂 SWINDON & CRICKLADE RAILWAY</td><td>🚂 SPA VALLEY RAILWAY</td></tr>
<tr><td>🚂 TANFIELD RAILWAY</td><td>🚂 STRATHSPEY RAILWAY</td></tr>
<tr><td>🚂 ULSTER FOLK & TRANSPORT</td><td>🚂 SWANAGE RAILWAY</td></tr>
<tr><td>🚂 VALE OF GLAMORGAN RAILWAY</td><td>🚂 TANFIELD RAILWAY</td></tr>
<tr><td>🚂 WEST SOMERSET RAILWAY</td><td>🚂 WELSHPOOL & LLANFAIR</td></tr>
</table>

0-6-0T

🚂 APPLEBY-FRODINGHAM RAILWAY

🚂 WEST LANCASHIRE LIGHT RLWY

0-6-0VCG

🚂 AVON VALLEY RAILWAY

🚂 BEAMISH

🚂 BATTLEFIELD LINE

0-6-0WT

🚂 BEAMISH

🚂 ARMLEY MILLS

🚂 BEER HEIGHTS

🚂 BRESSINGHAM STEAM

🚂 BLUEBELL RAILWAY

🚂 LEIGHTON BUZZARD RAILWAY

🚂 BODMIN & WENFORD RAILWAY

🚂 OLD KILN LIGHT RAILWAY

🚂 BO'NESS & KINNEIL RAILWAY

0-6-2

🚂 BRESSINGHAM STEAM

🚂 BRECON MOUNTAIN RAILWAY

🚂 BUCKINGHAMSHIRE RLWY CTRE

🚂 EAST ANGLIAN RAILWAY MUSEUM

ROLLING STOCK by WHEEL ARRANGEMENT

0-6-0ST — 0-6-2

ROLLING STOCK by WHEEL ARRANGEMENT

0-6-2 — 2-4-0DM

EAST SOMERSET RAILWAY

GREAT WHIPSNADE RAILWAY

KEIGHLEY & WORTH VALLEY

TELFORD STEAM RAILWAY

WELSHPOOL & LLANFAIR

0-6-2ST

ARMLEY MILLS

0-6-2T

BLUEBELL RAILWAY

CHURNET VALLEY RAILWAY

DIDCOT RAILWAY CENTRE

GREAT CENTRAL RAILWAY

KEIGHLEY & WORTH VALLEY

LAKESIDE & HAVERTHWAITE RLWY

NATIONAL RAILWAY MUSEUM

NORTH NORFOLK RAILWAY

NORTH YORKSHIRE MOORS RAILWAY

SITTINGBOURNE & KEMSLEY

SWINDON & CRICKLADE RAILWAY

TEIFI VALLEY RAILWAY

0-6-4

FAIRBOURNE & BARMOUTH

LAPPA VALLEY STEAM RAILWAY

0-6-4T

BARLEYLANDS MINIATURE RAILWAY

KIRKLEES LIGHT RAILWAY

RPSI

0-8-0

NATIONAL RAILWAY MUSEUM

NORTH YORKSHIRE MOORS RAILWAY

0-8-0DH

AVON VALLEY RAILWAY

0-8-0T

AMERTON RAILWAY

NORTH GLOUCESTERSHIRE RAILWAY

WELSHPOOL & LLANFAIR

WEST LANCASHIRE LIGHT RLWY

0-8-2

RAVENGLASS & ESKDALE

12W

STRATHSPEY RAILWAY

1CO-CO1

EAST LANCASHIRE RAILWAY

GREAT CENTRAL RAILWAY

NENE VALLEY RAILWAY

NORTHAMPTON & LAMPORT RAILWAY

WATERCRESS LINE

2 AXLE

RAILWORLD

2-10-0

BARLEYLANDS MINIATURE RAILWAY

BLUEBELL RAILWAY

BRESSINGHAM STEAM

CHURNET VALLEY RAILWAY

EAST LANCASHIRE RAILWAY

GLOUCESTERSHIRE WARWICKSHIRE

GREAT CENTRAL RAILWAY

MIDLAND RAILWAY CENTRE

NATIONAL RAILWAY MUSEUM

NENE VALLEY RAILWAY

NORTH YORKSHIRE MOORS RAILWAY

SEVERN VALLEY RAILWAY

2-2-0TG

BUCKINGHAMSHIRE RLWY CTRE

2-2-2

NATIONAL RAILWAY MUSEUM

RAILWAY AGE

STEAM

2-2-4T

NATIONAL RAILWAY MUSEUM

2-4-0

ISLE OF MAN RAILWAY

MIDLAND RAILWAY CENTRE

MOORS VALLEY RAILWAY

NATIONAL RAILWAY MUSEUM

RUISLIP LIDO RAILWAY

2-4-0 + 0-4-2T

MOORS VALLEY RAILWAY

2-4-0DM

ARMLEY MILLS

FFESTINIOG RAILWAY

2-4-0F

SITTINGBOURNE & KEMSLEY

2-4-0ST

BEER HEIGHTS

2-4-0STT

FFESTINIOG RAILWAY

2-4-0T

AMBERLEY WORKING MUSEUM

GROUDLE GLEN RAILWAY

MUSEUM OF SCIENCE & INDUSTRY

SOUTH DEVON RAILWAY

2-4-0WT

BUCKINGHAMSHIRE RLWY CTRE

NATIONAL RAILWAY MUSEUM

2-4-2

BEER HEIGHTS

EASTLEIGH LAKESIDE RAILWAY

EXMOOR STEAM RAILWAY

WESTON PARK RAILWAY

WINDMILL FARM RAILWAY

2-4-2T

NATIONAL RAILWAY MUSEUM

RUDYARD LAKE RAILWAY

ULSTER FOLK & TRANSPORT

2-4-2T & TENDER

BEER HEIGHTS

2-4-4T

MOORS VALLEY RAILWAY

2-6-0

BARLEYLANDS MINIATURE RAILWAY

BLUEBELL RAILWAY

BRESSINGHAM STEAM

BUCKINGHAMSHIRE RLWY CTRE

DARLINGTON RAILWAY PRES SOC

DIDCOT RAILWAY CENTRE

EAST LANCASHIRE RAILWAY

GLOUCESTERSHIRE WARWICKSHIRE

GREAT CENTRAL RAILWAY

KEIGHLEY & WORTH VALLEY

KENT & EAST SUSSEX RAILWAY

NATIONAL RAILWAY MUSEUM

NORTH YORKSHIRE MOORS RAILWAY

RPSI

SEVERN VALLEY RAILWAY

SOUTH DOWNS LIGHT RAILWAY

STRATHSPEY RAILWAY

WATERCRESS LINE

2-6-0 + 0-6-2

WELLS & WALSINGHAM

2-6-0T

ROYAL VICTORIA RAILWAY

2-6-2

BURE VALLEY RAILWAY

CLEETHORPES LIGHT RAILWAY

EASTLEIGH LAKESIDE RAILWAY

FAIRBOURNE & BARMOUTH

LLANGOLLEN RAILWAY

MOORS VALLEY RAILWAY

NATIONAL RAILWAY MUSEUM

PAIGNTON & DARTMOUTH RAILWAY

RAVENGLASS & ESKDALE

TRALEE & DINGLE RAILWAY

WELSH HIGHLAND RAILWAY

WELSHPOOL & LLANFAIR

2-6-2 + 2-6-2

BRECON MOUNTAIN RAILWAY

EXMOOR STEAM RAILWAY

2-6-2DM

ARMLEY MILLS

2-6-2T

BODMIN & WENFORD RAILWAY

BUCKINGHAMSHIRE RLWY CTRE

DIDCOT RAILWAY CENTRE

FFESTINIOG RAILWAY

KEIGHLEY & WORTH VALLEY

KIRKLEES LIGHT RAILWAY

MOORS VALLEY RAILWAY

MULL RAILWAY

NENE VALLEY RAILWAY

SEVERN VALLEY RAILWAY

ROLLING STOCK by WHEEL ARRANGEMENT

2-4-0DM — 2-6-2T

ROLLING STOCK by **WHEEL ARRANGEMENT**

2-6-2T — 4-4-0

SOUTH DEVON RAILWAY	MIDLAND RAILWAY CENTRE
TYSELEY LOCOMOTIVE WORKS	NATIONAL RAILWAY MUSEUM
VALE OF GLAMORGAN RAILWAY	NORTH YORKSHIRE MOORS RAILWAY
VALE OF RHEIDOL RAILWAY	PAIGNTON & DARTMOUTH RAILWAY
WATERCRESS LINE	SEVERN VALLEY RAILWAY
WELSHPOOL & LLANFAIR	SOMERSET & DORSET RAILWAY
WEST SOMERSET RAILWAY	SOUTH DEVON RAILWAY

2-6-4 / STEAM

BURE VALLEY RAILWAY	SWINDON & CRICKLADE RAILWAY
DONEGAL RAILWAY HERITAGE CTRE	TYSELEY LOCOMOTIVE WORKS
FAIRBOURNE & BARMOUTH	WATERCRESS LINE

2-6-4 T / WEST SOMERSET RAILWAY

BURE VALLEY RAILWAY

2-8-0GH

2-6-4DH

WINDMILL FARM RAILWAY	CLEETHORPES LIGHT RAILWAY
	WINDMILL FARM RAILWAY

2-6-4T

2-8-0T

BLUEBELL RAILWAY	SWANSEA VALE RAILWAY

2-8-2

BO'NESS & KINNEIL RAILWAY	EXMOOR STEAM RAILWAY
CHURNET VALLEY RAILWAY	RAVENGLASS & ESKDALE
EAST LANCASHIRE RAILWAY	WELSH HIGHLAND RAILWAY

2-8-2T

FOYLE VALLEY RAILWAY CENTRE	BUCKINGHAMSHIRE RLWY CTRE
LAKESIDE & HAVERTHWAITE RLWY	DIDCOT RAILWAY CENTRE
MIDLAND RAILWAY CENTRE	EAST LANCASHIRE RAILWAY

2W

MOORS VALLEY RAILWAY	SOUTH TYNEDALE RAILWAY

2W-2PM

MULL RAILWAY	WINDMILL FARM RAILWAY

4

NATIONAL RAILWAY MUSEUM	BEAMISH
NORTH YORKSHIRE MOORS RAILWAY	BRISTOL HARBOUR RAILWAY
RPSI	

4 WHEEL

SEVERN VALLEY RAILWAY	SPA VALLEY RAILWAY
ULSTER FOLK & TRANSPORT	WELSH HIGHLAND RAILWAY

2-8-0 / **4 + 4**

AVON VALLEY RAILWAY	BEAMISH

4-2-2

BODMIN & WENFORD RAILWAY	NATIONAL RAILWAY MUSEUM

4-4-0

CHURNET VALLEY RAILWAY	BLUEBELL RAILWAY
CONWY VALLEY	
DIDCOT RAILWAY CENTRE	
GLOUCESTERSHIRE WARWICKSHIRE	
GREAT CENTRAL RAILWAY	
KEIGHLEY & WORTH VALLEY	

🚂 BO'NESS & KINNEIL RAILWAY

🚂 MUSEUM OF SCIENCE & INDUSTRY

🚂 NATIONAL RAILWAY MUSEUM

🚂 NORTH YORKSHIRE MOORS RAILWAY

🚂 RPSI

🚂 ULSTER FOLK & TRANSPORT

🚂 WINDMILL FARM RAILWAY

4-4-0T

🚂 LONDON TRANSPORT MUSEUM

🚂 NORTH GLOUCESTERSHIRE RAILWAY

4-4-2

🚂 EASTLEIGH LAKESIDE RAILWAY

🚂 MULL RAILWAY

🚂 NATIONAL RAILWAY MUSEUM

🚂 RHYL MINIATURE RAILWAY

🚂 WINDMILL FARM RAILWAY

4-4-2T

🚂 BARLEYLANDS MINIATURE RAILWAY

🚂 BLUEBELL RAILWAY

🚂 NATIONAL RAILWAY MUSEUM

🚂 ROYAL VICTORIA RAILWAY

🚂 ULSTER FOLK & TRANSPORT

4-4W-4-4W-4DER

🚂 RHYL MINIATURE RAILWAY

4-4WDH

🚂 BEER HEIGHTS

4-6-0

🚂 BARLEYLANDS MINIATURE RAILWAY

🚂 BLUEBELL RAILWAY

🚂 BO'NESS & KINNEIL RAILWAY

🚂 BRESSINGHAM STEAM

🚂 BUCKINGHAMSHIRE RLWY CTRE

🚂 CAMBRIAN RAILWAY SOCIETY

🚂 DIDCOT RAILWAY CENTRE

🚂 EAST LANCASHIRE RAILWAY

🚂 GLOUCESTERSHIRE WARWICKSHIRE

🚂 GREAT CENTRAL RAILWAY

🚂 GREAT WESTERN RAILWAY MUSEUM

🚂 KEIGHLEY & WORTH VALLEY

🚂 LLANGOLLEN RAILWAY

🚂 MIDLAND RAILWAY CENTRE

🚂 MOORS VALLEY RAILWAY

🚂 NATIONAL RAILWAY MUSEUM

🚂 NENE VALLEY RAILWAY

🚂 NORTH NORFOLK RAILWAY

🚂 NORTH YORKSHIRE MOORS RAILWAY

🚂 NOTTINGHAM TRANSPORT CTRE

🚂 PAIGNTON & DARTMOUTH RAILWAY

🚂 PLYM VALLEY RAILWAY

🚂 PONTYPOOL & BLAENAVON RAILWAY

🚂 SEVERN VALLEY RAILWAY

🚂 SOUTH DEVON RAILWAY

🚂 SOUTH DOWNS LIGHT RAILWAY

🚂 STEAM

🚂 STRATHSPEY RAILWAY

🚂 SWANAGE RAILWAY

🚂 SWINDON & CRICKLADE RAILWAY

🚂 TYSELEY LOCOMOTIVE WORKS

🚂 ULSTER FOLK & TRANSPORT

🚂 WATERCRESS LINE

🚂 WEST SOMERSET RAILWAY

4-6-0DH

🚂 WINDMILL FARM RAILWAY

4-6-0T

🚂 LEIGHTON BUZZARD RAILWAY

4-6-2

🚂 AVON VALLEY RAILWAY

🚂 BARLEYLANDS MINIATURE RAILWAY

🚂 BLUEBELL RAILWAY

🚂 BODMIN & WENFORD RAILWAY

🚂 BRECON MOUNTAIN RAILWAY

🚂 BRESSINGHAM STEAM

🚂 CLEETHORPES LIGHT RAILWAY

🚂 EAST LANCASHIRE RAILWAY

🚂 EASTLEIGH LAKESIDE RAILWAY

🚂 GLOUCESTERSHIRE WARWICKSHIRE

🚂 GREAT CENTRAL RAILWAY

🚂 MIDLAND RAILWAY CENTRE

🚂 MOORS VALLEY RAILWAY

ROLLING STOCK by **WHEEL ARRANGEMENT**

4-4-0 — 4-6-2

ⱲⱲⱲ NATIONAL RAILWAY MUSEUM

ⱲⱲⱲ NENE VALLEY RAILWAY

ⱲⱲⱲ NORTH YORKSHIRE MOORS RAILWAY

ⱲⱲⱲ RAILWORLD

ⱲⱲⱲ ROMNEY HYTHE & DYMCHURCH

ⱲⱲⱲ SEVERN VALLEY RAILWAY

ⱲⱲⱲ SOUTH DOWNS LIGHT RAILWAY

ⱲⱲⱲ SWANAGE RAILWAY

ⱲⱲⱲ TANFIELD RAILWAY

ⱲⱲⱲ WATERCRESS LINE

ⱲⱲⱲ WEST SOMERSET RAILWAY

ⱲⱲⱲ WINDMILL FARM RAILWAY

4-6-2DE

ⱲⱲⱲ WINDMILL FARM RAILWAY

4-6-2DH

ⱲⱲⱲ WINDMILL FARM RAILWAY

4-6-4D

ⱲⱲⱲ RAVENGLASS & ESKDALE

4-6-4DM

ⱲⱲⱲ WINDMILL FARM RAILWAY

4-8-2

ⱲⱲⱲ ROMNEY HYTHE & DYMCHURCH

4-8-2 + 2-8-4

ⱲⱲⱲ MUSEUM OF SCIENCE & INDUSTRY

ⱲⱲⱲ WESTON PARK RAILWAY

4-8-4

ⱲⱲⱲ BUCKINGHAMSHIRE RLWY CTRE

ⱲⱲⱲ EASTLEIGH LAKESIDE RAILWAY

ⱲⱲⱲ NATIONAL RAILWAY MUSEUM

4W

ⱲⱲⱲ ALFORD VALLEY RAILWAY

ⱲⱲⱲ BARROW HILL ROUNDHOUSE

ⱲⱲⱲ BEER HEIGHTS

ⱲⱲⱲ BLUEBELL RAILWAY

ⱲⱲⱲ BRISTOL HARBOUR RAILWAY

ⱲⱲⱲ CAVAN & LEITRIM RAILWAY

ⱲⱲⱲ CHASEWATER RAILWAY

ⱲⱲⱲ DARLINGTON RAILWAY PRES SOC

ⱲⱲⱲ DERBY INDUSTRIAL MUSEUM

ⱲⱲⱲ DERWENT VALLEY

ⱲⱲⱲ EAST ANGLIA TRANSPORT MUSEUM

ⱲⱲⱲ EAST ANGLIAN RAILWAY MUSEUM

ⱲⱲⱲ FOXFIELD STEAM RAILWAY

ⱲⱲⱲ GARTELL LIGHT RAILWAY

ⱲⱲⱲ IRISH STEAM PRESERVATION SOC

ⱲⱲⱲ LAPPA VALLEY STEAM RAILWAY

ⱲⱲⱲ LEIGHTON BUZZARD RAILWAY

ⱲⱲⱲ MARKEATON PARK LIGHT RAILWAY

ⱲⱲⱲ NATIONAL TRAMWAY MUSEUM

ⱲⱲⱲ NIRT

ⱲⱲⱲ NORTH NORFOLK RAILWAY

ⱲⱲⱲ ROYAL VICTORIA RAILWAY

ⱲⱲⱲ RUDYARD LAKE RAILWAY

ⱲⱲⱲ SOUTH TYNEDALE RAILWAY

ⱲⱲⱲ STRATHSPEY RAILWAY

ⱲⱲⱲ SWANSEA VALE RAILWAY

ⱲⱲⱲ TALYLLYN RAILWAY

ⱲⱲⱲ ULSTER FOLK & TRANSPORT

ⱲⱲⱲ VINTAGE CARRIAGES TRUST

ⱲⱲⱲ WELSH HIGHLAND RAILWAY

4W - 4WT

ⱲⱲⱲ KIRKLEES LIGHT RAILWAY

4W BE

ⱲⱲⱲ TANFIELD RAILWAY

4W BOGIE

ⱲⱲⱲ ROYAL VICTORIA RAILWAY

4W PM

ⱲⱲⱲ BLUEBELL RAILWAY

4W VBGT

ⱲⱲⱲ MIDDLETON RAILWAY

4W WE

ⱲⱲⱲ TANFIELD RAILWAY

4W + 4W

ⱲⱲⱲ CHINNOR & PRINCES RISBOROUGH

4W + 4W BOGIE

ⱲⱲⱲ LAPPA VALLEY STEAM RAILWAY

4W4DM

ⱲⱲⱲ CLEETHORPES LIGHT RAILWAY

4W-4DM

ⱲⱲⱲ WINDMILL FARM RAILWAY

4W-4W

〰 **DIDCOT RAILWAY CENTRE**

〰 **ROYAL VICTORIA RAILWAY**

〰 **RUISLIP LIDO RAILWAY**

4W-4WDH

〰 **WINDMILL FARM RAILWAY**

4W-4WE

〰 **TANFIELD RAILWAY**

4W-4WWE

〰 **TANFIELD RAILWAY**

4WBE

〰 **ALMOND VALLEY HERITAGE TRUST**

〰 **AMBERLEY WORKING MUSEUM**

〰 **SOUTH TYNEDALE RAILWAY**

4WD

〰 **BUCKINGHAMSHIRE RLWY CTRE**

〰 **RUDYARD LAKE RAILWAY**

4WDE

〰 **ALMOND VALLEY HERITAGE TRUST**

4WDH

〰 **ALMOND VALLEY HERITAGE TRUST**

〰 **AMERTON RAILWAY**

〰 **AVON VALLEY RAILWAY**

〰 **BATTLEFIELD LINE**

〰 **BO'NESS & KINNEIL RAILWAY**

〰 **BURE VALLEY RAILWAY**

〰 **EAST LANCASHIRE RAILWAY**

〰 **FOXFIELD STEAM RAILWAY**

〰 **LEIGHTON BUZZARD RAILWAY**

4WDH TRAM

〰 **CLEETHORPES LIGHT RAILWAY**

4WDM

〰 **ABBEY PUMPING STATION**

〰 **ALMOND VALLEY HERITAGE TRUST**

〰 **AMBERLEY WORKING MUSEUM**

〰 **AMERTON RAILWAY**

〰 **ARMLEY MILLS**

〰 **AVON VALLEY RAILWAY**

〰 **BALA LAKE RAILWAY**

〰 **BATTLEFIELD LINE**

〰 **BICTON WOODLAND RAILWAY**

〰 **BODMIN & WENFORD RAILWAY**

〰 **BO'NESS & KINNEIL RAILWAY**

〰 **BRESSINGHAM STEAM**

〰 **CADEBY LIGHT RAILWAY**

〰 **CALEDONIAN RAILWAY**

〰 **CAMBRIAN RAILWAY SOCIETY**

〰 **CHASEWATER RAILWAY**

〰 **CORRIS RAILWAY MUSEUM**

〰 **DERWENT VALLEY**

〰 **DEVON RAILWAY CENTRE**

〰 **EAST LANCASHIRE RAILWAY**

〰 **EXMOOR STEAM RAILWAY**

〰 **FFESTINIOG RAILWAY**

〰 **FOXFIELD STEAM RAILWAY**

〰 **GREAT CENTRAL RAILWAY**

〰 **HOLLYCOMBE STEAM COLLECTION**

〰 **IRCHESTER NARROW GAUGE MUSEUM**

〰 **LAKESIDE & HAVERTHWAITE RLWY**

〰 **LAUNCESTON STEAM RAILWAY**

〰 **LEIGHTON BUZZARD RAILWAY**

〰 **NORTH GLOUCESTERSHIRE RAILWAY**

〰 **NORTHAMPTON & LAMPORT RAILWAY**

〰 **PRESTONGRANGE INDUSTRIAL**

〰 **RHYL MINIATURE RAILWAY**

〰 **SCOTTISH RAILWAY CENTRE**

〰 **SOUTH YORKSHIRE RAILWAY**

〰 **SWANSEA VALE RAILWAY**

〰 **WEST SOMERSET RAILWAY**

4WPM

〰 **ABBEY PUMPING STATION**

〰 **AMBERLEY WORKING MUSEUM**

〰 **AVON VALLEY RAILWAY**

〰 **CADEBY LIGHT RAILWAY**

〰 **DEVON RAILWAY CENTRE**

〰 **IRCHESTER NARROW GAUGE MUSEUM**

〰 **LEIGHTON BUZZARD RAILWAY**

〰 **NORTH GLOUCESTERSHIRE RAILWAY**

〰 **SWANAGE RAILWAY**

〰 **WINDMILL FARM RAILWAY**

ROLLING STOCK by WHEEL ARRANGEMENT

4w-4w — 4wPM

ROLLING STOCK by **WHEEL ARRANGEMENT**

4wVBT — Bo-BODE

4WVBT
- BATTLEFIELD LINE
- CHASEWATER RAILWAY
- MIDLAND RAILWAY CENTRE
- SOUTH YORKSHIRE RAILWAY

4WVBTG
- BUCKINGHAMSHIRE RLWY CTRE

6W
- BEAMISH
- BLUEBELL RAILWAY
- BODMIN & WENFORD RAILWAY
- CHASEWATER RAILWAY
- STRATHSPEY RAILWAY
- VINTAGE CARRIAGES TRUST

6WDM
- EAST LANCASHIRE RAILWAY
- IRCHESTER NARROW GAUGE MUSEUM

8W
- TALYLLYN RAILWAY

8W BOGIE
- RUDYARD LAKE RAILWAY

A1A-A1A
- BATTLEFIELD LINE
- EAST LANCASHIRE RAILWAY
- GREAT CENTRAL RAILWAY
- MIDLAND RAILWAY CENTRE
- MID-NORFOLK RAILWAY
- TYSELEY LOCOMOTIVE WORKS

ARTICULATED
- ROYAL VICTORIA RAILWAY

B-B
- EAST LANCASHIRE RAILWAY
- EASTLEIGH LAKESIDE RAILWAY
- SEVERN VALLEY RAILWAY
- WEST SOMERSET RAILWAY

BO-BO
- BALA LAKE RAILWAY
- BARROW HILL ROUNDHOUSE
- BATTLEFIELD LINE
- BODMIN & WENFORD RAILWAY
- BO'NESS & KINNEIL RAILWAY
- BROOKSIDE MINIATURE
- BURE VALLEY RAILWAY
- CALEDONIAN RAILWAY
- CHURNET VALLEY RAILWAY
- CONWY VALLEY
- EAST LANCASHIRE RAILWAY
- EASTLEIGH LAKESIDE RAILWAY
- FFESTINIOG RAILWAY
- GLOUCESTERSHIRE WARWICKSHIRE
- GREAT CENTRAL RAILWAY
- HEATHERSLAW LIGHT RAILWAY
- HOLLYBUSH GARDEN CENTRE
- KEIGHLEY & WORTH VALLEY
- KENT & EAST SUSSEX RAILWAY
- KERR MINIATURE RAILWAY
- LAKESIDE & HAVERTHWAITE RLWY
- LAVENDER LINE
- LONDON TRANSPORT MUSEUM
- MARKEATON PARK LIGHT RAILWAY
- MIDLAND RAILWAY CENTRE
- MULL RAILWAY
- NORTH NORFOLK RAILWAY
- NORTHAMPTON & LAMPORT RAILWAY
- PAIGNTON & DARTMOUTH RAILWAY
- RAILWORLD
- ROMNEY HYTHE & DYMCHURCH
- ROYAL VICTORIA RAILWAY
- RUDYARD LAKE RAILWAY
- SEVERN VALLEY RAILWAY
- SOUTH YORKSHIRE RAILWAY
- STRATHSPEY RAILWAY
- SWANAGE RAILWAY
- WATERCRESS LINE
- WELLINGTON COUNTRY PARK
- WEST SOMERSET RAILWAY
- YEOVIL RAILWAY CENTRE

BO-BODE
- CHINNOR & PRINCES RISBOROUGH
- NORTH YORKSHIRE MOORS RAILWAY

BO-BODH

🚂 **BOWES RAILWAY**

BOGIE

🚂 **HEATHERSLAW LIGHT RAILWAY**

🚂 **WELSH HIGHLAND RAILWAY**

C - C

🚂 **EAST LANCASHIRE RAILWAY**

🚂 **MIDLAND RAILWAY CENTRE**

🚂 **SEVERN VALLEY RAILWAY**

🚂 **WEST SOMERSET RAILWAY**

CO - BO

🚂 **EAST LANCASHIRE RAILWAY**

CO-CO

🚂 **BARROW HILL ROUNDHOUSE**

🚂 **EAST LANCASHIRE RAILWAY**

🚂 **GLOUCESTERSHIRE WARWICKSHIRE**

🚂 **GREAT CENTRAL RAILWAY**

🚂 **MIDLAND RAILWAY CENTRE**

🚂 **MID-NORFOLK RAILWAY**

🚂 **MUSEUM OF SCIENCE & INDUSTRY**

🚂 **NORTH NORFOLK RAILWAY**

🚂 **PONTYPOOL & BLAENAVON RAILWAY**

🚂 **SEVERN VALLEY RAILWAY**

🚂 **TYSELEY LOCOMOTIVE WORKS**

CO-CODE

🚂 **NORTH YORKSHIRE MOORS RAILWAY**

ROLLING STOCK by WHEEL ARRANGEMENT

Bo-BoDH — Co-CoDE

Rolling Stock by Builder

SECTION 5G

*This section shows who Built
the stock and where it can be
located*

**e.g. Barclay & Sons,
     Avon Valley Railway**

Once you have located a
railway/museum using this
section you can then refer
to the railway or museum's
detailed profile in section 1.

STEAM
RAILWAY

ALCO

- FFESTINIOG RAILWAY
- RAILWORLD

ALCOCK

- MULL RAILWAY

ALLEN

- TALYLLYN RAILWAY

AMERICAN LOCOMOTIVE CO

- WATERCRESS LINE

ARMSTRONG

- COLNE VALLEY RAILWAY
- DIDCOT RAILWAY CENTRE
- GREAT CENTRAL RAILWAY
- NOTTINGHAM TRANSPORT CTRE

ARN JUNG

- BRECON MOUNTAIN RAILWAY
- BREDGAR & WORMSHILL
- NORTH GLOUCESTERSHIRE RAILWAY

ARTISAIR

- WINDMILL FARM RAILWAY

ASHBURY

- BLUEBELL RAILWAY

ASSOCIATED EQUIPMENT CO

- DIDCOT RAILWAY CENTRE

ATKINSON

- ULSTER FOLK & TRANSPORT

AVONSIDE ENGINEERING CO

- AVON VALLEY RAILWAY
- BRISTOL HARBOUR RAILWAY
- COLNE VALLEY RAILWAY
- DIDCOT RAILWAY CENTRE
- EAST KENT LIGHT RAILWAY
- FOXFIELD STEAM RAILWAY
- GWILI RAILWAY
- LEIGHTON BUZZARD RAILWAY
- RPSI

BAGNALL

- AMBERLEY WORKING MUSEUM
- AMERTON RAILWAY
- BATTLEFIELD LINE
- BODMIN & WENFORD RAILWAY

- BO'NESS & KINNEIL RAILWAY
- BREDGAR & WORMSHILL
- BUCKINGHAMSHIRE RLWY CTRE
- CADEBY LIGHT RAILWAY
- CHASEWATER RAILWAY
- DARLINGTON RAILWAY CENTRE
- EAST ANGLIAN RAILWAY MUSEUM
- EMBSAY & BOLTON ABBEY RLWY
- FOXFIELD STEAM RAILWAY
- GREAT WESTERN RAILWAY MUSEUM
- GROUDLE GLEN RAILWAY
- KEW BRIDGE STEAM MUSEUM
- LAKESIDE & HAVERTHWAITE RLWY
- LAUNCESTON STEAM RAILWAY
- MANGAPPS RAILWAY MUSEUM
- MIDDLETON RAILWAY
- NORTH GLOUCESTERSHIRE RAILWAY
- NORTH NORFOLK RAILWAY
- PALLOT STEAM MUSEUM
- PEAK RAIL
- SITTINGBOURNE & KEMSLEY
- SPA VALLEY RAILWAY
- TANFIELD RAILWAY
- WELSH HIGHLAND RAILWAY
- WELSHPOOL & LLANFAIR
- WEST SOMERSET RAILWAY

BAGULEY

- AMERTON RAILWAY
- BALA LAKE RAILWAY
- BREDGAR & WORMSHILL
- BUCKINGHAMSHIRE RLWY CTRE
- CADEBY LIGHT RAILWAY
- DEVON RAILWAY CENTRE
- EMBSAY & BOLTON ABBEY RLWY
- FFESTINIOG RAILWAY
- FOXFIELD STEAM RAILWAY
- LEIGHTON BUZZARD RAILWAY
- SOUTH TYNEDALE RAILWAY
- TEIFI VALLEY RAILWAY

ROLLING STOCK by BUILDER

Alco — Baguley

⚬ TYSELEY LOCOMOTIVE WORKS	⚬ PONTYPOOL & BLAENAVON RAILWAY
⚬ WEST LANCASHIRE LIGHT RLWY	⚬ RUTLAND RAILWAY MUSEUM
BALDWIN LOCOMOTIVE WORKS	⚬ SCOTTISH RAILWAY CENTRE
⚬ ALMOND VALLEY HERITAGE TRUST	⚬ SITTINGBOURNE & KEMSLEY
⚬ BRECON MOUNTAIN RAILWAY	⚬ SOUTH YORKSHIRE RAILWAY
⚬ FFESTINIOG RAILWAY	⚬ SPA VALLEY RAILWAY
⚬ LEIGHTON BUZZARD RAILWAY	⚬ STRATHSPEY RAILWAY
⚬ NORTH YORKSHIRE MOORS RAILWAY	⚬ SWANSEA INDUSTRIAL MUSEUM
BARCLAY & SONS	⚬ SWANSEA VALE RAILWAY
⚬ ALMOND VALLEY HERITAGE TRUST	⚬ SWINDON & CRICKLADE RAILWAY
⚬ AVON VALLEY RAILWAY	⚬ TALYLLYN RAILWAY
⚬ BATTLEFIELD LINE	⚬ TANFIELD RAILWAY
⚬ BO'NESS & KINNEIL RAILWAY	⚬ WELSHPOOL & LLANFAIR
⚬ BOWES RAILWAY	**BARLOW**
⚬ BUCKINGHAMSHIRE RLWY CTRE	⚬ WINDMILL FARM RAILWAY
⚬ CALEDONIAN RAILWAY	**BARNES & CO**
⚬ CAMBRIAN RAILWAY SOCIETY	⚬ RHYL MINIATURE RAILWAY
⚬ CHASEWATER RAILWAY	**BATLEY**
⚬ COLNE VALLEY RAILWAY	⚬ ABBEY LIGHT RAILWAY
⚬ DERWENT VALLEY	⚬ ARMLEY MILLS
⚬ EAST ANGLIAN RAILWAY MUSEUM	⚬ WEST LANCASHIRE LIGHT RLWY
⚬ EAST KENT LIGHT RAILWAY	**BATTISON**
⚬ EAST LANCASHIRE RAILWAY	⚬ WINDMILL FARM RAILWAY
⚬ EAST SOMERSET RAILWAY	**BEER HEIGHTS LIGHT RAILWAY**
⚬ EMBSAY & BOLTON ABBEY RLWY	⚬ BEER HEIGHTS
⚬ FOXFIELD STEAM RAILWAY	**BELGE**
⚬ GIANTS CAUSEWAY & BUSHMILLS	⚬ EXMOOR STEAM RAILWAY
⚬ GREAT CENTRAL RAILWAY	**BERWIN ENGINEERING**
⚬ GWILI RAILWAY	⚬ LAPPA VALLEY STEAM RAILWAY
⚬ HOLLYCOMBE STEAM COLLECTION	**BEYER**
⚬ IRISH STEAM PRESERVATION SOC	⚬ BARROW HILL ROUNDHOUSE
⚬ ISLE OF WIGHT STEAM RAILWAY	⚬ BUCKINGHAMSHIRE RLWY CTRE
⚬ KEIGHLEY & WORTH VALLEY	⚬ EXMOOR STEAM RAILWAY
⚬ LAKESIDE & HAVERTHWAITE RLWY	⚬ FOXFIELD STEAM RAILWAY
⚬ LAVENDER LINE	⚬ ISLE OF MAN RAILWAY
⚬ LEIGHTON BUZZARD RAILWAY	⚬ LONDON TRANSPORT MUSEUM
⚬ MANGAPPS RAILWAY MUSEUM	⚬ MIDDLETON RAILWAY
⚬ MIDLAND RAILWAY CENTRE	⚬ MUSEUM OF SCIENCE & INDUSTRY
⚬ NATIONAL WATERWAYS MUSEUM	⚬ NARROW GAUGE RAILWAY MUSEUM
	⚬ NATIONAL TRAMWAY MUSEUM

- NORTH YORKSHIRE MOORS RAILWAY
- NORTHAMPTON & LAMPORT RAILWAY
- RPSI
- SEVERN VALLEY RAILWAY
- ULSTER FOLK & TRANSPORT
- WELSHPOOL & LLANFAIR

BIMPSON

- EASTLEIGH LAKESIDE RAILWAY

BIRMINGHAM CARRIAGE & WAGON CO

- BARROW HILL ROUNDHOUSE
- BO'NESS & KINNEIL RAILWAY
- CHASEWATER RAILWAY
- EAST ANGLIAN RAILWAY MUSEUM
- SEVERN VALLEY RAILWAY
- STRATHSPEY RAILWAY

BLACK

- BEAMISH
- BO'NESS & KINNEIL RAILWAY
- INDUSTRIAL RAILWAY MUSEUM

BLENKINSOP

- SOUTH TYNEDALE RAILWAY

BOOTH

- BLUEBELL RAILWAY
- GROUDLE GLEN RAILWAY

BOOTHS

- NORTH NORFOLK RAILWAY

BORROWS

- MIDDLETON RAILWAY
- TANFIELD RAILWAY

BOUGHTON

- ROYAL VICTORIA RAILWAY

BOWATERS

- SITTINGBOURNE & KEMSLEY

BOWERS

- ROYAL VICTORIA RAILWAY

BR

- BARROW HILL ROUNDHOUSE
- BRISTOL HARBOUR RAILWAY
- BUCKINGHAMSHIRE RLWY CTRE
- CALEDONIAN RAILWAY
- CHASEWATER RAILWAY
- CHINNOR & PRINCES RISBOROUGH
- CHURNET VALLEY RAILWAY
- DARLINGTON RAILWAY PRES SOC
- DARTMOOR RAILWAY
- DIDCOT RAILWAY CENTRE
- EAST SOMERSET RAILWAY
- EMBSAY & BOLTON ABBEY RLWY
- GLOUCESTERSHIRE WARWICKSHIRE
- GREAT CENTRAL RAILWAY
- GWILI RAILWAY
- KEITH & DUFFTOWN RAILWAY
- KENT & EAST SUSSEX RAILWAY
- LAVENDER LINE
- LLANGOLLEN RAILWAY
- MANGAPPS RAILWAY MUSEUM
- MID-NORFOLK RAILWAY
- NATIONAL RAILWAY MUSEUM
- NENE VALLEY RAILWAY
- NORTH NORFOLK RAILWAY
- NORTH YORKSHIRE MOORS RAILWAY
- NOTTINGHAM TRANSPORT CTRE
- PAIGNTON & DARTMOUTH RAILWAY
- PEAK RAIL
- PLYM VALLEY RAILWAY
- RAILWORLD
- SEVERN VALLEY RAILWAY
- SOUTH YORKSHIRE RAILWAY
- SPA VALLEY RAILWAY
- STRATHSPEY RAILWAY
- SWINDON & CRICKLADE RAILWAY
- TELFORD STEAM RAILWAY
- TIMOTHY HACKWORTH
- VALE OF GLAMORGAN RAILWAY
- VINTAGE CARRIAGES TRUST
- WATERCRESS LINE

BRCW

- BARROW HILL ROUNDHOUSE
- CALEDONIAN RAILWAY
- CHURNET VALLEY RAILWAY

AAW KENT & EAST SUSSEX RAILWAY

AAW NORTH NORFOLK RAILWAY

AAW NORTH YORKSHIRE MOORS RAILWAY

AAW NOTTINGHAM TRANSPORT CTRE

AAW SOUTH YORKSHIRE RAILWAY

AAW WATERCRESS LINE

BRE

AAW EMBSAY & BOLTON ABBEY RLWY

BRECON MOUNTAIN RAILWAY

AAW VALE OF RHEIDOL RAILWAY

BRITISH ELECTRIC VEHICLES

AAW WEST LANCASHIRE LIGHT RLWY

BROOK

AAW ALMOND VALLEY HERITAGE TRUST

BROWN

AAW MARKEATON PARK LIGHT RAILWAY

AAW MOORS VALLEY RAILWAY

AAW TALYLLYN RAILWAY

AAW WINDMILL FARM RAILWAY

BRUSH ELECTRICAL ENGINEERING

AAW BATTLEFIELD LINE

AAW GLOUCESTERSHIRE WARWICKSHIRE

AAW GREAT CENTRAL RAILWAY

AAW MIDDLETON RAILWAY

AAW MIDLAND RAILWAY CENTRE

AAW MID-NORFOLK RAILWAY

AAW WEST SOMERSET RAILWAY

BRW

AAW WATERCRESS LINE

CALEDONIAN RAILWAY

AAW NORTH YORKSHIRE MOORS RAILWAY

AAW STRATHSPEY RAILWAY

CASSEL

AAW AMERTON RAILWAY

CCLR

AAW CLEETHORPES LIGHT RAILWAY

CHATHAM & DOVER RAILWAY

AAW BUCKINGHAMSHIRE RLWY CTRE

AAW SPA VALLEY RAILWAY

CHEESEMAN

AAW BURE VALLEY RAILWAY

CHRZANOW

AAW APPLEBY-FRODINGHAM RAILWAY

AAW WEST LANCASHIRE LIGHT RLWY

CHURCHWARD

AAW DIDCOT RAILWAY CENTRE

CLARKE

AAW BARLEYLANDS MINIATURE RAILWAY

AAW BEER HEIGHTS

CLARKE & CO

AAW AMBERLEY WORKING MUSEUM

AAW ARMLEY MILLS

AAW AVON VALLEY RAILWAY

AAW BATTLEFIELD LINE

AAW BOWES RAILWAY

AAW BRESSINGHAM STEAM

AAW BUCKINGHAMSHIRE RLWY CTRE

AAW CADEBY LIGHT RAILWAY

AAW CAMBRIAN RAILWAY SOCIETY

AAW CHASEWATER RAILWAY

AAW DERWENT VALLEY

AAW DOWNPATRICK & ARDGLASS

AAW EAST LANCASHIRE RAILWAY

AAW EMBSAY & BOLTON ABBEY RLWY

AAW INDUSTRIAL RAILWAY MUSEUM

AAW KEIGHLEY & WORTH VALLEY

AAW LEADHILLS & WANLOCKHEAD

AAW MANGAPPS RAILWAY MUSEUM

AAW MIDDLETON RAILWAY

AAW MID-SUFFOLK LIGHT RAILWAY

AAW NENE VALLEY RAILWAY

AAW NIRT

AAW NORTH NORFOLK RAILWAY

AAW NOTTINGHAM TRANSPORT CTRE

AAW PEAK RAIL

AAW RPSI

AAW SOUTH TYNEDALE RAILWAY

AAW SOUTH YORKSHIRE RAILWAY

AAW SWANSEA VALE RAILWAY

AAW SWINDON & CRICKLADE RAILWAY

- 🚂 **TANFIELD RAILWAY**
- 🚂 **TEIFI VALLEY RAILWAY**
- 🚂 **VALE OF GLAMORGAN RAILWAY**
- 🚂 **VINTAGE CARRIAGES TRUST**
- 🚂 **WEST LANCASHIRE LIGHT RLWY**

CLARKSON
- 🚂 **RAVENGLASS & ESKDALE**

CLAYE
- 🚂 **KENT & EAST SUSSEX RAILWAY**

CLAYTON EQUIPMENT CO
- 🚂 **CHINNOR & PRINCES RISBOROUGH**

COCKERILL
- 🚂 **EXMOOR STEAM RAILWAY**
- 🚂 **MIDDLETON RAILWAY**
- 🚂 **NENE VALLEY RAILWAY**

COLBOURNE
- 🚂 **MOORS VALLEY RAILWAY**

COLEBOURNE
- 🚂 **MOORS VALLEY RAILWAY**

COLEBY
- 🚂 **KERR MINIATURE RAILWAY**

COLES
- 🚂 **BRISTOL HARBOUR RAILWAY**
- 🚂 **CHINNOR & PRINCES RISBOROUGH**
- 🚂 **NORTH YORKSHIRE MOORS RAILWAY**

COLLETT
- 🚂 **DIDCOT RAILWAY CENTRE**

CORK ST FOUNDRY
- 🚂 **ULSTER FOLK & TRANSPORT**

CORPET
- 🚂 **IRCHESTER NARROW GAUGE MUSEUM**

COWAN
- 🚂 **NORTH YORKSHIRE MOORS RAILWAY**
- 🚂 **PEAK RAIL**
- 🚂 **STRATHSPEY RAILWAY**
- 🚂 **SWANSEA VALE RAILWAY**

CRANE
- 🚂 **LAKESIDE & HAVERTHWAITE RLWY**

CRAVENS
- 🚂 **BLUEBELL RAILWAY**
- 🚂 **MANGAPPS RAILWAY MUSEUM**

- 🚂 **NORTH NORFOLK RAILWAY**
- 🚂 **NORTH YORKSHIRE MOORS RAILWAY**
- 🚂 **SITTINGBOURNE & KEMSLEY**

CREWE WORKS
- 🚂 **INDUSTRIAL RAILWAY MUSEUM**
- 🚂 **RAILWAY AGE**

CROMAR
- 🚂 **BEER HEIGHTS**

CROWHURST ENGINEERING
- 🚂 **WELLINGTON COUNTRY PARK**

CULVER
- 🚂 **MOORS VALLEY RAILWAY**

CURWEN
- 🚂 **BEER HEIGHTS**
- 🚂 **FAIRBOURNE & BARMOUTH**
- 🚂 **MULL RAILWAY**
- 🚂 **ROYAL VICTORIA RAILWAY**

DAVIES
- 🚂 **MULL RAILWAY**

DE WINTON
- 🚂 **LEIGHTON BUZZARD RAILWAY**

DEAN
- 🚂 **DIDCOT RAILWAY CENTRE**

DECAUVILLE
- 🚂 **AMBERLEY WORKING MUSEUM**
- 🚂 **BREDGAR & WORMSHILL**

DERBY WORKS
- 🚂 **PEAK RAIL**

DEUTZ
- 🚂 **CADEBY LIGHT RAILWAY**

DODMAN & CO
- 🚂 **KENT & EAST SUSSEX RAILWAY**

DREWRY
- 🚂 **AVON VALLEY RAILWAY**
- 🚂 **BALA LAKE RAILWAY**
- 🚂 **BREDGAR & WORMSHILL**
- 🚂 **CAVAN & LEITRIM RAILWAY**
- 🚂 **DERWENT VALLEY**
- 🚂 **EAST ANGLIAN RAILWAY MUSEUM**
- 🚂 **FFESTINIOG RAILWAY**
- 🚂 **LAVENDER LINE**

ROLLING STOCK by **BUILDER**

Clarke & Co — Drewry

ROLLING STOCK by **BUILDER**

Drewry — Fowler

- MANGAPPS RAILWAY MUSEUM
- MUSEUM OF ARMY TRANSPORT
- NORTH NORFOLK RAILWAY
- NORTH YORKSHIRE MOORS RAILWAY
- ROTHER VALLEY RAILWAY
- SOUTH TYNEDALE RAILWAY
- SOUTH YORKSHIRE RAILWAY
- SPA VALLEY RAILWAY
- WELSHPOOL & LLANFAIR

DUBS
- FOXFIELD STEAM RAILWAY
- ISLE OF MAN RAILWAY

DURSLEY
- ABBEY LIGHT RAILWAY

DYSON
- BARLEYLANDS MINIATURE RAILWAY

EASTLEIGH LAKESIDE RAILWAY
- EASTLEIGH LAKESIDE RAILWAY

EASTLEIGH LAKESIDE RLWY
- EASTLEIGH LAKESIDE RAILWAY

EDWARDS
- BURE VALLEY RAILWAY

ENGLAND
- DIDCOT RAILWAY CENTRE
- FFESTINIOG RAILWAY

ENGLISH ELECTRIC
- BARROW HILL ROUNDHOUSE
- BATTLEFIELD LINE
- BO'NESS & KINNEIL RAILWAY
- FOXFIELD STEAM RAILWAY
- GLOUCESTERSHIRE WARWICKSHIRE
- KEITH & DUFFTOWN RAILWAY
- MIDLAND RAILWAY CENTRE
- MID-NORFOLK RAILWAY
- MUSEUM OF SCIENCE & INDUSTRY
- NATIONAL TRAMWAY MUSEUM
- NENE VALLEY RAILWAY
- NORTH NORFOLK RAILWAY
- NORTH YORKSHIRE MOORS RAILWAY
- PONTYPOOL & BLAENAVON RAILWAY

- SOUTH TYNEDALE RAILWAY
- WATERCRESS LINE
- YEOVIL RAILWAY CENTRE

EXMOOR STEAM RAILWAY
- BROOKSIDE MINIATURE
- EXMOOR STEAM RAILWAY
- MARKEATON PARK LIGHT RAILWAY
- PERRYGROVE RAILWAY
- RUDYARD LAKE RAILWAY

FAIRBOURNE
- CLEETHORPES LIGHT RAILWAY

FALCON WORKS
- TALYLLYN RAILWAY

FAVELL
- SOUTH DOWNS LIGHT RAILWAY

FAVERDALE CARRIAGE & WAGON CO
- KENT & EAST SUSSEX RAILWAY

FORSHAW
- HOLLYBUSH GARDEN CENTRE

FOWLER
- ARMLEY MILLS
- BODMIN & WENFORD RAILWAY
- BREDGAR & WORMSHILL
- BUCKINGHAMSHIRE RLWY CTRE
- CAVAN & LEITRIM RAILWAY
- CHASEWATER RAILWAY
- DARLINGTON RAILWAY PRES SOC
- EAST KENT LIGHT RAILWAY
- EMBSAY & BOLTON ABBEY RLWY
- GREAT CENTRAL RAILWAY
- ALFORD VALLEY RAILWAY
- AMBERLEY WORKING MUSEUM
- BO'NESS & KINNEIL RAILWAY
- DERWENT VALLEY
- GREAT WHIPSNADE RAILWAY
- LAKESIDE & HAVERTHWAITE RLWY
- MIDDLETON RAILWAY
- MIDLAND RAILWAY CENTRE
- NIRT
- NORTHAMPTON & LAMPORT RAILWAY

- SCOTTISH RAILWAY CENTRE
- SOUTH YORKSHIRE RAILWAY
- SWANAGE RAILWAY
- SWINDON & CRICKLADE RAILWAY
- TANFIELD RAILWAY
- WELSHPOOL & LLANFAIR

FOX
- BRISTOL HARBOUR RAILWAY
- MANGAPPS RAILWAY MUSEUM

FREUDENSTEIN
- LEIGHTON BUZZARD RAILWAY

FRICHS OF AARHUS
- RAILWORLD

FUNKEY
- FFESTINIOG RAILWAY

GARRETT
- MUSEUM OF SCIENCE & INDUSTRY

GCR
- GREAT CENTRAL RAILWAY

GCW
- NORTH NORFOLK RAILWAY

GEC
- DARLINGTON RAILWAY PRES SOC

GER
- NORTH NORFOLK RAILWAY

GNR
- NORTH NORFOLK RAILWAY
- NORTH YORKSHIRE MOORS RAILWAY
- VINTAGE CARRIAGES TRUST

GNRI
- ULSTER FOLK & TRANSPORT

GOWER
- ROYAL VICTORIA RAILWAY

GRAFTON CRANE CO
- NORTH NORFOLK RAILWAY
- SPA VALLEY RAILWAY

GRANGE IRONWORKS
- BEAMISH

GRCW
- NORTH NORFOLK RAILWAY

GREATREX
- BROOKSIDE MINIATURE

- CONWY VALLEY
- HOLLYBUSH GARDEN CENTRE

GREEN
- ARMLEY MILLS

GREENWOOD
- ABBEY LIGHT RAILWAY
- ALMOND VALLEY HERITAGE TRUST
- ARMLEY MILLS
- WEST LANCASHIRE LIGHT RLWY

GSR INCHICORE
- ULSTER FOLK & TRANSPORT

GUEST
- SOUTH DOWNS LIGHT RAILWAY
- WINDMILL FARM RAILWAY

GUEST & SAUNDERS LIGHT ENGINEERING
- RHYL MINIATURE RAILWAY

GUINNESS
- WINDMILL FARM RAILWAY

GWR
- BLUEBELL RAILWAY
- BRISTOL HARBOUR RAILWAY
- BUCKINGHAMSHIRE RLWY CTRE
- DIDCOT RAILWAY CENTRE
- GLOUCESTERSHIRE WARWICKSHIRE
- LLANGOLLEN RAILWAY
- NATIONAL RAILWAY MUSEUM
- NORTH NORFOLK RAILWAY
- NORTH YORKSHIRE MOORS RAILWAY
- SEVERN VALLEY RAILWAY
- SOUTH DEVON RAILWAY
- STEAM
- TELFORD STEAM RAILWAY
- VALE OF GLAMORGAN RAILWAY
- VALE OF RHEIDOL RAILWAY

HACKWORTH
- TIMOTHY HACKWORTH

HALL
- SOUTH TYNEDALE RAILWAY

HANOMAG
- BRECON MOUNTAIN RAILWAY

ROLLING STOCK by **BUILDER**

Fowler — Hanomag

HARRISON & CAMM
NORTH NORFOLK RAILWAY

HARTMANN
MIDDLETON RAILWAY

HAWKS
BEAMISH

HAWKSWORTH
DIDCOT RAILWAY CENTRE

HAWTHORN
AVON VALLEY RAILWAY
BARROW HILL ROUNDHOUSE
BATTLEFIELD LINE
BEAMISH
BO'NESS & KINNEIL RAILWAY
BOWES RAILWAY
BUCKINGHAMSHIRE RLWY CTRE
CHASEWATER RAILWAY
COLNE VALLEY RAILWAY
DARLINGTON RAILWAY PRES SOC
DIDCOT RAILWAY CENTRE
EMBSAY & BOLTON ABBEY RLWY
FOXFIELD STEAM RAILWAY
GWILI RAILWAY
HOLLYCOMBE STEAM COLLECTION
ISLE OF WIGHT STEAM RAILWAY
INDUSTRIAL RAILWAY MUSEUM
LINCOLNSHIRE WOLDS RAILWAY
MIDLAND RAILWAY CENTRE
NORTH YORKSHIRE MOORS RAILWAY
NOTTINGHAM TRANSPORT CTRE
PEAK RAIL
PLYM VALLEY RAILWAY
RUTLAND RAILWAY MUSEUM
SITTINGBOURNE & KEMSLEY
SPA VALLEY RAILWAY
STRATHSPEY RAILWAY
TYSELEY LOCOMOTIVE WORKS
VALE OF GLAMORGAN RAILWAY

HAYDOCK FOUNDRY
FOXFIELD STEAM RAILWAY

HAYLOCK
MOORS VALLEY RAILWAY

HCS BULLOCK
EASTLEIGH LAKESIDE RAILWAY
KERR MINIATURE RAILWAY

HEAD WRIGHTSON
BEAMISH
KENT & EAST SUSSEX RAILWAY
NORTH YORKSHIRE MOORS RAILWAY
PEAK RAIL

HEATH
FOXFIELD STEAM RAILWAY

HEATHERSLAW LIGHT RAILWAY
HEATHERSLAW LIGHT RAILWAY

HENSCHEL
AMERTON RAILWAY
BREDGAR & WORMSHILL
NORTH GLOUCESTERSHIRE RAILWAY
SOUTH TYNEDALE RAILWAY
WEST LANCASHIRE LIGHT RLWY

HENSHAW
MANGAPPS RAILWAY MUSEUM

HEYWOOD
RAVENGLASS & ESKDALE

HIBBERD & CO
ABBEY PUMPING STATION
AMBERLEY WORKING MUSEUM
BOWES RAILWAY
BUCKINGHAMSHIRE RLWY CTRE
CAMBRIAN RAILWAY SOCIETY
CHOLSEY & WALLINGFORD RAILWAY
COLNE VALLEY RAILWAY
DEVON RAILWAY CENTRE
EAST LANCASHIRE RAILWAY
FFESTINIOG RAILWAY
LAVENDER LINE
LEIGHTON BUZZARD RAILWAY
SOUTH TYNEDALE RAILWAY
SOUTH YORKSHIRE RAILWAY
WEST LANCASHIRE LIGHT RLWY

HILL

- AVON VALLEY RAILWAY
- FOXFIELD STEAM RAILWAY
- MIDDLETON RAILWAY
- NORTH YORKSHIRE MOORS RAILWAY
- PEAK RAIL
- PLYM VALLEY RAILWAY
- SOUTH YORKSHIRE RAILWAY

HOLM

- NENE VALLEY RAILWAY

HORLOCK

- INDUSTRIAL RAILWAY MUSEUM

HOWARD

- BLUEBELL RAILWAY
- SOUTH DOWNS LIGHT RAILWAY

HUDELL

- SOUTH DOWNS LIGHT RAILWAY

HUDSON

- ABBEY LIGHT RAILWAY
- AMBERLEY WORKING MUSEUM
- ARMLEY MILLS
- BICTON WOODLAND RAILWAY
- BURE VALLEY RAILWAY
- CAVAN & LEITRIM RAILWAY
- GROUDLE GLEN RAILWAY
- LEIGHTON BUZZARD RAILWAY
- SITTINGBOURNE & KEMSLEY
- SOUTH TYNEDALE RAILWAY
- WELSH HIGHLAND RAILWAY
- WEST LANCASHIRE LIGHT RLWY

HUDSWELL

- AMBERLEY WORKING MUSEUM
- ARMLEY MILLS
- AVON VALLEY RAILWAY
- BATTLEFIELD LINE
- BOWES RAILWAY
- BRESSINGHAM STEAM
- BUCKINGHAMSHIRE RLWY CTRE
- CADEBY LIGHT RAILWAY
- CAMBRIAN RAILWAY SOCIETY

- CHASEWATER RAILWAY
- DERWENT VALLEY
- DOWNPATRICK & ARDGLASS
- EAST LANCASHIRE RAILWAY
- EMBSAY & BOLTON ABBEY RLWY
- INDUSTRIAL RAILWAY MUSEUM
- KEIGHLEY & WORTH VALLEY
- LEADHILLS & WANLOCKHEAD
- MANGAPPS RAILWAY MUSEUM
- MIDDLETON RAILWAY
- MID-SUFFOLK LIGHT RAILWAY
- NENE VALLEY RAILWAY
- NIRT
- NORTH NORFOLK RAILWAY
- NOTTINGHAM TRANSPORT CTRE
- PEAK RAIL
- RPSI
- SOUTH TYNEDALE RAILWAY
- SOUTH YORKSHIRE RAILWAY
- SWANSEA VALE RAILWAY
- SWINDON & CRICKLADE RAILWAY
- TANFIELD RAILWAY
- TEIFI VALLEY RAILWAY
- VALE OF GLAMORGAN RAILWAY
- VINTAGE CARRIAGES TRUST
- WEST LANCASHIRE LIGHT RLWY

HUGHES LOCO & TRAMWAY ENG WORKS

- TALYLLYN RAILWAY

HUMPHRIES

- CONWY VALLEY

HUNSLET

- ABBEY LIGHT RAILWAY
- ALMOND VALLEY HERITAGE TRUST
- AMBERLEY WORKING MUSEUM
- AMERTON RAILWAY
- ARMLEY MILLS
- BALA LAKE RAILWAY
- BATTLEFIELD LINE
- BICTON WOODLAND RAILWAY

ROLLING STOCK by BUILDER

Hill — Hunslet

WW BODMIN & WENFORD RAILWAY

WW BO'NESS & KINNEIL RAILWAY

WW BOWES RAILWAY

WW BUCKINGHAMSHIRE RLWY CTRE

WW BURE VALLEY RAILWAY

WW CAMBRIAN RAILWAY SOCIETY

WW CAVAN & LEITRIM RAILWAY

WW CHURNET VALLEY RAILWAY

WW COLNE VALLEY RAILWAY

WW DIDCOT RAILWAY CENTRE

WW EMBSAY & BOLTON ABBEY RLWY

WW FFESTINIOG RAILWAY

WW FOXFIELD STEAM RAILWAY

WW GLOUCESTERSHIRE WARWICKSHIRE

WW GROUDLE GLEN RAILWAY

WW GWILI RAILWAY

WW INDUSTRIAL RAILWAY MUSEUM

WW IRCHESTER NARROW GAUGE MUSEUM

WW KEIGHLEY & WORTH VALLEY

WW KENT & EAST SUSSEX RAILWAY

WW KEW BRIDGE STEAM MUSEUM

WW LAKESIDE & HAVERTHWAITE RLWY

WW LAUNCESTON STEAM RAILWAY

WW LAVENDER LINE

WW LEADHILLS & WANLOCKHEAD

WW LEIGHTON BUZZARD RAILWAY

WW LLANBERIS LAKE RAILWAY

WW MIDDLETON RAILWAY

WW MIDLAND RAILWAY CENTRE

WW MUSEUM OF ARMY TRANSPORT

WW NARROW GAUGE RAILWAY MUSEUM

WW NENE VALLEY RAILWAY

WW NIRT

WW NORTH GLOUCESTERSHIRE RAILWAY

WW NORTH NORFOLK RAILWAY

WW NORTH YORKSHIRE MOORS RAILWAY

WW NOTTINGHAM TRANSPORT CTRE

WW OLD KILN LIGHT RAILWAY

WW SEVERN VALLEY RAILWAY

WW SITTINGBOURNE & KEMSLEY

WW SNOWDON MOUNTAIN RAILWAY

WW SOUTH TYNEDALE RAILWAY

WW SOUTH YORKSHIRE RAILWAY

WW SWANAGE RAILWAY

WW SWANSEA VALE RAILWAY

WW TALYLLYN RAILWAY

WW TANFIELD RAILWAY

WW TEIFI VALLEY RAILWAY

WW TRALEE & DINGLE RAILWAY

WW VALE OF GLAMORGAN RAILWAY

WW WATERCRESS LINE

WW WELSH HIGHLAND RAILWAY

WW WELSHPOOL & LLANFAIR

WW WEST LANCASHIRE LIGHT RLWY

HURST

WW DIDCOT RAILWAY CENTRE

WW EAST ANGLIAN RAILWAY MUSEUM

WW KENT & EAST SUSSEX RAILWAY

WW NORTH NORFOLK RAILWAY

JAMES

WW BLUEBELL RAILWAY

JENNINGS

WW AMBERLEY WORKING MUSEUM

WW KERR MINIATURE RAILWAY

WW TALYLLYN RAILWAY

JONES

WW LAKESIDE & HAVERTHWAITE RLWY

WW ROYAL VICTORIA RAILWAY

JUBILEE

WW WINDMILL FARM RAILWAY

KEEF

WW BICTON WOODLAND RAILWAY

WW GARTELL LIGHT RAILWAY

WW LEIGHTON BUZZARD RAILWAY

WW MARKEATON PARK LIGHT RAILWAY

WW TELFORD STEAM RAILWAY

WW WELLS & WALSINGHAM

KENT CONSTRUCTION & ENG CO

- CHASEWATER RAILWAY
- DEVON RAILWAY CENTRE

KERR

- BUCKINGHAMSHIRE RLWY CTRE
- CAVAN & LEITRIM RAILWAY
- FOXFIELD STEAM RAILWAY
- GREAT WHIPSNADE RAILWAY
- LEIGHTON BUZZARD RAILWAY
- NARROW GAUGE RAILWAY MUSEUM
- RAVENGLASS & ESKDALE
- SEVERN VALLEY RAILWAY
- SITTINGBOURNE & KEMSLEY
- TALYLLYN RAILWAY
- TEIFI VALLEY RAILWAY
- WELSHPOOL & LLANFAIR
- WEST LANCASHIRE LIGHT RLWY

KIRKLAND

- SOUTH DOWNS LIGHT RAILWAY

KIRKLEES LIGHT RAILWAY

- KIRKLEES LIGHT RAILWAY

KITSON & CO

- DIDCOT RAILWAY CENTRE
- NORTH YORKSHIRE MOORS RAILWAY
- NORTHAMPTON & LAMPORT RAILWAY
- SOUTH DEVON RAILWAY
- ULSTER FOLK & TRANSPORT

KOPPEL

- ABBEY LIGHT RAILWAY
- AMBERLEY WORKING MUSEUM
- BREDGAR & WORMSHILL
- CADEBY LIGHT RAILWAY
- DOWNPATRICK & ARDGLASS
- LEADHILLS & WANLOCKHEAD
- LEIGHTON BUZZARD RAILWAY
- OLD KILN LIGHT RAILWAY
- RAILWORLD
- SOUTH TYNEDALE RAILWAY
- WELSH HIGHLAND RAILWAY
- WEST LANCASHIRE LIGHT RLWY

KRAUSS

- ROMNEY HYTHE & DYMCHURCH

KRUPP

- BRESSINGHAM STEAM

LA MEUSE

- BREDGAR & WORMSHILL

LANCING CARRIAGE WORKS

- EAST ANGLIAN RAILWAY MUSEUM

LEIGHTON BUZZARD RAILWAY

- LEIGHTON BUZZARD RAILWAY

LEWIN

- BEAMISH

LISTER & CO

- AMBERLEY WORKING MUSEUM
- BURE VALLEY RAILWAY
- CADEBY LIGHT RAILWAY
- CLEETHORPES LIGHT RAILWAY
- DEVON RAILWAY CENTRE
- KEW BRIDGE STEAM MUSEUM
- LAPPA VALLEY STEAM RAILWAY
- LEIGHTON BUZZARD RAILWAY
- NORTH GLOUCESTERSHIRE RAILWAY
- RHYL MINIATURE RAILWAY
- WEST LANCASHIRE LIGHT RLWY
- WINDMILL FARM RAILWAY

LMS

- BO'NESS & KINNEIL RAILWAY
- BRISTOL HARBOUR RAILWAY
- CHURNET VALLEY RAILWAY
- GLOUCESTERSHIRE WARWICKSHIRE
- LLANGOLLEN RAILWAY
- NORTH NORFOLK RAILWAY
- NORTH YORKSHIRE MOORS RAILWAY
- SEVERN VALLEY RAILWAY
- STRATHSPEY RAILWAY

LNER

- BO'NESS & KINNEIL RAILWAY
- EAST ANGLIAN RAILWAY MUSEUM
- NORTH NORFOLK RAILWAY
- NORTH YORKSHIRE MOORS RAILWAY
- SEVERN VALLEY RAILWAY

ROLLING STOCK by BUILDER

Kent Construction & Eng Co — LNER

ROLLING STOCK by BUILDER

LNER — Moss

STRATHSPEY RAILWAY

WATERCRESS LINE

LNWR
KENT & EAST SUSSEX RAILWAY

NORTH NORFOLK RAILWAY

LOMAS
BROOKSIDE MINIATURE

LONDON
BUCKINGHAMSHIRE RLWY CTRE

SPA VALLEY RAILWAY

LONDON & NORTH WESTERN RAILWAY
BUCKINGHAMSHIRE RLWY CTRE

LONDON & SOUTH WEST RAILWAY
BUCKINGHAMSHIRE RLWY CTRE

LSWR
BLUEBELL RAILWAY

NORTH YORKSHIRE MOORS RAILWAY

SOUTH DEVON RAILWAY

WATERCRESS LINE

MANCHESTER WORKS
CHASEWATER RAILWAY

MANKTELOW
MOORS VALLEY RAILWAY

MANNING
ARMLEY MILLS

AVON VALLEY RAILWAY

BLUEBELL RAILWAY

BUCKINGHAMSHIRE RLWY CTRE

GREAT WHIPSNADE RAILWAY

KENT & EAST SUSSEX RAILWAY

MIDDLETON RAILWAY

NARROW GAUGE RAILWAY MUSEUM

SEVERN VALLEY RAILWAY

MARDYKE
ROYAL VICTORIA RAILWAY

MARSH & CO
BEER HEIGHTS

MOORS VALLEY RAILWAY

MULL RAILWAY

MARSHALLS
TALYLLYN RAILWAY

MCEWAN
BEAMISH

MCW
NORTH NORFOLK RAILWAY

METCALFE
SOUTH DOWNS LIGHT RAILWAY

METRO CAMMELL
EAST SOMERSET RAILWAY

METROPOLITAN CAMMELL
CHINNOR & PRINCES RISBOROUGH

CHURNET VALLEY RAILWAY

KENT & EAST SUSSEX RAILWAY

MANGAPPS RAILWAY MUSEUM

NORTH NORFOLK RAILWAY

NORTH YORKSHIRE MOORS RAILWAY

SPA VALLEY RAILWAY

METROPOLITAN CARRIAGE & WAGON CO
KENT & EAST SUSSEX RAILWAY

MANGAPPS RAILWAY MUSEUM

NORTH YORKSHIRE MOORS RAILWAY

STRATHSPEY RAILWAY

TALYLLYN RAILWAY

VINTAGE CARRIAGES TRUST

WELSH HIGHLAND RAILWAY

MIDLAND & SCOTTISH RAILWAY
BUCKINGHAMSHIRE RLWY CTRE

MIDLAND RAILWAY
KENT & EAST SUSSEX RAILWAY

VINTAGE CARRIAGES TRUST

MILLS
ROYAL VICTORIA RAILWAY

MILNER
FAIRBOURNE & BARMOUTH

MILNER ENG
CONWY VALLEY

MILNER ENGINEERING
WESTON PARK RAILWAY

MINI RAIL
LAPPA VALLEY STEAM RAILWAY

MOSS
WINDMILL FARM RAILWAY

MOTOR RAIL

- ABBEY LIGHT RAILWAY
- ABBEY PUMPING STATION
- AMBERLEY WORKING MUSEUM
- AMERTON RAILWAY
- ARMLEY MILLS
- BRESSINGHAM STEAM
- CADEBY LIGHT RAILWAY
- CHASEWATER RAILWAY
- CORRIS RAILWAY MUSEUM
- DERBY INDUSTRIAL MUSEUM
- DEVON RAILWAY CENTRE
- EAST ANGLIA TRANSPORT MUSEUM
- EAST ANGLIAN RAILWAY MUSEUM
- EAST LANCASHIRE RAILWAY
- EXMOOR STEAM RAILWAY
- FFESTINIOG RAILWAY
- IRCHESTER NARROW GAUGE MUSEUM
- LAKESIDE & HAVERTHWAITE RLWY
- LAUNCESTON STEAM RAILWAY
- LEADHILLS & WANLOCKHEAD
- LEIGHTON BUZZARD RAILWAY
- MIDLAND RAILWAY CENTRE
- NORTH GLOUCESTERSHIRE RAILWAY
- NOTTINGHAM TRANSPORT CTRE
- PERRYGROVE RAILWAY
- ULSTER FOLK & TRANSPORT
- WEST LANCASHIRE LIGHT RLWY

MOUSE BOILER WORKS

- MULL RAILWAY

MUIR HILL

- ABBEY LIGHT RAILWAY

MUL HAUSER

- SOUTH TYNEDALE RAILWAY

NASMYTH

- MIDLAND RAILWAY CENTRE
- ULSTER FOLK & TRANSPORT

NEIL SIMKINS

- WESTON PARK RAILWAY

NEILSON & CO

- BLUEBELL RAILWAY
- BO'NESS & KINNEIL RAILWAY
- BRESSINGHAM STEAM
- CHASEWATER RAILWAY
- INDUSTRIAL RAILWAY MUSEUM

NELSON & CO

- DIDCOT RAILWAY CENTRE
- EAST ANGLIAN RAILWAY MUSEUM
- KENT & EAST SUSSEX RAILWAY
- NORTH NORFOLK RAILWAY

NER

- BEAMISH
- NORTH YORKSHIRE MOORS RAILWAY

NORTH BRITISH LOCOMOTIVE CO

- BARROW HILL ROUNDHOUSE
- BO'NESS & KINNEIL RAILWAY
- BUCKINGHAMSHIRE RLWY CTRE
- GREAT CENTRAL RAILWAY
- GWILI RAILWAY
- LLANGOLLEN RAILWAY
- MIDLAND RAILWAY CENTRE
- NORTH YORKSHIRE MOORS RAILWAY
- SCOTTISH RAILWAY CENTRE
- SEVERN VALLEY RAILWAY
- SWANSEA VALE RAILWAY
- ULSTER FOLK & TRANSPORT

NORTH DORSET LOCO WORKS

- GARTELL LIGHT RAILWAY

NSR

- CHURNET VALLEY RAILWAY

NYDQUIST

- NENE VALLEY RAILWAY

ORENSTEIN

- ABBEY LIGHT RAILWAY
- AMBERLEY WORKING MUSEUM
- BREDGAR & WORMSHILL
- CADEBY LIGHT RAILWAY
- DOWNPATRICK & ARDGLASS
- LEADHILLS & WANLOCKHEAD

ROLLING STOCK by **BUILDER**

Motor Rail — Orenstein

ﾑﾑﾜ LEIGHTON BUZZARD RAILWAY

ﾑﾑﾜ OLD KILN LIGHT RAILWAY

ﾑﾑﾜ RAILWORLD

ﾑﾑﾜ SOUTH TYNEDALE RAILWAY

ﾑﾑﾜ WELSH HIGHLAND RAILWAY

ﾑﾑﾜ WEST LANCASHIRE LIGHT RLWY

PAXMAN

ﾑﾑﾜ RAVENGLASS & ESKDALE

ﾑﾑﾜ ROMNEY HYTHE & DYMCHURCH

PEACOCK

ﾑﾑﾜ BARROW HILL ROUNDHOUSE

ﾑﾑﾜ BUCKINGHAMSHIRE RLWY CTRE

ﾑﾑﾜ EXMOOR STEAM RAILWAY

ﾑﾑﾜ FOXFIELD STEAM RAILWAY

ﾑﾑﾜ ISLE OF MAN RAILWAY

ﾑﾑﾜ LONDON TRANSPORT MUSEUM

ﾑﾑﾜ MIDDLETON RAILWAY

ﾑﾑﾜ NARROW GAUGE RAILWAY MUSEUM

ﾑﾑﾜ NATIONAL TRAMWAY MUSEUM

ﾑﾑﾜ NORTH YORKSHIRE MOORS RAILWAY

ﾑﾑﾜ NORTHAMPTON & LAMPORT RAILWAY

ﾑﾑﾜ RPSI

ﾑﾑﾜ SEVERN VALLEY RAILWAY

ﾑﾑﾜ ULSTER FOLK & TRANSPORT

ﾑﾑﾜ WELSHPOOL & LLANFAIR

PECKETT & SONS

ﾑﾑﾜ AMBERLEY WORKING MUSEUM

ﾑﾑﾜ APPLEBY-FRODINGHAM RAILWAY

ﾑﾑﾜ BATTLEFIELD LINE

ﾑﾑﾜ BREDGAR & WORMSHILL

ﾑﾑﾜ BRISTOL HARBOUR RAILWAY

ﾑﾑﾜ BUCKINGHAMSHIRE RLWY CTRE

ﾑﾑﾜ CADEBY LIGHT RAILWAY

ﾑﾑﾜ CALEDONIAN RAILWAY

ﾑﾑﾜ CAMBRIAN RAILWAY SOCIETY

ﾑﾑﾜ CHASEWATER RAILWAY

ﾑﾑﾜ DERBY INDUSTRIAL MUSEUM

ﾑﾑﾜ EMBSAY & BOLTON ABBEY RLWY

ﾑﾑﾜ FOXFIELD STEAM RAILWAY

ﾑﾑﾜ GIANTS CAUSEWAY & BUSHMILLS

ﾑﾑﾜ GREAT WESTERN RAILWAY MUSEUM

ﾑﾑﾜ IRCHESTER NARROW GAUGE MUSEUM

ﾑﾑﾜ KEIGHLEY & WORTH VALLEY

ﾑﾑﾜ KENT & EAST SUSSEX RAILWAY

ﾑﾑﾜ LINCOLNSHIRE WOLDS RAILWAY

ﾑﾑﾜ MIDDLETON RAILWAY

ﾑﾑﾜ MIDLAND RAILWAY CENTRE

ﾑﾑﾜ NORTHAMPTON & LAMPORT RAILWAY

ﾑﾑﾜ RUTLAND RAILWAY MUSEUM

ﾑﾑﾜ SITTINGBOURNE & KEMSLEY

ﾑﾑﾜ SOMERSET & DORSET RAILWAY

ﾑﾑﾜ SOUTH DEVON RAILWAY

ﾑﾑﾜ SPA VALLEY RAILWAY

ﾑﾑﾜ SWANAGE RAILWAY

ﾑﾑﾜ SWANSEA INDUSTRIAL MUSEUM

ﾑﾑﾜ SWANSEA VALE RAILWAY

ﾑﾑﾜ TELFORD STEAM RAILWAY

ﾑﾑﾜ TIMOTHY HACKWORTH

ﾑﾑﾜ TYSELEY LOCOMOTIVE WORKS

ﾑﾑﾜ ULSTER FOLK & TRANSPORT

ﾑﾑﾜ WEST SOMERSET RAILWAY

ﾑﾑﾜ YEOVIL RAILWAY CENTRE

PERMAQUIP

ﾑﾑﾜ NORTH YORKSHIRE MOORS RAILWAY

PERRYGROVE RAILWAY

ﾑﾑﾜ PERRYGROVE RAILWAY

PICKERING & CO

ﾑﾑﾜ KENT & EAST SUSSEX RAILWAY

ﾑﾑﾜ NORTH YORKSHIRE MOORS RAILWAY

ﾑﾑﾜ PEAK RAIL

PLANET

ﾑﾑﾜ CAMBRIAN RAILWAY SOCIETY

ﾑﾑﾜ IRISH STEAM PRESERVATION SOC

ﾑﾑﾜ NIRT

ﾑﾑﾜ SWANAGE RAILWAY

PORTER

ﾑﾑﾜ BUCKINGHAMSHIRE RLWY CTRE

PRATT

ﾑﾑﾜ BEAMISH

PRESSED STEEL CO
- BARROW HILL ROUNDHOUSE
- CHASEWATER RAILWAY
- CHINNOR & PRINCES RISBOROUGH
- LAVENDER LINE
- MANGAPPS RAILWAY MUSEUM
- NORTH NORFOLK RAILWAY
- NORTH YORKSHIRE MOORS RAILWAY
- NORTHAMPTON & LAMPORT RAILWAY
- NOTTINGHAM TRANSPORT CTRE
- PLYM VALLEY RAILWAY

RANSOMES
- AMBERLEY WORKING MUSEUM
- BLUEBELL RAILWAY
- KENT & EAST SUSSEX RAILWAY
- NORTH YORKSHIRE MOORS RAILWAY

RAPIDO RAIL
- RHYL MINIATURE RAILWAY

RAPIER
- AMBERLEY WORKING MUSEUM
- BLUEBELL RAILWAY
- KENT & EAST SUSSEX RAILWAY
- NORTH YORKSHIRE MOORS RAILWAY

RAVENGLASS & ESKDALE RAILWAY
- HEATHERSLAW LIGHT RAILWAY
- RAVENGLASS & ESKDALE
- RUISLIP LIDO RAILWAY

RCW
- NORTH YORKSHIRE MOORS RAILWAY

ROBERTS & CO
- BEAMISH
- CHASEWATER RAILWAY
- DIDCOT RAILWAY CENTRE
- NORTH NORFOLK RAILWAY
- NORTH YORKSHIRE MOORS RAILWAY
- PEAK RAIL

RODLEY
- DERWENT VALLEY
- DINGLES STEAM VILLAGE
- KENT & EAST SUSSEX RAILWAY

- NORTH YORKSHIRE MOORS RAILWAY
- PEAK RAIL
- VALE OF GLAMORGAN RAILWAY
- WINDMILL FARM RAILWAY

ROGERS
- AMBERLEY WORKING MUSEUM

ROWAN OAK ENGINEERING
- MOORS VALLEY RAILWAY

RSH
- BUCKINGHAMSHIRE RLWY CTRE

RUSTON
- BEAMISH
- BO'NESS & KINNEIL RAILWAY
- BRISTOL HARBOUR RAILWAY
- DEVON RAILWAY CENTRE
- ELSECAR HERITAGE CENTRE
- IRISH STEAM PRESERVATION SOC
- WEST SOMERSET RAILWAY

RUSTON & HORNSBY LTD
- ABBEY LIGHT RAILWAY
- ABBEY PUMPING STATION
- AMBERLEY WORKING MUSEUM
- AMERTON RAILWAY
- AVON VALLEY RAILWAY
- BALA LAKE RAILWAY
- BATTLEFIELD LINE
- BICTON WOODLAND RAILWAY
- CADEBY LIGHT RAILWAY
- CALEDONIAN RAILWAY
- CHASEWATER RAILWAY
- CHINNOR & PRINCES RISBOROUGH
- COLNE VALLEY RAILWAY
- DARLINGTON RAILWAY PRES SOC
- DERWENT VALLEY
- EAST ANGLIA TRANSPORT MUSEUM
- EAST KENT LIGHT RAILWAY
- EMBSAY & BOLTON ABBEY RLWY
- FOXFIELD STEAM RAILWAY
- GARTELL LIGHT RAILWAY

ROLLING STOCK by BUILDER

Pressed Steel Co — Ruston & Hornsby Ltd

ROLLING STOCK by **BUILDER**

Ruston & Hornsby Ltd — Simplex

- GREAT CENTRAL RAILWAY
- GREAT WHIPSNADE RAILWAY
- GWILI RAILWAY
- HOLLYCOMBE STEAM COLLECTION
- INDUSTRIAL RAILWAY MUSEUM
- IRCHESTER NARROW GAUGE MUSEUM
- KENT & EAST SUSSEX RAILWAY
- LEADHILLS & WANLOCKHEAD
- LEIGHTON BUZZARD RAILWAY
- LINCOLNSHIRE WOLDS RAILWAY
- MIDDLETON RAILWAY
- MIDLAND RAILWAY CENTRE
- MID-SUFFOLK LIGHT RAILWAY
- NATIONAL TRAMWAY MUSEUM
- NIRT
- NORTH GLOUCESTERSHIRE RAILWAY
- NORTH NORFOLK RAILWAY
- NORTH YORKSHIRE MOORS RAILWAY
- NORTHAMPTON & LAMPORT RAILWAY
- NOTTINGHAM TRANSPORT CTRE
- PEAK RAIL
- PRESTONGRANGE INDUSTRIAL
- SCOTTISH RAILWAY CENTRE
- SEVERN VALLEY RAILWAY
- SITTINGBOURNE & KEMSLEY
- SOUTH YORKSHIRE RAILWAY
- SPA VALLEY RAILWAY
- SWANSEA VALE RAILWAY
- TALYLLYN RAILWAY
- TANFIELD RAILWAY
- WELSH HIGHLAND RAILWAY
- WEST LANCASHIRE LIGHT RLWY

SCHARTZKOPF
- BREDGAR & WORMSHILL

SDR
- SOUTH DEVON RAILWAY

SECR
- BLUEBELL RAILWAY

SENTINEL
- AVON VALLEY RAILWAY
- BATTLEFIELD LINE
- BUCKINGHAMSHIRE RLWY CTRE
- CAMBRIAN RAILWAY SOCIETY
- CHASEWATER RAILWAY
- EAST LANCASHIRE RAILWAY
- EAST SOMERSET RAILWAY
- EMBSAY & BOLTON ABBEY RLWY
- FOXFIELD STEAM RAILWAY
- GWILI RAILWAY
- MIDDLETON RAILWAY
- MIDLAND RAILWAY CENTRE
- NIRT
- SOUTH YORKSHIRE RAILWAY
- TANFIELD RAILWAY
- WEST SOMERSET RAILWAY

SEVERN LAMB
- BALA LAKE RAILWAY
- BEER HEIGHTS
- LAPPA VALLEY STEAM RAILWAY
- RUISLIP LIDO RAILWAY
- WINDMILL FARM RAILWAY

SHARP
- RPSI

SHELDON
- NORTH YORKSHIRE MOORS RAILWAY
- PEAK RAIL
- STRATHSPEY RAILWAY
- SWANSEA VALE RAILWAY

SHILDON WAGON WORKS
- PEAK RAIL

SIEMENS - SCHUKERT
- BEAMISH

SIMKINS
- FAIRBOURNE & BARMOUTH
- KERR MINIATURE RAILWAY
- WELLS & WALSINGHAM

SIMPLEX
- ABBEY LIGHT RAILWAY

☷ ALMOND VALLEY HERITAGE TRUST	☷ GREAT CENTRAL RAILWAY
☷ AMBERLEY WORKING MUSEUM	☷ KENT & EAST SUSSEX RAILWAY
☷ AMERTON RAILWAY	☷ NORTH NORFOLK RAILWAY
☷ CADEBY LIGHT RAILWAY	☷ NORTH YORKSHIRE MOORS RAILWAY
☷ EAST ANGLIAN RAILWAY MUSEUM	☷ PEAK RAIL
☷ FOXFIELD STEAM RAILWAY	☷ SPA VALLEY RAILWAY
☷ GIANTS CAUSEWAY & BUSHMILLS	☷ WATERCRESS LINE
☷ TALYLLYN RAILWAY	**STANDARD RAILWAY WAGON CO**
☷ TEIFI VALLEY RAILWAY	☷ NORTH YORKSHIRE MOORS RAILWAY
SITTINGBOURNE & KEMSLEY LIGHT RAILWAY	☷ RAILWORLD
☷ SITTINGBOURNE & KEMSLEY	**STANHOPE**
SMALLWOOD	☷ RUDYARD LAKE RAILWAY
☷ EASTLEIGH LAKESIDE RAILWAY	**STEPHENSON**
SMITH	☷ AVON VALLEY RAILWAY
☷ DERWENT VALLEY	☷ BARROW HILL ROUNDHOUSE
☷ DINGLES STEAM VILLAGE	☷ BATTLEFIELD LINE
☷ HOLLYBUSH GARDEN CENTRE	☷ BEAMISH
☷ KENT & EAST SUSSEX RAILWAY	☷ BO'NESS & KINNEIL RAILWAY
☷ NORTH YORKSHIRE MOORS RAILWAY	☷ BOWES RAILWAY
☷ PEAK RAIL	☷ COLNE VALLEY RAILWAY
☷ RUDYARD LAKE RAILWAY	☷ DARLINGTON RAILWAY PRES SOC
☷ VALE OF GLAMORGAN RAILWAY	☷ DIDCOT RAILWAY CENTRE
☷ WINDMILL FARM RAILWAY	☷ EMBSAY & BOLTON ABBEY RLWY
SMITH & SONS	☷ FOXFIELD STEAM RAILWAY
☷ PLYM VALLEY RAILWAY	☷ GWILI RAILWAY
☷ SPA VALLEY RAILWAY	☷ INDUSTRIAL RAILWAY MUSEUM
SOCIETE FRANCO BELGE	☷ LINCOLNSHIRE WOLDS RAILWAY
☷ WELSH HIGHLAND RAILWAY	☷ MIDLAND RAILWAY CENTRE
☷ WELSHPOOL & LLANFAIR	☷ NATIONAL RAILWAY MUSEUM
SOUTH TYNEDALE RAILWAY PRESERVATION SOCIETY	☷ NORTH YORKSHIRE MOORS RAILWAY
☷ SOUTH TYNEDALE RAILWAY	☷ NOTTINGHAM TRANSPORT CTRE
SOUTHAMPTON UNIVERSITY	☷ PEAK RAIL
☷ EASTLEIGH LAKESIDE RAILWAY	☷ SPA VALLEY RAILWAY
SPENCE	☷ STRATHSPEY RAILWAY
☷ AMBERLEY WORKING MUSEUM	☷ ULSTER FOLK & TRANSPORT
SR	☷ VALE OF GLAMORGAN RAILWAY
☷ BLUEBELL RAILWAY	**STEWART**
☷ COLNE VALLEY RAILWAY	☷ BRESSINGHAM STEAM
☷ DIDCOT RAILWAY CENTRE	☷ RPSI
☷ GLOUCESTERSHIRE WARWICKSHIRE	

ROLLING STOCK by **BUILDER**

Simplex — Stewart

STRACHAN

- ∷ **MANGAPPS RAILWAY MUSEUM**

STUART & CO

- ∷ **BUCKINGHAMSHIRE RLWY CTRE**
- ∷ **CAVAN & LEITRIM RAILWAY**
- ∷ **FOXFIELD STEAM RAILWAY**
- ∷ **GREAT WHIPSNADE RAILWAY**
- ∷ **LEIGHTON BUZZARD RAILWAY**
- ∷ **NARROW GAUGE RAILWAY MUSEUM**
- ∷ **RAVENGLASS & ESKDALE**
- ∷ **SEVERN VALLEY RAILWAY**
- ∷ **SITTINGBOURNE & KEMSLEY**
- ∷ **TALYLLYN RAILWAY**
- ∷ **TEIFI VALLEY RAILWAY**
- ∷ **WELSHPOOL & LLANFAIR**
- ∷ **WEST LANCASHIRE LIGHT RLWY**

SWINDON WORKS

- ∷ **PEAK RAIL**

SWISS LOCOMOTIVE WORKS

- ∷ **SNOWDON MOUNTAIN RAILWAY**

T M A ENGINEERING

- ∷ **HOLLYBUSH GARDEN CENTRE**
- ∷ **ROMNEY HYTHE & DYMCHURCH**

TALYLLYN RAILWAY

- ∷ **TALYLLYN RAILWAY**

TAYLOR

- ∷ **KIRKLEES LIGHT RAILWAY**

TAYLOR & HUBBARD

- ∷ **KENT & EAST SUSSEX RAILWAY**
- ∷ **SPA VALLEY RAILWAY**

THAKEHAM

- ∷ **CADEBY LIGHT RAILWAY**

THOMPSON

- ∷ **LEIGHTON BUZZARD RAILWAY**

TISDALE

- ∷ **TALYLLYN RAILWAY**

TISDALES

- ∷ **TALYLLYN RAILWAY**

TR

- ∷ **TALYLLYN RAILWAY**

TRACKED HOVER CRAFT

- ∷ **RAILWORLD**

TRALSER

- ∷ **NIRT**

TRAMCAR CO

- ∷ **ARMLEY MILLS**
- ∷ **CADEBY LIGHT RAILWAY**
- ∷ **IRCHESTER NARROW GAUGE MUSEUM**
- ∷ **ULSTER FOLK & TRANSPORT**

TREDOMEN ENGINEERING

- ∷ **LEIGHTON BUZZARD RAILWAY**

TUBIZE

- ∷ **WELSHPOOL & LLANFAIR**

VALENTE

- ∷ **SOUTH TYNEDALE RAILWAY**

VERE

- ∷ **MULL RAILWAY**

VICTOR

- ∷ **ALMOND VALLEY HERITAGE TRUST**

VOLANTE

- ∷ **WINDMILL FARM RAILWAY**

VULCAN FOUNDRY

- ∷ **ALDERNEY RAILWAY**
- ∷ **COLNE VALLEY RAILWAY**
- ∷ **EAST KENT LIGHT RAILWAY**
- ∷ **EAST SOMERSET RAILWAY**
- ∷ **GREAT CENTRAL RAILWAY**
- ∷ **LAVENDER LINE**
- ∷ **MANGAPPS RAILWAY MUSEUM**
- ∷ **MUSEUM OF SCIENCE & INDUSTRY**
- ∷ **ROTHER VALLEY RAILWAY**
- ∷ **SEVERN VALLEY RAILWAY**
- ∷ **SPA VALLEY RAILWAY**
- ∷ **STRATHSPEY RAILWAY**

WALKER

- ∷ **BRISTOL HARBOUR RAILWAY**
- ∷ **MANGAPPS RAILWAY MUSEUM**
- ∷ **ULSTER FOLK & TRANSPORT**
- ∷ **WINDMILL FARM RAILWAY**

WALKERS

- ∷ **DONEGAL RAILWAY HERITAGE CTRE**

WALLSEND

- ∷ **BEAMISH**

WARDLE & CO

- ARMLEY MILLS
- AVON VALLEY RAILWAY
- BLUEBELL RAILWAY
- BUCKINGHAMSHIRE RLWY CTRE
- GREAT WHIPSNADE RAILWAY
- KENT & EAST SUSSEX RAILWAY
- MIDDLETON RAILWAY
- NARROW GAUGE RAILWAY MUSEUM
- SEVERN VALLEY RAILWAY

WATERFIELD

- PERRYGROVE RAILWAY

WATKINS

- BURE VALLEY RAILWAY

WELSH HIGHLAND RAILWAY

- WELSH HIGHLAND RAILWAY

WHALLEY

- WESTON PARK RAILWAY

WHITE

- BEER HEIGHTS

WHITWORTH

- COLNE VALLEY RAILWAY
- DIDCOT RAILWAY CENTRE
- GREAT CENTRAL RAILWAY
- NORTH YORKSHIRE MOORS RAILWAY
- NOTTINGHAM TRANSPORT CTRE

WICKHAM

- AVON VALLEY RAILWAY
- PEAK RAIL
- SOUTH TYNEDALE RAILWAY

WILSON

- ARMLEY MILLS
- MIDLAND RAILWAY CENTRE
- ULSTER FOLK & TRANSPORT

WINGROVE

- AMBERLEY WORKING MUSEUM

WINSON ENGINEERING

- BURE VALLEY RAILWAY

WINTON

- NARROW GAUGE RAILWAY MUSEUM

WISEMAN

- SOUTH DOWNS LIGHT RAILWAY

WOLVERTON WORKS

- NOTTINGHAM TRANSPORT CTRE

WORSDELL

- NOTTINGHAM TRANSPORT CTRE

YORKSHIRE ENGINE CO

- APPLEBY-FRODINGHAM RAILWAY
- CHURNET VALLEY RAILWAY
- EMBSAY & BOLTON ABBEY RLWY
- FOXFIELD STEAM RAILWAY
- GWILI RAILWAY
- NENE VALLEY RAILWAY
- ROMNEY HYTHE & DYMCHURCH
- SOUTH YORKSHIRE RAILWAY

ROLLING STOCK by **BUILDER**

Wardle & Co — Yorkshire Engine Co

Rolling Stock by Designer

SECTION 5H

This section shows who Designed the stock and where it can be located

e.g. C B Collett, East Somerset Railway

Once you have located a railway/museum using this section you can then refer to the railway or museum's detailed profile in section 1.

ADAMS

- 🚂 **BLUEBELL RAILWAY**
- 🚂 **ISLE OF WIGHT STEAM RAILWAY**

ALCOCK

- 🚂 **MULL RAILWAY**

ATKINSON

- 🚂 **ULSTER FOLK & TRANSPORT**

AVONSIDE ENGINEERING CO

- 🚂 **BRISTOL HARBOUR RAILWAY**
- 🚂 **SOUTH TYNEDALE RAILWAY**

BAGNALL

- 🚂 **KEW BRIDGE STEAM MUSEUM**

BARCLAY

- 🚂 **STRATHSPEY RAILWAY**
- 🚂 **TALYLLYN RAILWAY**

BATE

- 🚂 **TALYLLYN RAILWAY**

BEATTIE

- 🚂 **BUCKINGHAMSHIRE RLWY CTRE**

BEER HEIGHTS LIGHT RAILWAY

- 🚂 **BEER HEIGHTS**

BEYER

- 🚂 **BARROW HILL ROUNDHOUSE**
- 🚂 **FOXFIELD STEAM RAILWAY**
- 🚂 **ULSTER FOLK & TRANSPORT**

BLACK

- 🚂 **INDUSTRIAL RAILWAY MUSEUM**

BOWERS

- 🚂 **ROYAL VICTORIA RAILWAY**

BR

- 🚂 **BRISTOL HARBOUR RAILWAY**
- 🚂 **CALEDONIAN RAILWAY**
- 🚂 **GLOUCESTERSHIRE WARWICKSHIRE**
- 🚂 **NORTH NORFOLK RAILWAY**
- 🚂 **RAILWORLD**
- 🚂 **SOUTH YORKSHIRE RAILWAY**
- 🚂 **STRATHSPEY RAILWAY**
- 🚂 **WATERCRESS LINE**

BRCW

- 🚂 **CALEDONIAN RAILWAY**
- 🚂 **NORTH NORFOLK RAILWAY**
- 🚂 **WATERCRESS LINE**

BREDIN

- 🚂 **ULSTER FOLK & TRANSPORT**

BRW

- 🚂 **WATERCRESS LINE**

BUDDLE

- 🚂 **BEAMISH**

BULLEID

- 🚂 **AVON VALLEY RAILWAY**
- 🚂 **BLUEBELL RAILWAY**
- 🚂 **GLOUCESTERSHIRE WARWICKSHIRE**
- 🚂 **GREAT CENTRAL RAILWAY**
- 🚂 **NATIONAL RAILWAY MUSEUM**
- 🚂 **NENE VALLEY RAILWAY**
- 🚂 **SEVERN VALLEY RAILWAY**
- 🚂 **VINTAGE CARRIAGES TRUST**
- 🚂 **WATERCRESS LINE**

BURY

- 🚂 **NATIONAL RAILWAY MUSEUM**

CANTLIE

- 🚂 **NATIONAL RAILWAY MUSEUM**

CASSEL

- 🚂 **AMERTON RAILWAY**

CHAPMAN

- 🚂 **BEAMISH**

CHURCHWARD

- 🚂 **DIDCOT RAILWAY CENTRE**
- 🚂 **GLOUCESTERSHIRE WARWICKSHIRE**
- 🚂 **PAIGNTON & DARTMOUTH RAILWAY**
- 🚂 **SEVERN VALLEY RAILWAY**
- 🚂 **STEAM**

CLARKE

- 🚂 **NENE VALLEY RAILWAY**

CLIFFORD

- 🚂 **ULSTER FOLK & TRANSPORT**

COLBOURNE

- 🚂 **MOORS VALLEY RAILWAY**

COLES

- 🚂 **BRISTOL HARBOUR RAILWAY**

COLLETT

- 🚂 **BLUEBELL RAILWAY**
- 🚂 **BUCKINGHAMSHIRE RLWY CTRE**
- 🚂 **DIDCOT RAILWAY CENTRE**

ROLLING STOCK by DESIGNER

Adams — Collett

ROLLING STOCK by DESIGNER

Collett — Hawksworth

EAST SOMERSET RAILWAY
- EAST SOMERSET RAILWAY
- GLOUCESTERSHIRE WARWICKSHIRE
- LLANGOLLEN RAILWAY
- NATIONAL RAILWAY MUSEUM
- PAIGNTON & DARTMOUTH RAILWAY
- SEVERN VALLEY RAILWAY
- SOUTH DEVON RAILWAY
- STEAM
- TELFORD STEAM RAILWAY

CREWE WORKS
- INDUSTRIAL RAILWAY MUSEUM

CROSSKEY
- ROYAL VICTORIA RAILWAY

CULVER
- MOORS VALLEY RAILWAY

CURWEN
- BEER HEIGHTS
- FAIRBOURNE & BARMOUTH
- MULL RAILWAY
- ROYAL VICTORIA RAILWAY

DAVIES
- MULL RAILWAY

DEAN
- STEAM

DEUTZ
- GIANTS CAUSEWAY & BUSHMILLS

DUBS
- FOXFIELD STEAM RAILWAY

EDWARDS
- BURE VALLEY RAILWAY

ENGLISH ELECTRIC
- BARROW HILL ROUNDHOUSE
- BATTLEFIELD LINE
- EAST KENT LIGHT RAILWAY
- GLOUCESTERSHIRE WARWICKSHIRE
- NORTH NORFOLK RAILWAY
- WATERCRESS LINE

EVANS
- FOXFIELD STEAM RAILWAY

EXMOOR STEAM RAILWAY
- PERRYGROVE RAILWAY

FALCON DESIGN
- FOXFIELD STEAM RAILWAY

FOSTER
- NATIONAL RAILWAY MUSEUM

FOWLER
- AVON VALLEY RAILWAY
- EAST SOMERSET RAILWAY
- GREAT CENTRAL RAILWAY
- LLANGOLLEN RAILWAY
- MIDLAND RAILWAY CENTRE
- SEVERN VALLEY RAILWAY
- ULSTER FOLK & TRANSPORT

FOX
- BRISTOL HARBOUR RAILWAY

GEOGHEGAN
- NARROW GAUGE RAILWAY MUSEUM
- ULSTER FOLK & TRANSPORT

GNRI
- ULSTER FOLK & TRANSPORT

GREATREX
- HOLLYBUSH GARDEN CENTRE

GREENLY
- RHYL MINIATURE RAILWAY
- ROMNEY HYTHE & DYMCHURCH

GRESLEY
- BO'NESS & KINNEIL RAILWAY
- GREAT CENTRAL RAILWAY
- NATIONAL RAILWAY MUSEUM
- SEVERN VALLEY RAILWAY
- STRATHSPEY RAILWAY
- WATERCRESS LINE

HACKWORTH
- TIMOTHY HACKWORTH

HANTON
- RUDYARD LAKE RAILWAY

HAWKSWORTH
- BUCKINGHAMSHIRE RLWY CTRE
- GLOUCESTERSHIRE WARWICKSHIRE
- KENT & EAST SUSSEX RAILWAY
- STEAM

HAWTHORN
- INDUSTRIAL RAILWAY MUSEUM

HAYLOCK
- MOORS VALLEY RAILWAY

HEAD
- BEAMISH

HENSCHEL
- AMERTON RAILWAY

HEYWOOD
- PERRYGROVE RAILWAY

HILL
- KENT & EAST SUSSEX RAILWAY
- NORTH NORFOLK RAILWAY

HLR
- HEATHERSLAW LIGHT RAILWAY

HOLDEN
- NORTH NORFOLK RAILWAY

HOLM
- NENE VALLEY RAILWAY
- RAILWORLD

HOLMES
- BO'NESS & KINNEIL RAILWAY

HORLOCK
- INDUSTRIAL RAILWAY MUSEUM

HORNSBY
- NIRT

HOWDEN
- ULSTER FOLK & TRANSPORT

HUDSWELL
- NENE VALLEY RAILWAY

HUGHES LOCO & TRAMWAY ENG WORKS
- TALYLLYN RAILWAY

HUNSLET
- BARLEYLANDS MINIATURE RAILWAY
- BEER HEIGHTS
- INDUSTRIAL RAILWAY MUSEUM
- KEW BRIDGE STEAM MUSEUM
- NORTH NORFOLK RAILWAY
- OLD KILN LIGHT RAILWAY
- ROYAL VICTORIA RAILWAY

IVATT
- BUCKINGHAMSHIRE RLWY CTRE

- ROYAL VICTORIA RAILWAY
- SEVERN VALLEY RAILWAY
- STRATHSPEY RAILWAY
- WATERCRESS LINE

JENNINGS
- TALYLLYN RAILWAY

KEEF
- TELFORD STEAM RAILWAY

KERR
- TALYLLYN RAILWAY

KIRKLEES LIGHT RAILWAY
- KIRKLEES LIGHT RAILWAY

KIRTLEY
- MIDLAND RAILWAY CENTRE

KITSON
- ULSTER FOLK & TRANSPORT

KOPPE
- OLD KILN LIGHT RAILWAY
- RAILWORLD

LEWIN
- BEAMISH

LISTER
- KEW BRIDGE STEAM MUSEUM

LMS
- BRISTOL HARBOUR RAILWAY
- PEAK RAIL
- STRATHSPEY RAILWAY
- SWANSEA VALE RAILWAY
- WATERCRESS LINE

LOMAS
- BROOKSIDE MINIATURE

MACDOUGALL
- BEER HEIGHTS

MACINTOSH
- BO'NESS & KINNEIL RAILWAY
- STRATHSPEY RAILWAY

MANKTELOW
- MOORS VALLEY RAILWAY

MARDYKE
- ROYAL VICTORIA RAILWAY

MARSH
- BEER HEIGHTS

ROLLING STOCK by **DESIGNER**

Hawthorn — Marsh

MOORS VALLEY RAILWAY	
MULL RAILWAY	
MARTENS	
ROMNEY HYTHE & DYMCHURCH	
MARTIN	
WELLS & WALSINGHAM	
MAUNSELL	
BLUEBELL RAILWAY	
GREAT CENTRAL RAILWAY	
VINTAGE CARRIAGES TRUST	
WATERCRESS LINE	
MEREDITH	
ULSTER FOLK & TRANSPORT	
MILNER	
FAIRBOURNE & BARMOUTH	
MINISTRY OF SUPPLY	
STRATHSPEY RAILWAY	
MOTOR RAIL	
AMERTON RAILWAY	
ULSTER FOLK & TRANSPORT	
NEILSON	
INDUSTRIAL RAILWAY MUSEUM	
NORTH BRITISH	
BARROW HILL ROUNDHOUSE	
NYDQUIST	
NENE VALLEY RAILWAY	
RAILWORLD	
ORENSTEIN	
OLD KILN LIGHT RAILWAY	
RAILWORLD	
PEACOCK	
BARROW HILL ROUNDHOUSE	
FOXFIELD STEAM RAILWAY	
ULSTER FOLK & TRANSPORT	
PECKETT	
BRISTOL HARBOUR RAILWAY	
FOXFIELD STEAM RAILWAY	
TELFORD STEAM RAILWAY	
ULSTER FOLK & TRANSPORT	
RAILWAY	
PEAK RAIL	

RASTRICK
NATIONAL RAILWAY MUSEUM

RAVENSGLASS
HEATHERSLAW LIGHT RAILWAY

RICHARDSON
ROMNEY HYTHE & DYMCHURCH

RIDDLES
BO'NESS & KINNEIL RAILWAY
DARLINGTON RAILWAY PRES SOC
GREAT CENTRAL RAILWAY
MIDLAND RAILWAY CENTRE
NATIONAL RAILWAY MUSEUM
NENE VALLEY RAILWAY
SEVERN VALLEY RAILWAY
WATERCRESS LINE

ROBINSON
GREAT CENTRAL RAILWAY

ROMNEY HYTHE & DYMCHURCH RAILWAY
ROMNEY HYTHE & DYMCHURCH

RUSTON
AMERTON RAILWAY
BRISTOL HARBOUR RAILWAY
NIRT

SCHUKERT
BEAMISH

SECR
PEAK RAIL
VINTAGE CARRIAGES TRUST

SEVERN LAMB
BEER HEIGHTS

SHARP
MOORS VALLEY RAILWAY

SIEMENS
BEAMISH

SIMKINS
WELLS & WALSINGHAM

SMITH
HEATHERSLAW LIGHT RAILWAY
HOLLYBUSH GARDEN CENTRE

SOUTH TYNEDALE RAILWAY PRESERVATION SOCIETY
SOUTH TYNEDALE RAILWAY

SR

- PLYM VALLEY RAILWAY

STANDARD RAILWAY WAGON CO

- RAILWORLD

STANHOPE

- RUDYARD LAKE RAILWAY

STANIER

- BO'NESS & KINNEIL RAILWAY
- GLOUCESTERSHIRE WARWICKSHIRE
- GREAT CENTRAL RAILWAY
- LLANGOLLEN RAILWAY
- MIDLAND RAILWAY CENTRE
- NATIONAL RAILWAY MUSEUM
- NOTTINGHAM TRANSPORT CTRE
- SEVERN VALLEY RAILWAY
- STRATHSPEY RAILWAY

STEPHENSON

- BEAMISH
- NATIONAL RAILWAY MUSEUM
- STEAM
- ULSTER FOLK & TRANSPORT

STIRLAND

- BROOKSIDE MINIATURE
- RUDYARD LAKE RAILWAY

STROUDLEY

- ISLE OF WIGHT STEAM RAILWAY
- KENT & EAST SUSSEX RAILWAY

STUART

- TALYLLYN RAILWAY

SULZER

- WATERCRESS LINE

TAYLOR

- KIRKLEES LIGHT RAILWAY

THOMPSON

- GREAT CENTRAL RAILWAY

TRACKED HOVER CRAFT

- RAILWORLD

TREVITHICK

- RAILWAY AGE

URIE

- WATERCRESS LINE

VERE

- MULL RAILWAY

WALKER

- BRISTOL HARBOUR RAILWAY
- ULSTER FOLK & TRANSPORT

WATKINS

- BURE VALLEY RAILWAY

WESTERN REGION BR SCALE

- ROYAL VICTORIA RAILWAY

WILSON

- ULSTER FOLK & TRANSPORT

WORSDELL

- BEAMISH
- NORTH NORFOLK RAILWAY

ROLLING STOCK by DESIGNER

SR — Worsdell

SECTION 6

Railways/Museums are listed by country, by county

The facilities available are displayed in the form of a grid. This can be used in two different ways. You can search for a particular facility in order to see which railways/museums offer it

e.g. Restaurant, Great Whipsnade Railway, Brookside Miniature

Or, you can look at a particular railway/ museum to see what facilities they have available

e.g. Railway Age, Disabled Access, Souvenir Shop, Children's Events and Facilities for Hire

Once you have located a railway/museum using this section you can then refer to the railway or museum's detailed profile in section 1.

Facilities Available at Stations

by Country by County By Category

	Café	Restaurant	Buffet	Disabled access	Cinema	Slide shows	Movie shows	Ticket office	Advanced booking	Through ticketing	Platform tickets	Line permit needed	Photo Line side permit	Waiting room	Guided Tours	Driver footplate experience	Training courses	Courses - how to drive Locos	Courses - how to renovate	History lectures	Enthusiast galas	Left luggage office	Souvenir shop	Books for sale	Videos for sale	Photos for sale	Paintings/drawings for sale	Film for sale	CD's for sale	Tapes for sale	Models for sale	Main Credit Cards taken	Children's events	Santa Special	"Thomas" event	Lecture room	Function room	Facilities for Hire	Trains for Hire
ENGLAND																																							
BEDFORDSHIRE																																							
GREAT WHIPSNADE RAILWAY	●	●		●				●	●		●																					●					●		
LEIGHTON BUZZARD RAILWAY	●			●				●	●		●			●	●						●		●	●	●	●	●	●	●	●	●	●	●	●				●	●
BERKSHIRE																																							
WELLINGTON COUNTRY PARK				●																												●	●	●					
BRISTOL																																							
AVON VALLEY RAILWAY	●														●	●		●					●	●	●							●		●	●				
BRISTOL HARBOUR RAILWAY				●																	●		●																
BRISTOL HARBOUR RAILWAY				●					●							●							●	●	●	●					●	●						●	●
BUCKINGHAMSHIRE																																							
BUCKINGHAMSHIRE RLWY CTRE	●			●														●					●	●								●		●	●			●	
CAMBRIDGESHIRE																																							
NENE VALLEY RAILWAY	●			●				●			●		●	●	●	●				●	●		●	●	●	●	●	●	●	●		●	●	●	●		●	●	●
RAILWORLD			●	●	●										●					●			●													●		●	
CHANNEL ISLANDS																																							
ALDERNEY RAILWAY																							●	●									●	●					●
PALLOT STEAM MUSEUM				●										●									●	●															
CHESHIRE																																							
BROOKSIDE MINIATURE	●	●		●				●						●	●		●				●		●	●	●	●	●	●			●	●	●	●			●	●	●
RAILWAY AGE				●																			●										●					●	
CLEVELAND																																							
TEESIDE SMALL GAUGE RAILWAY				●																																			
CORNWALL																																							
BODMIN & WENFORD RAILWAY	●			●												●		●			●		●	●	●						●			●	●				
LAPPA VALLEY STEAM RAILWAY	●			●				●															●	●	●							●		●					
LAUNCESTON STEAM RAILWAY	●		●	●				●						●									●	●	●	●	●	●		●	●								
COUNTY DURHAM																																							
BEAMISH	●								●					●									●	●	●	●	●	●			●	●					●	●	
DARLINGTON RAILWAY CENTRE	●			●									●		●					●	●		●	●	●							●	●	●	●			●	
DARLINGTON RAILWAY PRES SOC				●									●																					●	●				

www.hccsteamrailway.com

Facilities Available at Stations

by Country by Category

Railway	Trains for Hire	Facilities for Hire	Function room	Lecture room	"Thomas" event	Santa Special	Children's events	Main Credit Cards taken	Models for sale	Tapes for sale	CD's for sale	Film for sale	Paintings/drawings for sale	Photos for sale	Videos for sale	Books for sale	Souvenir shop	Left luggage office	Enthusiast galas	History lectures	Courses - how to renovate	Courses - how to drive Locos	Training courses	Driver footplate experience	Guided Tours	Waiting room	Photo Line side permit	Line permit needed	Platform tickets	Through ticketing	Advanced booking	Ticket office	Movie shows	Slide shows	Cinema	Disabled access	Buffet	Restaurant	Café
TANFIELD RAILWAY	●	●	●	●		●	●		●				●			●	●		●						●						●					●			●
TIMOTHY HACKWORTH						●	●										●																						
CUMBRIA																																							
LAKESIDE & HAVERTHWAITE RLWY						●											●																			●		●	●
RAVENGLASS & ESKDALE	●	●				●	●		●			●	●	●	●	●	●		●					●						●		●			●	●			●
SOUTH TYNEDALE RAILWAY	●	●				●		●	●			●	●	●	●	●	●		●					●					●			●				●			●
DERBYSHIRE																																							
BARROW HILL ROUNDHOUSE																●	●																			●			●
DERBY INDUSTRIAL MUSEUM																●	●																			●	●		●
MARKEATON PARK LIGHT RAILWAY						●											●																					●	
MIDLAND RAILWAY CENTRE	●	●	●			●		●	●	●	●	●		●	●	●	●							●	●							●				●		●	●
NATIONAL TRAMWAY MUSEUM				●			●	●								●	●											●								●			●
PEAK RAIL	●	●	●	●		●	●	●							●	●	●		●					●								●				●			●
DEVON																																							
BEER HEIGHTS																●	●									●					●	●				●	●	●	●
BICTON WOODLAND RAILWAY								●							●	●	●																						
BIDEFORD RAILWAY MUSEUM								●								●	●																			●	●		
DARTMOOR RAILWAY								●									●																						●
DINGLES STEAM VILLAGE							●		●				●				●					●																	●
EXMOOR STEAM RAILWAY								●									●																						●
GORSE BLOSSOM MINIATURE								●									●																						●
LYNTON & BARNSTAPLE RAILWAY					●	●		●							●	●	●																			●			
PAIGNTON & DARTMOUTH RAILWAY	●	●	●		●	●		●								●	●					●		●								●				●			●
PLYM VALLEY RAILWAY																	●																						
SOUTH DEVON RAILWAY	●	●	●	●	●	●	●	●	●						●	●	●		●													●				●			●
DORSET																																							
SWANAGE RAILWAY						●	●	●							●	●	●		●					●												●		●	
ESSEX																																							
AUDLEY END MINIATURE RAILWAY						●	●		●								●																			●	●		
AUDLEY END MINIATURE RAILWAY						●	●		●								●																			●			
BARLEYLANDS MINIATURE RAILWAY																																						●	●
COLNE VALLEY RAILWAY	●	●			●	●	●	●								●	●		●					●		●						●				●			●

Facilities Available at Stations

by Country by County By Category

England

FACILITIES AVAILABLE AT STATIONS

Railway	Café	Restaurant	Buffet	Disabled access	Cinema	Slide shows	Movie shows	Ticket office	Advanced booking	Through ticketing	Platform tickets	Line permit needed	Photo Line side permit	Waiting room	Guided Tours	Driver footplate experience	Training courses	Courses - how to drive Locos	Courses - how to renovate	History lectures	Enthusiast galas	Left luggage office	Souvenir shop	Books for sale	Videos for sale	Photos for sale	Paintings/drawings for sale	Film for sale	CD's for sale	Tapes for sale	Models for sale	Main Credit Cards taken	Children's events	Santa Special	"Thomas" event	Lecture room	Function room	Facilities for Hire	Trains for Hire
EAST ANGLIAN RAILWAY MUSEUM	•					•		•						•		•							•									•		•	•				•
MANGAPPS RAILWAY MUSEUM				•				•															•	•										•	•			•	•
GLOUCESTERSHIRE																																							
DEAN FOREST RAILWAY	•			•		•		•	•		•		•	•	•	•		•			•		•	•	•	•	•	•			•	•		•	•				•
GLOUCESTERSHIRE WARWICKSHIRE	•			•	•			•						•	•	•		•		•	•		•	•	•	•						•	•	•	•			•	•
NATIONAL WATERWAYS MUSEUM	•		•	•																				•															
PERRYGROVE RAILWAY	•		•	•				•						•	•	•							•	•		•							•	•					•
WINCHCOMBE RAILWAY																								•															
HAMPSHIRE																																							
EASTLEIGH LAKESIDE RAILWAY	•		•	•				•								•	•	•					•	•	•	•	•	•	•			•	•	•	•				
HOLLYCOMBE STEAM COLLECTION				•											•								•	•	•	•													
IRCHESTER NARROW GAUGE MUSEUM				•																			•	•	•	•											•	•	
MOORS VALLEY RAILWAY	•		•	•				•	•	•		•	•			•					•		•	•	•	•	•	•			•	•	•	•	•			•	•
ROYAL VICTORIA RAILWAY				•				•	•					•		•					•		•	•	•	•					•	•		•					•
WATERCRESS LINE	•			•				•															•	•	•	•						•		•	•				
ISLE OF MAN																																							
GROUDLE GLEN RAILWAY	•													•							•		•																•
ISLE OF MAN RAILWAY				•				•	•					•				•			•		•	•	•	•	•							•					•
ISLE OF WIGHT																																							
ISLE OF WIGHT STEAM RAILWAY	•			•				•			•			•	•			•			•		•	•	•	•		•				•		•	•				•
KENT																																							
BREDGAR & WORMSHILL	•																																						
EAST KENT LIGHT RAILWAY			•	•																				•	•	•	•							•					
KENT & EAST SUSSEX RAILWAY	•		•	•				•	•		•		•	•	•	•	•	•		•	•		•	•	•	•	•	•	•		•	•		•	•			•	•
ROMNEY HYTHE & DYMCHURCH	•		•					•	•		•			•	•	•		•			•		•	•	•	•	•				•	•		•	•	•	•	•	•
SITTINGBOURNE & KEMSLEY	•			•																	•		•	•	•									•					•
SPA VALLEY RAILWAY				•				•													•		•		•							•		•					
LANCASHIRE																																							
EAST LANCASHIRE RAILWAY	•			•							•					•		•			•		•			•					•			•	•				•
ST ANNES MINI RAILWAY				•																	•													•					
WEST LANCASHIRE LIGHT RLWY																					•		•										•	•					•
WINDMILL FARM RAILWAY	•			•																														•					

Facilities Available at Stations

FACILITIES AVAILABLE AT STATIONS

Steam Railway Directory

Facility \ Railway (by Country by County By Category)	ABBEY PUMPING STATION	CADEBY LIGHT RAILWAY	GREAT CENTRAL RAILWAY	SNIBSTON DISCOVERY PARK	CLEETHORPES LIGHT RAILWAY	LINCOLNSHIRE WOLDS RAILWAY	GREAT COCKCROW RAILWAY	KEW BRIDGE STEAM MUSEUM	LONDON TRANSPORT MUSEUM	OLD STATION MUSEUM	RUISLIP LIDO RAILWAY	SCIENCE MUSEUM	MUSEUM OF SCIENCE & INDUSTRY	CHASEWATER RAILWAY	HOLLYBUSH GARDEN CENTRE	TYSELEY LOCOMOTIVE WORKS	VINTAGE TRAINS	BRESSINGHAM STEAM	BURE VALLEY RAILWAY	FORNCETT INDUSTRIAL MUSEUM	MID-NORFOLK RAILWAY	NORTH NORFOLK RAILWAY	WELLS & WALSINGHAM	NIRT	NORTHAMPTON & LAMPORT RAILWAY
LEICESTERSHIRE																									
LINCOLNSHIRE (NORTH EAST)																									
LONDON (GREATER)																									
MANCHESTER (GREATER)																									
MIDLANDS (WEST)																									
NORFOLK																									
NORTHAMPTONSHIRE																									
Trains for Hire			●		●				●							●		●				●	●		●
Facilities for Hire			●		●				●		●					●		●	●	●	●			●	●
Function room									●									●							
Lecture room																		●							
"Thomas" event																		●	●			●			●
Santa Special		●	●								●			●				●	●			●			●
Children's events		●									●							●	●			●			●
Main Credit Cards taken			●					●				●						●							●
Models for sale					●			●										●							
Tapes for sale																									
CD's for sale																									
Film for sale																									
Paintings/drawings for sale								●										●							
Photos for sale																									
Videos for sale		●			●	●			●			●				●	●	●				●			
Books for sale	●	●	●	●	●	●	●	●	●			●		●		●	●	●				●			
Souvenir shop	●	●	●	●	●	●	●	●				●		●		●	●	●			●	●			●
Left luggage office																									
Enthusiast galas		●		●					●								●								
History lectures					●											●									
Courses - how to renovate																									
Courses - how to drive Locos					●											●	●							●	
Training courses																									
Driver footplate experience		●										●													
Guided Tours			●		●	●			●			●												●	
Waiting room						●								●				●							
Photo Line side permit						●																			
Line permit needed		●																●							
Platform tickets		●									●										●				
Through ticketing																									
Advanced booking		●																							
Ticket office		●		●	●		●		●					●				●	●		●	●		●	
Movie shows													●					●							
Slide shows																									
Cinema																									
Disabled access	●		●	●				●	●	●			●		●	●		●	●		●	●		●	●
Buffet			●	●										●				●				●	●		
Restaurant									●	●	●		●											●	
Café	●	●			●			●	●		●	●		●				●	●		●	●		●	

Facilities Available at Stations

by Country by County By Category

	NORTHUMBERLAND	HEATHERSLAW LIGHT RAILWAY	NOTTINGHAMSHIRE	NOTTINGHAM TRANSPORT CTRE	OXFORDSHIRE	CHINNOR & PRINCES RISBOROUGH	CHOLSEY & WALLINGFORD RAILWAY	DIDCOT RAILWAY CENTRE	RUTLAND	RUTLAND RAILWAY MUSEUM	SHROPSHIRE	BLISTSHILL VICTORIAN TOWN	CAMBRIAN RAILWAY SOCIETY	TELFORD STEAM RAILWAY	WESTON PARK RAILWAY	SOMERSET	EAST SOMERSET RAILWAY	GARTELL LIGHT RAILWAY	SOMERSET & DORSET RAILWAY	WEST SOMERSET RAILWAY	STAFFORDSHIRE	AMERTON RAILWAY	CHURNET VALLEY RAILWAY	FOXFIELD STEAM RAILWAY	HILCOTE VALLEY RAILWAY	RUDYARD LAKE RAILWAY	SUFFOLK	EAST ANGLIA TRANSPORT MUSEUM	MID-SUFFOLK LIGHT RAILWAY	SURREY	OLD KILN LIGHT RAILWAY	SUSSEX (EAST)
Trains for Hire						●		●						●			●			●				●								
Facilities for Hire		●				●		●						●			●			●				●								
Function room								●																							●	
Lecture room																								●							●	
"Thomas" event						●	●	●						●			●		●	●			●	●								
Santa Special		●		●		●	●	●		●			●	●			●			●		●	●	●		●					●	
Children's events		●				●	●	●		●		●		●			●			●				●		●			●			
Main Credit Cards taken						●	●	●				●	●	●			●			●				●								
Models for sale						●	●	●					●				●			●				●								
Tapes for sale						●																										
CD's for sale								●												●												
Film for sale							●	●						●			●			●				●								
Paintings/drawings for sale								●						●			●			●											●	
Photos for sale						●		●						●			●			●		●									●	
Videos for sale						●	●	●		●		●		●			●		●	●		●		●							●	
Books for sale		●				●	●	●		●		●	●	●			●		●	●		●						●	●		●	
Souvenir shop		●				●	●	●		●		●	●	●			●		●	●		●	●	●	●			●	●		●	
Left luggage office																																
Enthusiast galas				●				●					●	●	●		●			●		●		●		●			●		●	
History lectures																															●	
Courses - how to renovate																																
Courses - how to drive Locos		●																		●			●			●						
Training courses		●												●						●			●									
Driver footplate experience		●						●						●			●			●						●						
Guided Tours								●						●										●							●	
Waiting room		●				●	●							●			●														●	
Photo Line side permit														●						●												
Line permit needed														●																		
Platform tickets																	●			●												
Through ticketing								●																								
Advanced booking		●					●	●									●															
Ticket office						●	●	●						●			●			●		●		●	●							
Movie shows																																
Slide shows																								●								
Cinema																																
Disabled access						●	●					●		●	●		●		●	●				●	●				●		●	
Buffet						●																		●							●	
Restaurant								●									●					●										
Café		●					●	●					●	●				●		●			●	●	●			●	●		●	

Facilities Available at Stations

by Country by County By Category

Railway	Trains for Hire	Facilities for Hire	Function room	Lecture room	"Thomas" event	Santa Special	Children's events	Main Credit Cards taken	Models for sale	Tapes for sale	CD's for sale	Film for sale	Paintings/drawings for sale	Photos for sale	Videos for sale	Books for sale	Souvenir shop	Left luggage office	Enthusiast galas	History lectures	Courses - how to renovate	Courses - how to drive Locos	Training courses	Driver footplate experience	Guided Tours	Waiting room	Photo Line side permit	Line permit needed	Platform tickets	Through ticketing	Advanced booking	Ticket office	Movie shows	Slide shows	Cinema	Disabled access	Buffet	Restaurant	Café
SUSSEX (WEST)																																							
BLUEBELL RAILWAY					●	●		●							●	●	●		●																	●		●	
LAVENDER LINE	●	●				●	●	●	●						●	●	●							●					●							●	●		
ROTHER VALLEY RAILWAY						●										●	●																			●	●		
AMBERLEY WORKING MUSEUM								●							●	●	●		●				●													●			●
LITTLEHAMPTON MINIATURE RLWY																																				●		●	
SOUTH DOWNS LIGHT RAILWAY					●										●	●			●					●												●			
TYNE AND WEAR																																							
BOWES RAILWAY															●	●	●							●	●							●				●			●
MONKWEARMOUTH STATION MUSEUM								●												●												●				●			●
NORTH TYNESIDE STEAM RAILWAY			●			●	●										●								●											●		●	
STEPHENSON RAILWAY MUSEUM						●	●																													●		●	
WARWICKSHIRE																																							
BATTLEFIELD LINE	●				●	●	●	●				●			●	●	●	●	●					●		●	●	●	●		●	●				●	●		●
WILTSHIRE																																							
STEAM			●	●	●	●			●				●		●	●	●								●							●				●			●
SWINDON & CRICKLADE RAILWAY	●	●	●	●	●		●								●	●	●		●					●												●		●	●
WORCESTERSHIRE																																							
KIDDERMINSTER RAILWAY MUSEUM		●	●	●	●		●								●	●	●									●										●			●
SEVERN VALLEY RAILWAY	●	●	●	●	●	●	●	●	●						●	●	●	●	●				●	●		●	●	●	●		●	●				●			●
YORKSHIRE (EAST)																																							
MUSEUM OF ARMY TRANSPORT									●							●																				●			●
YORKSHIRE (NORTH)																																							
DERWENT VALLEY																										●						●				●			
EMBSAY & BOLTON ABBEY RLWY	●	●	●	●	●	●	●		●						●	●	●																			●	●		●
NATIONAL RAILWAY MUSEUM		●	●	●	●	●	●		●						●	●	●						●		●											●	●		●
NORTH YORKSHIRE MOORS RAILWAY	●	●	●	●	●	●	●								● ●	● ●	●		●					●	●	●	●				●	●				●			
YORKSHIRE (SOUTH)																																							
ELSECAR HERITAGE CENTRE						●											●								●											●			
YORKSHIRE (WEST)																																							
ABBEY LIGHT RAILWAY		● ●														● ●			●			●		●															
ARMLEY MILLS				●													●																			●			●

538 Section 6.

Facilities Available at Stations

by Country by County By Category

Facilities	KEIGHLEY & WORTH VALLEY	KIRKLEES LIGHT RAILWAY	MIDDLETON RAILWAY	VINTAGE CARRIAGES TRUST
Trains for Hire	●	●		
Facilities for Hire	●			
Function room				
Lecture room				
"Thomas" event	●	●	●	
Santa Special	●	●	●	
Children's events	●	●	●	
Main Credit Cards taken	●	●	●	●
Models for sale	●			
Tapes for sale				
CD's for sale				
Film for sale			●	
Paintings/drawings for sale				
Photos for sale	●			
Videos for sale	●			
Books for sale	●		●	
Souvenir shop	●	●	●	●
Left luggage office				
Enthusiast galas		●		
History lectures				
Courses - how to renovate				
Courses - how to drive Locos				
Training courses				
Driver footplate experience	●			
Guided Tours				
Waiting room	●			
Photo Line side permit				
Line permit needed				
Platform tickets				
Through ticketing				
Advanced booking				
Ticket office	●	●		
Movie shows				
Slide shows				
Cinema				
Disabled access	●	●		●
Buffet				
Restaurant				
Café	●			

Facilities Available at Stations

by Country by County By Category

Facility	Donegal Rly Heritage Ctre	Fintown & Glenties Rly	Tralee & Dingle Rly	Cavan & Leitrim Rly	Irish Steam Preservation Soc	Giants Causeway & Bushmills	RPSI	Downpatrick & Ardglass	Ulster Folk & Transport	Foyle Valley Rly Centre
Trains for Hire						•	•	•		
Facilities for Hire							•	•		
Function room									•	
Lecture room									•	
"Thomas" event										
Santa Special		•		•			•	•		•
Children's events		•		•	•		•	•		•
Main Credit Cards taken							•		•	•
Models for sale										
Tapes for sale										
CD's for sale										
Film for sale										
Paintings/drawings for sale										
Photos for sale							•			
Videos for sale							•	•	•	
Books for sale				•			•	•	•	
Souvenir shop	•		•	•	•		•	•	•	
Left luggage office										
Enthusiast galas										
History lectures										
Courses - how to renovate										
Courses - how to drive Locos										
Training courses										
Driver footplate experience								•		
Guided Tours							•	•		
Waiting room							•			
Photo Line side permit										
Line permit needed										
Platform tickets										
Through ticketing										
Advanced booking							•	•		
Ticket office							•	•	•	•
Movie shows										
Slide shows										
Cinema										
Disabled access			•		•		•	•	•	•
Buffet							•			
Restaurant								•		
Café	•							•	•	

IRELAND
- COUNTY DONEGAL
- DONEGAL RAILWAY HERITAGE CTRE
- FINTOWN & GLENTIES RAILWAY
- COUNTY KERRY
- TRALEE & DINGLE RAILWAY
- COUNTY LEITRIM
- CAVAN & LEITRIM RAILWAY
- COUNTY LAOIS
- IRISH STEAM PRESERVATION SOC

NORTHERN IRELAND
- COUNTY ANTRIM
- GIANTS CAUSEWAY & BUSHMILLS
- RPSI
- COUNTY DOWN
- DOWNPATRICK & ARDGLASS
- ULSTER FOLK & TRANSPORT
- COUNTY LONDONDERRY
- FOYLE VALLEY RAILWAY CENTRE

Facilities Available at Stations

by Country by County By Category

SCOTLAND

Railway (by County)	Facilities available
ABERDEENSHIRE	
ALFORD VALLEY RAILWAY	Santa Special; Children's events; Disabled access
ANGUS	
CALEDONIAN RAILWAY	Trains for Hire; Facilities for Hire; Santa Special; Children's events; Photos for sale; Videos for sale; Books for sale; Souvenir shop; Left luggage office; Enthusiast galas; Driver footplate experience; Guided Tours; Waiting room; Advanced booking; Ticket office; Disabled access; Buffet
KERR MINIATURE RAILWAY	Disabled access; Buffet
ARGYLL AND BUTE	
MULL RAILWAY	Trains for Hire; Main Credit Cards taken; Paintings/drawings for sale; Photos for sale; Videos for sale; Books for sale; Souvenir shop; Guided Tours; Through ticketing; Advanced booking; Ticket office
AYRSHIRE	
SCOTTISH RAILWAY CENTRE	Main Credit Cards taken; Models for sale; Paintings/drawings for sale; Photos for sale; Videos for sale; Books for sale; Souvenir shop; Disabled access; Café
FIFE	
ST ANDREWS	History lectures; Guided Tours; Café
GLASGOW (CITY OF)	
GLASGOW MUSEUM OF TRANSPORT	Models for sale; Videos for sale; Books for sale; Souvenir shop; Guided Tours; Disabled access; Restaurant
HIGHLANDS	
GLENFINNAN STATION MUSEUM	Videos for sale; Books for sale; Training courses
STRATHSPEY RAILWAY	Trains for Hire; Facilities for Hire; Santa Special; Main Credit Cards taken; Film for sale; Videos for sale; Books for sale; Souvenir shop; Enthusiast galas; Driver footplate experience; Waiting room; Photo Line side permit; Line permit needed; Platform tickets; Through ticketing; Advanced booking; Ticket office; Disabled access
LANARKSHIRE	
LEADHILLS & WANLOCKHEAD	Models for sale; Books for sale; Souvenir shop; Disabled access
LANARKSHIRE (NORTH)	
SUMMERLEE HERITAGE PK	Books for sale; Souvenir shop; Disabled access; Café
LOTHIAN (EAST)	
PRESTONGRANGE INDUSTRIAL	Facilities for Hire; Children's events; Disabled access
LOTHIAN (WEST)	
ALMOND VALLEY HERITAGE TRUST	Main Credit Cards taken; Ticket office; Disabled access; Café
BO'NESS & KINNEIL RAILWAY	Trains for Hire; Facilities for Hire; Santa Special; Videos for sale; Books for sale; Souvenir shop; Enthusiast galas; Driver footplate experience; Buffet
MORAY	
KEITH & DUFFTOWN RAILWAY	Trains for Hire; Facilities for Hire; Santa Special; Models for sale; Books for sale; Souvenir shop; Disabled access; Café

Facility categories (column headers): Trains for Hire · Facilities for Hire · Function room · Lecture room · "Thomas" event · Santa Special · Children's events · Main Credit Cards taken · Models for sale · Tapes for sale · CD's for sale · Film for sale · Paintings/drawings for sale · Photos for sale · Videos for sale · Books for sale · Souvenir shop · Left luggage office · Enthusiast galas · History lectures · Courses - how to renovate · Courses - how to drive Locos · Training courses · Driver footplate experience · Guided Tours · Waiting room · Photo Line side permit · Line permit needed · Platform tickets · Through ticketing · Advanced booking · Ticket office · Movie shows · Slide shows · Cinema · Disabled access · Buffet · Restaurant · Café

Facilities Available at Stations

by Country by County By Category

Facility columns (left to right):
Trains for Hire · Facilities for Hire · Function room · Lecture room · "Thomas" event · Santa Special · Children's events · Main Credit Cards taken · Models for sale · Tapes for sale · CD's for sale · Film for sale · Paintings/drawings for sale · Photos for sale · Videos for sale · Books for sale · Souvenir shop · Left luggage office · Enthusiast galas · History lectures · Courses - how to renovate · Courses - how to drive Locos · Training courses · Driver footplate experience · Guided Tours · Waiting room · Photo Line side permit · Line permit needed · Platform tickets · Through ticketing · Advanced booking · Ticket office · Movie shows · Slide shows · Cinema · Disabled access · Buffet · Restaurant · Café

WALES

CARMARTHENSHIRE
- GWILI RAILWAY
- TEIFI VALLEY RAILWAY

CEREDIGION
- VALE OF RHEIDOL RAILWAY

CONWY
- CONWY VALLEY

DENBIGHSHIRE
- GOLDEN VALLEY LIGHT RAILWAY
- LLANGOLLEN RAILWAY
- RHYL MINIATURE RAILWAY

GLAMORGAN (VALE OF)
- VALE OF GLAMORGAN RAILWAY

GWYNEDD
- BALA LAKE RAILWAY
- FAIRBOURNE & BARMOUTH
- FFESTINIOG RAILWAY
- INDUSTRIAL RAILWAY MUSEUM
- LLANBERIS LAKE RAILWAY
- NARROW GAUGE RAILWAY MUSEUM
- SNOWDON MOUNTAIN RAILWAY
- TALYLLYN RAILWAY
- WELSH HIGHLAND RAILWAY
- WELSH HIGHLAND RAILWAY
- WELSH SLATE MUSEUM

MERTHYR TYDFIL
- BRECON MOUNTAIN RAILWAY

POWYS
- CORRIS RAILWAY MUSEUM
- WELSHPOOL & LLANFAIR

Facilities Available at Stations

by Country by County By Category

FACILITIES AVAILABLE AT STATIONS

Facility	SWANSEA			TORFAEN		
	SWANSEA	SWANSEA INDUSTRIAL MUSEUM	SWANSEA VALE RAILWAY	TORFAEN	GRIFFITHSTOWN RAILWAY MUSEUM	PONTYPOOL & BLAENAVON RAILWAY
Trains for Hire			●			
Facilities for Hire			●			
Function room					●	
Lecture room						
"Thomas" event						●
Santa Special			●			●
Children's events			●			
Main Credit Cards taken						
Models for sale						
Tapes for sale						
CD's for sale						
Film for sale						
Paintings/drawings for sale						
Photos for sale						
Videos for sale						
Books for sale						
Souvenir shop			●			
Left luggage office						
Enthusiast galas						
History lectures						
Courses - how to renovate						
Courses - how to drive Locos						
Training courses						
Driver footplate experience			●			
Guided Tours						
Waiting room						
Photo Line side permit						
Line permit needed						
Platform tickets						
Through ticketing						
Advanced booking						
Ticket office						●
Movie shows						
Slide shows						
Cinema						
Disabled access		●	●		●	
Buffet						
Restaurant						
Café			●		●	

© HCC Publishing Ltd

A-Z of Organisations

SECTION 7

This section shows a list of organisations with their contact details and the railways/museums under their jurisdiction

e.g. Heritage Railway Association, Welsh Highland Railway

Once you have located a railway/museum using this section you can then refer to the railway or museum's detailed profile in section 1.

BRITAINS GREAT LITTLE RAILWAYS

64 Bullars Rd, Southampton, **Hampshire,** SO18 1GS,
England.
(T) 02380 334044

- **BROOKSIDE MINIATURE**
- **EASTLEIGH LAKESIDE RAILWAY**
- **FAIRBOURNE & BARMOUTH**
- **PERRYGROVE RAILWAY**
- **SOUTH DOWNS LIGHT RAILWAY**

ENGLISH TOURISM COUNCIL

Thames Tower, Blacks Rd, London, **London (Greater),** W6
9EL, England.
(T) 020 8563 3000

- **GLOUCESTERSHIRE WARWICKSHIRE**

GREAT LITTLE TRAINS OF WALES

Talyllyn Railway, Wharf Station, Tywyn, **Gwynedd,** LL36 9EY,
Wales.

- **WELSH HIGHLAND RAILWAY**

HEART OF ENGLAND TOURIST BOARD

Larkhill Rd, Worcester, **Worcestershire,** WR5 2EZ, England.
(T) 01905 761100

- **GLOUCESTERSHIRE WARWICKSHIRE**

HERITAGE RAILWAY ASSOCIATION

Turnpike Hse, Maidstone Rd, Marden, Tonbridge, **Kent,** TN12
9AB, England.

- **ALMOND VALLEY HERITAGE TRUST**
- **AMBERLEY WORKING MUSEUM**
- **AVON VALLEY RAILWAY**
- **BALA LAKE RAILWAY**
- **BARROW HILL ROUNDHOUSE**
- **BATTLEFIELD LINE**
- **BLUEBELL RAILWAY**
- **BODMIN & WENFORD RAILWAY**
- **BO'NESS & KINNEIL RAILWAY**
- **BOWES RAILWAY**
- **BREDGAR & WORMSHILL**
- **BRISTOL HARBOUR RAILWAY**
- **BUCKINGHAMSHIRE RLWY CTRE**
- **BURE VALLEY RAILWAY**

- **CADEBY LIGHT RAILWAY**
- **CALEDONIAN RAILWAY**
- **CAMBRIAN RAILWAY SOCIETY**
- **CHASEWATER RAILWAY**
- **CHINNOR & PRINCES RISBOROUGH**
- **CHOLSEY & WALLINGFORD RAILWAY**
- **CHURNET VALLEY RAILWAY**
- **CLEETHORPES LIGHT RAILWAY**
- **COLNE VALLEY RAILWAY**
- **CONWY VALLEY**
- **CORRIS RAILWAY MUSEUM**
- **DARLINGTON RAILWAY CENTRE**
- **DARTMOOR RAILWAY**
- **DEAN FOREST RAILWAY**
- **DIDCOT RAILWAY CENTRE**
- **DONEGAL RAILWAY HERITAGE CTRE**
- **DOWNPATRICK & ARDGLASS**
- **EAST ANGLIA TRANSPORT MUSEUM**
- **EAST ANGLIAN RAILWAY MUSEUM**
- **EAST KENT LIGHT RAILWAY**
- **EAST LANCASHIRE RAILWAY**
- **EMBSAY & BOLTON ABBEY RLWY**
- **FFESTINIOG RAILWAY**
- **FOXFIELD STEAM RAILWAY**
- **FOYLE VALLEY RAILWAY CENTRE**
- **GLOUCESTERSHIRE WARWICKSHIRE**
- **GREAT CENTRAL RAILWAY**
- **GREAT WHIPSNADE RAILWAY**
- **GWILI RAILWAY**
- **HOLLYCOMBE STEAM COLLECTION**
- **INDUSTRIAL RAILWAY MUSEUM**
- **IRCHESTER NARROW GAUGE MUSEUM**

A-Z of **ORGANISATIONS**

Britains Great Little Railways — Heritage Railway Association

IRISH STEAM PRESERVATION SOC	PEAK RAIL
IRISH TRACTION GROUP	PLYM VALLEY RAILWAY
ISLE OF WIGHT STEAM RAILWAY	PONTYPOOL & BLAENAVON RAILWAY
KEIGHLEY & WORTH VALLEY	RAILWORLD
KEITH & DUFFTOWN RAILWAY	RAVENGLASS & ESKDALE
KENT & EAST SUSSEX RAILWAY	ROMNEY HYTHE & DYMCHURCH
KIRKLEES LIGHT RAILWAY	ROTHER VALLEY RAILWAY
LAKESIDE & HAVERTHWAITE RLWY	RPSI
LAUNCESTON STEAM RAILWAY	RUISLIP LIDO RAILWAY
LAVENDER LINE	RUTLAND RAILWAY MUSEUM
LEADHILLS & WANLOCKHEAD	SCOTTISH RAILWAY CENTRE
LEIGHTON BUZZARD RAILWAY	SEVERN VALLEY RAILWAY
LINCOLNSHIRE WOLDS RAILWAY	SITTINGBOURNE & KEMSLEY
LLANBERIS LAKE RAILWAY	SNOWDON MOUNTAIN RAILWAY
LLANGOLLEN RAILWAY	SOMERSET & DORSET RAILWAY
LONDON TRANSPORT MUSEUM	SOUTH DEVON RAILWAY
MANGAPPS RAILWAY MUSEUM	SOUTH TYNEDALE RAILWAY
MIDDLETON RAILWAY	SOUTH YORKSHIRE RAILWAY
MIDLAND RAILWAY CENTRE	SPA VALLEY RAILWAY
MID-NORFOLK RAILWAY	STEAM
MID-SUFFOLK LIGHT RAILWAY	STRATHSPEY RAILWAY
MULL RAILWAY	SWANAGE RAILWAY
NATIONAL RAILWAY MUSEUM	SWANSEA VALE RAILWAY
NATIONAL TRAMWAY MUSEUM	SWINDON & CRICKLADE RAILWAY
NATIONAL WATERWAYS MUSEUM	TALYLLYN RAILWAY
NENE VALLEY RAILWAY	TANFIELD RAILWAY
NIRT	TEIFI VALLEY RAILWAY
NORTH NORFOLK RAILWAY	TELFORD STEAM RAILWAY
NORTH TYNESIDE STEAM RAILWAY	VALE OF GLAMORGAN RAILWAY
NORTH YORKSHIRE MOORS RAILWAY	VALE OF RHEIDOL RAILWAY
NORTHAMPTON & LAMPORT RAILWAY	VINTAGE CARRIAGES TRUST
NOTTINGHAM TRANSPORT CTRE	WATERCRESS LINE

WELLS & WALSINGHAM	**DEAN FOREST RAILWAY**
WELSH HIGHLAND RAILWAY	**DERBY INDUSTRIAL MUSEUM**
WELSH HIGHLAND RAILWAY	**DERWENT VALLEY**
WELSHPOOL & LLANFAIR	**DIDCOT RAILWAY CENTRE**
WEST LANCASHIRE LIGHT RLWY	**EAST ANGLIA TRANSPORT MUSEUM**
WEST SOMERSET RAILWAY	**EAST ANGLIAN RAILWAY MUSEUM**
WINDMILL FARM RAILWAY	**EAST LANCASHIRE RAILWAY**
YEOVIL RAILWAY CENTRE	**EAST SOMERSET RAILWAY**

LICHFIELD DISTRICT TOURISM ASSOCIATION

Donegal Hse, Bore St, Lichfield, **Staffordshire,** WS13 6NE,
England.
(T) 01543 308209   (F) 01543 308211

CHASEWATER RAILWAY

SOUTHERN FEDERATION OF MODEL ENGINEERING

35 Rivershill, Watton, Stone, **Hertfordshire,** SG14 3SD,
England.
(T) 01920 830629

SOUTH DOWNS LIGHT RAILWAY

SWINDON BOROUGH COUNCIL

Civic Offices, Euclid St, Swindon, **Wiltshire,** SN1 2JH,
England.
(T) 01793 463725

STEAM

TRANSPORT TRUST

202 Lambeth Rd, London, **London (Greater),** SE1 7JW,
England.
(T) 020 7928 6464   (F) 020 7928 6565

ABBEY PUMPING STATION	**EMBSAY & BOLTON ABBEY RLWY**
AMBERLEY WORKING MUSEUM	**GREAT CENTRAL RAILWAY**
BALA LAKE RAILWAY	**GWILI RAILWAY**
BATTLEFIELD LINE	**HOLLYCOMBE STEAM COLLECTION**
BLUEBELL RAILWAY	**ISLE OF WIGHT STEAM RAILWAY**
BO'NESS & KINNEIL RAILWAY	**KENT & EAST SUSSEX RAILWAY**
BRESSINGHAM STEAM	**LAKESIDE & HAVERTHWAITE RLWY**
BURE VALLEY RAILWAY	**LAPPA VALLEY STEAM RAILWAY**
CADEBY LIGHT RAILWAY	**LAUNCESTON STEAM RAILWAY**
CHASEWATER RAILWAY	**LEIGHTON BUZZARD RAILWAY**
COLNE VALLEY RAILWAY	**LLANGOLLEN RAILWAY**

LONDON TRANSPORT MUSEUM

MIDLAND RAILWAY CENTRE

MULL RAILWAY

MUSEUM OF ARMY TRANSPORT

NATIONAL RAILWAY MUSEUM

NATIONAL TRAMWAY MUSEUM

NENE VALLEY RAILWAY

NORTH NORFOLK RAILWAY

NORTH YORKSHIRE MOORS RAILWAY

RPSI

SCOTTISH RAILWAY CENTRE

SEVERN VALLEY RAILWAY

SITTINGBOURNE & KEMSLEY

Heritage Railway Association — Transport Trust

A-Z of ORGANISATIONS

A-Z of TV/Film Appearances

SECTION 8

This is a list of TV programmes/Films that railways have appeared in. Also showing where they are located

e.g. Casualty, Bristol Harbour Railway, Bristol, England

Once you have located a railway/museum using this section you can then refer to the railway or museum's detailed profile in section 1.

ACT OF WILL

BEAMISH, COUNTY DURHAM, England

ALL CREATURES GREAT AND SMALL

NORTH YORKSHIRE MOORS RAILWAY,
YORKSHIRE (NORTH), England

ALL THE KINGS MEN

NORTH NORFOLK RAILWAY, NORFOLK, England

ART ATTACK

KENT & EAST SUSSEX RAILWAY, KENT, England

BIRDS OF A FEATHER

WATERCRESS LINE, HAMPSHIRE, England

BROTHER TO THE OX

ABBEY LIGHT RAILWAY, YORKSHIRE (WEST),
England

BUDWEISER BEER COMMERCIAL

VINTAGE CARRIAGES TRUST, YORKSHIRE
(WEST), England

CAMOMILE LAWN

DIDCOT RAILWAY CENTRE, OXFORDSHIRE,
England

CANTERVILLE GHOST

EAST SOMERSET RAILWAY, SOMERSET, England

CASUALTY

BRISTOL HARBOUR RAILWAY, BRISTOL, England

NORTH YORKSHIRE MOORS RAILWAY,
YORKSHIRE (NORTH), England

CENTRAL NEWS

PERRYGROVE RAILWAY, GLOUCESTERSHIRE,
England

CLARISSA AND THE COUNTRY MAN

MULL RAILWAY, ARGYLL AND BUTE, Scotland

CLASSIC TRAINS

LEIGHTON BUZZARD RAILWAY, BEDFORDSHIRE,
England

COLLECTORS LOT

PERRYGROVE RAILWAY, GLOUCESTERSHIRE,
England

COUNTRY WAYS

SPA VALLEY RAILWAY, KENT, England

DAD'S ARMY

NORTH NORFOLK RAILWAY, NORFOLK, England

DARLING BUDS OF MAY

KENT & EAST SUSSEX RAILWAY, KENT, England

DECHRAU CANU DECHRAU CANMOL

GWILI RAILWAY, CARMARTHENSHIRE, Wales

DIRTY DOZEN - NEXT MISSION

NENE VALLEY RAILWAY, CAMBRIDGESHIRE,
England

DISNEY ADVENTURES

GLOUCESTERSHIRE WARWICKSHIRE,
GLOUCESTERSHIRE, England

DISTANT BRIDGES

BEAMISH, COUNTY DURHAM, England

DR WHO

BUCKINGHAMSHIRE RLWY CTRE,
BUCKINGHAMSHIRE, England

FIRST GREAT TRAIN ROBBERY

RPSI, COUNTY ANTRIM, Northern Ireland

FRED DIBNAH

TIMOTHY HACKWORTH, COUNTY DURHAM,
England

FRENCH LIEUTENANT'S WOMAN

PAIGNTON & DARTMOUTH RAILWAY, DEVON,
England

GLASS

WATERCRESS LINE, HAMPSHIRE, England

GOLDENEYE

NENE VALLEY RAILWAY, CAMBRIDGESHIRE,
England

GREAT DAY OUT

BREDGAR & WORMSHILL, KENT, England

GREAT KADINSKY

WATERCRESS LINE, HAMPSHIRE, England

HANOVER ST

EAST SOMERSET RAILWAY, SOMERSET, England

TV / FILM APPEARANCES

Act of Will — Hanover St

HARRY POTTER

NORTH YORKSHIRE MOORS RAILWAY,
YORKSHIRE (NORTH), England

HEARTBEAT

NORTH YORKSHIRE MOORS RAILWAY,
YORKSHIRE (NORTH), England

HENO

GWILI RAILWAY, CARMARTHENSHIRE, Wales

HIGH HEELS AND LOW LIFES

WATERCRESS LINE, HAMPSHIRE, England

HISTORY OF BRITISH ART

VINTAGE CARRIAGES TRUST, YORKSHIRE
(WEST), England

HOLIDAY

BEER HEIGHTS, DEVON, England

FFESTINIOG RAILWAY, GWYNEDD, Wales

VINTAGE CARRIAGES TRUST, YORKSHIRE
(WEST), England

HOURS

VINTAGE CARRIAGES TRUST, YORKSHIRE
(WEST), England

INSPECTOR MORSE.

DIDCOT RAILWAY CENTRE, OXFORDSHIRE,
England

JEEVES & WOOSTER

GLOUCESTERSHIRE WARWICKSHIRE,
GLOUCESTERSHIRE, England

LAST DAYS OF PATTON

NENE VALLEY RAILWAY, CAMBRIDGESHIRE,
England

LEAGUE OF GENTLEMEN

VINTAGE CARRIAGES TRUST, YORKSHIRE
(WEST), England

LONDON'S BURNING

NENE VALLEY RAILWAY, CAMBRIDGESHIRE,
England

LOVE ON A BRANCH LINE

NORTH NORFOLK RAILWAY, NORFOLK, England

MICHAEL COLLINS

RPSI, COUNTY ANTRIM, Northern Ireland

MINIATURE RAILWAY MEMORIES

KERR MINIATURE RAILWAY, ANGUS, Scotland

MONARCH OF THE GLEN

STRATHSPEY RAILWAY, HIGHLANDS, Scotland

MONOCLED MUTINEER

BEAMISH, COUNTY DURHAM, England

OCTOPUSSY

NENE VALLEY RAILWAY, CAMBRIDGESHIRE,
England

OFF THE RAILS

KENT & EAST SUSSEX RAILWAY, KENT, England

LEIGHTON BUZZARD RAILWAY, BEDFORDSHIRE,
England

ON THE RECORD

KENT & EAST SUSSEX RAILWAY, KENT, England

OUR FRIENDS IN THE NORTH

BEAMISH, COUNTY DURHAM, England

OUT AND ABOUT

LAKESIDE & HAVERTHWAITE RLWY, CUMBRIA,
England

PEAK PRACTICE

PEAK RAIL, DERBYSHIRE, England

PIE IN THE SKY

WATERCRESS LINE, HAMPSHIRE, England

POIROT

NORTH YORKSHIRE MOORS RAILWAY,
YORKSHIRE (NORTH), England

RAILWAY CHILDREN

BLUEBELL RAILWAY, SUSSEX (EAST), England

KEIGHLEY & WORTH VALLEY, YORKSHIRE
(WEST), England

VINTAGE CARRIAGES TRUST, YORKSHIRE
(WEST), England

RAILWAY WITH A HEART OF GOLD
AAW **TALYLLYN RAILWAY**, GWYNEDD, Wales

RIVERS OF WALES
AAW **FFESTINIOG RAILWAY**, GWYNEDD, Wales

SHADOWLANDS
AAW **GREAT CENTRAL RAILWAY**, LEICESTERSHIRE, England

SHERLOCK HOLMES
AAW **NORTH YORKSHIRE MOORS RAILWAY**, YORKSHIRE (NORTH), England

AAW **VINTAGE CARRIAGES TRUST**, YORKSHIRE (WEST), England

SHERLOCK HOLMES MURDER ROOMS
AAW **NORTH NORFOLK RAILWAY**, NORFOLK, England

SONGS OF PRAISE
AAW **TIMOTHY HACKWORTH**, COUNTY DURHAM, England

SONS & LOVERS
AAW **BEAMISH**, COUNTY DURHAM, England

SOUTHERN STEAM
AAW **BREDGAR & WORMSHILL**, KENT, England

AAW **HOLLYCOMBE STEAM COLLECTION**, HAMPSHIRE, England

AAW **KENT & EAST SUSSEX RAILWAY**, KENT, England

AAW **SPA VALLEY RAILWAY**, KENT, England

SPIKE MILLIGAN'S PUCKOON
AAW **ULSTER FOLK & TRANSPORT**, COUNTY DOWN, Northern Ireland

TIME TOURISTS
AAW **AMBERLEY WORKING MUSEUM**, SUSSEX (WEST), England

TOMORROW'S WORLD
AAW **VINTAGE CARRIAGES TRUST**, YORKSHIRE (WEST), England

TWEENIES
AAW **PEAK RAIL**, DERBYSHIRE, England

TWRIO
AAW **GWILI RAILWAY**, CARMARTHENSHIRE, Wales

UNKNOWN SOLDIER
AAW **VINTAGE CARRIAGES TRUST**, YORKSHIRE (WEST), England

VIEW TO A KILL
AAW **AMBERLEY WORKING MUSEUM**, SUSSEX (WEST), England

WIND IN THE WILLOWS
AAW **BLUEBELL RAILWAY**, SUSSEX (EAST), England

WORLD IN ACTION
AAW **BROOKSIDE MINIATURE**, CHESHIRE, England

Y CLEDDRAUCOLL
AAW **GWILI RAILWAY**, CARMARTHENSHIRE, Wales

Y GYNDDEIRIG
AAW **GWILI RAILWAY**, CARMARTHENSHIRE, Wales

Y PALMANT AUR
AAW **GWILI RAILWAY**, CARMARTHENSHIRE, Wales

TV / FILM APPEARANCES

Railway with a Heart of Gold — Y Palmant Aur

NOTES

NOTES

STEAM
RAILWAY